## Periodic Table
(Based on Carbon 12 = 12.000)

P9-COO-624

**Legend:**

| 6 | Atomic number |
|---|---|
| C | Symbol |
| Carbon | Name |
| 12.011 | Atomic mass |

Solid · Liquid · Gas

**Transition Elements**

| 1 IA | 2 IIA | 3 IIIB | 4 IVB | 5 VB | 6 VIB | 7 VIIB | 8 | 9 VIIIB | 10 | 11 IB | 12 IIB | 13 IIIA | 14 IVA | 15 VA | 16 VIA | 17 VIIA | 18 O (Noble Gases) |
|---|---|---|---|---|---|---|---|---|---|---|---|---|---|---|---|---|---|
| 1 H Hydrogen 1.00794 | | | | | | | | | | | | | | | | | 2 He Helium 4.00260 |
| 3 Li Lithium 6.941 | 4 Be Beryllium 9.01218 | | | | | | | | | | | 5 B Boron 10.811 | 6 C Carbon 12.011 | 7 N Nitrogen 14.0067 | 8 O Oxygen 15.9994 | 9 F Fluorine 18.998403 | 10 Ne Neon 20.179 |
| 11 Na Sodium 22.98977 | 12 Mg Magnesium 24.305 | | | | | | | | | | | 13 Al Aluminum 26.98154 | 14 Si Silicon 28.0855 | 15 P Phosphorus 30.97376 | 16 S Sulphur 32.066 | 17 Cl Chlorine 35.453 | 18 Ar Argon 39.948 |
| 19 K Potassium 39.0983 | 20 Ca Calcium 40.078 | 21 Sc Scandium 44.95591 | 22 Ti Titanium 47.88 | 23 V Vanadium 50.9415 | 24 Cr Chromium 51.9961 | 25 Mn Manganese 54.9380 | 26 Fe Iron 55.847 | 27 Co Cobalt 58.9332 | 28 Ni Nickel 58.69 | 29 Cu Copper 63.546 | 30 Zn Zinc 65.39 | 31 Ga Gallium 69.723 | 32 Ge Germanium 72.59 | 33 As Arsenic 74.9216 | 34 Se Selenium 78.96 | 35 Br Bromine 79.904 | 36 Kr Krypton 83.80 |
| 37 Rb Rubidium 85.4678 | 38 Sr Strontium 87.62 | 39 Y Yttrium 88.9059 | 40 Zr Zirconium 91.224 | 41 Nb Niobium 92.9064 | 42 Mo Molybdenum 95.94 | 43 Tc Technetium 97.9072 | 44 Ru Ruthenium 101.07 | 45 Rh Rhodium 102.9055 | 46 Pd Palladium 106.42 | 47 Ag Silver 107.8682 | 48 Cd Cadmium 112.41 | 49 In Indium 114.82 | 50 Sn Tin 118.710 | 51 Sb Antimony 121.75 | 52 Te Tellurium 127.60 | 53 I Iodine 126.9045 | 54 Xe Xenon 131.29 |
| 55 Cs Cesium 132.9054 | 56 Ba Barium 137.33 | 71 Lu Lutetium 174.967 | 72 Hf Hafnium 178.49 | 73 Ta Tantalum 180.9479 | 74 W Tungsten 183.85 | 75 Re Rhenium 186.207 | 76 Os Osmium 190.2 | 77 Ir Iridium 192.22 | 78 Pt Platinum 195.08 | 79 Au Gold 196.9665 | 80 Hg Mercury 200.59 | 81 Tl Thallium 204.383 | 82 Pb Lead 207.2 | 83 Bi Bismuth 208.9804 | 84 Po Polonium 208.9824 | 85 At Astatine 209.9871 | 86 Rn Radon 222.0176 |
| 87 Fr Francium 223.0197 | 88 Ra Radium 226.0254 | 103 Lr Lawrencium 260.1054 | 104 Unq 261 | 105 Unp 262 | 106 Unh 263 | 107 Uns 264 | 108 Uno 265 | 109 Une 266 | | | | | | | | | |

**Rare Earth Elements**

Lanthanide Series:

| 57 La Lanthanum 138.9055 | 58 Ce Cerium 140.12 | 59 Pr Praseodymium 140.9077 | 60 Nd Neodymium 144.24 | 61 Pm Promethium 144.9128 | 62 Sm Samarium 150.36 | 63 Eu Europium 151.96 | 64 Gd Gadolinium 157.25 | 65 Tb Terbium 158.9254 | 66 Dy Dysprosium 162.50 | 67 Ho Holmium 164.9304 | 68 Er Erbium 167.26 | 69 Tm Thulium 168.9342 | 70 Yb Ytterbium 173.04 |
|---|---|---|---|---|---|---|---|---|---|---|---|---|---|

Actinide Series:

| 89 Ac Actinium 227.0278 | 90 Th Thorium 232.0381 | 91 Pa Protactinium 231.0359 | 92 U Uranium 238.0289 | 93 Np Neptunium 237.0482 | 94 Pu Plutonium 244.0642 | 95 Am Americium 94.0614 | 96 Cm Curium 247.0703 | 97 Bk Berkelium 247.0703 | 98 Cf Californium 251.0796 | 99 Es Einsteinium 252.0828 | 100 Fm Fermium 257.0951 | 101 Md Mendelevium 258.0986 | 102 No Nobelium 259.1009 |
|---|---|---|---|---|---|---|---|---|---|---|---|---|---|

# PHYSICS

## CONCEPTS AND CONNECTIONS

**Igor Nowikow**

**Brian Heimbecker**

**Don Bosomworth,** Physics Advisor

**IRWIN PUBLISHING**
Toronto/Vancouver, Canada

Copyright © 2001 by Irwin Publishing

National Library of Canada Cataloguing in Publication Data

Nowikow, Igor
 Physics: concepts and connections

Includes index.
ISBN 0-7725-2872-1

1. Physics.  I. Heimbecker, Brian.  II. Bosomworth, Don.  III. Title.

QC23.N68 2001     530     C2001-930662-8

All rights reserved. It is illegal to reproduce any portion of this book in any form or by any means, electronic or mechanical, including photocopy, recording or any information storage and retrieval system now known or to be invented, without the prior written permission of the publisher, except by a reviewer who wishes to quote brief passages in connection with a review written for inclusion in a magazine, newspaper, or broadcast.
 Any request for photocopying, recording, taping, or for storing of informational and retrieval systems, of any part of this book should be directed in writing CAN-COPY (Canadian Reprography Collective), One Yonge Street, Suite 1900, Toronto, ON  M5E 1E5.

Cover and text design: Dave Murphy/ArtPlus Ltd.
Page layout: Leanne O'Brien/ArtPlus Ltd.
Illustration: Donna Guilfoyle, Sandy Sled/ArtPlus Ltd., Imagineering, Dave McKay, Sacha Warunkiw, Jane Whitney
ArtPlus Ltd. production co-ordinator: Kristi Moreau
Project developer: Doug Panasis
Editor: Lina Mockus-O'Brien
Editorial: Jim MacLachlan, Mark Philpott, Lee Geller, Joyce Tannassee
Photo research: Susan Berger
Indexer: May Look

Published by
Irwin Publishing Ltd.
325 Humber College Blvd.
Toronto, ON  M9W 7C3

Printed and bound in Canada
1 2 3 4  04 03 02 01

French edition
ISBN 2-89310-872-5
available from Chenelière/McGraw-Hill

# Acknowledgements

The authors and publisher would like to thank the following reviewers for their insights and suggestions.

Ray Donatelli, Teacher, Mississauga, Peel District School Board

Bob Wevers, Teacher, Toronto, Toronto District School Board

David Miller, Teacher, Niagara Falls, District School Board of Niagara

Lisa McEntee, Teacher, Fenelon Falls, Trillium/Lakelands District School Board

Vince Weeks, Teacher, Burlington, Halton District School Board

Jim Buckley, Teacher, Milton, Halton Catholic District School Board

Peter Masher, Faculty of Engineeering, McMaster University

Martin Gabber, Teacher, Whitby, Durham District School Board

Al Perry, Teacher, Brockville, Upper Canada District School Board

Paul Gragg, Teacher, Ottawa, Ottawa-Carlton District School Board

Pat Durst, Bias Reviewer, formerly York Region District School Board


Igor Nowikow would like to thank the following students for their contribution.

*Problem Solvers:* Ryan Van Wert, Amy Leung, Andrew Buckler, Sook Young Chang, Praveena Sivananthan, Ashley Pitcher

*Solution Inputters:* Sandra Tso, Chris Jones, Andrew Brown, Jennie Baek, Neil Hooey, Dickson Kwan

*Student Researchers:* Andrew Brown, Jennifer Harper, Candice Moxley, Hossein N-Marandi, Ashvini Nimkar, Janet Tse, Drew Henderson, Aleem Kherani, Angel Lo, John So, Henry Tu, Garrett Wright, Young Chang, Adam Jones, Alinda Kim, Robert Lee, Erin McGregor, Sevil N-Marandi, Joanna Wice

### Dedication
To my wife Jane and my children Melissa and Cameron for enduring patiently the trials and tribulations of a driven author, and to all my students for keeping me energized on the job.

Brian Heimbecker would like to thank the following students for their contribution.

*Problem Solvers and Solution Inputters:* David Badregon, Jonathan Aiello, Maria-Anna Piorkowska, Jennifer Walsh

*Student Researchers:* Angela Baldesarra, Nicole Bradley, David Carlini, Vanessa Chiaravalloti, Kaitlyn Chircop, Joel Couture, Thomas Crocker, Ashleigh Davidson, Lorenzo De Novellis, Marco Di Lorenzo, Christian Dover, Karen Finney, Chantal Gauthier, Michelle Gilmour, Erica Gismondi, Lawrence Gubert, Samantha Gowland, Tara Grozier, Ryan Hayes, David Heilman, Sarah Higginson, Stephanie Kadlicko, Josh Kavanagh, Jesse Kerpan, Ryan Kershaw, Alicja Krol, Keith Maiato, Vanessa Mann, Jennifer McNeil, Caroline Namedynski, Joanne Namedynski, Iva Pavlic, Tara Ross, Robert Vangerven, Maria Venditti

### Dedication
To Laurie, Alyssa and Emma for making "the text book" possible.
This book is for all students and teachers because physics is for everyone.

The authors would like to thank Bob McCloskey for his photo contributions, for writing the unit introductions, and for editing the STSE articles.

# Table of Contents

# To the Student

Physics is for everyone. It is more than simply the study of the physical universe. It is much more interesting, diverse, and far more extreme. In physics, we observe nature, seek regularities in the data, and attempt to create mathematical relationships that we can use as tools to study new situations. Physics is not just the study of unrelated concepts, but rather how everything we do profoundly affects society and the environment.

## Features

### Flowcharts

The flowcharts in this book are visual summaries that graphically show you the interconnections among the concepts presented at the end of each section and chapter. They help you organize the methods and ideas put forward in the course. The flowcharts come in three flavors: Connecting the Concepts, Method of Process, and Putting It All Together. They are introduced as you need them to help you review and remember what you have learned.

### Examples

The examples in this book are loaded with both textual and visual cues, so you can use them to teach yourself to do various problems. They are the next-best thing to having the teacher there with you.

### Applying the Concepts

At the end of most subsections, we have included a few simple practice questions that give you a chance to use and manipulate new equations and try out newly introduced concepts. Many of these sections also include extensions of new concepts into the areas of society, technology, and the environment to show you the connection of what you are studying to the real world.

## End-of-chapter STSE

Every chapter ends with a feature that deals exclusively with how our studies impact on society and the environment. These articles attempt to introduce many practical applications of the chapter's physics content by challenging you to be conscious of your responsibility to society and the environment. Each feature presents three challenges. The first and most important is to answer and ask more questions about the often-dismissed societal implications of what we do. These sections also illustrate how the knowledge and application of physics are involved in various career opportunities in Canada. Second, you are challenged to evaluate various technologies by performing correlation studies on related topics. Finally, you are challenged to design or build something that has a direct correlation to the topic at hand.

## Exercises

Like a good musician who needs to practise his or her instrument regularly, you need to practise using the skills and tools of physics in order to become good at them. Every chapter ends with an extensive number of questions to give you a chance to practise. Conceptual questions challenge you to think about the concepts you have learned and apply them to new situations. The problems involve numeric calculations that give you a chance to apply the equations and methods you have learned in the chapter. In many cases, the problems in this textbook require you to connect concepts or ideas from other sections of the chapter or from other parts of the book.

**EXERCISES**

## Labs

"Physics is for everyone" is re-enforced by moving learning into the practical and tactile world of the laboratory. You will learn by doing labs that stress verification and review of concepts. By learning the concepts first and applying them in the lab setting, you will internalize the physics you are studying. During the labs, you will use common materials as well as more high-tech devices.

**L A B**

## Appendices

The appendices provide brief, concise summaries of mathematical methods that have been developed throughout the book. They also provide you with detailed explanations on how to organize a lab report, evaluate data, and make comparisons and conclusions using results obtained experimentally. They explain uncertainty analysis techniques, including some discussion on statistical analysis for experiments involving repetitive measurements.

We hope that using this book will help you gain greater enjoyment in learning about the world around us.

Igor Nowikow, Brian Heimbecker

Toronto, 2001

# Motion and Forces

A

Everything around you is in motion — vehicles in the streets, children in the playground, planets in their orbits, the blood coursing through your arteries and veins.

In this unit, you learn to describe and analyze motions; you will learn the causes of motion, and how to apply your analysis to examples in nature and in technology.

The foundations for these studies were laid down more than 300 years ago by Galileo in Italy and Isaac Newton in England. Within 100 years, their insights into motions and forces were being applied, especially in England, to transform work and production.

Machinery replaced hand labour; the pace of life quickened; world populations began to expand. For many people, the quality of life improved greatly. However, the fruits of scientific technology are not evenly spread. We still have much to do.

A Venus-Williams tennis serve has been clocked at 200 km/h. Baseball pitches seldom travel much above 150 km/h. How can you account for the difference?

In this unit, you will learn how to relate the speed of a ball to its mass and the force that is exerted upon it. You will also be able to apply your analysis to many other kinds of motion. In the case of hockey pucks, you will see how the force of friction on the ice will affect the speed. Then, in the following unit on energy and power, you will be able to relate the force and motion of balls and pucks to the strength and endurance of the athlete who hits or throws them.

This study of the motions of objects and the forces that act on them is called **mechanics**. You will begin by describing and analyzing motions without regard to the forces that are acting on the moving objects. This branch of mechanics is called **kinematics**. It was first developed around 1605 by Galileo, who was the first to study motion by mathematical analysis rather than by fuzzy philosophical talk about the causes of various kinds of motions. Galileo's work was extended by Isaac Newton in the 1660s to take account of the forces acting on moving objects. That study is called **dynamics**.

The study of forces acting on objects at rest is called **statics**. Statics was well analyzed by Archimedes about 250 BC. You will find some work on statics in Chapter 5.

## Timeline: The History of Mechanics

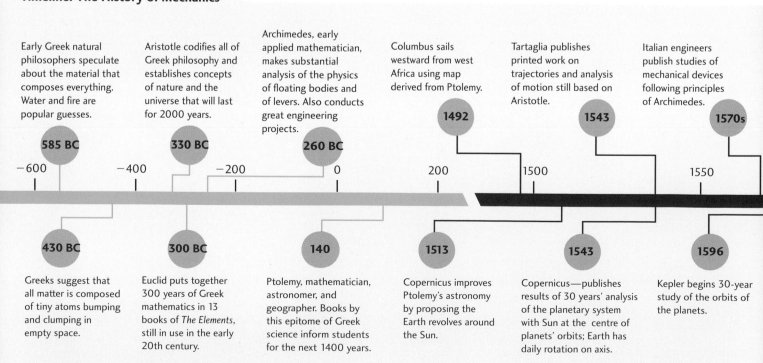

Early Greek natural philosophers speculate about the material that composes everything. Water and fire are popular guesses.
**585 BC**

Aristotle codifies all of Greek philosophy and establishes concepts of nature and the universe that will last for 2000 years.
**330 BC**

Archimedes, early applied mathematician, makes substantial analysis of the physics of floating bodies and of levers. Also conducts great engineering projects.
**260 BC**

Columbus sails westward from west Africa using map derived from Ptolemy.
**1492**

Tartaglia publishes printed work on trajectories and analysis of motion still based on Aristotle.
**1543**

Italian engineers publish studies of mechanical devices following principles of Archimedes.
**1570s**

−600    −400    −200    0    200    1500    1550

**430 BC**
Greeks suggest that all matter is composed of tiny atoms bumping and clumping in empty space.

**300 BC**
Euclid puts together 300 years of Greek mathematics in 13 books of *The Elements*, still in use in the early 20th century.

**140**
Ptolemy, mathematician, astronomer, and geographer. Books by this epitome of Greek science inform students for the next 1400 years.

**1513**
Copernicus improves Ptolemy's astronomy by proposing the Earth revolves around the Sun.

**1543**
Copernicus—publishes results of 30 years' analysis of the planetary system with Sun at the centre of planets' orbits; Earth has daily rotation on axis.

**1596**
Kepler begins 30-year study of the orbits of the planets.

Aristotle believed that there were two distinct types of motion: terrestrial and celestial. He imagined that the heavens (Moon, Sun, planets, and stars) were made of a special perfect material. When Copernicus made Earth a planet, the distinction between heavens and Earth began to decline. However, when Galileo compared shadows on the Moon with those on Earth, philosophers and theologians strongly opposed the idea. Yet in his physics, Galileo still felt restricted to motions on Earth.

Descartes was the first to make the radical claim that there was no distinction between heavens and Earth. His was a universal philosophy of nature; whereas for Aristotle, nature stopped just within the Moon's orbit. Descartes promised more than he could deliver. He lacked adequate proofs for his theories.

Newton's genius was to imagine a space without gravity, while proposing the principle of gravitation that filled the universe with force. Besides his fertile imagination, Newton possessed a truly exceptional capacity for mathematics. Starting from Descartes' analytical geometry, Newton invented calculus to be able to solve problems in motion that Galileo had posed.

The publication of Newton's *Mathematical Principles of Natural Philosophy (Principia)* in 1687 marked the firm establishment of a physics in which careful experimental measurements provided full support for imaginative mathematical theories. Newton handled the trajectories of comets and cannonballs with equal ease using the same equations.

Galileo always stressed that his science depended on a combination of conclusive mathematical proofs and sensible experiments. If Newton is physics, then Galileo is the father of physics.

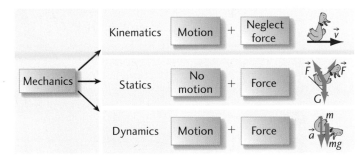

By 1604, Galileo has derived a new theory from analyzing experiments. He finds objects fall distances proportional to the square of the time.

**1604**

After being condemned for Earth's motion in 1633, Galileo publishes result of a lifetime of motion studies in his *Two New Sciences*.

**1638**

Royal Society of London for the promotion of Natural Knowledge chartered by Charles II. Businessmen and scientists combine to advance English commerce.

**1662**

Huygens in Holland publishes mechanical study of his new pendulum clock, accurate to 10 s per day — a gigantic improvement.

**1672**

Sir Isaac Newton is knighted by Queen Anne and elected president of the Royal Society, which he dominated until his death in 1727.

**1704**

Application of steam engine to machine spinning of cotton leads to great expansion of textile industry in Britain, giving it economic and technological domination in the world.

**1785**

1600    1650    1700    1750    1800

**1602**

Galileo begins experimenting with pendulums and rolling balls down inclined ramps. His earlier theories of motion had not fitted experience.

**1610**

Kepler publishes first two laws of planetary motion. Galileo publishes discovery with telescope of Jupiter's moon and roughness of the Moon's surface.

**1644**

Descartes publishes his theory that all motion is caused by whirls of atoms in his *Principles of Philosophy.*

**1666**

Newton (age 24) lays foundations for calculus, experimental optics, and notion of "gravity extending to the orb of the moon."

**1687**

Newton's *Mathematical Principles of Natural Philosophy* builds on Kepler and Galileo to describe forces and motions on Earth and on planets and comets.

**1769**

Patents awarded to Watt for improved steam engine; and to Arkwright for harnessing water power to spin cotton.

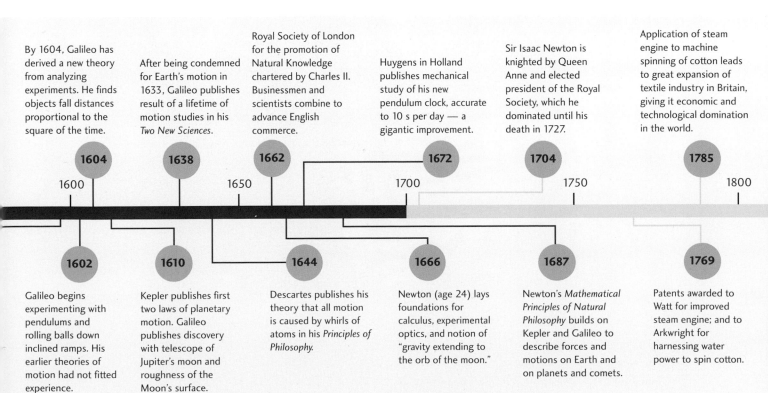

# 1

# Displacement-Time Graphs

## Chapter Outline

### By the end of this chapter, you will be able to

- analyze simple motion data
- draw displacement-time graphs
- derive velocity values from a displacement-time graph
- distinguish between instantaneous and average values of velocity

**Fig.1.1** Riding a roller coaster

# ▸ 1.1 Introduction

Riding a roller coaster (Fig. 1.1) is like training for a shuttle space mission. The long, initial climb builds the expectation of the ride ahead, like sitting in the shuttle waiting for countdown. The ensuing free fall causes an adrenaline rush associated with the thrill of ever-increasing speed, like during the blast-off. In mere moments you are buffeted rudely around a sharp corner, causing your body to experience $g$-forces approaching those of a test pilot. As you fly over the tops of the loops, you momentarily feel weightless, causing that queasy, empty feeling in your stomach. Perhaps you are a good candidate for the vomiting studies conducted on some missions. Then, to settle your insides, at the bottom of the loop your weight increases drastically, becoming equivalent to that of Jupiter's gravitational pull (Fig. 1.2). Your speed is finally brought to zero by the frictional arrester mechanism at the end of the ride. You leave rubber-legged but ready for more.

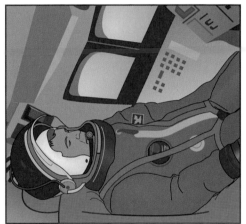

**Fig.1.2** At the bottom of the loop of the roller coaster, your weight is equivalent to Jupiter's gravitational pull

In the next few chapters, you will develop your understanding of the basic principles behind such motions. These principles belong to the branch of physics called **mechanics**, the study of motions and forces.

In order to develop a method of studying such motions, we will use the following approach:

Observe the event → Measure and record data → Analyze data by graph and calculation → Generate theories and equations

**Fig.1.3** Steps in the study of motion

In the process of learning how to analyze data, we will adopt a set of rules used for the manipulation of numbers. These rules are introduced in boxes in the text when the need for them arises. They are also summarized in the Appendices.

1. Describe the various sections of a roller coaster ride and a drive in a car over hilly and winding roads in terms of motion. Save your descriptions to compare later after studying this unit.
2. Define in your own words "distance," "position," "displacement," "speed," "velocity," "acceleration." Again, save these definitions in order to compare them later.
3. What careers would involve aspects of the terms mentioned in Question 2?

Roller coasters have been around for hundreds of years. In 15th century Russia, people were sliding down ice slides, some of which were on top of wooden structures. Soon, carts with wheels were being used, and in the 1800s, the carts were pulled up to the top of the hill by mechanical means. Loops were attempted with some disastrous results. John Miller patented over 100 improvements to the roller coaster, many in the area of safety.

4. Research the history of safety in roller coaster rides. Compare the excitement features of early versions of roller coasters to those of today (height of drops, number of loops, radii of turns, maximum speeds, length of ride, and passenger orientation).

**Fig.1.4** Winnipeg Beach roller coaster, 1927

## ▶ 1.2 Terms and Units

To start, we will study the roller coaster called "Superman the Escape" (Fig. 1.5).

In our initial studies, we will observe its motion only, without regard to any underlying causes. This sub-branch of mechanics is called **kinematics**, the study of motion. In later chapters, after building up a physics language, we will add forces to the picture. This is the study called **dynamics**, the cause of motion.

In order to discuss observed events, we must create a common language associated with this type of study. When you discuss the thrill aspects of your ride, you make reference to the distance you fall, the speeds you reach, and the $g$-forces you experience. But what exactly is a "$g$"? and what is the difference between speed and acceleration? How are distance, height, speed, and acceleration related? These are the questions you will be able to answer by the end of the next two chapters.

The Superman ride is rated as the coaster that generates the fastest speed: a mind-boggling 160 km/h! You travel up 127 m, about the height of a 35-storey building. The duration of the ride is a mere 28 s, covering a distance of 375 m.

When looking over the basic data of Superman the Escape (Table 1.1), you notice that technical terms all have a number and a unit associated with them. In physics, we always include a unit with the value, even in

**Fig.1.5** Superman the Escape

calculations. For example, the total distance covered by moving up the ride, then down again is 127 m + 127 m = 254 m.

Now consider the quantity, 254 m. Although it tells us the distance, we need more information in order to explain exactly what this value represents. The directions "up" and "down" are required. It's just like giving a friend directions to your house. He or she could hardly get there with the statement "Just walk 0.6 km, you can't miss it." Direction must also be specified. In physics, quantities with direction are called **vectors**. On the other hand, a quantity without a direction is called a **scalar**.

> **Scalars** are quantities that are specified by a value (magnitude) only and no direction.

Examples of scalars: age, 16 years; height, 155 cm; temperature, 20°C; hair loss rate, 5 hairs/hour; distance, 127 m; and speed, 161 km/h.

> **Vectors** are quantities that are specified by both a magnitude and a direction.

Examples of vectors: displacement, 127 m [up], 50 km [north]; velocity, 161 km/h [down], 10 m/s [west].

Notice there is a distinction between distance and displacement as well as speed and velocity. One is a scalar, the other is a vector.

**Distance** is a measure of the total travel of the object, regardless of direction. When you ride your bike around a track (Fig. 1.6A), the odometer clicks off the distance travelled. **Displacement** is the net travel of an object as measured from its starting point to its end point in a straight line. No matter how many times you complete the loop of the track on your bike, if you stop where you started, your displacement is zero. Displacement requires a direction.

**Average speed** is associated with the distance travelled. It is the distance per unit time. **Average velocity** is the displacement per unit time, and requires a direction. The tricky part comes in dealing with an **instantaneous velocity** or **instantaneous speed**. This is a measurement done at one moment in time. In this case, *the magnitude of velocity is called speed.*

| **Table 1.1** |
| :---: |
| ***Superman the Escape —*** |
| **Basic Data** |

Type of coaster: reverse free fall

Height: 127 m

Top speed: 160 km/h

Length: 375 m

Max. *g*-force: 4.5 *g*s

Acceleration: 0 to 160 km/h in 7 s

Zero gravity free fall: 6.5 s

Ride vehicles: two 6 t 15-passenger trains

Opening date: March 15, 1997

Ride designer: Intamin AG

**Fig.1.6A**   Displacement and distance

500 m  Total distance is 500 m (1 loop)

**1** Total displacement is zero after 1 complete loop

**2** Displacement is 10 m [W] from the start

**EXAMPLE 1** **Using the terms correctly**

(a) Victoria, BC is 4491 km from Toronto, ON (Fig. 1.6B). 4491 km is a measure of distance.

(b) To get to Victoria from Toronto, you must fly 4491 km [west]. 4491 km [west] is the displacement.

(c) Windsor, ON is 2153 km from Halifax, NS. 2153 km [east] is the displacement (Fig. 1.6B).

(d) On average, the roller coaster moved at 51 km/h. 51 km/h is an average speed.

(e) When the car moves downward near the bottom of the ride at 160 km/h, 160 km/h [down] is an instantaneous velocity. If you omit the direction, then your speed is 160 km/h. Sometimes a confusion occurs between *speed* and *average speed* because the term *average* is left out in many cases when referring to average speed. On the roller coaster ride in Fig. 1.6C, the displacement from start to finish is 540 m [E], while the distance travelled is 960 m. The average speed over the length of the ride is 51 km/h, while the instantaneous velocity near the bottom of the loop is 160 km/h [down].

**Fig.1.6B**

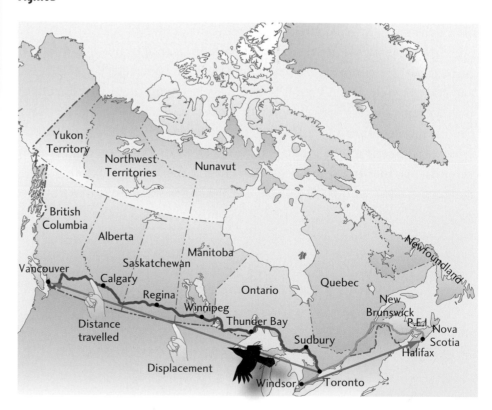

$\vec{d} = 540\text{m[E]}$

**Fig.1.6C** Speeds and accelerations vary over different parts of the ride. In part A, riders are accelerating. In B, the speed is constant; and in C, the ride slows to a stop.

## Standard Units

Depending on the country you are in or the age of the person you are talking to, you will hear various units of measurement. In the United States, the length of the Superman ride is given as 1235 ft with a top speed of 100 mph. A horse-racing enthusiast might call the length of the track 1.9 furlongs. Back in ancient times, a Greek or Roman might have called the distance 800 or 720 cubits—the unit varied from place to place. Now, to keep measurements and calculations uniform around the world, scientists mostly use SI units from the *Système International d'Unités*.

> For distance and displacement, we will use metres as often as possible (unit m). For time, seconds are used as often as possible (unit s).

Therefore, for speed and velocity, the unit of choice becomes metres per second (m/s).

## Unit Analysis

Although we use SI units wherever possible, there are times when we have to convert a measurement from one unit to another. This is no different than converting amounts of money from the currency of one country to that of another. If 1 franc equals 14 yen, then the fraction of the two equal values is one. This **equivalent fraction** is

$$\frac{1 \text{ franc}}{14 \text{ yen}} = 1$$

If you have 17 francs, divide by the equivalent fraction. When you solve for the number of yen, you get $17 \times 14 = 238$ yen. If you have 500 yen, multiply by the equivalent fraction and you get 35.7 francs.

**DEFINING UNITS**

**Metre** was once defined by two marks on a bar of platinum-iridium alloy kept at 0°C. Nowadays, for greater precision, it is 1 650 763 .73 wavelengths of an orange-red light created by an atomic process in krypton-86. The number is not a nice, even one because it must match the original two lines on the bar standard. **Second** is the time required for 9 192 631 770 vibrations of a particular wavelength of light emitted by a cesium-133 atom.

**OTHER UNITS**

There are other systems of measurement used throughout history and different parts of the world. The CGS (centimetre, gram, second) system is metric. British engineers used a pound-force and a mass unit of 1 slug ≈ 32 lb.

| Prefixes of the Metric System | | |
|---|---|---|
| Factor | Prefix | Symbol |
| $10^{18}$ | exa | E |
| $10^{15}$ | peta | P |
| $10^{12}$ | tera | T |
| $10^{9}$ | giga | G |
| $10^{6}$ | mega | M |
| $10^{3}$ | kilo | k |
| $10^{2}$ | hecto | h |
| 10 | deka | da |
| $10^{-1}$ | deci | d |
| $10^{-2}$ | centi | c |
| $10^{-3}$ | milli | m |
| $10^{-6}$ | micro | μ |
| $10^{-9}$ | nano | n |
| $10^{-12}$ | pico | p |
| $10^{-15}$ | femto | f |
| $10^{-18}$ | atto | a |

## EXAMPLE 2 — Converting units

Calculate the number of seconds in seven years. (The unit for year is a.)

**Given**

Assuming all values are exact, we have

1 a = 365 d     1 d = 24 h     1 h = 60 min     1 min = 60 s

### Solution

From each relation, make an equivalent fraction. Arrange to have the larger time unit in the denominator of each fraction. Then multiply 7 a by the sequence of fractions.

$$7\text{ a} = 7\text{ a} \times \frac{365\text{ d}}{1\text{ a}} \times \frac{24\text{ h}}{1\text{ d}} \times \frac{60\text{ min}}{1\text{ h}} \times \frac{60\text{ s}}{1\text{ min}} = 2.2075 \times 10^{8}\text{ s}$$

$$7\text{ a} = 7\text{ a} \times \frac{365\text{ d}}{1\text{ a}} \times \frac{24\text{ h}}{1\text{ d}} \times \frac{60\text{ min}}{1\text{ h}} \times \frac{60\text{ s}}{1\text{ min}} = 2.2075 \times 10^{8}\text{ s}$$

Notice how the unit fractions (where numerator and denominator are equal) are arranged so successive units cancel. There are approximately 220 million seconds in seven years, or 0.22 Gs (giga seconds).

Unit analysis can also be used to establish relations among measured quantities. If you know the proper units for a quantity, you should be able to invent a formula for it that you may have forgotten. The next example shows how to find the formula for density if you remember that a unit for density is grams per litre.

## EXAMPLE 3 — Unit analysis

The density of helium gas is 0.18 g/L. What is the volume of 50 g of helium?

### Solution and Connection to Theory

**Given**

Density, $D = 0.18$ g/L     mass, $m = 50$ g     volume, $V = ?$

You probably remember that the quantities must be either multiplied or divided. You might try $D \times m$, $\frac{D}{m}$, or $\frac{m}{D}$. In each case, put the units in and see what the result is. Eventually you should find that

$$V = \frac{50\text{ g}}{0.18\text{ g/L}} = \frac{50}{0.18}\text{ g} \times \frac{\text{L}}{\text{g}} = 2.8 \times 10^{2}\text{ L}$$

Since the volume has to be in litres, you combine the units of the given quantities so that grams cancel and litres are in the numerator. So the formula must be

$$V = \frac{m}{D}$$

which is deduced from knowing the unit for density. This example shows that you can manipulate units in the same way as numbers or algebraic expressions.

## Vector and Scalar Notation

To represent a vector quantity symbolically, we draw an arrow above the variable symbol. When referring to the magnitude or the scalar part of the vector, the arrow is omitted. Thus, when quoting a value for $\vec{d}$, a direction must be given.

**EXAMPLE 4**  **When to use the vector arrow**

| | |
|---|---|
| $\vec{d}$ = 200 m [south] | $d$ = 200 m |
| $\vec{v}$ = 20 m/s [down] | $v$ = 20 m/s |

In math, the scalar part of the vector is also represented as $|\vec{d}|$. The $|\ |$ are called absolute value bars.

1. Sketch the path of a short trip you took using only
   a) scalar quantities.
   b) vector quantities.
2. In your own words, describe the difference between
   a) average speed and average velocity.
   b) instantaneous speed and instantaneous velocity.
3. The Range Rover 4.0 SE has the following specifications, as taken from *The Car and Driver*, 1995:
   0–60 mph (miles per hour) in 10.5 s
   Top speed: 113 mph
   Fuel consumption: 14 mpg (miles per gallon)
   Convert these values to metric. Show all steps and cancellations.
4. a) Use the definition of a second and calculate the number of vibrations light undergoes in 1 h 32 s.
   b) Use the definition of the metre to calculate the number of wavelengths in a 150 mm ruler.
5. Research the progression of the standardization process of the metre and the second.

# 1.3 The Meaning of Negatives in Kinematics

**Fig.1.7** Nothing is implied by the negative sign except direction

To most people, the word "negative" carries with it certain connotations. You have a negative bank balance, you're in debt; you're feeling rather negative, you're somewhat down and out; the temperature is negative, it's cold (Fig. 1.7). But in kinematics, the negative sign attached to a one-dimensional vector indicates only one thing: the vector's direction. Although you can choose which directions are + and −, we will use **the standard reference system** as default. As shown in Fig. 1.8, for geographical directions, we make [N] and [E] positive, and [S] and [W] negative. In space, we call up [U] and right [R] positive and down [D] and left [L] negative. In particular cases, you may wish to deviate from the standard system. Whenever you do, be sure to specify which directions you are taking to be positive. Otherwise, most people will assume you are using the standard system.

a)  b)  c)

**Fig.1.8** Standard directions used for vectors (a and b) are based on the Cartesian coordinate system (c)

### EXAMPLE 5 Using the terms correctly

For vertical motion in the standard reference system, *up is positive* and *down is negative*. So, early in your roller coaster ride, you might have a velocity of $\vec{v}$ = 2.8 m/s. This means that you are moving *up* at 2.8 m/s. Later, a velocity of $\vec{v}$ = −44 m/s means that you are moving *down* at 44 m/s.

### EXAMPLE 6 Using the terms correctly

Using the standard reference system, consider the displacement of the car at the top of Superman to be zero. Then, as the car reaches a speed of 160 km/h at the bottom of the track, the displacement is $\vec{d}$ = −127 m.

Before continuing with the kinematics of roller coasters, we need to take a closer look at how we work with data numbers.

## SIGNIFICANT DIGITS AND DECIMAL PLACES

Measured quantities, such as 1.7 m and 1.700 m, reflect the precision of an instrument. The second value was measured by a more precise instrument and hence generated more significant digits. The number of digits represents the accuracy of a measurement. In calculations involving measurements, *the final answer should have the same number of significant digits as the least accurate measurement* (the measurement with the fewest digits).

A **significant digit** is (a) any non-zero number, (b) any zero between non-zero numbers, (c) any trailing zero after a decimal (e.g., 2.3300 m), (d) any trailing zeros before a decimal if the value is a known measurement (e.g. 300 m).

## CALCULATING WITH MEASUREMENTS

When measurements are multiplied or divided, the *number of significant digits* in the answer must be limited to the number of digits in the least accurate measurement. Example: The area of the hall carpet is 3.42 m $\times$ 0.96 m = 3.3 m² (not 3.2832 or even 3.28).

When measurements are added or subtracted, the *number of decimal places* in the result is the same as the number of decimal places in the measurement with the fewest decimal places. Example: 2.0056 m + 4.03 m = 6.0356 m, which is rounded off to 6.04 m.

Rounding off when the digit is 5: In order not to round up more than down when using large quantities of data, we round differently depending on whether the digit before 5 is odd or even. Odd numbers round up: 34.35 m is rounded to 34.4 m, and even numbers stay the same: 34.45 m becomes 34.4 m.

1. Draw a numbered Cartesian graph like in Fig. 1.8(c). Use the $y$ direction up and the $x$ direction right as positive. Draw on the graph what you believe the motion of a fly would be. Describe what you've drawn using the terms "up," "down," "right," and "left." Then replace these terms with the terms "positive" and "negative," and $y$ and $x$.

2. State the number of significant digits for the following values:
   a) 3211 m
   b) 20001 cm
   c) 2001000 mm
   d) 0.002 m
   e) 0.02000 cm
   f) 200.000 m

3. Round the following to one decimal place:
   a) 3.125 m
   b) 3.25 m
   c) 3.35 m
   d) 3.55 m
   e) 3.3500001 m

4. Find the answer to the following operations, correct to the right number of decimal places.
   a) 2.301 m + 1.4444 m
   b) 321.66 m − 12.1 m
   c) 120 s − 0.110 s
   d) 670.3546 s + 1.2 s
   e) 22.3456 s + 239.239.234 s + 200.1 s

5. Provide the answer to the correct number of significant digits:
   a) 1.2 m $\times$ 3.33 m
   b) $\dfrac{1.0 \text{ m}}{0.3 \text{ m}}$
   c) $\dfrac{1.0000}{0.30000}$
   d) $\dfrac{1}{3.00000000}$
   e) $\dfrac{1.000000000}{3}$

# 1.4 Three Steps to Graphical Analysis

Now we can collect data from the ride. Consider the horizontal section of the ride, marked B (Fig. 1.9). Imagine a tape measure stretched out along the track from a marked point. As your friends' car reaches the mark, start your stopwatch. Record the displacements from that point at each 1.0 s interval, with the results, as shown in Fig. 1.9. They are displayed in Table 1.2.

### Table 1.2

| Time (s) | Displacement (m) |
|----------|------------------|
| 0        | 0                |
| 1.0      | 15               |
| 2.0      | 30               |
| 3.0      | 45               |
| 4.0      | 60               |
| 5.0      | 75               |
| 6.0      | 90               |
| 7.0      | 105              |

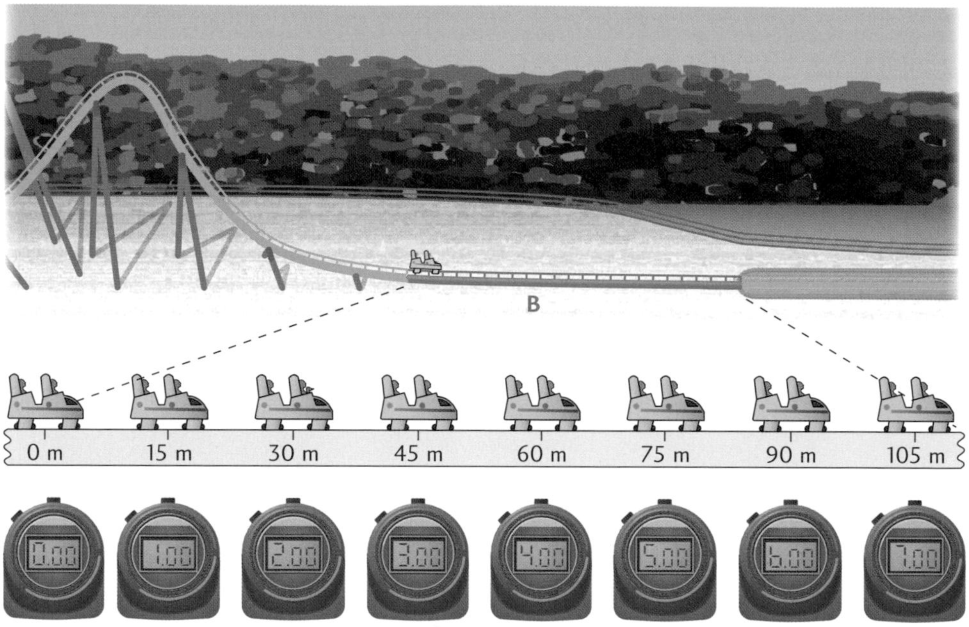

**Fig.1.9** Constant motion section of the ride

The motion is easier to visualize if the data are plotted on a graph. The quantity you controlled (choosing time intervals) is normally assigned to the x axis. Then plot the points indicated by each pair of measurements, with time along the x axis and displacement along the y axis, as in Fig. 1.10A. Label the axes, including the units, and draw the line of best fit.

Since the direction of travel does not change, you only need to use the scalar part of the displacement. You should also note that we started the stopwatch at 0 m for convenience. A $\vec{d}$-$t$ graph's origin is just the starting point of the motion. In other words, a person moving with a constant velocity of 15 m/s [N] can be doing so in Toronto, Vancouver, or St. John's. The motion is the same, but the initial starting position is different.

The data in Table 1.3 and the corresponding graph in Fig. 1.10B are shown as having started 3.0 s later than the graph in Fig. 1.10A, but the sections of both graphs that describe the motion of section B of the roller coaster are identical.

Graphs are one of the tools of trade for a physicist. The graph is like a carpenter's hammer (Fig. 1.11): it's hard to get along without one. Like the carpenter, who builds structures of wood using the hammer, physicists build understanding using the graph.

There are only a few basic things you can do with a hammer. Similarly, there are only three things you can do with a graph.

### Table 1.3

| Time (s) | Displacement (m) |
|----------|------------------|
| 3.0      | 80               |
| 4.0      | 95               |
| 5.0      | 110              |
| 6.0      | 125              |
| 7.0      | 140              |
| 8.0      | 155              |
| 9.0      | 170              |
| 10.0     | 185              |

**Fig. 1.10A** A displacement-time graph of a section of the ride

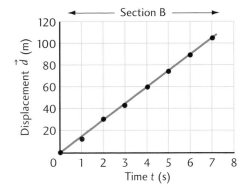

**Fig. 1.10B** The graph of section B of the ride is the same, regardless of when we start timing

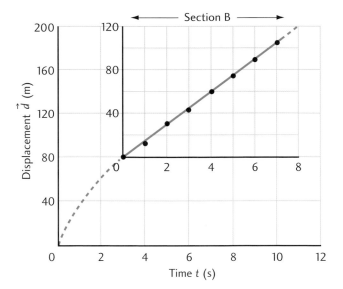

The three steps of graphical analysis:

1. You can read values off the graph.
2. You can find slope(s) of the graph.
3. You can calculate the area between the curve and the x-axis of the graph.

Regardless of the source of your data, these are the three analytical skills you will need. Whether you are a physicist, economist, statistician, or poet, if you have data on a graph, these are the ways you can get the most information from your measurements.

**Fig.1.11** The right tools for the right job?

1. Convert the following values to the units specified:
   **a)** 389 s to   i) months   ii) minutes   iii) years   iv) microseconds
   **b)** 5.0 a to   i) months   ii) minutes   iii) days   iv) seconds
2. For the following $y$ and $x$ axes respectively, what units would the slope have?
   **a)** m and s      **b)** m/s and s     **c)** m and $s^{-1}$     **d)** m/s and $s^{-1}$
3. Understanding size is important in dealing with various topics in physics. For the following examples, find the size of the object using scientific notation as well as an appropriate metric prefix: a galaxy, planet Saturn, a city, an airplane, an insect, a cell, a bacterium, an atom, and an atom's nucleus.

# 1.5 Analysis of Straight-Line $\vec{d}$-t Graphs

The graphing tool just described can be used on many different sizes and shapes of graphs. We begin with the simple straight line, but it won't be long before you will see more complicated graphs. We will take the three steps one at a time.

| Different Ways to Indicate Beginning and End Values of Displacement | |
|---|---|
| Initial value | Final value |
| $\vec{d}_1$ | $\vec{d}_2$ |
| $\vec{d}_0$ | $\vec{d}_f$ |
| $\vec{d}_i$ | $\vec{d}_f$ |
| $\vec{d}_0$ | $\vec{d}$ |
| $\vec{d}$ | $\vec{d}'$ |
| $\vec{d}'$ | $\vec{d}''$ |

## Reading the Graph

We start our analysis by simply reading the graph. Follow the sequence shown in Fig. 1.12A to go from $t = 4.6$ s up to the graph line and then across to 70 m for displacement. That is the displacement from the chosen origin at that moment. By this method, you are finding an instantaneous displacement. The graph will show you where your friend is at any given time. So this **read** procedure gives you *instantaneous* values of displacement.

## Finding the Slope of the Graph

For the section of roller coaster we have chosen, the resultant graph is simply a straight line with a constant slope. Therefore, we can calculate the slope anywhere on the line and obtain the same value. The procedure for calculating the slope is shown in Fig. 1.12B.

The slope is given by the formula

$$\text{slope} = \frac{\text{rise}}{\text{run}}$$

**Fig.1.12A** The steps in the *read* procedure are (1) choose a value on the time axis, 4.6 s; (2) look up to the point on the graph at that time; (3) look horizontally to the displacement axis and read 70 m.

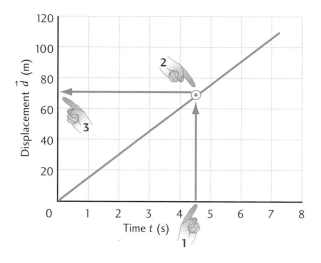

**Fig.1.12B** Calculating slope on a $\vec{d}$-t graph

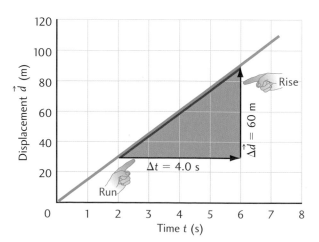

UNIT A: Motion and Forces

For the run, choose a large time interval, preferably one that is a whole number, or at least one that will be easy to divide by. Here (Fig. 1.12B) we start the interval at $t_1 = 2.0$ s and extend it to $t_2 = 6.0$ s. The displacement values at those times are $d_1 = 30$ m and $d_2 = 90$ m. So the run is

$$\Delta t = t_2 - t_1 = 6.0 \text{ s} - 2.0 \text{ s} = 4.0 \text{ s}$$

The sign $\Delta$ (Greek letter delta) means **difference**.

and the rise is

$$\Delta \vec{d} = \vec{d}_2 - \vec{d}_1 = 90 \text{ m} - 30 \text{ m} = 60 \text{ m}$$

The slope is

$$\text{slope} = \frac{\Delta \vec{d}}{\Delta t} = \frac{60 \text{ m}}{4.0 \text{ s}} = 15 \text{ m/s}$$

Notice that the value obtained for the slope has the units m/s, the units for **velocity**. We have just generated our first kinematics equation

$$\vec{v} = \frac{\Delta \vec{d}}{\Delta t}$$

Thus, by using one of the three possible graph manipulations plus unit analysis, you have gained a deeper understanding of the event. From the graph, you found that the car was moving at a constant velocity of 15 m/s. We can generalize this analysis by the summary statement

The slope of a displacement-time graph is the velocity of the object.

Example 7 will show you how to analyze a graph without knowing any data in advance.

## EXAMPLE 7    Analysis of a negative slope

The sky surfer in Fig. 1.13A has reached terminal velocity (fall at a constant speed). The graph in Fig. 1.13B shows his changing vertical displacement relative to a photographer with a telescopic lens on a nearby cliff. The upward direction is positive. What is the velocity of the sky surfer?

### Solution and Connection to Theory

**Read:** At $t = 0$, $\vec{d} = 200$ m. The motion begins when the object is 200 m away from a reference point. Then, notice that $\vec{d} = 0$ m at $t = 4$ s. The displacement is decreasing. So, if the positive direction is up, the motion is downward and negative.

**Slope:** Choose a time interval (say from $t_1 = 2.0$ s to $t_2 = 6.0$ s) and read the corresponding values for displacement, $\vec{d}_1 = 100$ m and $\vec{d}_2 = -100$ m. The slope of the line gives the velocity of the motion.

**Fig.1.13A**    A sky surfer

$$\vec{v} = \frac{\Delta \vec{d}}{\Delta t} = \frac{\vec{d_2} - \vec{d_1}}{t_2 - t_1}$$

$$= \frac{-100\text{m} - 100 \text{ m}}{6.0 \text{ s} - 2.0 \text{ s}}$$

$$= \frac{-200 \text{ m}}{4.0 \text{ s}} = -50 \text{ m/s}$$

The negative sign indicates that the velocity is downward. The surfer's velocity is 50 m/s [D].

**Fig.1.13B** Finding the velocity for a negative slope in Example 7

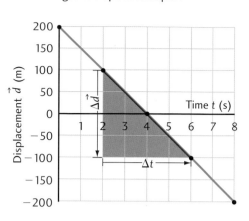

## Finding the Area Under the Graph

The area under the graph of Fig. 1.14 is a triangle, which can be calculated by $\frac{1}{2}$ base × height. On our graph, the base is $\Delta t$ = 6.0 s, and the height is $\Delta \vec{d}$ = 90 m. By substituting values and units into the formula for the area of a triangle, we obtain 270 m·s. Again, we look at the units to try to gain some insight into the situation. Unit analysis has yielded the combination m·s. In this case, finding the area doesn't give us any useful information. However, the process of finding the area is useful, as you will see in the next chapter. In the meantime, you can review various formulas for area in Fig. 1.15.

**Fig.1.14** Finding the area under a $\vec{d}$-t graph. What quantity has the units m·s?

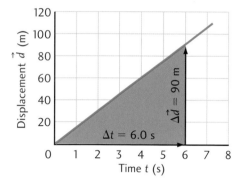

**Fig.1.15** Areas under straight-line graphs use standard formulas;

(a) $A = l\,w$,

(b) $A = -l\,w$,

(c) $A = \frac{1}{2}(l_1 + l_2)w$,

(d) $A = -\frac{1}{2}(l_1 + l_2)w$

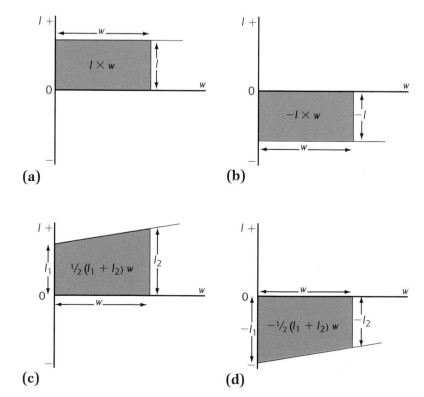

**Fig.1.16** Summary of Analyzing Straight-line $\vec{d}$-t Graphs

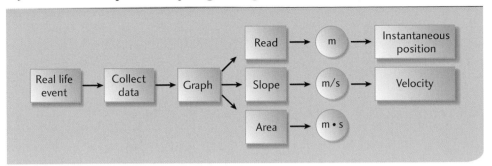

1. Copy the graphs in Fig. 1.15(c) and (d). Add time scales to them. Take the slope at three different intervals for each graph. If your values for slope are not the same, explain why.
2. For the graphs from Question 1, calculate the areas at three different time intervals for each graph.

# 1.6 Analysis of Curved-Line $\vec{d}$-t Graphs

From our last graph, we could calculate the slope on any part of the graph and arrive at the same answer. Thus, the velocities were always the same. We can write this as

$$\vec{v_1} = \vec{v_2} = \vec{v}_{const}$$

Now we'll look at the section of the ride you pay the big bucks for, the free fall (section A). Once again, we'll set $\vec{d_1} = 0.0$ m and $t_1 = 0.0$ s, and take a series of displacement-time measurements. This time, the corresponding graph (Fig. 1.17) generates a curve.

**Fig.1.17** Section A of the roller coaster (free fall)

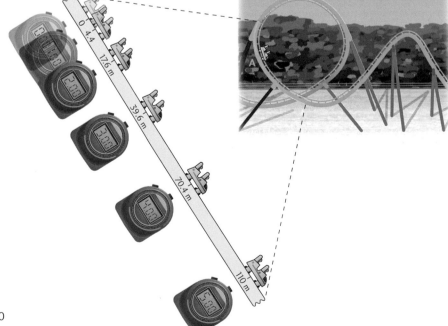

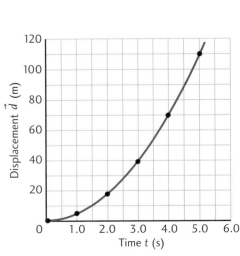

## Reading the Graph

You can read values from a curved-line graph just as easily as from a straight-line graph. You can still read off instantaneous displacements at chosen time instants.

## Calculating the Slope of the Graph

The process of finding slopes is more involved for a curved-line graph because the slope of the line changes with time. As you can see from Fig. 1.17, the slope is increasing. This means that the velocity is increasing. To understand the motion, we draw tangents at several points along the curve (A, B, and C in Fig. 1.18).

**Fig.1.18** Slopes of the $\vec{d}$-t graph of Fig. 1.17 are taken at points A, B, and C

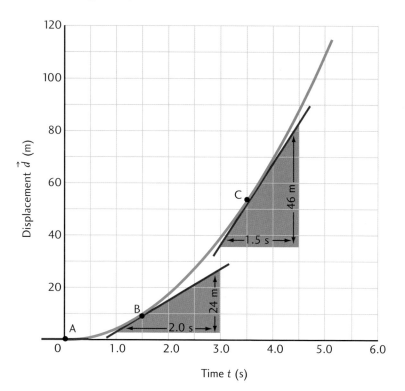

|         | Table 1.4    |                |
|---------|--------------|----------------|
| Point   | Time (s)     | Velocity (m/s) |
| A       | 0.0          | 0.0            |
| B       | 1.5          | 12             |
| C       | 3.5          | 31             |

A tangent is a line touching the curve at one point. In Fig. 1.18, the tangent at point A is horizontal, so its slope is zero. The tangents at points B and C are drawn according to the method outlined in Fig. 1.19. The values of the slopes are then calculated. The triangles in Fig. 1.18 show values of run and rise for the tangents at B and C.

At point B,
$$\text{rise} = \vec{d}_2 - \vec{d}_1$$
$$= 26\ \text{m} - 2\ \text{m}$$
$$= 24\ \text{m}$$

$$\text{run} = t_2 - t_1$$
$$= 3.0\ \text{s} - 1.0\ \text{s}$$
$$= 2.0\ \text{s}$$

At point C,
$$\text{rise} = \vec{d}_2 - \vec{d}_1$$
$$= 81\ \text{m} - 35\ \text{m}$$
$$= 46\ \text{m}$$

$$\text{run} = t_2 - t_1$$
$$= 4.5\ \text{s} - 3.0\ \text{s}$$
$$= 1.5\ \text{s}$$

UNIT A: Motion and Forces

Now calculate the velocities using the rise-over-run formula.

$$\vec{v}_B = \frac{\Delta \vec{d}}{\Delta t} = \frac{24\ \text{m}}{2.0\ \text{s}} = 12\ \text{m/s}$$

$$\vec{v}_C = \frac{\Delta \vec{d}}{\Delta t} = \frac{46\ \text{m}}{1.5\ \text{s}} = 31\ \text{m/s}$$

From the $\vec{d}$-$t$ graph in Fig. 1.18, we have determined three values of velocity, as shown in Table 1.4.

From unit analysis, we can see that slope is still a velocity. However, we have now calculated a velocity at one specific point only, not for the entire graph. This means that we have found an **instantaneous velocity**. To get an idea of the overall motion of this part of the roller coaster from the graph in Fig. 1.18, we check the slopes at the points A, B, and C. We can see that the slopes become steeper and their values increase as the motion progresses. Since slope represents velocity, we can say that the object is speeding up. The action of changing your velocity is called **acceleration**, a topic that will be treated in detail in the next chapter.

## PROCEDURE FOR DRAWING A TANGENT TO A CURVE

**Fig.1.19**

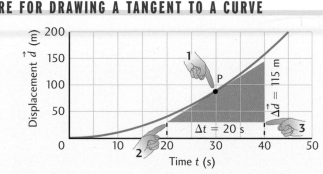

(1) Choose point P on the curve.
(2) Draw a straight line parallel to the direction of the curve at that point. The line touches the curve at P only; and the "angles" between the curve and the line on either side of P are equal.
(3) Then draw a rise-run triangle and calculate the slope.

$$\frac{\Delta \vec{d}}{\Delta t} = \frac{\vec{d}_2 - \vec{d}_1}{t_2 - t_1} = \frac{140\text{m} - 25\ \text{m}}{40\ \text{s} - 20\ \text{s}} = \frac{115\ \text{m}}{20\ \text{s}} = 5.8\ \text{m/s}$$

Now we move to the last section of the ride, section C. Instead of the normal braking action on the wheels, our ride ends up running through a pool of water. The water serves as a brake (Fig. 1.20A).

Once again, the action has produced a curve. This means that the velocities are changing. Drawing tangents at the points indicated, we see their slopes getting smaller; they are less steep. Therefore, the velocity is decreasing, i.e., the car is slowing down to a stop. The point where it stops is the place where the tangent has a slope of zero and is parallel to the time axis. The process of slowing down is also called *acceleration* because the velocity is changing.

Once again, we construct tangents at points A, B, and C.

**Fig.1.20A** $\vec{d}$-$t$ graph of section C of the roller coaster

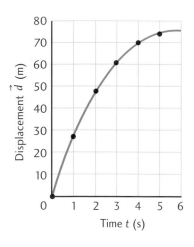

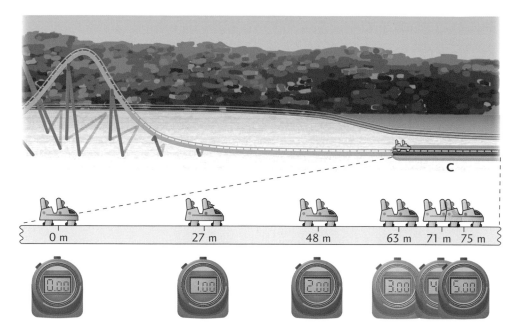

**Fig.1.20B** Finding the slopes of the tangents

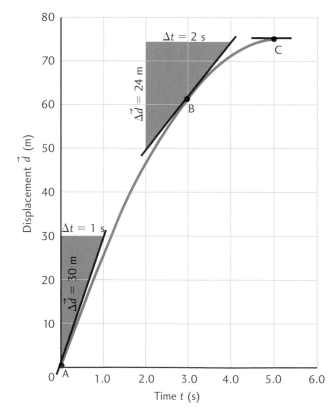

We now calculate the values of the slopes at A, B, and C in Fig. 1.20B.

$$\text{At A, } \vec{v} = \frac{\Delta \vec{d}}{\Delta t} = \frac{30 \text{ m} - 0 \text{ m}}{1.0 \text{ s} - 0.0 \text{ s}} = \frac{30 \text{ m}}{1.0 \text{ s}} = 30 \text{ m/s}$$

$$\text{At B, } \vec{v} = \frac{\Delta \vec{d}}{\Delta t} = \frac{74 \text{ m} - 50 \text{ m}}{4.0 \text{ s} - 2.0 \text{ s}} = \frac{24 \text{ m}}{2.0 \text{ s}} = 12 \text{ m/s}$$

At point C, the tangent is horizontal; therefore, the velocity is zero.

From the $\vec{d}$-$t$ graph in Fig. 1.20B, we have determined three values of velocity, as shown in Table 1.5.

| Table 1.5 | | |
| --- | --- | --- |
| Point | Time (s) | Velocity (m/s) |
| A | 0.0 | 30 |
| B | 3.0 | 12 |
| C | 5.0 | 0.0 |

The concept chart in Fig. 1.21 shows the various kinds of motion that are indicated by $\vec{d}$-$t$ graphs of various shapes.

UNIT A: Motion and Forces

**Fig.1.21** Summary of $\vec{d}$-$t$ Graph Analysis

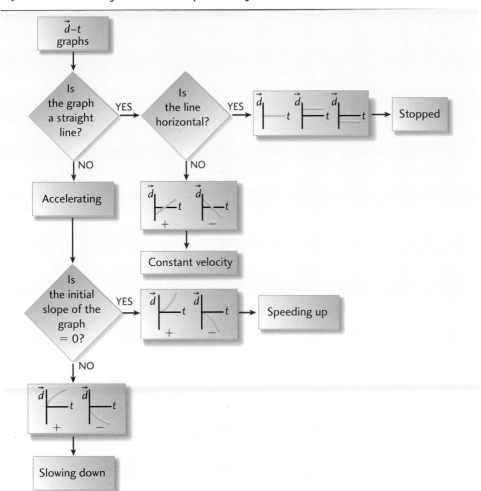

1. Copy the graphs in Fig. 1.18 and Fig. 1.20B. For each, calculate the value of the instantaneous velocity at four different times. Relate the shape of the graph to an actual event in terms of its implied action.
2. **a)** Choose a situation involving a person, car, or other object and sketch a $\vec{d}$-$t$ graph with various sections of straight lines and curves involving your object. Describe what is happening to the object as depicted by your graph.
   **b)** Describe the same event in terms of slopes at various points on the graph.

# 1.7 Average and Instantaneous Velocities

From the slope of the tangent, we found instantaneous velocities using a displacement-time graph. The tangent was drawn at one point on the graph. But what if we draw a line connecting two individual points on the graph, as illustrated in Fig. 1.22?

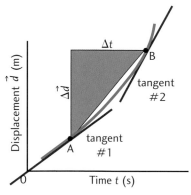

**Fig.1.22** The slope of the secant joining A to B is the average velocity of that portion of the motion. That slope lies between the values of the slopes of the tangents at A and B.

This case is very different from the one discussed in Section 1.6. Here we deal with two different points on the graph. The slope of line AB lies in between the slopes of the two tangents calculated at the ends of the selected time period. Its value represents the **average velocity**.

Over the interval from A to B,

$$\vec{v}_{avg} = \frac{\Delta \vec{d}}{\Delta t}$$

In Fig. 1.22, you can see that there is a large chunk of information lost in this process. The lost information is the part of the curve in the time period we've selected. This is because we are representing that part of the graph with a straight line. If you decrease the interval in time (i.e., bring points A and B closer together), your average velocity value gets closer to the instantaneous velocity value. The greater the time span used (i.e., the farther apart points A and B), the more detail of the event you lose.

**Fig.1.23** Average vs. Instantaneous Velocity

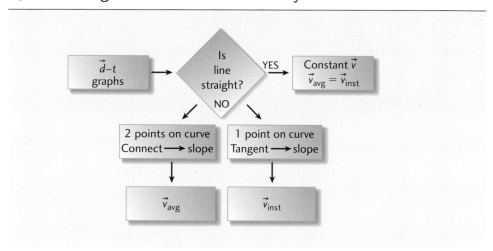

## A Closer Look at Our First Equation

The equation $\vec{v} = \frac{\Delta \vec{d}}{\Delta t}$ was obtained by analyzing the $\vec{d}$-$t$ graph. The question we must ask here is, which $\vec{v}$ are we calculating? There is a variety of possibilities. There is $\vec{v}_1$, the initial velocity, $\vec{v}_2$, the final velocity, $\vec{v}_{avg}$, the average velocity, and $\Delta \vec{v}$, the change in velocity $(\vec{v}_2 - \vec{v}_1)$.

When two points for the calculation of the slope were on the curve (rather than a tangent at one point), the velocity calculated was $\vec{v}_{avg}$. We can also find an average by adding two numbers and dividing the result by two. Thus,

$$\vec{v}_{avg} = \frac{\vec{v}_1 + \vec{v}_2}{2}$$

We combine this with our initial formula for $\vec{v}_{avg}$, $\vec{v}_{avg} = \frac{\Delta\vec{d}}{\Delta t}$, to produce

$$\frac{\Delta\vec{d}}{\Delta t} = \frac{\vec{v}_1 + \vec{v}_2}{2}$$

By rearranging the formula, we obtain one of the standard five kinematics equations

$$\Delta\vec{d} = \tfrac{1}{2}(\vec{v}_1 + \vec{v}_2)\Delta t$$

**Fig.1.24** Overview of $\vec{d}$-t Graph Manipulations

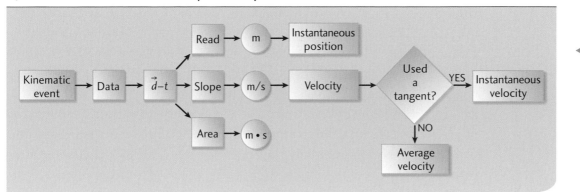

1. **a)** For Fig. 1.20A, calculate the instantaneous velocities at the beginning and end of the graph.
   **b)** Find the average velocity of the whole trip graphically.
   **c)** Average the two instantaneous values. Are the values of b) and c) equal? Should they be?
2. **a)** Draw a graph representing a drive from a non-congested area of traffic to a congested area of traffic. Label each section of the graph. Also label distance and time on the graph.
   **b)** Calculate the maximum and minimum velocity for this drive.
   **c)** Calculate the average velocity for the whole trip.
   **d)** Should the value in part c) equal the value in part b)? Explain.
3. Study the layout of the roller coaster in Fig. 1.25. Assign a sign convention to the directions of motion and a reasonable scale for the heights and lengths. Find the places where
   **a)** the speed is increasing in a positive direction.
   **b)** the speed is decreasing in a positive direction.
   **c)** the speed is increasing in a negative direction.
   **d)** the speed is decreasing in a negative direction.
   **e)** Draw a $\vec{d}$-t graph representing the motion of the roller coaster in the up-and-down direction. Save your graph for the next chapter, when you will use it to calculate acceleration.
   **f)** Describe the effects that you would feel in each section.

**Fig.1.25**

Motion of ride

# Travel Routes

In recent years, the urbanization of the Canadian landscape has meant an increased dependence on our transportation infrastructure. For example, a person who works in downtown Toronto or Vancouver but lives in the suburbs may need to travel for more than an hour each way, often using several different types of transportation systems. The increase in traffic congestion has been matched by an increase in driver frustration. At times, frustrated commuters exhibit uncharacteristically bizarre and aggressive behaviour. This condition is known as "road rage." Driving a car might mean choosing a longer route that can be travelled faster instead of taking a more direct route that's slower due to traffic backup. In Southern Ontario, highway 407, an electronic toll route, offers travel in less time, but at a cost to the user. Drivers can also use regular radio traffic reports and new dynamically updated road signs to aid them in selecting the best route.

Traffic reporters get their information from overhead aircraft or from travellers using mobile phones. Maps are now more accessible over the Internet, and some cars are being outfitted with satellite-aided navigation systems called GPS (Global Positioning Systems). Although information is now more accessible, commuters still need to analyze the information to make the best travel plan. Even the best plans can still be foiled by weather conditions or transit system failures. Several travel options are always advisable.

**Fig.STSE.1.1**   An updateable road sign on the freeway

## Design a Study of Societal Impact

To relieve traffic congestion, some cities have designated lanes on their urban expressways as car-pool lanes. Which cities in Canada use car-pool lanes? Do traffic statistics support the effectiveness of car-pool lanes?

Research variables that would affect the reliability or efficiency of various transportation systems on a day-to-day, seasonal, or annual basis.

What other factors may be involved in deciding whether or not to use public transit?

## Design an Activity to Evaluate

The map in Fig. STSE.1.2 shows two routes plotted from a point of origin to the same destination. Using the map and the other transportation information supplied, complete the following series of steps for both routes.

**Fig.STSE.1.2**

**Fig.STSE.1.3**

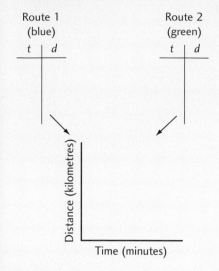

1. Create a table of values to record the distance-versus-time data (see Fig. STSE.1.3).
2. Plot a distance-versus-time graph for both routes on one set of axes.
3. On each curve, draw a tangent at the point that represents the maximum instantaneous velocity for the entire trip. Calculate the values of these maximum velocities.
4. What is the average speed of the entire trip for each route? Show all calculations and appropriate additions to the graphs.
5. Which route is faster?
6. Choose the route you feel may be more unreliable on a day-to-day basis to get to work or school on time. Support your decision by describing the aspects of the trip that may be time consuming.

**Travel information:**

The trip is from Woodbridge to Pickering Village (refer to the map). Map scale is 14 mm = 10 km.

**Route 1: Blue Dots**

- Dots show position at 20-minute intervals.
- Xs represent a stop of 5 minutes.
- This commuter takes a taxi from Woodbridge to the Weston GO Train station. She then boards a train to get to Ajax, and finally takes a taxi from the Ajax station to her final destination.

**Route 2: Green Dots**

- Dots show position at 20-minute intervals.
- Xs represent a stop of 10 minutes (traffic jam).
- This route is by car all the way.

## Build a Structure

Use a map of your school, city, province, or even the entire country to plan the fastest way to travel from one place to another. Do this activity as a group competition or project. If you do a project, consider a number of different transportation systems, such as walking, skate boarding, biking, driving, rail, or air travel.

## You should be able to

*Understand Basic Concepts:*
- Differentiate between scalars and vectors.
- Define values in standard units.
- Set up and apply systems that use positive and negative to designate direction.
- Manipulate data, keeping track of significant digits and decimal places.
- Convert and manipulate units.
- Differentiate between average and instantaneous velocity using examples.
- Differentiate between average and instantaneous velocity using slopes from a $\vec{d}$-$t$ graph.
- Use the method of tangents to find instantaneous velocity from the slope of a $\vec{d}$-$t$ graph.
- Use graphical methods to find average speed values using a $\vec{d}$-$t$ graph.
- Apply unit analysis to other situations not involving displacement and time.

*Develop Skills of Inquiry and Communication:*
- Design and carry out experiments identifying different types of one-dimensional motion.
- Interpret patterns and trends in data drawn by hand or by computer and infer linear and non-linear relationships among the variables ($\vec{d}$, $\vec{v}$, $\vec{a}$, and $t$) using $\vec{d}$-$t$ graphs.
- Analyze the $\vec{d}$-$t$ graph by using the methods **Read**, **Slope**, and **Area**.
- Interpret the results of the processes **Read**, **Slope**, and **Area**.
- Analyze $\vec{d}$-$t$ graphs involving uniform, stopped, and accelerating motion (positive and negative).
- Apply the concepts of graphical analysis to other graph situations.

*Relate Science to Technology, Society, and the Environment:*
- Relate sizes of objects in our macro world, the micro world, and the cosmos to estimated values.
- Analyze the different aspects of a roller coaster ride in terms of thrill components and safety aspects.
- Evaluate today's road systems that are designed to speed up the flow of traffic.
- Design and evaluate routes between different places on a map.

## Equations

$$\text{Slope} = \frac{\text{rise}}{\text{run}}$$

$$\Delta\vec{d} = \frac{(\vec{v}_1 + \vec{v}_2)\,\Delta t}{2} \quad \text{or} \quad \vec{v}_{\text{avg}} = \frac{\Delta\vec{d}}{\Delta t}$$

## Conceptual Questions

1. The number of decimal places in a measurement along with the unit is an indicator of the precision of an instrument. Describe what kind of instruments can be used to produce measurements of 1 m, 1.0 m, 1.00 m, 1.000 m, and 1.000 000 m.

2. Having measured an object and found it to be 1.0 m, you then split it into three equal pieces and quote the value 0.333 333 333 m as the length of one of these pieces. This is what your calculator produces when you divide 1.0 by 3. Is this value reasonable? What is it implying?

3. Using dollars and cents as the units for any numbers you wish to use, explain why keeping your units consistent is important when adding and subtracting quantities.

4. Name three other scalar and vector quantities besides the ones mentioned in this chapter.

5. Design an odometer and a speedometer that can be used to measure vector quantities. Remember, we now have access to satellite mapping systems.

6. State three examples where the displacement is equal in magnitude to the distance travelled but not equal to the actual distance travelled.

7. Using examples, explain why two vectors of equal magnitude are not necessarily equal.

8. You have bought a Ferrari. On your trip, you had an average speed of 180 km/h, yet an average velocity of 2 km/h (magnitude only). How is this possible?

9. Do all the people on the rotor ride (Fig. 1.26) have the same velocities and speeds at any given time? Explain.

**Fig.1.26**

Motion of ride

10. Sketch a $\vec{d}$-$t$ representation of a typical 100 m dash. Remember that sprinters do not increase their speed for the full 100 m. In many cases, they slow down near the end.

11. Sketch a $\vec{d}$-$t$ graph for the 400 m run. Why is it different from the 100 m sketch? How can these graphs be used to help improve performance for an athlete?

12. Look at the $\vec{d}$-$t$ graph in Fig. 1.27. Explain which parts of the graph you would use to find the average speed, the average velocity, and the instantaneous velocity.

**Fig.1.27**

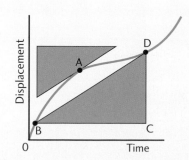

**13. a)** Consider the west direction to be positive. A person is moving at –50 km/h, at a place +300 km from the starting point. Describe where she is and which way she is travelling.

**b)** Using the standard reference frame, describe the Superman ride mentioned in the chapter in terms of displacement and velocity.

**14.** Can an object have
  **a)** a positive velocity and a negative displacement?
  **b)** a negative velocity and a displacement of zero?
  **c)** a value for distance and an average speed of zero?
  Explain each case.

## Problems

### ▷ 1.2 Terms and Units

**15.** Convert the following times. All units must be shown as well as cancellations.
  **a)** 20 minutes to seconds
  **b)** 6.5 hours to minutes
  **c)** 0.6 days to hours
  **d)** 4.5 years to seconds
  **e)** 453 seconds to hours
  **f)** 0.35 minutes to years

**16.** For a time of 250 s, state the value using each prefix. Use both decimal and scientific notation.
  **a)** micro
  **b)** milli
  **c)** kilo
  **d)** mega

**17.** Convert the following speeds. Show all units as well as cancellations.
  **a)** 25 km/h to m/s
  **b)** 150 km/h to m/s
  **c)** 2.0 m/s to km/h
  **d)** 50 m/s to km/h

**18. a)** An average person is 175 cm tall. How many people could you stack one on top of another to reach the top of the CN Tower (553 m)?

**b)** If 1 inch = 2.54 cm and 12 inches = 1 foot, how tall is the CN Tower in feet?

**19. a)** The maximum speed reached by a standing skate boarder is about 14.7 m/s. Would the skateboarder get a ticket in a 30 km/h speed zone?

**b)** A snail crawls 100 times slower than a normal human walk (3 km/h). How many times slower than the human is the snail?

**20.** For the roller coaster in Fig. 1.28, estimate the displacement and distance travelled for the following sections:
  **a)** A to B        **b)** B to C        **c)** C to B
  **d)** B to D        **e)** A to D

**Fig.1.28**

C

B                                        D

A

**21.** Four people set out to measure a field's perimeter. They find that Side A = 20.0 m, Side B = 12 m, Side C = 20.005 m, and Side D = 11.99998 m. Taking into account significant digits,
  **a)** what is the perimeter, in metres and in millimetres?
  **b)** what is the sum of A + B?

c) of C + D?

d) of B + D?

e) What would account for the different number of decimal places in the measurements?

**22.** What is the difference in heights for the following measurements?

a) 50.7 m and 30.2 m

b) 50.7 m and 2 m

c) 2356.9076 cm and 3567.2 m

d) 30.9 km and 30.9 mm

## 1.3 The Meaning of Negatives in Kinematics

**23.** For the paths taken in Fig. 1.29, state the displacement using the standard reference system.

**Fig.1.29**

(a)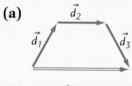

(b)

(c)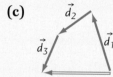

(d)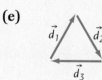

(e)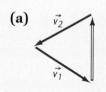

1 cm = 50 m

**24.** For the motions in Fig. 1.30, describe the velocity in terms of a reference system where north is negative and east is positive.

**Fig.1.30**

(a)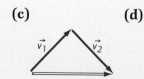

(b)

(c)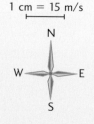

(d)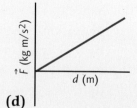

1 cm = 15 m/s

**25.** A person is walking 3 km/h in a train that is moving 70 km/h west. In the standard reference system, what are the person's two possible velocities as measured by a cop using a radar gun parked on the side of the road?

## 1.4 Three Steps to Graphical Analysis

**26.** Copy the graphs in Fig. 1.31 into your notebook and draw a line of best fit for each. Indicate any points that are anomalies.

**Fig.1.31**

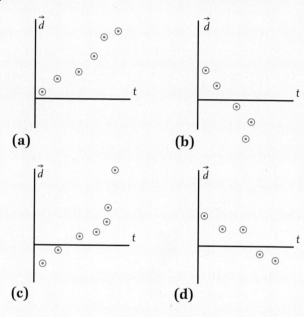

(a)     (b)

(c)     (d)

**27.** For the graphs in Fig. 1.32, state the units for

a) slopes taken from the graphs.

b) areas taken from the graphs.

**Fig.1.32**

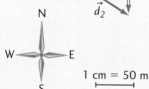

(a)     (b)

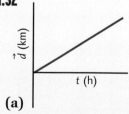

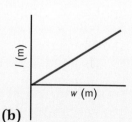

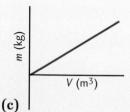

(c)     (d)

## ▶ 1.5 Analysis of Straight-Line $\vec{d}$-t Graphs

**28.** For the graph in Fig. 1.33, describe what the person is doing in each marked section.

**Fig.1.33**

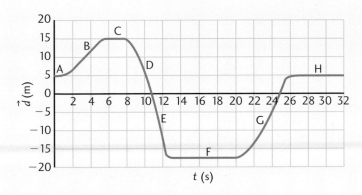

**29.** For the graph in Fig. 1.34, calculate
   **a)** the slope for each section.
   **b)** the area for each section (this is practice for the next chapter).

**Fig.1.34**

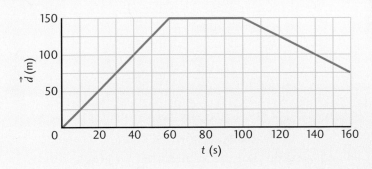

**30.** Find the velocity for each section in Fig. 1.34.

**31.** Using the data in Fig. 1.35 for a Formula 1 car,
   **a)** plot a labelled $\vec{d}$-t graph and find the velocity of the car.
   **b)** Convert the velocity to km/h.

**Fig.1.35**

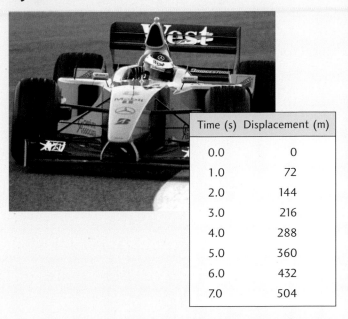

| Time (s) | Displacement (m) |
|---|---|
| 0.0 | 0 |
| 1.0 | 72 |
| 2.0 | 144 |
| 3.0 | 216 |
| 4.0 | 288 |
| 5.0 | 360 |
| 6.0 | 432 |
| 7.0 | 504 |

**32.** The X-15A-2 travels at about six times the speed of sound (Mach 6). Use the data in Fig. 1.36 to create a $\vec{d}$-t graph. Find the velocity and convert it to km/h.

**Fig.1.36**

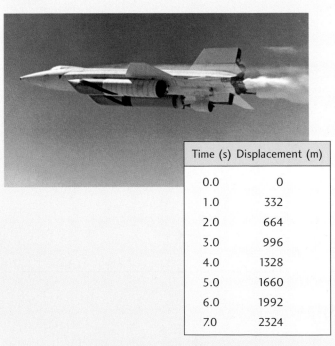

| Time (s) | Displacement (m) |
|---|---|
| 0.0 | 0 |
| 1.0 | 332 |
| 2.0 | 664 |
| 3.0 | 996 |
| 4.0 | 1328 |
| 5.0 | 1660 |
| 6.0 | 1992 |
| 7.0 | 2324 |

**33.** Use the tickertape data in Fig. 1.37 to create a $\vec{d}$-t table and a $\vec{d}$-t graph, then find the object's velocity. The period of the ticker (time between dots) is 0.40 s.

**Fig.1.37**

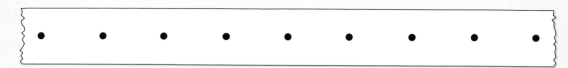

**34.** Graph the data from Fig. 1.37. Assume that all measurements of displacement are *negative*.

### ▶ 1.6 Analysis of Curved-Line $\vec{d}$-t Graphs

**35.** Copy the graphs in Fig. 1.38 into your notebook and draw curves of best fit. Then draw in three representative tangents for each curve.

**Fig.1.38**

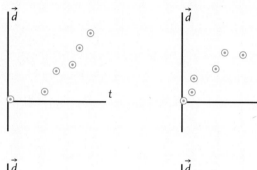

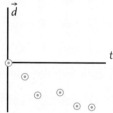

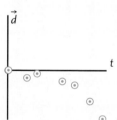

**36.** Describe what is happening in the following graph by identifying motion sections. Assume positive is up.

**Fig.1.39**

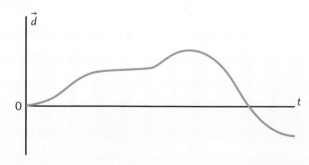

**37.** Copy the graph in Fig. 1.39 into your notebook and draw one tangent per section.

**38.** Copy the graphs in Fig. 1.40 into your note-book. Draw a tangent at the point indicated and find its slope.

**Fig.1.40**

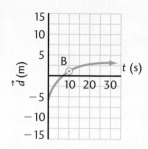

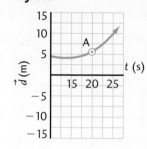

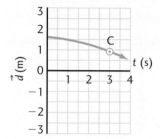

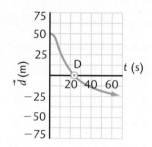

**39.** For the following data of a car, draw a $\vec{d}$-t graph and describe the motion. Draw tangents at 2, 4, and 6 s, and find their slopes. Convert the values to km/h.

| Time (s) | Displacement (m) |
|----------|------------------|
| 0.0 | 0.0 |
| 1.0 | 5.0 |
| 2.0 | 15 |
| 3.0 | 30 |
| 4.0 | 55 |
| 5.0 | 70 |
| 6.0 | 80 |
| 7.0 | 90 |

**40. a)** For the tickertape data in Fig. 1.41, meas-ure the displacements, create a $\vec{d}$-t chart, then plot the values on a $\vec{d}$-t graph. Find the curve of best fit, draw four tangents, and find their slopes. Is this object speed-ing up or slowing down? ($T = 0.05$ s)

**b)** Change your displacement values to nega-tive. Repeat the graphing procedure and find the slopes of the tangents. Is the object speeding up or slowing down?

**Fig.1.41**

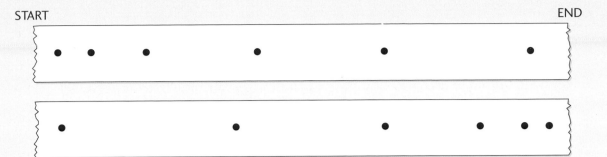

START                                                                 END

**Fig.1.42**

**41. a)** For the tickertape data in Fig. 1.42, measure the displacements, create a $\vec{d}$-$t$ chart, then plot the values on a $\vec{d}$-$t$ graph. Find the curve of best fit, draw four tangents, and find their slopes. Is this object speeding up or slowing down? ($T = 0.05$ s)

   **b)** Change your displacement values to negative. Repeat the graphing procedure and find the slopes of the tangents. Is the object speeding up or slowing down?

▶ **1.7 Average and Instantaneous Velocities**

**42.** For the graph in Fig. 1.43, find the average velocity between the points indicated.

**Fig.1.43**

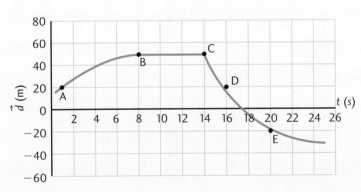

**Fig.1.44**

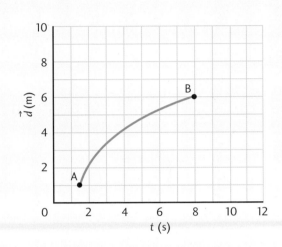

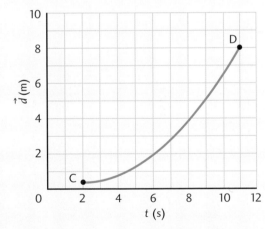

**43.** For the graphs in Fig. 1.44, find the average velocity, as well as the instantaneous velocities at the beginning and end of the time period indicated. Calculate the average of the instantaneous values and compare them to the average velocity obtained graphically.

**44.** A person walks 50 m [up] a flight of stairs in 1.0 min, then waits 125 s while being hooked up to a bungee cord. He jumps off, falls 55 m in 5.0 s, then stops and bounces back 10 m in 1.0 s before eventually coming to rest. Draw a representative $\vec{d}$-$t$ graph. Remember to include a slowing-down section as the free fall was 50 m in height. You can add extra sections for the person bouncing to a complete stop if you wish.

## Purpose

To study the relationship between the instrument used in an experiment and its method of use by measuring different objects with rulers of different precision.

## Equipment

Small ruler with mm markings

Metre stick with cm markings (do not use the side with mm on it)

Metre stick taped up so no markings are present

## Procedure

Measure and record the following three lengths using each of the three rulers.

a) A person's foot

b) A person's height while he or she is free standing (you are not allowed to use a wall to help you)

c) The length of the room

NOTE: Keep track of the number of times you lift the ruler.

Assign a procedural and instrumental uncertainty for each of the measurements (see Appendix A). Justify briefly the procedural uncertainties. Summarize them in a table.

## Discussion

1. Do the measurements agree without the uncertainties? Explain any discrepancy.

2. Do the measurements agree with the uncertainties included?

3. Which instrument is best suited to measure each object?

4. Is aligning an object with the measuring device significant for the various objects?

## Conclusion

State the relationship between the precision of an instrument and the manner in which it is used in an experiment.

| Data Table | | | | | | | | |
|---|---|---|---|---|---|---|---|---|
| Object | Unmarked metre stick | | | Marked metre stick | | | Small ruler | |
| | (m) | #lifts | | (cm) | #lifts | | (mm) | #lifts |
| Foot length | | | | | | | | |
| Person's height | | | | | | | | |
| Room length | | | | | | | | |
| Uncertainty | | | | | | | | |

## Purpose

To analyze an example of constant velocity.

## Equipment

Tickertape apparatus: power supply, clacker or sparker, tickertape
Metre stick
Graph paper
Tape

**Fig.Lab.1.1**

Ticker tape

Motion of tape

Clacker

## Procedure

1. Assuming that the period for the tickertape system is known, run a tape of about 1 m through the recorder. Try to keep a steady pull, one that is not too slow (produces too many dots) and not too sharp (produces mainly an accelerating action and too few dots).

2. Study the tape and tear off the beginning section where the dots are increasing in spacing. Study the end and tear off any tape which has an obviously decreasing set of dots. You should have at least 10 dots left on your tape.

## Data

1. Measure the distance from the first point left on your tape to each of the points on the ticker-tape. **Do not measure the spacing between consecutive dots!** Always measure the distance from the first dot.

2. Create a $\vec{d}$-t chart. If the period of the clacker is an awkward value, then use it as a multiplication factor for the time and place it in the heading of your chart. Example: If $T = 0.032$ s is the period of the clacker, then the chart heading for time should read "Time ($\times$ 0.032 s)." Then the numbers which are used in the actual chart are just the dot numbers, 1 to whatever number of dots you have.

## Uncertainty

Assign an instrumental uncertainty for the ruler you used (see Appendix A). If you felt there was a procedural component as well, then assign a value to it. Add the two. It may be possible that some points have a different uncertainty if the tickertape is long or the ruler is short.

## Analysis

1. Produce a $\vec{d}$-t graph. If the uncertainties in $\vec{d}$ are visible on the graph, use an error bar for each. If not, use a dot inside a small circle.

2. Draw a line of best fit through the points.

3. Find three slopes from the graph. Include units when you calculate the slopes. Remember to factor in the period for the run part of the slope calculation (if necessary).

4. Average the slope value, then find the percent deviation (see Appendix A) for each value of the slope (compare it to the average).

5. Calculate the uncertainty in the slopes.

6. Produce a chart summarizing your results.

## Discussion

1. How do you know that the slope from a $\vec{d}$-t graph is speed?

2. Why did you cut off the beginning points and possibly the end points on the tickertape?

3. What would happen if you used these points in drawing a best-fit line?

4. Were your deviations zero or close to zero? If not, account for the difference.

5. Another method of finding the distance from the beginning of the tickertape to a given dot would have been to add up the spaces between dots. Why does this method produce a larger uncertainty?

## Conclusion

State the speed of the tickertape along with an uncertainty for it.

## LAB 1.3 Acceleration

### Purpose

To analyze the motion of an accelerating object.

### Equipment

Tickertape apparatus: power supply, clacker or sparker, tickertape
Toy car, 100 g–200 g mass, Metre stick
Graph paper, Tape, Pulley

**Fig.Lab.1.2**

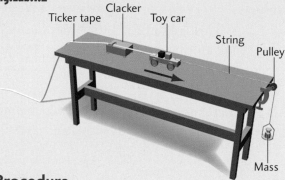

### Procedure

1. Clamp the clacker to the back of the lab station.
2. Cut a piece of tickertape no longer than the height of the lab station. Set the toy car in front of the clacker. Feed the tickertape through the clacker and tape it to the back of the car.
3. Attach the pulley to the front edge of the lab station.
4. Run the string from the front of the toy car over the pulley. Tie the mass to the end of the string.
5. Start the sparker or clacker and let go of the car. It will travel to the edge of the table where someone should be ready to catch it.
6. Repeat the experiment for each member in the group.

### Alternate Procedures

1. If a smart pulley is available, use it in place of the one in the experiment to collect the data.
2. If a sonic ranger is available, place it behind the car to collect the required data as the car moves away.

### Data

1. Measure the distance from the first point on your tape to each of the points on the tickertape. **Do not measure the spacing between consecutive dots!** Always measure the distance from the first dot.

2. Create a $\vec{d}$-$t$ chart. If the period is an awkward value, then use it as a multiplication factor for the time and place it in the heading of your chart. Example: If $T = 0.032$ s is the period of the clacker, than the chart heading for time should read "Time ($\times$ 0.032 s)." Then the numbers which are used in the actual chart are just the dot numbers, 1 to whatever number of dots you have.

### Uncertainty

Assign an instrumental uncertainty for the ruler you used. If you felt there was a procedural component as well, assign a value to it. Add the two. It may be possible that some points have a different uncertainty if the tickertape is long or the ruler is short.

### Analysis

1. Produce a $\vec{d}$-$t$ graph. If the uncertainties in $\vec{d}$ are visible on the graph, use an error bar for each. If not, use a dot inside a small circle.
2. Draw a curve of best fit through the points.
3. Select three different times along the graph. At these times, draw a tangent and find its slope. Include units in your calculations. Remember to factor in the period of the clacker for the run part of the slope calculation.
4. Produce a chart summarizing your results.
5. Optional: Calculate the uncertainties in the slopes.

### Discussion

1. Explain why the beginning section of the graph is curved.
2. Does the graph ever become truly straight?
3. What factors are acting on the car to limit its speed?
4. What is the slope of the graph at time zero?
5. How do you know that the car is speeding up in terms of the rise part of the slope calculation?

### Conclusion

Summarize the action of the car.

### Extension

Design and carry out an experiment to collect the required data and graph the motion of an object that is slowing down.

# Velocity-Time Graphs

## Chapter Outline

**By the end of this chapter, you will be able to**

- determine acceleration from a velocity-time graph
- determine displacement from a velocity-time graph
- solve problems in straight-line motions using equations of kinematics

## 2.1 Analysis of Velocity-Time Graphs

In the last chapter, we found velocities from displacement-time graphs by taking slopes at given times. In this chapter, we will use these values to create velocity-time graphs and analyze them using the three primary analysis methods for graphs, learned in the last chapter.

### Constant-Velocity Graphs

A motorcyclist travelling along a straight, level road passed markers at 40 m, 100 m, and 160 m at the times you can read on the graph in Fig. 2.1(a). This $\vec{d}\text{-}t$ graph is a straight line. Slopes at three points on the graph are recorded in the table of Fig. 2.1(b), and plotted on the $\vec{v}\text{-}t$ graph in Fig. 2.1(c). The horizontal line of the $\vec{v}\text{-}t$ graph shows that the velocity of the motorcyclist remained constant as time passed. Use the read, slope, and area techniques of graph analysis to discover what information can be gleaned from a $\vec{v}\text{-}t$ graph.

**Fig.2.1**

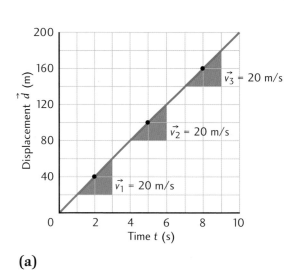

(a)

| Time (s) | Velocity (m/s) |
|----------|----------------|
| 2.0 | 20 |
| 5.0 | 20 |
| 8.0 | 20 |

(b)

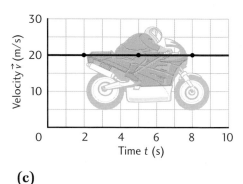

(c)

### Reading the Graph

In Fig. 2.2, the units on the $y$ axis are **m/s**, which indicates velocity. Since you are reading a given velocity at a given time, reading this graph allows you to find **instantaneous velocities**.

**Fig.2.2**

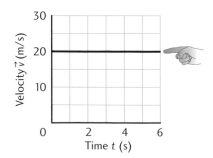

### Finding the Slope of the Graph

To find the slope of the graph in Fig. 2.2, note that the horizontal graph has no rise. Thus, for any value of $\Delta t$, the value of $\Delta \vec{v}$ will be zero. The value of the slope will be

$$\text{slope} = \frac{\Delta \vec{v}}{\Delta t} = \frac{0 \text{ m/s}}{3.0 \text{ s}} = 0 \, \frac{\text{m}}{\text{s}} \times \frac{1}{3.0 \text{ s}} = 0 \text{ m/s}^2$$

UNIT A: Motion and Forces

The slope calculation produces a value of zero with units of **m/s²**. This is the change in velocity over a given time period. We can see that if an object has a constant velocity, its acceleration must be zero.

The process of changing the velocity is called **acceleration.** The units for acceleration are $\frac{\text{distance}}{(\text{time})^2}$. By finding the slope of the $\vec{v}$-$t$ graph, we have produced the following equation:

$$\vec{a} = \frac{\vec{v_2} - \vec{v_1}}{t_2 - t_1} \qquad \text{or} \qquad \vec{a} = \frac{\Delta \vec{v}}{\Delta t}$$

Calculating the slope from two points on the $\vec{v}$-$t$ graph gives us the **average acceleration**. The slope of the *tangent* on the $\vec{v}$-$t$ graph gives us the **instantaneous acceleration**.

### Finding the Area Under the Graph

Consider positive to be north. In Fig. 2.3(a), the area under the graph forms a rectangle, so its area is obtained by the relationship $l \times w$ (length times width). In our case, the length is time and the width is velocity. We can represent the area of the $\vec{v}$-$t$ graph as $\vec{v}$ times $t$. By doing a unit analysis, we see that

$$\frac{\text{m}}{\text{s}} \times \text{s} = \text{m}$$

indicating that the area represents a distance. In other words, the area represents the displacement of the object during the chosen time interval.

$$\text{area} = \vec{v} \times \Delta t = 20 \, \frac{\text{m}}{\text{s}} \times 5.0 \text{ s} = 100 \text{ m}$$

$$\therefore \Delta \vec{d} = 100 \text{ m [N]}$$

The displacement is in the positive direction because the area is positive. If the velocity is negative, as in Fig. 2.3(b), the displacement is also negative.

$$\text{area} = \vec{v} \times \Delta t = -15 \, \frac{\text{m}}{\text{s}} \times 5.0 \text{ s} = -75 \text{ m}$$

$$\therefore \Delta \vec{d} = 75 \text{ m [S]}$$

The results of this analysis are summarized in Fig. 2.4.

**ACCELERATION UNITS**

Another unit for acceleration is km/h². However, ordinary observations would more likely produce accelerations of (km/h)/s. For example, we talk about a car changing its velocity at a rate of 20 km/h each second. This is written as (20 km/h)/s, which becomes 5.6 m/s² in the SI system.

**Fig.2.3**

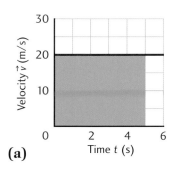

**(a)**

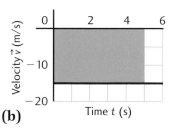

**(b)**

**Fig.2.4** Three Graph Analysis Techniques for a $\vec{v}$-$t$ Graph

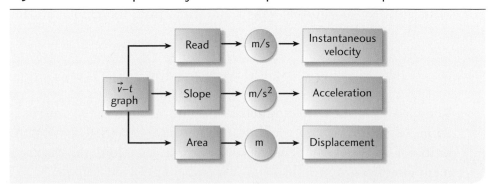

## Graphs with Changing Velocity

On a performance test, a Honda Civic produced the $\vec{d}$-$t$ graph in Fig. 2.5(a). As you saw in Chapter 1, a curved $\vec{d}$-$t$ graph means that velocity is changing. Finding the slope of this graph at four different times gives the velocities, as shown in Fig. 2.5(b). Plotting these points gives the $\vec{v}$-$t$ graph in Fig. 2.5(c).

**Fig.2.5**

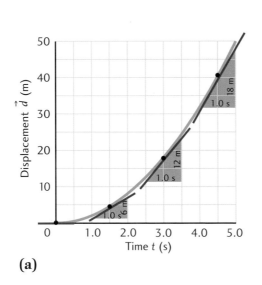

(a)

| Time (s) | Velocity (m/s) |
|----------|----------------|
| 0.0 | 0.0 |
| 1.5 | 6.0 |
| 3.0 | 12 |
| 4.5 | 18 |

(b)

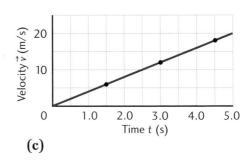

(c)

### Finding the Slope of the Graph

Figure 2.5(c) shows a steadily increasing velocity. If the velocity increases, the object is accelerating. To find the acceleration, we find the slope of the $\vec{v}$-$t$ graph.

$$\vec{a} = \frac{\Delta \vec{v}}{\Delta t} = \frac{\vec{v}_2 - \vec{v}_1}{t_2 - t_1} = \frac{18 \text{ m/s} - 6 \text{ m/s}}{4.5 \text{ s} - 1.5 \text{ s}} = \frac{12 \text{ m/s}}{3.0 \text{ s}} = 4.0 \text{ m/s}^2$$

The value for the acceleration is a positive number. The sign indicates that the acceleration is in the same direction as the velocity (eastward), which means that the car is speeding up. Its acceleration is 4.0 m/s² [E].

### Finding the Area Under the Graph

The area under the graph in Fig. 2.6 is a triangle. The area of a triangle is $\frac{1}{2}$(base)(height). By substituting values and units from the graph into the equation, we obtain $\frac{1}{2}$(velocity)(time). Thus

**Fig.2.6**

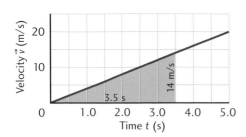

$$\Delta \vec{d} = \tfrac{1}{2} (\vec{v} \times \Delta t) = \tfrac{1}{2} \left( 14 \, \frac{\text{m}}{\text{s}} \times 3.5 \text{ s} \right) = 24.5 \text{ m}$$

Rounded off to the correct number of significant digits, the answer is 24 m. As in the last case, the units for time have cancelled, leaving the units for displacement. The value is positive; therefore, the displacement after 3.5 s is 24 m [E].

EXAMPLE 1 **Working with negative motion**

Repeating the test drive in Fig. 2.5 in a westward direction produced the $\vec{v}$-$t$ graph in Fig. 2.7. Calculate the acceleration and reconstruct the $\vec{d}$-$t$ graph.

**Fig.2.7**

### Solution and Connection to Theory

a) *Finding acceleration.* In the standard reference system, westward is negative. Hence the velocities are negative. But that does not change the process of finding the slope. In Fig. 2.7, the slope of the $\vec{v}$-$t$ graph gives an acceleration of $-4.0$ m/s$^2$ or 4.0 m/s$^2$ [W]. Although the acceleration turns out to be negative, it's in the same direction as the velocity. Therefore, the object is speeding up.

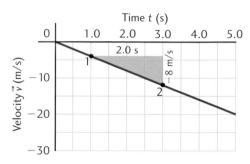

$$\vec{a} = \frac{\text{rise}}{\text{run}} = \frac{\vec{v_2} - \vec{v_1}}{t_2 - t_1} = \frac{-12 \text{ m/s} - (-4 \text{ m/s})}{3.0 \text{ s} - 1.0 \text{ s}} = \frac{-8 \text{ m/s}}{2.0 \text{ s}} = -4 \text{ m/s}^2$$

Once again, the acceleration is 4 m/s$^2$ [W].

b) *Finding displacement.* To find displacement, we once again find the area. This time, the area is *under* the time axis and stretches down to the velocity line. Three areas are shown in Fig. 2.8(a). Figure 2.8(b) is a table of displacements represented by the areas under the velocity graph. These points are then plotted in Fig. 2.8(c) and joined with a smooth curve. Fig. 2.8(c) is a $\vec{d}$-$t$ graph constructed from a $\vec{v}$-$t$ graph.

**Fig.2.8**

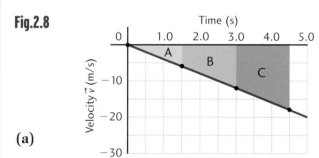

**(a)**

$$A = \tfrac{1}{2}(1.5 \text{ s})(-6.0 \text{ m/s}) = -4.5 \text{ m}$$
$$A + B = \tfrac{1}{2}(3.0 \text{ s})(-12 \text{ m/s}) = -18 \text{ m}$$
$$A + B + C = \tfrac{1}{2}(4.5 \text{ s})(-18 \text{ m/s}) = -40.5 \text{ m}$$

| Time (s) | Displacement (m) | |
|---|---|---|
| 0.0 | | 0.0 |
| 1.5 | A | −4.5 |
| 3.0 | A + B | −18.0 |
| 4.5 | A + B + C | −40.5 |

**(b)**

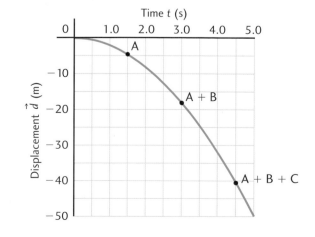

**(c)**

If the velocity values are negative as time passes, then displacements calculated from the $\vec{v}$-t graph will be negative. Figure 2.9 shows a constantly increasing negative velocity from rest: $-40$ m/s at 3.0 s. At that point, the displacement is

$$\Delta \vec{d} = \tfrac{1}{2}(\vec{v} \times \Delta t)$$

$$= \tfrac{1}{2}\left(-40 \, \frac{m}{s} \times 3.0 \, s\right)$$

$$= -60 \, m$$

You might say, "If you run backwards, then you'll end up farther back."

**Fig.2.9**

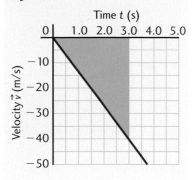

---

| EXAMPLE 2 | **When velocity and acceleration have different signs** |

For the slowing-down portion of the roller coaster ride, find the acceleration.

### *Solution and Connection to Theory*

**Given**

For this case, we will use the $\vec{d}$-t graph in Fig. 2.10.

Figure 2.10 shows the process of creating the $\vec{v}$-t graph (c) from slopes on the $\vec{d}$-t graph (a). To find the acceleration, take the slope of the $\vec{v}$-t graph.

$$\vec{a} = \frac{\Delta \vec{v}}{\Delta t} = \frac{6 \, m/s - 18 \, m/s}{4.0 \, s - 2.0 \, s} = \frac{-12 \, m/s}{2.0 \, s} = -6.0 \, m/s^2$$

The velocities are eastward and positive. The acceleration is negative; therefore, it must be westward: $6.0 \, m/s^2$ [W].

**Fig.2.10**

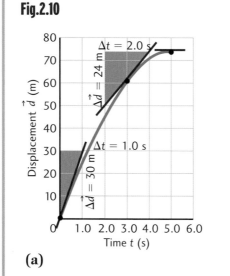

(a)

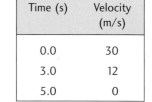

| Time (s) | Velocity (m/s) |
|----------|----------------|
| 0.0 | 30 |
| 3.0 | 12 |
| 5.0 | 0 |

(b)

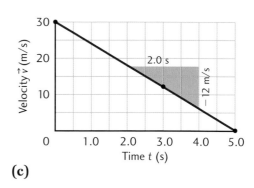

(c)

In this case, the acceleration sign is negative, yet the velocities are all positive. This means that the object is slowing down.

The flow chart of Fig. 2.11 shows how to determine from your calculations whether an object is slowing down or speeding up.

**Fig.2.11** Determining the Action of the Object

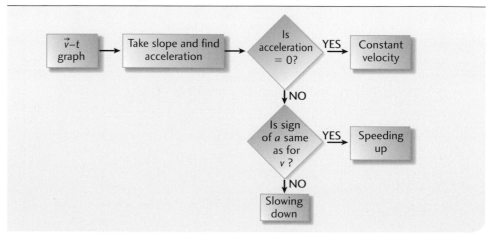

EXAMPLE 3 **A lot of travelling and ending up nowhere**

**Fig.2.12A**

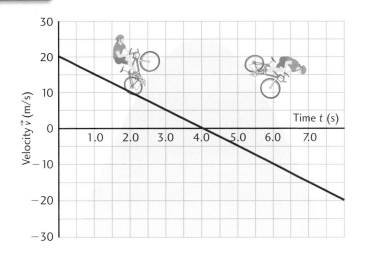

Figure 2.12A is a $\vec{v}$-$t$ graph of a cyclist's motion. The cyclist, travelling at 20 m/s, arrives at the bottom of a hill, climbs up the hill to a stop, then coasts back down again. Find the total displacement as well as the acceleration for each section.

### Solution and Connection to Theory

a) *Displacement.* First calculate the areas of sections A and B, making sure to keep track of the signs (Fig. 2.12B). Add the two parts to find the total displacement. Consider up the hill to be the positive direction.

**Fig.2.12B**

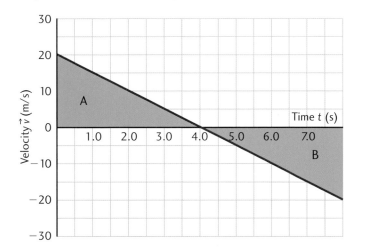

$$\Delta\vec{d}_A = \tfrac{1}{2}(\vec{v} \times \Delta t) = \tfrac{1}{2}\left(20\,\frac{\text{m}}{\text{s}} \times 4.0\,\text{s}\right) = 40\,\text{m}$$

$$\Delta\vec{d}_B = \tfrac{1}{2}(\vec{v} \times \Delta t) = \tfrac{1}{2}\left(-20\,\frac{\text{m}}{\text{s}} \times 4.0\,\text{s}\right) = -40\,\text{m}$$

$$\Delta\vec{d}_{\text{total}} = \Delta\vec{d}_A + \Delta\vec{d}_B = 40\,\text{m} + (-40\,\text{m}) = 0\,\text{m}$$

The total displacement is zero. The change in position from the start of the motion to its finish is zero; the cyclist is back at the bottom of the hill.

(b) *Acceleration.* To calculate the acceleration, take the slope of the line, as shown in Fig. 2.13. Both the negative and the positive sections have the same acceleration.

**Fig.2.13**

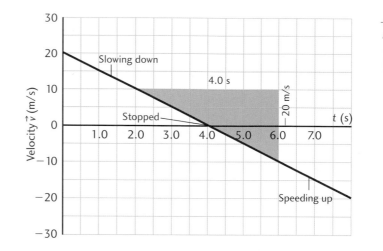

$$\vec{a} = \frac{\vec{v_2} - \vec{v_1}}{t_2 - t_1} = \frac{-10 \text{ m/s} - 10 \text{ m/s}}{6.0 \text{ s} - 2.0 \text{ s}} = \frac{-20 \text{ m/s}}{4.0 \text{ s}} = -5.0 \text{ m/s}^2$$

The acceleration for the whole trip is 5.0 m/s² [down]. Note that in section A, the velocities are positive and the acceleration is negative. According to Fig. 2.11 (Connecting the Concepts), this means that the object is slowing down. In section B, the velocities are negative and the acceleration is negative. This means that the object is speeding up.

## Average Velocity

The three graphical analysis procedures on a $\vec{v}$-$t$ graph give you instantaneous velocities, acceleration, and displacement. To find **average velocity** ($\vec{v}_{avg}$), we use the definition

$$\vec{v}_{avg} = \frac{\Delta \vec{d}}{\Delta t}$$

The average velocity is the total displacement divided by the total time.

We know that the area under the $\vec{v}$-$t$ graph represents how far the object has gone in any direction. Therefore, if we divide the area by the time, we can find the average velocity.

EXAMPLE 4    **Calculating average velocities graphically**

For the cyclist in Fig. 2.12, calculate the average velocity over the first 6.0 s.

## Solution and Connection to Theory

Area A in Fig. 2.14 represents the displacement over the first 4.0 s, and area B represents the displacement for the next 2.0 s.

The net displacement is the sum of the two areas.

$$\Delta\vec{d} = \frac{1}{2}\left(20\,\frac{m}{s} \times 4.0\ s\right) + \frac{1}{2}\left(-10\,\frac{m}{s} \times 2.0\ s\right) = 40\ m - 10\ m = 30\ m$$

The positive value indicates that the net displacement is up.

A net displacement of 30 m [up] during 6.0 s gives an average velocity of

$$\vec{v}_{avg} = \frac{\Delta\vec{d}}{\Delta t} = \frac{30\ m}{6.0\ s} = 5.0\ m/s$$

**Fig.2.14**

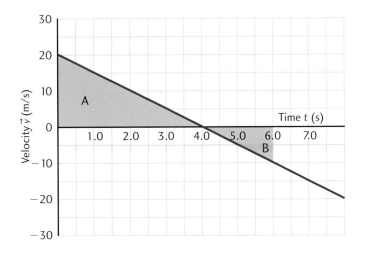

Thus the average velocity is 5.0 m/s [up].

All the information that can be derived from a $\vec{v}$-$t$ graph is summarized in Fig. 2.15.

**Fig.2.15** Information Obtained from a $\vec{v}$-$t$ Graph

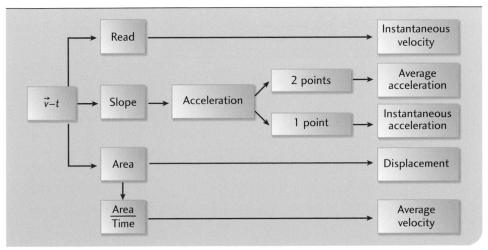

1. For Fig. 2.12, find the cyclist's speed and distance from where he started at 2.0 s and 7.0 s.

2. Draw a representative $\vec{v}$-$t$ graph showing
   **a)** uniform motion forward.     **d)** speeding up backward.
   **b)** uniform motion backward.   **e)** slowing down forward.
   **c)** speeding up forward.       **f)** slowing down backward.

3. For the graphs in Question 2, produce simple scales ranging from 0–5 s and 0–5 m/s. Then calculate the following for each graph:
   **a)** Acceleration
   **b)** Total displacement
   **c)** Average velocity

4. From the $\vec{d}$-$t$ graph in Fig. 1.18, generate a corresponding $\vec{v}$-$t$ graph.

5. The greatest acceleration possible in free fall is 9.8 m/s². Compare the accelerations from the graph you drew in Section 1.7, Applying the Concepts, Question 3(e). Modify any measurements to the graph if the values for acceleration do not make sense. Keep this graph for later analysis in studying the forces acting on you during the ride.

**Fig.2.16**

## ▶ 2.2 Moving from One Graph to Another

Figure 2.17 summarizes all the possible $\vec{d}$-$t$ motions with their corresponding $\vec{v}$-$t$ graphs and acceleration values. We can use the graph segments shown here to create $\vec{v}$-$t$ graph sketches from $\vec{d}$-$t$ graphs and vice versa.

**Fig.2.17**

| | $\vec{d}$–$t$ graphs | $\vec{v}$–$t$ graphs | Velocity | Acceleration | Example |
|---|---|---|---|---|---|
| Stopped | 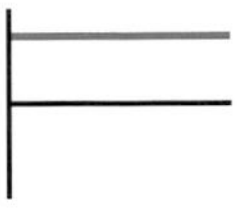 |  | $\vec{v} = 0$ | $\vec{a} = 0$ |  |
| | 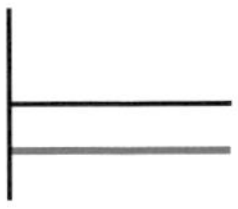 |  | $\vec{v} = 0$ | $\vec{a} = 0$ |  |
| Constant velocity | 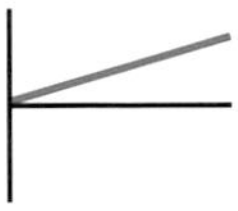 | 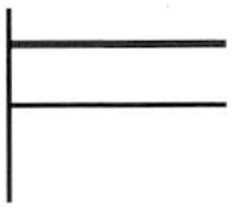 | $\vec{v} > 0$ | $\vec{a} = 0$ |  |
| |  | 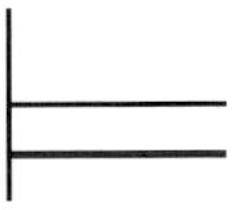 | $\vec{v} < 0$ | $\vec{a} = 0$ |  |
| Speeding up |  | 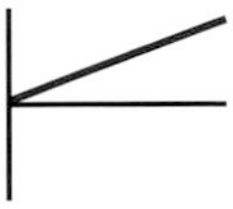 | $\vec{v} > 0$ | $\vec{a} > 0$ |  |
| |  | 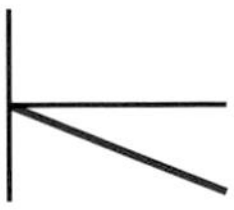 | $\vec{v} < 0$ | $\vec{a} < 0$ |  |
| Slowing down | 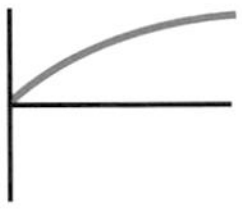 | 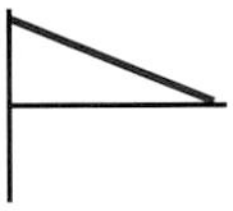 | $\vec{v} > 0$ | $\vec{a} < 0$ |  |
| | 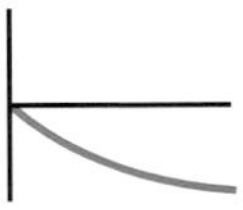 | 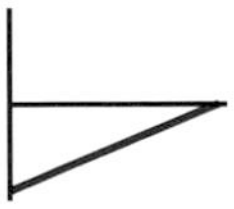 | $\vec{v} < 0$ | $\vec{a} > 0$ |  |

Each $\vec{v}$-$t$ graph can be generated from its corresponding $\vec{d}$-$t$ graph by taking slopes of the $\vec{d}$-$t$ graph at selected times and plotting them on a $\vec{v}$-$t$ graph.

## Fig.2.18 Constructing a $\vec{v}$-t graph from a $\vec{d}$-t graph

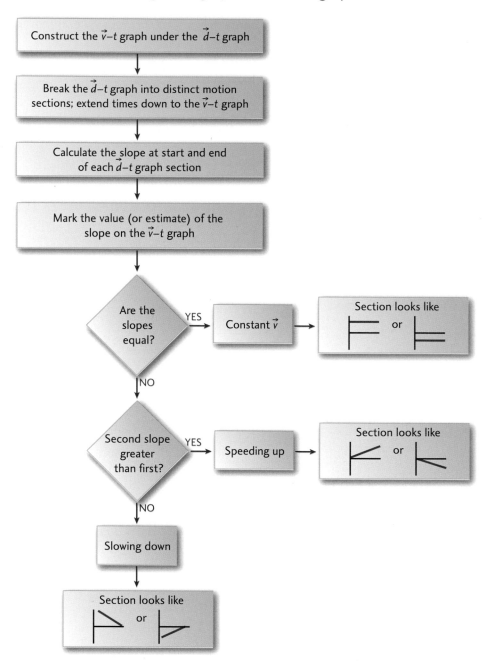

Construct the $\vec{v}$–t graph under the $\vec{d}$–t graph

Break the $\vec{d}$–t graph into distinct motion sections; extend times down to the $\vec{v}$–t graph

Calculate the slope at start and end of each $\vec{d}$–t graph section

Mark the value (or estimate) of the slope on the $\vec{v}$–t graph

Are the slopes equal? — YES → Constant $\vec{v}$ → Section looks like ... or ...

NO

Second slope greater than first? — YES → Speeding up → Section looks like ... or ...

NO

Slowing down

Section looks like ... or ...

To construct a $\vec{v}$-t graph from a complex $\vec{d}$-t graph, follow the procedure outlined in Fig. 2.18. Use the graphical summary in Fig. 2.17 to choose the appropriate corresponding shapes.

## EXAMPLE 5   Converting a $\vec{d}$-t graph to a $\vec{v}$-t graph

From the $\vec{d}$-t graph in Fig. 2.19, construct the corresponding $\vec{v}$-t graph.

## Solution and Connection to Theory

These are the steps for transferring the slopes of tangents on the $\vec{d}$-t graph to values on the $\vec{v}$-t graph at the appropriate instants of time (see Fig. 2.19):

1. Draw $\vec{v}$-t axes beneath the $\vec{d}$-t graph and make the time axis the same as the one on the $\vec{d}$-t graph.
2. Mark each point on the $\vec{d}$-t graph where the shape of the graph changes — these are actually points where the object's acceleration changes.
3. Draw vertical lines from each marked point down to the $\vec{v}$-t graph.
4. Draw a tangent to the $\vec{d}$-t graph at each of the marked points and calculate its slope (velocity).
5. Mark the value of the velocity for each point at the corresponding time on the $\vec{v}$-t graph.
6. Join the points, and check that the lines match the motion, as described in the chart of Fig. 2.18.

The resulting $\vec{v}$-t graph describes the same motion as the original $\vec{d}$-t graph.

**METRES PER SECOND**[?]

Many of our common actions involve constant acceleration, but there are cases where acceleration changes. The name given to this phenomenon is **jerk** (j), or in Britain, **jolt**. It is represented by $\frac{\Delta a}{\Delta t}$, with units m/s³. Jerk is a measure of effects such as the discomfort level of passengers (like sitting beside a new driver). Using computer controllers, train designers try to keep the jerk to less than 2 m/s³. Names in the continuing sloping process of graphs have been suggested: jerk (m/s³), snap (m/s⁴), crackle (m/s⁵), and pop (m/s⁶).

**Fig.2.19**

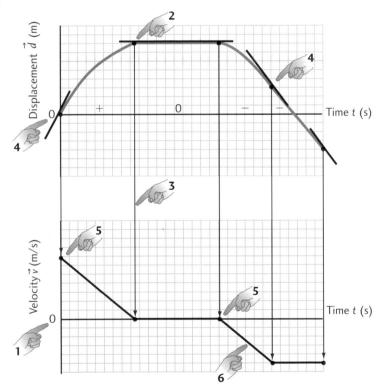

> Each $\vec{d}$-t graph can be generated from the $\vec{v}$-t graph by taking areas at selected times on the $\vec{v}$-t graph and plotting them on the $\vec{d}$-t graph.

The procedure for constructing a $\vec{d}$-t graph from a complex $\vec{v}$-t graph is outlined in Fig. 2.20. Use the graph summary of Fig. 2.17 to choose the appropriate corresponding shapes.

**Fig.2.20** Constructing a $\vec{d}$-$t$ graph from a $\vec{v}$-$t$ graph

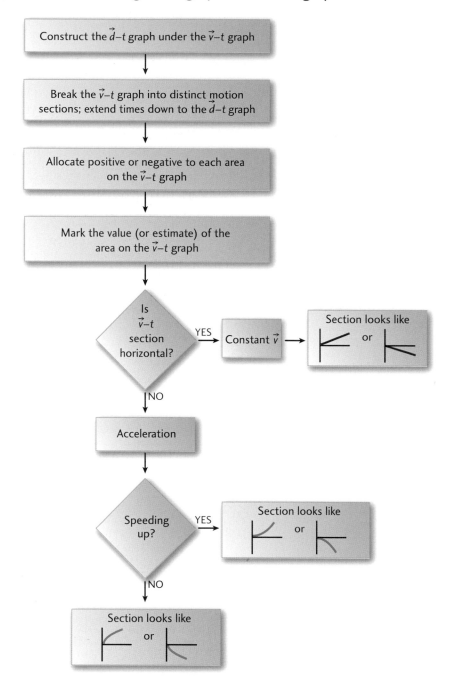

---

**EXAMPLE 6** **Converting a $\vec{v}$-$t$ graph to a $\vec{d}$-$t$ graph**

From the $\vec{v}$-$t$ graph in Fig. 2.21A, construct the corresponding $\vec{d}$-$t$ graph.

### Solution and Connection to Theory

These are the steps for transferring the areas of sections on the $\vec{v}$-$t$ graph to values on the $\vec{d}$-$t$ graph at the appropriate instants of time (see Fig. 2.21B):

**Fig.2.21A**

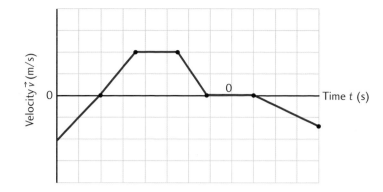

1. Draw $\vec{d}\text{-}t$ axes beneath the $\vec{v}\text{-}t$ graph and make the time axis the same as the one on the $\vec{d}\text{-}t$ graph.
2. Divide the area under the $\vec{v}\text{-}t$ graph into a series of sections with defined areas (positive and negative triangles and rectangles).
3. Mark the points on the $\vec{v}\text{-}t$ graph at the end of each section, indicating whether the motion is positive or negative.
4. Draw vertical lines from each marked point down to the $\vec{v}\text{-}t$ graph.
5. Calculate or estimate the area (displacement) of each section of the $\vec{v}\text{-}t$ graph, noting in particular whether it is positive or negative. Mark the value of the displacement for each point at the corresponding time on the $\vec{d}\text{-}t$ graph.
6. Join the points using the curved shapes of Fig. 2.17, and check that the lines match the motion as described in the chart of Fig. 2.20.

The resulting $\vec{d}\text{-}t$ graph describes the same motion as the original $\vec{v}\text{-}t$ graph.

**Fig.2.21B**

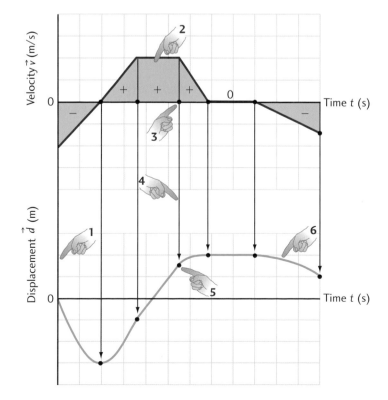

1. In Section 2.1 Question 2, you generated six $\vec{v}$-$t$ graphs representing
   a) uniform motion forward,
   b) uniform motion backward,
   c) speeding up forward,
   d) speeding up backward,
   e) slowing down forward, and
   f) slowing down backward. For each of these graphs, generate a corresponding $\vec{a}$-$t$ and $\vec{d}$-$t$ graph with values.
2. Sketch a map of a short trip to and from your favourite place.
   a) Sketch a $\vec{v}$-$t$ graph for your trip.
   b) Sketch a $\vec{d}$-$t$ graph based on your $\vec{v}$-$t$ graph. Try to have the areas add up to zero (if in the story you arrived back at the same place).
   c) Sketch a corresponding $\vec{a}$-$t$ graph.

**Computer-enhanced Bus Transportation**

The traffic light control systems used on today's streets are part of a sophisticated computer system that monitors car traffic density and rate of flow to allow for efficient streaming in and out of the city. In today's society, everyone wants to get to their destinations quickly. With many commuters driving to work, the number of cars has grown to the point of clogging routes in and out of the city. The number of commuters taking public transit, on the other hand, has declined. The biggest commuter complaint is that buses are too slow and stop too often. To remedy this problem, a new device has been added to traffic control systems that keeps green lights on slightly longer when a city bus approaches an intersection. Here's how it works. Each bus has a transmitter attached to the front of the vehicle. The traffic control system detects the bus's signal through an antenna embedded in the road and determines if keeping the green light on longer will cause other problems in the traffic grid. The time extension of the green light is no longer than ten seconds. The bus is also tracked through a computer system. Dispatchers can inform bus drivers whether they are behind or ahead of schedule so that they can adjust their speed. As a result, the time of bus travel has been cut by 25%.

3. a) Describe the different types of traffic conditions in a city. Relate each condition to the time of day, time of year, weather, road conditions, possible accidents, and car problems. Organize the situations in chart form and provide visual examples for each case.
   b) How do you think the timing of the lights is set to allow for efficient traffic flow? Consider cases where the lights are timed for a certain speed or volume of traffic.
   c) What differences in timing patterns are there between rush-hour traffic and off-hours traffic?
   d) Design a study that could be used to investigate local traffic in your community.

**Fig.2.22**  To increase efficiency of passenger pickup, passengers get on at the front of the bus and get off at the back of the bus

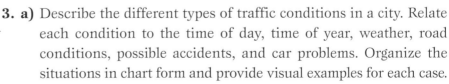

UNIT A: Motion and Forces

**e)** Speculate whether main streets that are all one way (as in Hamilton) are more efficient than two-way main streets in cities like Toronto.

**f)** In terms of the environment, why is it better for commuters to take a bus rather than a car to get to and from work?

# 2.3 Creating Equations

Equations are extremely handy since they are more versatile than graphs. To get the full complement of equations, we start with two we have used before. They can be constructed from the $\vec{v}$-$t$ graph in Fig. 2.23A.

The graph shows a motion that has a velocity of $\vec{v}_1$ at time $t_1$ and that increases with *constant* acceleration to velocity $\vec{v}_2$ at time $t_2$. We can construct the first equation by taking the slope of this graph, and the second equation by calculating the area under the graph.

**Equation 1.** Find the slope of the graph: rise $= \vec{v}_2 - \vec{v}_1$, and run $= \Delta t$.

$$\vec{a} = \frac{\vec{v}_2 - \vec{v}_1}{\Delta t}$$

Rearrange to make a linear equation.

**Fig.2.23A**

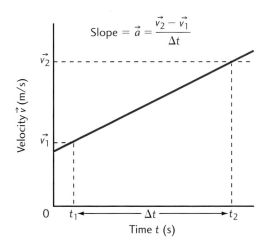

$$\vec{v}_2 = \vec{v}_1 + \vec{a}\Delta t \qquad \text{(Eq. 1)}$$

**Equation 2.** Find the displacement of the motion from the area of the trapezoid that has a base of $\Delta t$ and heights $\vec{v}_2$ and $\vec{v}_1$.

**Fig.2.23B**

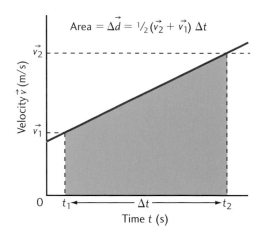

Area $= \Delta \vec{d} = \frac{1}{2}(\vec{v_2} + \vec{v_1}) \Delta t$

Velocity $\vec{v}$ (m/s)

$\vec{v_2}$

$\vec{v_1}$

0  $t_1$  $\Delta t$  $t_2$

Time $t$ (s)

$$\Delta \vec{d} = \tfrac{1}{2}(\vec{v_2} + \vec{v_1})\Delta t \quad \text{(Eq. 2)}$$

Note that since these two equations were constructed from a straight-line $\vec{v}$-$t$ graph, they can apply only to motions that have constant acceleration.

Each of these equations contains four quantities. That means that if you know the values of any three of the four, the fourth quantity can be calculated. In total, there are five quantities in these two equations: $\Delta \vec{d}$, $\vec{a}$, $\vec{v_2}$, $\vec{v_1}$, and $\Delta t$. Therefore, there should be five equations, each containing four of the variables. We can manipulate the two equations; we have to create the other three.

**Fig.2.24**  Jim Carrey

## Method of Generating Equations

The general procedure is to express one of the quantities in terms of three others in one equation and then to substitute that expression into the other equation. As a result, the quantity you choose to express will not be present in the new equation. By doing this in turn for $\vec{v_2}$, $\vec{v_1}$, and $\Delta t$ in Equation 1, we can produce the three other desired equations.

The substitution process works because you have two expressions for the same quantity: It is like referring to a person by his two different names. Whether a teacher says, "Please be seated, Mr. Carrey"; or "Sit down, Jim!" we expect the same result in either case. In mathematics, you can depend on the equals sign. Either expression for the quantity will give the same result. Expressed algebraically, if $a = b$ and $b = c + d$,

then      $a = \underline{c + d}$

$b = \quad b$

In Equation 1, you have

$$\vec{v_2} = \vec{v_1} + \vec{a}\Delta t \quad \text{(Eq. 1)}$$

Substitute the expression for $\vec{v}_2$ into Equation 2:

$$\Delta\vec{d} = \tfrac{1}{2}(\vec{v}_2 + \vec{v}_1)\Delta t \quad \text{(Eq. 2)}$$

$$\Delta\vec{d} = \tfrac{1}{2}(\vec{v}_1 + \vec{a}\Delta t + \vec{v}_1)\Delta t$$

$$\Delta\vec{d} = \vec{v}_1\Delta t + \tfrac{1}{2}\vec{a}\Delta t^2 \quad \text{(Eq. 3)}$$

Similarly, you can isolate $\vec{v}_1$ in Equation 1.

$$\vec{v}_1 = \vec{v}_2 - \vec{a}\Delta t$$

Substitute for $\vec{v}_1$ in Equation 2:

$$\Delta\vec{d} = \tfrac{1}{2}(\vec{v}_2 + \vec{v}_1)\Delta t \quad \text{(Eq. 2)}$$

$$\Delta\vec{d} = \tfrac{1}{2}(\vec{v}_2 + \vec{v}_2 - \vec{a}\Delta t)\Delta t$$

$$\Delta\vec{d} = \vec{v}_2\Delta t - \tfrac{1}{2}\vec{a}\Delta t^2 \quad \text{(Eq. 4)}$$

Finally, isolate $\Delta t$ in Equation 1 and substitute it into Equation 2.

$$\Delta t = \frac{\vec{v}_2 - \vec{v}_1}{\vec{a}} \quad \text{(Eq. 1)}$$

$$\Delta\vec{d} = \tfrac{1}{2}(\vec{v}_2 + \vec{v}_1)\frac{\vec{v}_2 - \vec{v}_1}{\vec{a}}$$

$$\Delta\vec{d} = \frac{\tfrac{1}{2}(\vec{v}_2^{\,2} - \vec{v}_1^{\,2})}{\vec{a}}$$

$$2\vec{a}\Delta\vec{d} = \vec{v}_2^{\,2} - \vec{v}_1^{\,2}$$

$$\vec{v}_2^{\,2} = \vec{v}_1^{\,2} + 2\vec{a}\Delta\vec{d} \quad \text{(Eq. 5)}$$

These are the five fundamental equations used in kinematics. Since they were derived from graphs involving constant acceleration, *they are only applicable in problems that have **constant** acceleration.* In Fig. 2.25, you can see a summary of the steps involved in deriving these equations.

**MATH TIP**

By $\Delta t^2$ we mean $(\Delta t)^2$. If ever we need to find the difference of the squares of two times, we will write $\Delta(t^2)$.

$$\Delta t^2 = (\Delta t)^2 = (t_2 - t_1)^2$$
$$\Delta(t^2) = t_2^2 - t_1^2$$

**MATH TIP**

Remember that

$$(a + b)(a - b) = a^2 - b^2$$

**Fig.2.25** Deriving the Five Kinematics Equations

1. Use the following two equations to derive $\vec{a} = \dfrac{\Delta \vec{v}}{\Delta t}$:

$$\Delta \vec{d} = \vec{v}_1 \Delta t + \tfrac{1}{2}\vec{a}\Delta t^2 \quad \text{and} \quad \Delta \vec{d} = \left(\dfrac{\vec{v}_1 + \vec{v}_2}{2}\right)\Delta t$$

2. Use the following two equations to derive $\vec{a} = \dfrac{\Delta \vec{v}}{\Delta t}$:

$$\Delta \vec{d} = \vec{v}_1 \Delta t + \tfrac{1}{2}\vec{a}\Delta t^2 \quad \text{and} \quad \Delta \vec{d} = \vec{v}_2 \Delta t - \tfrac{1}{2}\vec{a}\Delta t^2$$

3. In your own words, state the method of generating a new equation from two other equations.

# ▶ 2.4 Solving Problems Using Equations

Each of the five equations has four variables. The key to problem solving is to match the question's givens and the desired quantity to one of the equations. One of the equations will have the right combination of variables. That's the one you need.

You can use Table 2.1 to establish a routine for solving motion problems. For the motion to be unique, there must be three given quantities. The problem asks you to find a fourth quantity. Look for the line in the table that has check marks beside the three given variables as well as the missing variable you need. Use the equation in that line.

| | **Table 2.1** | | | | | |
|---|---|---|---|---|---|---|
| | **The Five Equations of Linear Kinematics** | | | | | |
| No. | Equation | $\Delta \vec{d}$ | $\vec{a}$ | $\vec{v}_2$ | $\vec{v}_1$ | $\Delta t$ |
| 1 | $\vec{v}_2 = \vec{v}_1 + \vec{a}\Delta t$ | | ✔ | ✔ | ✔ | ✔ |
| 2 | $\Delta \vec{d} = \tfrac{1}{2}(\vec{v}_2 + \vec{v}_1)\Delta t$ | ✔ | | ✔ | ✔ | ✔ |
| 3 | $\Delta \vec{d} = \vec{v}_1 \Delta t + \tfrac{1}{2}\vec{a}\Delta t^2$ | ✔ | ✔ | | ✔ | ✔ |
| 4 | $\Delta \vec{d} = \vec{v}_2 \Delta t - \tfrac{1}{2}\vec{a}\Delta t^2$ | ✔ | ✔ | ✔ | | ✔ |
| 5 | $\vec{v}_2^2 = \vec{v}_1^2 + 2\vec{a}\Delta \vec{d}$ | ✔ | ✔ | ✔ | ✔ | |

**EXAMPLE 7**   **Selecting the correct equation**

Kitty O'Neal, a female dragster, reached a speed of 628 km/h from rest in 3.72 s. How far did she travel in that time?

### *Solution and Connection to Theory*

Translate the problem into symbolic terms.

**Given:**

$\vec{v}_1 = 0$ km/h      $\vec{v}_2 = 628$ km/h      $\Delta t = 3.72$ s

Determine the quantity you are asked to find:      $\Delta \vec{d} = ?$

The four variables in this problem are $\vec{v}_1$, $\vec{v}_2$, $\Delta t$, and $\Delta \vec{d}$. Find the equation in Table 2.2 that has these variables only. In this case, the equation is Equation 2, $\Delta \vec{d} = \frac{1}{2}(\vec{v}_2 + \vec{v}_1)\,\Delta t$.

Now you can convert the units and substitute into the equation to find the desired quantity.

Once you have a match between the variables and the equation, you might have to rearrange the equation, then substitute values along with the units into the equation and solve. The steps in the process are summarized in Fig. 2.26.

**Fig.2.26** Method of Solving Problems Using Equations

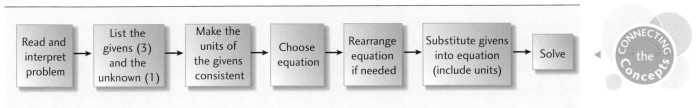

### EXAMPLE 8  Illustrating the method of solving motion problems

Consider a Ferrari, moving at 20.0 km/h, that accelerates to 230 km/h in 7.50 s. As it does so, it covers an unknown distance. Find the distance covered.

#### Solution and Connection to Theory

Before you try to solve the problem, determine which kinematics variables the quantities given in the problem represent. Then determine which variable you are trying to find. This will help you determine which equation to use. In the case of the Ferrari, the givens are

$\vec{v}_1 = 20.0$ km/h     $\vec{v}_2 = 230$ km/h     $\Delta t = 7.50$ s

The unknown or asked for variable is $\Delta \vec{d}$.

The units of all quantities must be consistent. The easiest way to ensure consistency is to convert all units to SI. Here, that means converting the velocities from km/h to m/s.

**Given**

$\vec{v}_1 = 5.56$ m/s     $\vec{v}_2 = 63.9$ m/s     $\Delta t = 7.50$ s     $\Delta \vec{d} = ?$

Check the list of equations. There is only one equation that includes the four variables in the problem. The equation of choice is

$\Delta \vec{d} = \frac{1}{2}(\vec{v}_1 + \vec{v}_2)\Delta t$

**UNITS TIP**

Convert km/h to m/s

$\dfrac{1 \text{ km}}{1 \text{ h}} = 1\dfrac{\cancel{\text{km}}}{\cancel{\text{h}}} \times \dfrac{1\cancel{\text{h}}}{3600 \text{ s}} \times \dfrac{1000 \text{ m}}{1\cancel{\text{km}}}$

$= \dfrac{1000 \text{ m}}{3600 \text{ s}} = \dfrac{1}{3.6}$ m/s

To convert m/s to km/h, multiply by 3.6.

To convert km/h to m/s, divide by 3.6.

For example, $\dfrac{20.0 \text{ km/h}}{3.6} = 5.56$ m/s.

**Multiplying/dividing numbers:**
Always keep the *least* number of *significant digits* in the answer based on the numbers used to obtain the final value. For example, 69.46 × 7.50 = 520.950. The number with the fewest significant digits is 7.50. Therefore, there should be only three significant digits in the answer, which rounds off to 521.

**Adding/subtracting numbers:**
Always keep the *least* number of *decimal places* in the answer based on the numbers used to obtain the final value. For example, 5.56 + 63.9 = 69.46. The number with the fewest decimal places is 63.9. Therefore, there should be only one decimal place in the answer, which rounds off to 69.5.
    Follow the order of operations and carry the extra decimal places and significant digits until the final answer. In other words, do not round off as you calculate; save it till the end.

**Safety tip:** Use the derived $\Delta\vec{d}$ only when you have to because you could have made an error in calculating it.

**Fig.2.27**

Rearrangement is not necessary; therefore, substitute the values and solve.

$$\Delta\vec{d} = \tfrac{1}{2}(5.56 \text{ m/s} + 63.9 \text{ m/s})7.50 \text{ s} = 260.475 \text{ m}$$

which rounds off to 260 m. Therefore, the Ferrari travelled 260 m.

Notice that the units cancelled to leave metres, the correct unit for displacement. The number of digits in the calculation should also be taken into consideration.

---

**EXAMPLE 9**    **Practising solving equations**

For the Ferrari in Example 8, calculate the acceleration.

### Solution and Connection to Theory

**Given**

$\vec{v}_1 = 5.56 \text{ m/s}$     $\vec{v}_2 = 63.9 \text{ m/s}$     $\Delta t = 7.50 \text{ s}$     $\Delta\vec{d} = 260 \text{ m}$     $\vec{a} = ?$

In this case, there are four equations that we can use. We will choose

$$\vec{v}_2 = \vec{v}_1 + \vec{a}\Delta t$$

because it has the three original variables that were given.

We arrange this equation to get

$$\vec{a} = \frac{\vec{v}_2 - \vec{v}_1}{\Delta t}$$

$$\vec{a} = \frac{(63.9 \text{ m/s} - 5.56 \text{ m/s})}{7.50 \text{ s}} = 7.78 \text{ m/s}^2.$$

Thus, the acceleration of the Ferrari is 7.78 m/s². We can check this answer by using another equation.

$$\vec{v}_2^{\,2} = \vec{v}_1^{\,2} + 2\vec{a}\Delta\vec{d}$$

This equation must be rearranged for $\vec{a}$.

$$\vec{a} = \frac{\vec{v}_2^{\,2} - \vec{v}_1^{\,2}}{2\Delta\vec{d}}$$

$$= \frac{(63.9 \text{ m/s})^2 - (5.56 \text{ m/s})^2}{2(260.475 \text{ m})}$$

$$= \frac{4052 \frac{\text{m}^2}{\text{s}^2}}{520.95 \text{ m}} = 7.78 \text{ m/s}^2$$

Notice how the units have cancelled to produce the correct unit for acceleration, m/s². Also note that the smallest number of significant digits in the values is three. Therefore, the answer must be rounded off to three digits. As an exercise, calculate the acceleration using two other equations.

## EXAMPLE 10  Air bag acceleration

Air bags are life savers when it comes to serious collisions. However, an air bag deploys with such explosive force that it is unsafe to use for children and small adults. Calculate the acceleration of the air bag if it deploys in 30 milliseconds (ms) and moves out a distance of 40 cm.

**Fig.2.28**

### Solution and Connection to Theory

**Given**

$\vec{v}_1 = 0$ m/s

$\Delta t = 30$ ms $= 3 \times 10^{-2}$ s

$\Delta \vec{d} = 40$ cm $= 0.40$ m

The relevant equation to use is Equation 3, rearranged to solve for $\vec{a}$.

$$\vec{a} = \frac{2\Delta\vec{d}}{\Delta t^2} = \frac{2(0.40 \text{ m})}{(3 \times 10^{-2} \text{ s})^2} = 8.9 \times 10^2 \text{ m/s}^2$$

To get an idea of the explosive intensity, note that this value is more than 90 times the acceleration due to gravity (9.8 m/s$^2$).

## EXAMPLE 11  Velocity in free fall

Newton was sitting under his apple tree when, unexpectedly, a duck fell on his head. Ignoring air resistance and any flapping of wings, find the velocity the duck had when making contact with Newton's head if the duck fell from a height of 3.5 m and the acceleration due to the gravity of Earth is 9.8 m/s$^2$.

### Solution and Connection to Theory

**Fig.2.29**

**Given**

Since everything is moving downward, we will set down to be the positive direction.

$\vec{a} = 9.8$ m/s$^2$     $\vec{v}_1 = 0.0$ m/s (started at rest)     $\Delta\vec{d} = 3.5$ m     $\vec{v}_2 = ?$

The equation of choice is

$$\vec{v}_2^2 = \vec{v}_1^2 + 2\vec{a}\Delta\vec{d}$$
$$= (0 \text{ m/s})^2 + 2(9.8 \text{ m/s}^2)(3.5 \text{ m})$$
$$= 68.6 \text{ m}^2/\text{s}^2$$
$$\vec{v}_2 = \pm 8.3 \text{ m/s}$$

Since the duck is moving down, the positive answer is correct.

The bird landed on Newton's head at 8.3 m/s and that would have hurt! Of course, with air resistance, the velocity would have been lower. Note: You could have solved this problem in two steps. First, you could have calculated the time it took to fall using the equation

$$\Delta \vec{d} = \vec{v}_1 \Delta t + \tfrac{1}{2}\vec{a}\Delta t^2$$

and then found $\vec{v}_2$ using any of the equations containing the variable $\vec{v}_2$.

**Fig.2.30** The Overall Picture

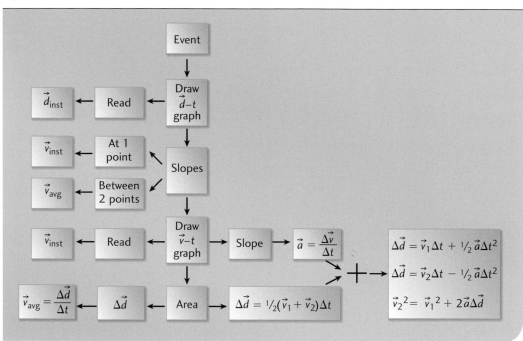

1. a) Calculate the take-off speed of a Boeing 747 if it accelerates at 4.0 m/s² and takes 40.0 s to reach this speed from rest.
   b) Calculate the distance travelled by the plane during takeoff in two different ways.
2. a) An arresting device on a carrier deck stops a plane in 152 m. If the plane is arriving at 66.7 m/s, find the acceleration of the plane.
   b) Find the time this process takes.
   c) Verify the displacement of the plane in two different ways.
3. a) A Russian MiG-25, nicknamed the "Foxbat," flies at 3395 km/h. Convert its speed to m/s.
   b) A sneeze takes 0.5 s. Find the distance the plane flies in the time it takes you to complete one sneeze.
   c) Find the plane's average acceleration if it takes 12.0 s to reach this speed from rest.
   d) From what speed must the plane start in order to reach its final speed in 8.7 s?

UNIT A: Motion and Forces

## 407 ETR

**4.** The 407 Express Toll Route (ETR) is a fully automated express toll highway running east-west just north of Toronto. High-resolution video cameras record the entry point and exit point of a vehicle. The video image is fed into a computer that reads the license plate number of the vehicle, and calculates the bill that is sent to the user. Regular users of the system carry transponders. The transponder emits radio signals to the receiver, which saves on computer time in trying to decipher license plate numbers.

**Fig.2.31** A 407 ETR route map

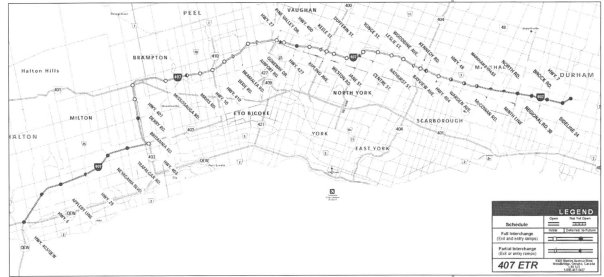

**a)** A physics teacher enters the 407 at the Markham interchange. She then exits onto Hwy 27 to go to the Irwin Publishing office to discuss the physics of ducks. If the trip is 31 km and took 21 min, how much did the trip cost, given that the entry time is 4:02, the exit time is 4:21, the cost per kilometre is $0.12, and a non-transponder charge of $1.50 plus an accounting fee of $2.00 are also levied?

**b)** Calculate the average speed of the vehicle.

**c)** The final exit time is not shown on the bill because the system is not used to produce electronic speeding tickets. What are the pros and cons of electronic ticketing? Would the fine reflect the true maximum speed of the vehicle? (Consider the difference between instantaneous and average velocity.)

**d)** Assume that electronic ticketing is done. What would you have to do to avoid getting caught speeding if you realize you have been travelling a 20 km route at 125 km/h when the speed limit is 100 km/h? (Calculate a value.)

**e)** The car gets 9.1 km/L. If gas costs $0.77 per litre, how much would the trip have cost using the regular, non-toll highway?

## Free Fall and Terminal Velocity

When a skydiver begins to fall toward the ground, her initial vertical velocity is zero. If she were falling in a vacuum, gravity would cause the skydiver to accelerate toward the ground at a rate of about 9.8 m/s². If this acceleration continued, an incredibly high speed would be reached before the parachute was opened. When an object falls through a medium like air, the velocity-versus-time graph looks very different from a fall through a vacuum. Figure STSE.2.1 shows that there is a point when the force of air resistance on the skydiver becomes sufficient to make the acceleration equal to zero. The skydiver then falls at constant speed, called the **terminal velocity**.

**Fig.STSE.2.1**

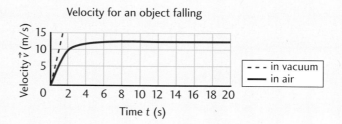

The value of the terminal velocity is dependent on the mass and size of the falling object as well as on the viscosity or thickness of the fluid within which the object is falling. The skydiver in Fig. STSE.2.2 has maximized his wind resistance by falling in the "spread eagle" position. This position produces the lowest possible terminal velocity. If the skydiver changes to a more vertical position, he will accelerate until he reaches a higher terminal velocity. When a parachute is opened (Fig. STSE.2.3), wind resistance increases. The result is negative acceleration and a lower terminal velocity that allows for a safe landing.

**Fig.STSE.2.2**

**Fig.STSE.2.3**

## Design a Study of Societal Impact

For most of us, our perspective of what happens when a parachute opens comes from the point of view of a video camera held by another skydiver. Explain why the first parachutist appears to move upward relative to the camera position.

Parachutists need to maximize their cross-sectional area, whereas the automobile industry wishes to reach a minimum effective area. Explain.

Transport trucks have air diverters on the roof of the truck cab. How do the diverters reduce wind drag?

Research a wind tunnel experiment designed to study wind or fluid drag on an object.

Parachutes are used to lift para-sailers, slow dragsters, and even help slow the space shuttle during landing. Research these parachute designs. What effective maximum drag force do they have?

## Design an Activity to Evaluate

Evaluate the terminal velocity of a falling body by doing a correlation study of at least one variable that affects its terminal velocity. For example, study the terminal velocity of a dandelion seed versus the number of "fluff shoots," or the terminal velocity of dry maple keys as they spin to the ground.

Try dropping various-sized marbles into liquids of different viscosity, such as shampoo or oil. Video tape the motion, with a stopwatch and metre stick in the background. Play the tape back frame by frame and record the distance-versus-time data. Use your knowledge of kinematics to calculate and plot the velocity-time graph. Find the terminal velocity of the marbles.

Use the graph in Fig. STSE.2.1 to determine how far the object fell from rest before it reached terminal velocity.

## Build a Structure

Design a parachute system that produces minimum velocity for a predetermined mass when released from the ceiling of the school gym.

Design a vehicle chassis that changes its drag force when placed in a fan-driven wind tunnel, as measured on a teathered newton spring scale.

## SPECIFIC EXPECTATIONS

### You should be able to

*Understand Basic Concepts:*

- Create $\vec{v}$-$t$ graphs from the slope values of $\vec{d}$-$t$ graphs.
- Analyze $\vec{v}$-$t$ graphs by using the methods **Read**, **Slope**, and **Area**.
- Differentiate between average and instantaneous acceleration using examples.
- Differentiate between average and instantaneous acceleration using slopes from a $\vec{v}$-$t$ graph.
- Calculate average velocity using graphical methods.
- Describe and explain different kinds of motion using examples and $\vec{v}$-$t$ graphs.
- Sketch a $\vec{v}$-$t$ graph given a $\vec{d}$-$t$ graph.
- Sketch a $\vec{d}$-$t$ graph given a $\vec{v}$-$t$ graph.
- Generate the five kinematics equations associated with motion with uniform acceleration.
- Solve problems involving the five equations using proper form.

*Develop Skills of Inquiry and Communication:*

- Interpret patterns and trends in data drawn by hand or by computer and infer linear and non-linear relationships among the variables ($\vec{d}$, $\vec{v}$, $\vec{a}$, and $t$) using $\vec{v}$-$t$ graphs.
- Analyze the $\vec{v}$-$t$ graph by using the methods **Read**, **Slope**, and **Area**.
- Interpret the results of the processes **Read**, **Slope**, and **Area**.
- Analyze $\vec{v}$-$t$ graphs involving uniform, stopped, and accelerating motion (positive and negative).
- Apply the concepts of graphical analysis to other graph situations.

*Relate Science to Technology, Society, and the Environment:*

- Evaluate traffic computer systems that were designed to decrease transportation pressures created by population growth in the cities.
- Relate the shapes of various parts of roller coasters to the thrills and sensations they cause.
- Evaluate and debate the pros and cons of a toll highways as well as possible future implications of electronic sensing on roads.
- Relate free-fall concepts to aspects of vehicle design.

### Equations

$$\vec{v}_{avg} = \frac{\Delta \vec{d}}{\Delta t} \qquad \vec{v}_{avg}\Delta t = \Delta \vec{d} \qquad \text{or} \qquad \Delta \vec{d} = \frac{(\vec{v}_1 + \vec{v}_2)\Delta t}{2}$$

$$\Delta \vec{d} = \vec{v}_1 \Delta t + \tfrac{1}{2}\vec{a}\Delta t^2$$

$$\Delta \vec{d} = \vec{v}_2 \Delta t - \tfrac{1}{2}\vec{a}\Delta t^2$$

$$\vec{a} = \frac{\Delta \vec{v}}{\Delta t}$$

$$\vec{v}_2^{\,2} = \vec{v}_1^{\,2} + 2\vec{a}\Delta \vec{d}$$

## Conceptual Questions

1. Figure 2.32 shows possible shapes of graphs. Interpret each graph, first as a $\vec{d}$-$t$ graph and then as a $\vec{v}$-$t$ graph, to describe the motion.

**Fig.2.32**

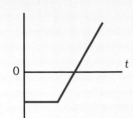
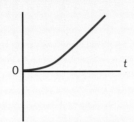
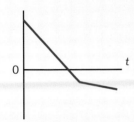
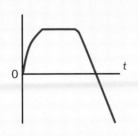

2. How does moving the $t$ axis up or down affect a $\vec{d}$-$t$ graph interpretation and a $\vec{v}$-$t$ graph interpretation?

3. a) A ball is thrown straight up into the air with an initial velocity, travels up, then comes back down into the person's hand. Draw a $\vec{v}$-$t$ graph representing its motion.
   b) The graph should show a constant acceleration. Why?
   c) In terms of the sign of the acceleration and the signs of the velocity sections, explain how your graph shows the ball speeding up and slowing down.
   d) Create a $\vec{d}$-$t$ sketch for this situation.
   e) How does each graph change if the ball lands lower than the position it started from?
   f) How does each graph change if the ball lands above its starting point?

4. Can an object be accelerating and not be moving? (Refer to Question 3 for a hint.)

5. Someone tells you she bought a child's toy that can accelerate at $10\,370$ km/h$^2$. This is actually a reasonable value. Explain why.

6. a) A sheet of paper and a bowling ball do not fall at the same rate on Earth. The bowling ball hits the ground first. Why?
   b) How can you modify the paper so that it hits the ground at the same time as the bowling ball?
   c) If the sheet of paper and the bowling ball fell in a vacuum box, which would land first? Explain.

7. Does an object dropped from a building reach the halfway point of its fall in half the time it takes it to drop? Explain.

8. Why can't the five kinematics equations be used if the acceleration is not constant?

9. Describe the process and considerations required in working out the time it takes for a yellow light to change to a red light at a given intersection.

10. Sketch three or more $\vec{v}$-$t$ graphs that represent impossible situations and explain why.

11. In a 100 m sprint, does the average speed of the sprinter represent his/her ability to catch someone ahead of him/her?

12. If we were to make $\vec{a}$-$t$ graphs, what shapes would they take for all the cases we have discussed in this chapter?

13. If a $\vec{v}$-$t$ graph has curved sections, what is happening to the acceleration? Provide examples for this case.

## Problems

### ▶ 2.1 Analysis of Velocity–Time Graphs

**14.** The following graph represents the motion of one of the fastest trains in the world, the TGV in France.

**Fig.2.33**

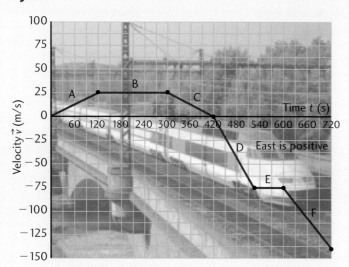

a) Describe the motion of the train. Consider the positive direction to be east.

b) How fast is the train moving at each of these times in km/h? (We have included one of the train's fastest runs ever, which is not typical of actual passenger trips.)
60 s, 240 s, 420 s, 480 s, 720 s

c) Calculate the accelerations for the lettered sections A–F.

d) How far has the train travelled in each of the lettered sections?

e) What is the total displacement of the train?

f) What is the average velocity for each of the lettered sections?

g) What is the average velocity for the whole trip?

h) What is the average speed for the trip?

**15.** The graph in Fig. 2.34 is for the fastest bird on Earth. The spine-tailed swift can reach a maximum speed of 170 km/h in free flight!

**Fig.2.34**

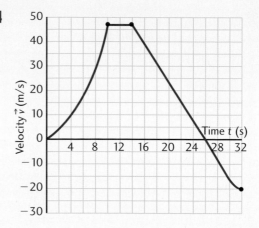

a) What is the velocity of the bird at these times? 4 s, 12 s, 18 s, 28 s

b) Calculate the acceleration at the following times: 4 s, 12 s, 18 s, 28 s.

c) When is the bird's velocity a maximum?

d) When is the bird's velocity a minimum?

e) When is the bird's acceleration a maximum?

f) When are the bird's accelerations zero?

**16.** Measure the tickertape in Fig. 2.35 and create a $\vec{d}$-t graph, followed by a $\vec{v}$-t graph. Calculate the acceleration. The time between dots is 0.032 s and the object starts from rest.

**17.** Measure the tickertape in Fig. 2.36 and create a $\vec{d}$-t graph, followed by a $\vec{v}$-t graph. Calculate the acceleration. The time between dots is 0.032 s.

**Fig.2.35**

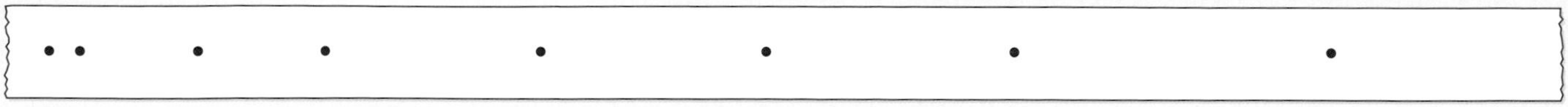

**Fig.2.36**

**18.** Create a $\vec{v}$-$t$ graph for a person moving up 50 m in a slow elevator, then waiting a short period of time before jumping off into a canyon using a bungee cord (Fig. 2.37). The person falls more than 50 m because of the stretch in the cord. Consider up as positive.

**Fig.2.37**

**19.** The following is a graph of a one-stage toy rocket launch from a cliff, followed by a free fall and a two-stage parachute descent. In your notebook, redraw the graph and
**a)** label each section.
**b)** calculate the accelerations for each section.

**Fig.2.38**

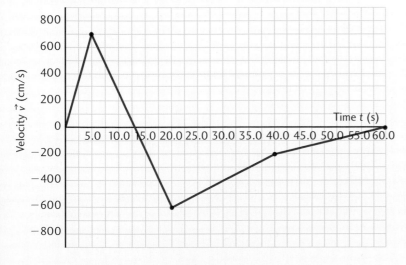

**20. a)** For the graph in Fig. 2.38, calculate the displacements for each section.
**b)** Find the total displacement.
**c)** Suggest possible scenerios to explain why the total displacement is not zero.

**21.** Consider the two-body problem in Fig. 2.39. The two vehicles were at the same position at time zero.

**Fig.2.39**

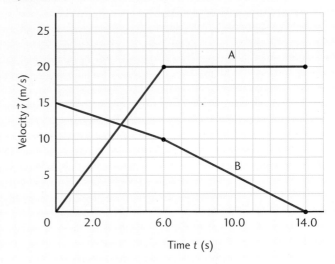

**a)** What was each vehicle doing at $t = 0$?
**b)** At what time are both vehicles travelling at the same velocity?
**c)** At any point on the graph, is either vehicle ever moving backward?
**d)** Describe the motion of each vehicle.
**e)** At the end of the graph, does vehicle A catch vehicle B?
**f)** How far apart are the vehicles at the moment they are travelling at the same speed?
**g)** What would have to be true for the graphs at the moment that vehicle A caught up with vehicle B?

▶ **2.2 Moving From One Graph to Another**

**22.** For the $\vec{d}$-$t$ graph in Fig. 2.40, sketch a $\vec{v}$-$t$ graph. Describe the motion depicted.

**Fig.2.40**

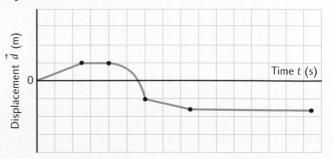

**23.** For the $\vec{d}$-$t$ graph in Fig. 2.41, sketch a $\vec{v}$-$t$ graph. Describe the motion depicted.

**Fig.2.41**

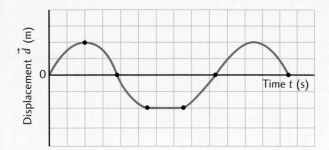

**24.** For the $\vec{d}$-$t$ graph in Fig. 2.42, create a $\vec{v}$-$t$ graph with values. Describe the motion.

**Fig.2.42**

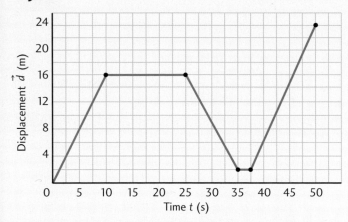

**25.** For the $\vec{d}$-$t$ graph in Fig. 2.43, create a $\vec{v}$-$t$ graph with values. Describe the motion.

**Fig.2.43**

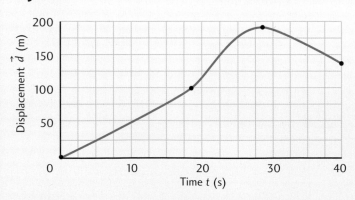

**26.** For the $\vec{v}$-$t$ graph in Fig. 2.44, sketch a corresponding $\vec{d}$-$t$ graph. Describe the motion.

**Fig.2.44**

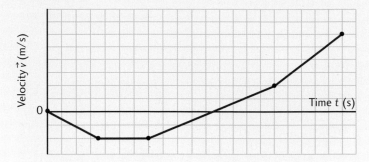

**27.** For the $\vec{v}$-$t$ graph in Fig. 2.45, sketch a corresponding $\vec{d}$-$t$ graph. Describe the motion.

**Fig.2.45**

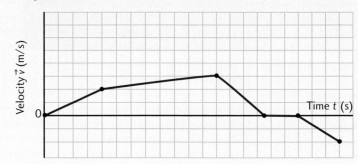

**28.** For the $\vec{v}$-$t$ graph in Fig. 2.46, create a $\vec{d}$-$t$ graph with values. Describe the motion.

**Fig.2.46**

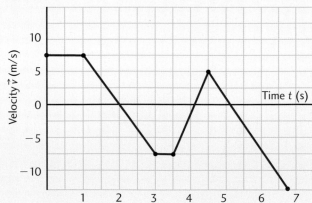

**29.** For the $\vec{v}$-$t$ graphs in Problems 26 and 27, sketch corresponding $\vec{a}$-$t$ graphs.

**30.** For the $\vec{v}$-$t$ graph in Problem 28, create an $\vec{a}$-$t$ graph with values.

## 2.3 Creating Equations

**31.** Below are two hypothetical equations among four variables. Derive the other equations needed to be able to solve problems when given the values of any two of the variables: $xy = p$ and $z = px$.

**32. a)** Derive an equation for the change in acceleration by using a graph analysis technique on an $\vec{a}$-$t$ graph. (Note: The name given to the change in acceleration per unit time is called *jerk* by some physicists.)

**b)** Write an equation for the area under the graph. What does this area represent?

## 2.4 Solving Problems Using Equations

### Displacement, Distance, Speed, and Velocity

**33.** Donovan Bailey ran the 100 m dash at the Atlanta Olympics in 9.84 s. Michael Johnson ran the 200 m in 19.32 s and the 400 m in 43.49 s. Find their average speed in each case.

**34.** How far will the TGV train travel in 45 s if its speed is 140 m/s? Express your answer in kilometres as well.

**35.** A sneeze causes you to momentarily shut your eyes. If this process takes 0.5 s and you are moving at 30 km/h, how far will you travel in that time?

**36.** Bacteria move at 100 μm/s. How long would it take one bacterium to move 1.0 m?

**37.** How far would a car move in 4.8 s if its velocity changed from 14.0 m/s to 16.0 m/s?

**38.** What is the displacement of a car accelerating from 15 m/s forward to 10 m/s forward in 8.0 s?

**39.** Apollo 10's re-entry speed was 39 897 km/h. How many seconds would it take the spacecraft to stop in a distance of $3.0 \times 10^6$ m?

**40.** The speed of light is $3.0 \times 10^8$ m/s. The speed of sound is 344 m/s. A flash of lightning occurs in a storm $1.0 \times 10^4$ m away. How many seconds does it take for us to see the lightning and hear the thunder?

**41.** How long would it take a laser beam to go to the Moon and back if the distance to the Moon is $3.8 \times 10^8$ m?

**42.** Jules Verne wrote a book called *Around the World in Eighty Days*. What was his average speed in m/s and km/h if the radius of the Earth is 6400 km?

**43.** What was the initial velocity of an object that moved 120 m in 5.60 s, reaching a final velocity of 15.0 m/s in that time? Was the object speeding up or slowing down?

### Acceleration

**44.** If Donovan Bailey reaches a top speed from rest of 10.2 m/s in 2.5 s, what is his acceleration?

**45.** If a sprinter accelerates at 2.2 m/s$^2$ for 2.5 s, what is her velocity after this time, assuming initial $\vec{v} = 0$?

**46.** If it takes 0.08 s for an air bag to stop a person, what is the acceleration of a person moving 13.0 m/s and coming to a complete stop in that time?

**47.** A fastball pitcher can throw a baseball at 100 km/h. If the windup and throw take 1.5 s, what is the acceleration of the ball?

**48.** A car moving at 10 m/s north ends up moving 10 m/s south after a period of 12 s. What is its acceleration?

**49.** An asteroid moving at $3.2 \times 10^4$ km/h slams into Earth. If it takes 3.5 s to bring the asteroid to rest (what's left of it), what was its acceleration?

**50.** An object accelerates at 9.8 m/s² when falling. How long does it take an object to change its speed from 4.5 m/s to 19.4 m/s?

**51.** What is an object's final velocity if it accelerates at 2.0 m/s² for 2.3 s from a velocity of 50 km/h?

**52.** What is an object's final velocity if it accelerates at $-2.0$ m/s² for 2.3 s from a velocity of 50 km/h?

**53.** What is an object's initial velocity if it accelerates at 2.0 m/s² for 2.3 s, attaining a velocity of $-50$ km/h?

## Acceleration and Displacement

**54.** Assuming no air resistance, how long does it take a penny to fall if it was dropped from the CN Tower (553 m)? Acceleration due to gravity is 9.8 m/s².

**55.** Assuming no air resistance, how long does it take a penny to fall if it was thrown down with an initial velocity of 5.0 m/s from the CN Tower (553 m)?

**56.** A car travelling at 40 km/h accelerates at 2.3 m/s² for 2.7 s. How far has it travelled in that time? What is its final velocity?

**57.** A car travelling at 40 km/h accelerates at $-2.3$ m/s² for 2.7 s. How far has it travelled in that time? What is its final velocity?

**58.** If 100 m sprinters accelerate from rest for 3.5 s at 2.8 m/s², how far have they run to this point? How long will it take them to complete the 100 m sprint, assuming they maintain their speed the rest of the way?

**59.** What is the average acceleration of the Blue Flame speed car if its initial velocity is 1000 km/h and it comes to a complete stop

in a distance of 2.0 km? Interpret the sign of your answer.

**60.** An object thrown up from a cliff at 10 m/s reaches a velocity of 20 m/s down as it lands. If the acceleration due to gravity is 9.8 m/s², what is the object's displacement? How long did it take for the object to land from the time it was thrown up?

**61.** If you accelerate (slow down) to a stop at $-0.8$ m/s² by applying brakes, how far do you travel when your initial velocity is
**a)** 10 km/h?　　**b)** 50 km/h?　　**c)** 90 km/h?
**d)** 140 km/h?

**62.** The Superman roller coaster reaches a velocity of 100 km/h in 7.0 s. What is its average acceleration in m/s²? How far has it travelled in that time? If you wish to calculate how many times faster your acceleration is than the acceleration due to the gravity (i.e., the number of $gs$ you pull), divide the acceleration by 9.8 m/s².

**63.** A car is slowing down at a rate of 20 km/h per second. How far does it travel if its original velocity is 50 km/h and its final velocity is 5 m/s?

**64.** Use the formula $\Delta \vec{d} = \vec{v}_1 \Delta t + \frac{1}{2}\vec{a}\Delta t^2$ and the following values to create a $\vec{d}$-$t$ chart. Then use the values you have generated to create a $\vec{d}$-$t$ graph. From the graph, take a series of tangents and their slopes and generate a $\vec{v}$-$t$ chart, followed by a $\vec{v}$-$t$ graph. From the graph, find the slope and compare it to the given acceleration. Given: $\vec{v}_1 = 10$ m/s, $\vec{a} = -10$ m/s², and time intervals of 0.2 s starting from 0.0 s and going to 2.2 s. Comment on what happened at the end of the motion.

**65.** A dragster accelerates from rest for a distance of 450 m at 14 m/s². A parachute is then used to slow it down to a stop. If the parachute gives the dragster an acceleration of $-7.0$ m/s², how far has the dragster travelled before stopping?

66. Two rugby players are running towards each other. They are 37 m apart. If one is accelerating from rest at 0.5 m/s² and the other was already moving at 3.1 m/s and maintains her speed,
    a) how long before they crunch together?
    b) how fast was the accelerating player going?
    c) how far has each player run?

67. Superwoman is hovering above the ground when a person free-falling goes by her at a terminal velocity of 140 km/h. Unfortunately, the parachute does not open. Fortunately, Superwoman is around. If it takes her 1.9 s to realize the person is in distress, what must her acceleration be if she is to catch the parachutist just before she hits the ground 1000 m below?

68. A police car stopped at a set of lights has a speeder pass it at 100 km/h. If the police car can accelerate at 3.6 m/s²,
    a) how long does it take to catch the speeder?
    b) how far would the police car have to go before it catches the speeder?
    c) what would its speed be when it caught up with the car? Is this speed reasonable?

# LAB 2.1 Acceleration Down an Incline

## Purpose

To find the acceleration of an object down an incline using graphing techniques.

## Equipment

Tickertape apparatus: power supply, clacker or sparker, tickertape
Metre stick, Graph paper, Tape
Clamp, Brick, Toy cart
Inclined plane or ramp that can be set at an angle

## Procedure

1. Set the ramp or inclined plane at approximately 20° to the horizontal.
2. Clamp the timer to the top of the incline.
3. Feed a piece of tickertape equal to the length of the table through the clacker or sparker and tape it to the back of the cart.
4. Place the brick on the cart, start the timer, and release the cart. Make sure that someone is ready to catch the cart at the bottom of the ramp.
5. Repeat Steps 3 and 4 for each member of your group.
6. Use a large protractor to measure the angle of your inclined plane to the horizontal.

## Data

1. Measure the distance from the first point on your tape to each of the points on the tickertape. **Do not measure the spacing between consecutive dots!** Always measure the distance from the first dot.
2. Create a $\vec{d}$-t chart. If the period is an awkward value, then use it as a multiplication factor for the time, and place it in the heading of your chart. Example: If $T = 0.032$ s, then the time column heading should read "Time ($\times$ 0.032 s)." Then the numbers used in the actual chart are just the dot numbers, 1 to whatever number of dots you have. If using all the dots gives you too many values, use groups of five or ten dots as your time interval.

## Uncertainty (see Appendix A)

Assign an instrumental uncertainty for the ruler you used. If you felt there was a procedural component as well, then assign a value to it. Add the two. It may be possible that some points have a different uncertainty if the tickertape is long or the ruler is short.

## Analysis

1. Produce a $\vec{d}$-t graph. If the uncertainties in $\vec{d}$ are visible on the graph, use an error bar for each. If not, use a dot inside a small circle.
2. Draw a curve of best fit through the points. (The curve is parabolic in shape.)
3. Select four time instances spaced out along the graph. At these times, draw a tangent and find its slope. Include units when you calculate them. Remember to multiply in the period for the "run" part of the slope calculation.
4. Calculate the uncertainties in the slopes.
5. Produce a $\vec{v}$-t chart summarizing your results. Include in your chart $\vec{v} = 0$ at $t = 0$.
6. Use the $\vec{v}$-t chart to create a $\vec{v}$-t graph.
7. Draw a line of best fit. Include error bars, if appropriate.
8. Find the slope of the $\vec{v}$-t graph, including units.

## Discussion

1. Why might using the brick improve your results in this experiment?
2. What effect would counting the first few dots incorrectly have on your $\vec{v}$-t graph?
3. The accepted value for acceleration on an inclined plane is $9.8(\sin\theta)$m/s$^2$, where $\theta$ is the angle the slope makes with the horizontal. Calculate the accepted value of acceleration for your experiment.
4. Give possible reasons for the difference between your answer and the accepted value.
5. Should each group in the class have the same answer? Discuss.

## Conclusion

Give your value for acceleration, with units, and state whether it agrees with the theoretical value.

## Purpose

To find the acceleration due to gravity using graphing techniques.

## Equipment

Tickertape apparatus: power supply, clacker or sparker, tickertape
100 g – 200 g mass
Metre Stick, Graph paper, Tape

## Procedure

1. Attach the tickertape to the mass.
2. Feed the tickertape through the sparker or clacker.
3. Make sure the tickertape is lying flat on the table so as not to snag in your apparatus. Position the mass on the edge of the table, ready to fall.
4. Start the clacker/sparker and gently nudge the mass off the table.

## Data

1. Measure the distance from the first point on your tape to each of the points on the tickertape. **Do not measure the spacing between consecutive dots!** Always measure the distance from the first dot.
2. Create a $\vec{d}$-t chart. If the period is an awkward value, then use it as a multiplication factor for the time, and place it in the heading of your chart. Example: If $T = 0.032$ s, then the time column heading should read "Time ($\times$ 0.032 s)." Then the numbers used in the actual chart are just the dot numbers, 1 to whatever number of dots you have.

## Uncertainty (see Appendix A)

Assign an instrumental uncertainty for the ruler you used. If you felt there was a procedural component as well, then assign a value to it. Add the two. It may be possible that some points have a different uncertainty if the tickertape is long or the ruler is short.

## Analysis

1. Produce a $\vec{d}$-t graph. If the uncertainties in $\vec{d}$ are visible on the graph, use an error bar for each. If not, use a dot inside a small circle.
2. Draw a curve of best fit through the points. (The curve is parabolic in shape.)
3. Select three time instances spaced out along the graph. At these times, draw a tangent and find its slope. Include units when you calculate them. Remember to multiply in the period for the "run" part of the slope calculation.
4. Calculate the uncertainties in the slopes.
5. Produce a $\vec{v}$-t chart summarizing your results. Include in your chart $\vec{v} = 0$ at $t = 0$.
6. Use the $\vec{v}$-t chart to create a $\vec{v}$-t graph.
7. Draw a line of best fit. Include error bars if appropriate.
8. Find the slope.
9. By how much does your calculated value differ from the accepted value of the slope ($9.8$ m/s$^2$)?
10. Optional: Find the uncertainty in the slope. (See Appendix B.)

## Discussion

1. Why have we not used the car in this experiment as we did in the acceleration experiment?
2. If your points do not line up in a straight line on the $\vec{v}$-t graph, explain possible reasons for this.
3. Was your value for the acceleration equal to the accepted value within an acceptable range? If not, explain what factors may have affected the value. If it fell in the acceptable range, postulate factors that could affect the result in a minor way.

## Conclusion

State your value of acceleration and whether it agrees with the theoretical value.

# 3

# Motion in Two Dimensions

## Chapter Outline

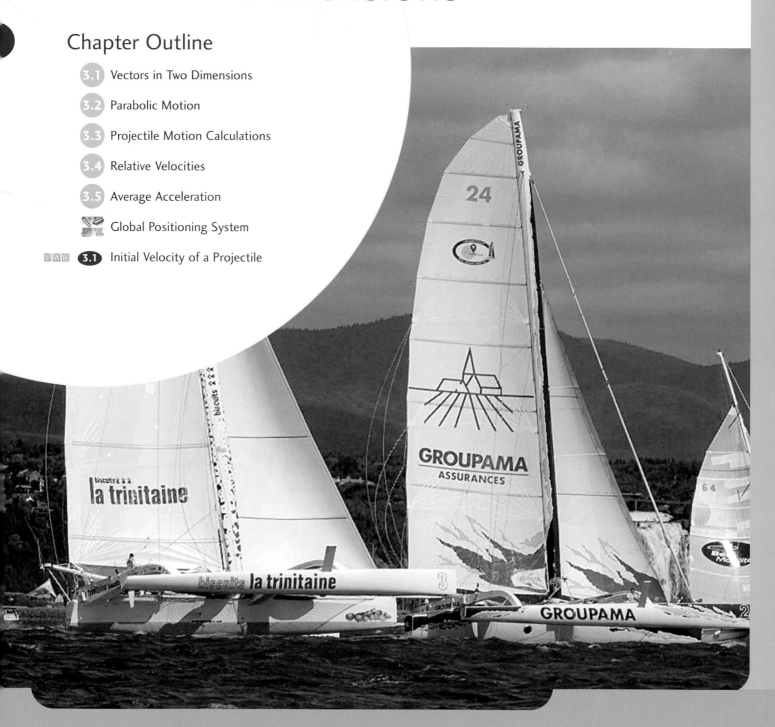

**By the end of this chapter, you will be able to**

- add vectors in two dimensions
- calculate the range of hurled projectiles
- calculate velocities relative to different media

# 3.1 Vectors in Two Dimensions

In order to extend our study of motion to two dimensions, we first need to describe the processes involved in manipulating vectors. The two-dimensional plane's directions will be referred to as $x$ and $y$. Positive $y$ will be in the upward direction, and positive $x$ will be to the right. Notice that the two directions are at 90° to each other and are referred to as an **orthogonal system**.

## Vectors

Vectors are quantities that possess both **magnitude** and **direction**. The direction element of the vector is represented by an arrow, where the beginning of the arrow is termed the **tail** and the end of the arrow is the **head**. To specify the angle of the vector, we use the compass system (north, south, east, and west) or the up, down, right, and left directions, along with an angle. It is best to keep the angle between 0° and 90° for future trigonometric calculations. Notice in Fig. 3.1 that the direction of the vector can be specified by two different angles. These angles are complementary and thus add up to 90°.

**Fig.3.1**

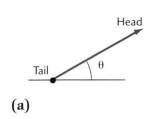

**(a)**

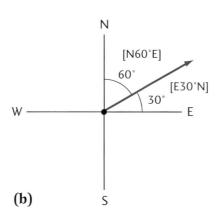

**(b)**

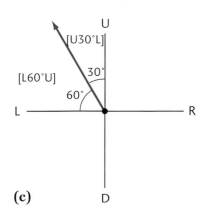

**(c)**

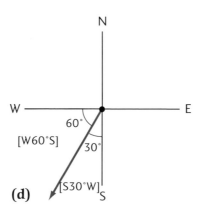

**(d)**

## Adding Vectors

Having learned to add from an early age, we are used to the meaning of the "+" sign. For scalar quantities, there is no debate as to the final result: 4 + 3 always equals 7. But if we use vector quantities, the answer "7" is obtained only if the two vectors are collinear (in the same direction). Otherwise, values anywhere from −1 to 7 are all possible, depending on the angle between the vectors. In Fig. 3.2, you can see that when the two vectors point in opposite directions, the total will be a minimum. The closer the two vectors are to being collinear, the closer their sum will be to the maximum value of 7.

**Fig.3.2**   What is 4 + 3?

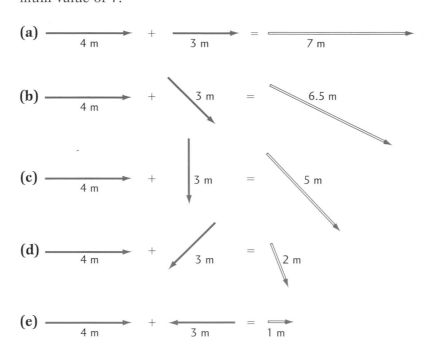

(a)   4 m   +   3 m   =   7 m

(b)   4 m   +   3 m   =   6.5 m

(c)   4 m   +   3 m   =   5 m

(d)   4 m   +   3 m   =   2 m

(e)   4 m   +   3 m   =   1 m

**Fig.3.3**   Connecting vectors

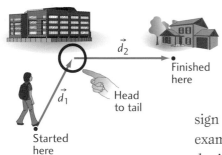

Now consider the vector diagram of $\vec{d}_1 + \vec{d}_2$, illustrated in Fig. 3.3. This diagram represents a walk you took. From home, you walked to your favourite place (perhaps school?), then you went over to a friend's house.

The diagram of the walk is naturally represented by arrows. The process of your trip demonstrates the method of adding vectors. The **head-to-tail** connection of the vectors is how you interpret the "+" sign in a vector addition equation. The vector additions shown in Fig. 3.4 are examples involving displacement vectors and velocity vectors. As long as you don't mix different types of variables in one diagram (e.g., velocity and displacement), the head-to-tail connection means vector addition.

In the trip of Fig. 3.3, your net displacement is the vector drawn straight from your starting point to your final location. It is called the **resultant vector**. Resultants are indicated in Fig. 3.4 by the vectors with hollow shafts. Like a sum in algebra, the resultant is the result of addition, only this time we are adding vectors rather than numbers. Note that *the resultant vector is specified by both a magnitude and a direction*. When adding distances travelled, the resultant vector is called the **total displacement**. The resultant vectors in Fig. 3.4 are described properly in Fig. 3.5. Notice how a magnitude and a direction are given. You should be able to specify direction in another way for each resultant vector.

**Fig.3.4** Addition of vectors

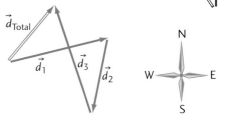

**Fig.3.5** Resultant vectors

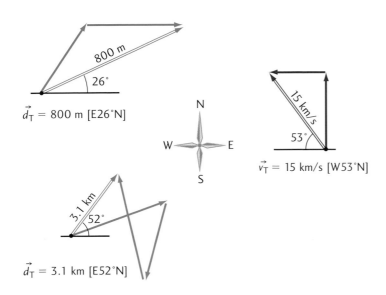

$\vec{d}_T = 800 \text{ m } [\text{E}26°\text{N}]$

$\vec{v}_T = 15 \text{ km/s } [\text{W}53°\text{N}]$

$\vec{d}_T = 3.1 \text{ km } [\text{E}52°\text{N}]$

In summary, the "+" sign in vector addition is an instruction to connect the vectors head to tail. When the vectors are collinear, you can simply add them. When the vectors are not collinear, you must construct a vector diagram or use trigonometry. To calculate the resultant of two vectors, the trigonometry for solving the triangle is straightforward. If your problem contains more than two vectors to add, you will normally find it easier to use **components**. Using this method, you resolve each vector into components in the $x$ and $y$ directions. Then add the magnitudes of the components in each direction, and solve the final right-angle triangle. Its hypotenuse is the resultant vector (see Fig. 3.6A).

## TRIGONOMETRY REVIEW

**Fig.3.6A**

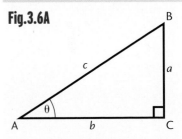

For a right-angle triangle with sides $a$ and $b$ forming the right angle, $c$ is the hypotenuse. Pythagoras' theorem states

$$a^2 + b^2 = c^2$$

Using the basic trigonometric ratios, $\theta$ can be found in one of three ways:

sine: $\sin\theta = \dfrac{a}{c} = \dfrac{\text{opposite}}{\text{hypotenuse}}$

cosine: $\cos\theta = \dfrac{b}{c} = \dfrac{\text{adjacent}}{\text{hypotenuse}}$

tangent: $\tan\theta = \dfrac{a}{b} = \dfrac{\text{opposite}}{\text{adjacent}}$

---

**EXAMPLE 1**   **Finding the resultant vector**

A student runs to school, covering a distance of 0.50 km in a direction given by [N20°E] as measured from the starting point. She then trudges over to a friend's house 0.30 km away due west from the school. And finally the two friends go off to the mall 0.80 km away in a direction given by [W50°S] from the friend's house. What is the total displacement of the student?

## VECTOR COMPONENTS

A vector can be resolved into **components**, which are perpendicular to each other. When they are added, their sum is equal to the vector. In Fig. 3.6B, vector $\vec{v}$ is resolved into components $v_x$ and $v_y$, where

$$v_x = v\cos\theta \text{ and } v_y = v\sin\theta$$

You could also use the complementary angle and get

$$v_x = v\sin\beta \text{ and } v_y = v\cos\beta$$

Choose whichever angle is most suitable in the given problem.

**Fig. 3.6B**

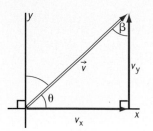

## *Solution and Connection to Theory*

### Given

$$\vec{d}_1 = 0.50 \text{ km [N20°E]} \qquad \vec{d}_2 = 0.30 \text{ km [W]} \qquad \vec{d}_3 = 0.80 \text{ km [W50°S]}$$

The vector equation is

$$\vec{d}_1 + \vec{d}_2 + \vec{d}_3 = \vec{d}_{total}$$

First set a scale: 1 cm represents 0.10 km. Then construct the vector diagram, as shown in Fig. 3.7, drawing the vectors to scale. Make sure the vectors are connected head to tail, with the correct angles.

**Fig. 3.7**

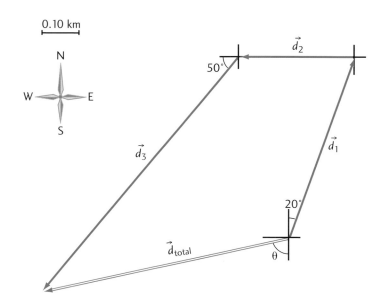

Find the resultant vector (total displacement) by drawing a line from the starting point to the end point. It should measure 6.6 cm. From the scale, this represents 0.66 km. Using a protractor, now measure the angle, θ, of the total displacement at its tail from one of the cardinal directions (i.e., N, S, E, W). It is 78° westward from south. So, the net displacement is 0.66 km [S78°W] (or 0.66 km [W12°S]).

For a trigonometric solution, you could break the figures into triangles and solve for the length and direction of the resultant. However, a more common way is to calculate the net displacement using a pair of components that are perpendicular to each other. Ordinarily, you will choose standard directions for the pair of components. As shown in Fig. 3.8, choose components along the N-S and E-W directions. Choose north and east as positive. Add the components first in the E-W direction (call the resultant $d_x$), then those in the N-S direction (for $d_y$). Finally, add the two component sums using Pythagoras' theorem and trigonometric ratios.

**Fig.3.8**

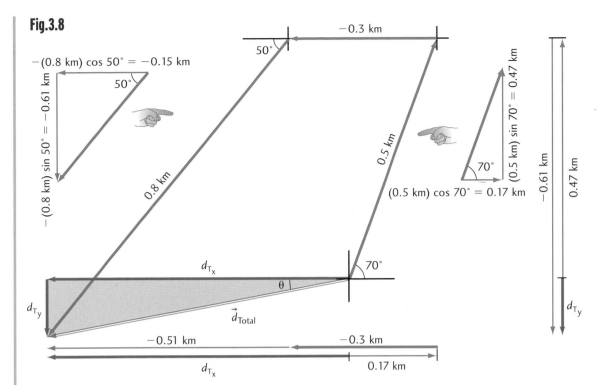

**E-W:** Adding all the horizontal components,

$$d_{T_x} = d_{1_x} + d_{2_x} + d_{3_x}$$
$$= (0.5 \text{ km})\cos 70° - 0.3 \text{ km} - (0.8 \text{ km})\cos 50°$$
$$= 0.17 \text{ km} - 0.3 \text{ km} - 0.51 \text{ km} = -0.64 \text{ km}$$

**N-S:** Adding all the vertical components,

$$d_{T_y} = d_{1_y} + d_{2_y} + d_{3_y}$$
$$= (0.5 \text{ km})\sin 70° + 0 - (0.8 \text{ km})\sin 50°$$
$$= 0.47 \text{ km} - 0.61 \text{ km} = -0.14 \text{ km}$$

Now use Pythagoras' theorem to calculate the sum of the two components, and the tangent ratio to find the angle of the resultant vector.

$$\vec{d}_{total} = d_{T_x} + d_{T_y} \qquad d^2_{total} = d^2_{T_x} + d^2_{T_y}$$
$$d_{total} = \sqrt{d^2_{T_x} + d^2_{T_y}} = \sqrt{(-0.64 \text{ km})^2 + (-0.14 \text{ km})^2}$$
$$= \sqrt{0.4292 \text{ km}^2} = 0.66 \text{ km}$$

To calculate the angle, substitute **magnitudes** of sides into the equation.

$$\theta = \tan^{-1} \frac{d_{T_y}}{d_{T_x}} = \tan^{-1} \frac{0.14 \text{ km}}{0.64 \text{ km}} = \tan^{-1} 0.219 = 12°$$

You can get the correct direction by checking the signs of $d_{T_x}$ and $d_{T_y}$. Since they are both negative, the components of the resultant displacement are 0.64 km [W] and 0.14 km [S]. Combine those directions with $\theta = 12°$ to find the student's resultant displacement, which is 0.66 km [W12°S].

**Fig.3.9** Method for Solving Vector Addition Problems

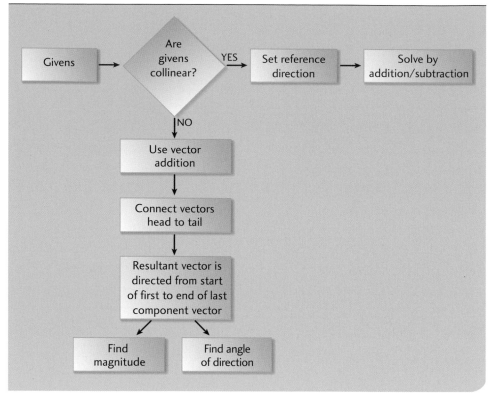

1. Find the components in the $x$ and $y$ directions for the following displacements:
   **a)** 20 km [S30°E]    **b)** 40 km [W60°N]    **c)** 10 m [N10°E]
   **d)** 5 km [S24°W]    **e)** 12 m [N45°W]    **f)** 10 km [N90°E]
2. A person walks 20 m [N20°E], then 120 m [N50°W], then 150 m [W], and finally 30 m [S75°E]. Find the person's final displacement using a scaled diagram and the trigonometric method.
3. Using a real example, explain in your own words the trigonometric method of solving two-dimensional displacement problems.

# ▶ 3.2 Parabolic Motion

When you throw a ball in outer space, the ball will leave your hands and travel in a straight line forever, unless it runs into an object or encounters a gravitational field. When you throw the same ball on Earth, it doesn't travel in a straight line but in an arc, finally coming to rest on the ground. Of course, we know that Earth causes all objects to fall. Our ball is moving forward, as it would in outer space, and falling at the same time. The combination of these two actions produces the curved motion we see. The term **projectile motion** is used to describe events where the object moves under the influence of gravity and is not self powered.

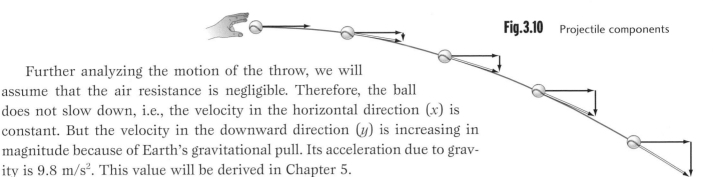

**Fig.3.10**   Projectile components

Further analyzing the motion of the throw, we will assume that the air resistance is negligible. Therefore, the ball does not slow down, i.e., the velocity in the horizontal direction ($x$) is constant. But the velocity in the downward direction ($y$) is increasing in magnitude because of Earth's gravitational pull. Its acceleration due to gravity is 9.8 m/s². This value will be derived in Chapter 5.

The trajectory of a ball in Fig. 3.10 shows the two components of projectile motion. Since the horizontal velocity is constant, the $x$ velocity vector is the same length throughout the motion. Since gravity causes a downward acceleration, the $y$ velocity vector gets progressively longer.

When you add these two velocity vectors, you obtain the resultant velocity at any given moment. This is indicated by a hollow vector on the diagram (Fig. 3.10). In summary, as the motion proceeds in time, the velocity component in the $y$ direction increases in length. The velocity vector in the $x$ direction stays the same length. When you combine a horizontal constant motion with an accelerating vertical motion, you produce **parabolic** (curved) motion.

In Fig. 3.11, you can see how the angle of launch of a volleyball or a football can affect the range of a parabolic trajectory. The **range** is the displacement in the horizontal direction, $x$.

**Fig.3.11**   Launch angle affects range

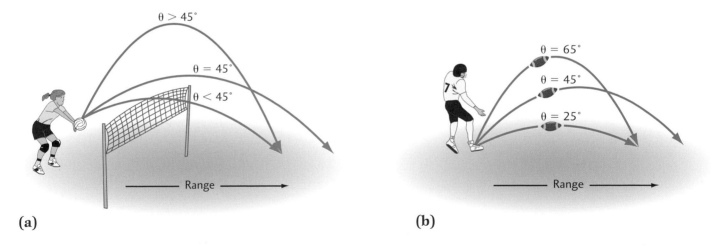

(a)

(b)

## Timing a Parabolic Trajectory

**Fig.3.12**   Vertical and horizontal components are independent

How long will it take the baseball thrown in Fig. 3.10 to hit the ground? The answer may surprise you. If the ball is thrown exactly horizontally, it will stay in the air for exactly the same length of time as a ball dropped from the same height, no matter how fast you throw it!

Figure 3.12 is a strobe photo of two balls released at exactly the same moment. Ball A drops straight down, while ball B is projected horizontally. Horizontal lines are superimposed on the photograph. You can see that

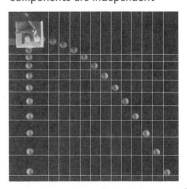

**Fig.3.13** Changing the initial vertical velocity

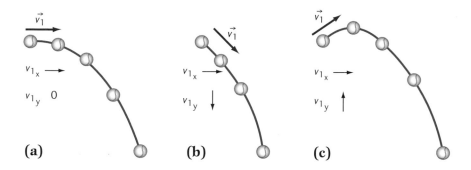

**(a)**　　　　　**(b)**　　　　　**(c)**

both balls cross the lines together. The objects are *falling* at the *same rate* and will land at the same time. The initial push only caused ball B to travel farther in the horizontal (*x*) direction. It still fell the same vertical distance, at the same rate as the dropped ball (A).

If you wish to have a clear winner, Fig. 3.13 shows two other possible cases. If you wish ball B to land first, then you could throw it downward, thereby giving it an initial velocity in the *y* direction (as in (b), in the direction of acceleration). If you throw the object upward, as in (c), again it will have an initial velocity in the *y* direction. However, this time the ball will cover a greater vertical distance (go up, stop, then come down) and land last.

**Fig.3.14** 2D Motion Summary

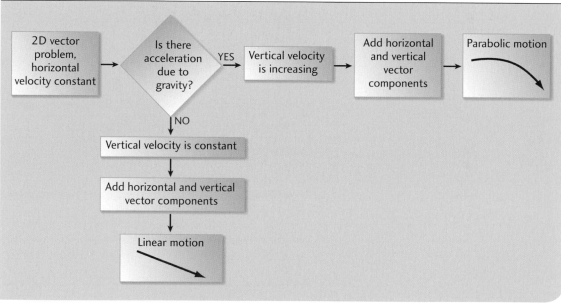

1. A cannonball is shot from a cannon simultaneously as another cannonball is dropped from the same height. Why do both cannonballs land at the same time? Assume the cannon is pointed horizontally.
2. What would happen to your answer for Question 1 if the cannon was not pointed horizontally?
3. How would air and spin affect the answer to Question 1?

# 3.3 Projectile Motion Calculations

In Chapter 2, we used the kinematics equations for one-dimensional motions only. The key to solving two-dimensional problems is to break them up into two one-dimensional parts, then recombine them to produce a final answer. The problem set-up will now have a set of givens in the $x$ direction and another set in the $y$ direction.

We will develop the process for solving such two-dimensional projectile problems in a series of steps. First, consider a horizontally fired cannon. We will set up the situation in Example 2, and then perform the calculations in Example 3. Next, consider a cannon that points upward at an angle in order to gain a greater range. Example 4 contains calculations to find the range. Example 5 calculates the maximum height achieved in the cannon shot.

---

**EXAMPLE 2**    **Setting up a projectile problem**

The Great Projecto, a circus duck, is shot at 40 m/s out of a horizontal cannon at the top of a cliff 100 m high. Derive the equations that represent the horizontal and vertical components of the motion.

### *Solution and Connection to Theory*

We will assume a standard sign reference system. The first step is to set up givens for components in the $x$ and $y$ directions.

$x$}   $v_{1_x} = v_{2_x} = 40$ m/s (horizontal velocity is constant)

     $a_x = 0$      $\Delta d_x = ?$      $\Delta t = ?$

$y$}   $v_{1_y} = 0$      $a_y = -9.8$ m/s$^2$      $\Delta d_y = -100$ m.      $\Delta t = ?$

$\Delta d_y$ is negative because Projecto travels downward, the negative direction.

The problem is now ready to be solved. The unknowns are time, and displacement in the horizontal direction, which is referred to as the *range*. Figure 3.15 shows Projecto shooting out with an initial horizontal velocity only; as he sails through the air, he develops an ever-increasing vertical velocity downward.

**Fig.3.15**

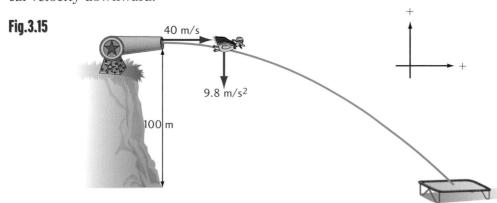

From the givens, you can see that there is a $\Delta t$ in each dimension. Since this is the time from firing to landing, $\Delta t$ is the same in both directions. So, if you can find a value for time in one of the directions, you can use that value in equations for the other direction.

**Choice of Equation.** The variables used in the $x$ direction are $\Delta t$, $\Delta \vec{d}$, $\vec{a}$, and $\vec{v}_1$. The equation containing all four of these variables is

$$\Delta \vec{d} = \vec{v}_1 \Delta t + \tfrac{1}{2} \vec{a} \Delta t^2$$

This equation simplifies to $\Delta d_x = v_x \Delta t$ because the acceleration in the $x$ direction is zero and the velocity is constant.

The variables in the $y$ direction are the same as those in the $x$ direction, hence we can use the same equation:

$$\Delta d_y = v_{1_y} \Delta t + \tfrac{1}{2} a_y \Delta t^2$$

**Fig.3.16** Solving Projectile Problems

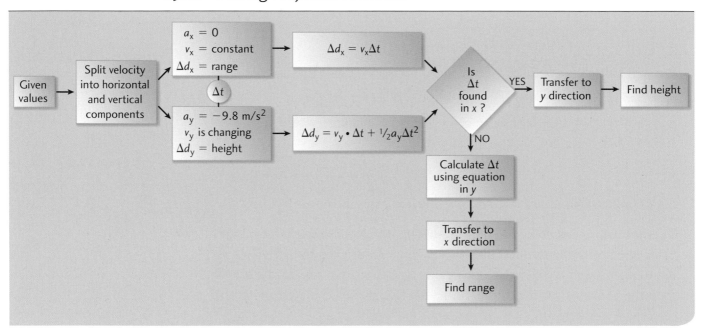

Now let's finish the cannon problem.

EXAMPLE 3    **Finding the range**

The Great Projecto is shot out of a horizontal cannon at 40 m/s. If the cannon is sitting at the top of a cliff 100 m high, how far will the duck travel?

### Solution and Connection to Theory

**Given**

$x\}$   $v_{1_x} = v_{2_x} = 40$ m/s   $a_x = 0$   $\Delta d_x = ?$   $\Delta t = ?$

$y\}$   $v_{1_y} = 0$   $a_y = -9.8$ m/s$^2$   $\Delta d_y = -100$ m   $\Delta t = ?$

In the $y$ direction, there is only one unknown. Solve in this direction first.

$$\Delta d_y = v_{1_y}\Delta t + \tfrac{1}{2}a_y\Delta t^2$$

$v_{1_y} = 0$, therefore $\Delta t^2 = \dfrac{2\Delta d_y}{a_y}$

$$\Delta t = \pm\sqrt{\frac{2\Delta d_y}{a_y}} = \pm\sqrt{\frac{2(-100\text{m})}{-9.8\ \text{m/s}^2}} = \pm 4.5\ \text{s}$$

Since time must be positive, $\Delta t = +4.5$ s. Now we use this value of time to calculate the range.

$$\Delta d_x = v_x\Delta t \quad a_x = 0; \text{ therefore, } \Delta d_x = 40 \text{ m/s } (4.5 \text{ s}) = 180 \text{ m}$$

During the 4.5 s that Projecto took to fall 100 m in the $y$ direction, he travelled 180 m in the $x$ direction.

---

**EXAMPLE 4**   **Projection angled upward**

A cannonball is shot out of a cannon with a horizontal velocity component of 40 m/s and a vertical velocity component of 20 m/s [up]. If the cannon is sitting at the top of a cliff 100 m high, how far will the cannonball travel?

**Fig.3.17A**

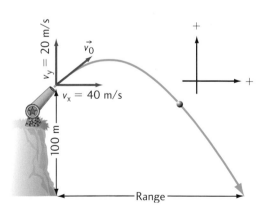

### Solution and Connection to Theory

This problem is very much like Example 3, except it has a vertical velocity component. This means that the cannonball is being fired at an angle upwards from the cliff top.

**Given**

$x\}$   $v_{1_x} = v_{2_x} = 40$ m/s   $a_x = 0$   $\Delta d_x = ?$   $\Delta t = ?$

$y\}$   $v_{1_y} = 20$ m/s   $a_y = -9.8$ m/s$^2$   $\Delta d_y = -100$ m   $\Delta t = ?$

Notice in Fig. 3.17A that the height of the cliff is still 100 m, as it was in Examples 2 and 3. In this example, the object travelled higher than the cliff top, but the definition of displacement is final position minus initial position, which is just the height of the cliff. If we were to stop the problem at a different moment, then the displacement would be different. As before, solve first in the $y$ direction.

## QUADRATIC FORMULA

Given the quadratic equation

$ax^2 + bx + c = 0$,

the solution is

$$x = \frac{-b \pm \sqrt{b^2 - 4ac}}{2a}$$

## ALTERNATIVE APPROACH

Use $v_{2_y}^2 = v_{1_y}^2 + 2a_y \Delta d_y$ to find $v_{2_y}$

Then use

$v_{2_y} = v_{1_y} + a_y \Delta t$ to find $\Delta t$.

$$\mathbf{y}\} \qquad \Delta d_y = v_{1_y} \Delta t + \tfrac{1}{2} a_y \Delta t^2$$

$$-100\ \text{m} = (20\ \text{m/s})\ \Delta t + \tfrac{1}{2}(-9.8\ \text{m/s}^2)\ \Delta t^2$$

This is a quadratic equation in $\Delta t$.

$$(-4.9\ \text{m/s}^2)\ \Delta t^2 + (20\ \text{m/s})\ \Delta t + 100\ \text{m} = 0$$

Using the quadratic formula,

$$\Delta t = \frac{-20\ \text{m/s} \pm \sqrt{(20\ \text{m/s})^2 - 4(-4.9\ \text{m/s}^2)(100\ \text{m})}}{2(-4.9\ \text{m/s}^2)}$$

$$= \frac{-20\ \text{m/s} \pm \sqrt{400\ \text{m}^2/\text{s}^2 + 1960\ \text{m}^2/\text{s}^2}}{-9.8\ \text{m/s}^2}$$

$$= \frac{-20\ \text{m/s} \pm 48.6\ \text{m/s}}{-9.8\ \text{m/s}^2} = \frac{-68.6\ \text{m/s}}{-9.8\ \text{m/s}^2} \ \text{or} \ \frac{28.6\ \text{m/s}}{-9.8\ \text{m/s}^2}$$

This gives $\Delta t = 7.0$ s and $-2.9$ s. Note that the units cancel to produce the correct unit for $\Delta t$.

A negative time does not apply in real life, so the correct value for $\Delta t$ is 7.0 s. Now substitute 7.0 s for $\Delta t$ in the equation for the $x$ direction.

$a_x = 0$; therefore, $\Delta d_x = v_{1_x} \Delta t \qquad \Delta d_x = 40\ \text{m/s}(7.0\ \text{s}) = 280\ \text{m}$

Because this projectile spent more time in the air than the one in Example 3, it managed to travel a greater distance, 280 m instead of 180 m.

## NEGATIVE TIME

We can give a meaning to the negative time by illustrating the problem using a parabola. The quadratic equation for $\Delta t$ describes a motion for a vertical displacement of 100 m for the initial velocity components given in the problem. Those same values could also be achieved by starting at the ground 2.9 s earlier, and firing a projectile upward. After 2.9 s, the upward velocity of the projectile would be 20 m/s. Mathematically, that earlier portion of the motion is the part of the parabola to the left of the vertical axis, as shown in Fig. 3.17B.

**Fig. 3.17B**

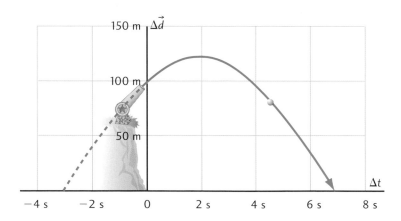

To find the maximum height of the shot, modify the solution as shown in Example 5.

EXAMPLE 5 **Maximum height of a projectile**

For the cannonball in Example 4, find its maximum height.

*Solution and Connection to Theory*

**Given**

We need the $y$ direction only because the maximum height involves the displacement in the $y$ direction only.

$y\}$   $v_{1_y} = 20$ m/s   $v_{2_y} = 0$ m/s   $a_y = -9.8$ m/s$^2$   $\Delta d_y = ?$   $\Delta t = ?$

The final velocity is zero because at the maximum height, the cannonball stops moving up.

The formula of choice for this case is

$$\vec{v}_2^2 = \vec{v}_1^2 + 2\vec{a}\Delta\vec{d}$$

Then $\Delta d_y = \dfrac{v_{2_y}^2 - v_{1_y}^2}{2a_y} = \dfrac{(0 \text{ m/s})^2 - (20 \text{ m/s})^2}{2(-9.8 \text{ m/s}^2)} = \dfrac{-400 \text{ m}^2/\text{s}^2}{-19.6 \text{ m/s}^2} = 20$ m

The cannonball will rise 20 m above its original location.

**Fig.3.18**   Finding Maximum Height

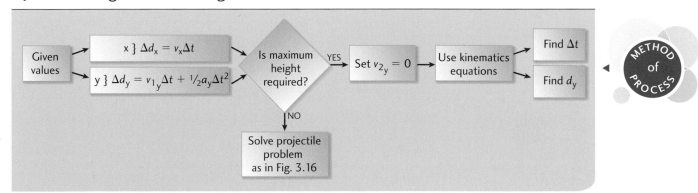

## Finding Final Velocity

To find the final velocity of the projectile as it hits the ground, we need to find the values of the two vector components that comprise it. In the $x$ direction, the final velocity is the same as the initial velocity because there is no horizontal acceleration. Then we calculate the final velocity in the $y$ direction from the given data. We get the resultant final velocity by adding the two components using the head-to-tail method. With a scale diagram, you can measure the magnitude and direction of the final velocity. For a more precise value, use Pythagoras' theorem and the inverse tangent of the ratio of the magnitudes of the components.

EXAMPLE 6    Finding the final velocity

What is the final velocity of the Great Projecto, if he is shot out of a cannon with a horizontal velocity component of 19 m/s and a vertical component of 23 m/s? For his stunt, he lands in a net 2.0 m above the point of launch and 70 m away (Fig. 3.20A).

**Fig. 3.20A**

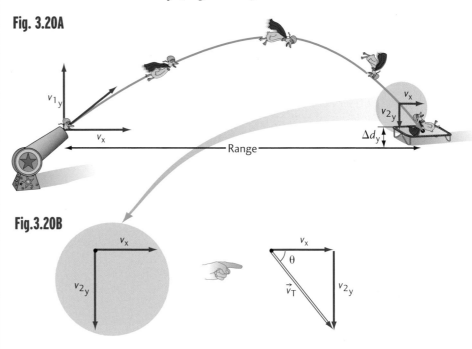

A circus cannon fired Emanuel Zacchini over three Ferris wheels that were 18 m high. Launch velocity was 37 m/s [R53°U] (Fig. 3.19). He travelled horizontally 69 m. A net was placed at that location. Many performers black out momentarily as they accelerate in the barrel. They must regain consciousness before landing, or risk breaking their necks.

**Fig.3.19**    Human cannonball

**Fig.3.20B**

## Solution and Connection to Theory

### Given

$x$}    $v_x = 19$ m/s. Because the velocity is constant in the $x$ direction, this value is also the final $x$ velocity.

$y$}    $a_y = -9.8$ m/s²    $\Delta d_y = 2.0$ m    $v_{1_y} = 23$ m/s    $v_{2_y} = ?$

The formula of choice is

$$\vec{v}_2^{\,2} = \vec{v}_1^{\,2} + 2\vec{a}\Delta\vec{d}$$

$$v_{2_y} = \pm\sqrt{(23 \text{ m/s})^2 + 2(-9.8 \text{ m/s}^2)2.0 \text{ m}} = \pm 22 \text{ m/s}$$

We obtain two answers (a positive and a negative) because Projecto is two metres above the point of launch at two different times. Just after leaving the cannon (up two metres vertically), his vertical velocity is 22 m/s [up]. As he reaches the net, he has a vertical velocity of 22 m/s [down]. Here, we are interested in the final velocity only.

The final vector can be calculated from the given values using the formulas

$$v_2^2 = v_{2_x}^2 + v_{2_y}^2 \text{ and } \theta = \tan^{-1}\frac{v_{2_y}}{v_{2_x}}$$

Because Projecto is moving downward, the velocity is negative. Therefore, $v_{2_y} = -22$ m/s. Now we combine the $x$ and $y$ components of the final velocity from Fig. 3.20A by connecting them head to tail.

In Fig. 3.20B, the final velocity vector was obtained by adding the two components. The resulting vector diagram is a right-angle triangle. Using Pythagoras' theorem,

$$v_T = \sqrt{(19 \text{ m/s})^2 + (-22 \text{ m/s})^2} = 29 \text{ m/s}$$

If you used a scale diagram, then measure the angle. If not, use the tangent function, substituting the magnitudes of the components.

$$\theta = \tan^{-1} \frac{22 \text{ m/s}}{19 \text{ m/s}} = 49°$$

To find the compass directions, we check the signs of the components, $v_x$ (+) and $v_{2_y}$ (−). The signs tell us that Projecto was moving to the right and down. His final velocity is 29 m/s [R49°D].

**Fig.3.21** Finding Final Projectile Velocity

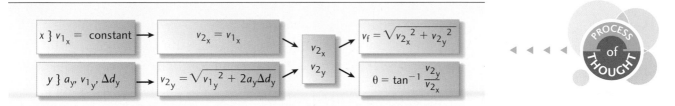

**Fig.3.22** Complete Projectile Overview

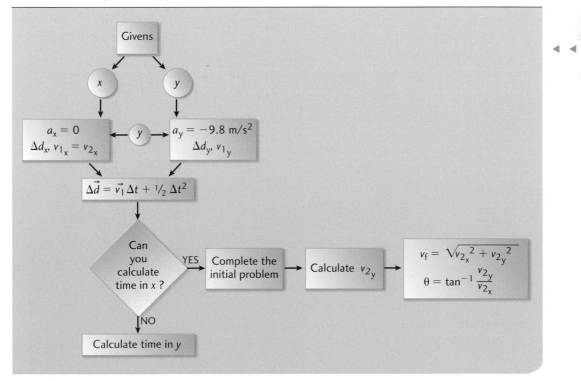

1. **a)** Calculate the time an object takes to fall 100 m if it starts from rest.
   **b)** Calculate the time it takes the object to reach the ground if the object has an initial velocity of 10 m/s upward.
   **c)** Calculate the time it takes the object to reach the ground if the object has an initial velocity of 10 m/s downward.
   **d)** Assuming that the object had a horizontal velocity of 10.0 m/s, find the range for a), b), and c).

2. A soccer ball is kicked at 25 m/s at an angle of 25° to the ground. Find
   **a)** the time it takes the ball to reach the maximum height in its trajectory.
   **b)** the maximum height of the ball.
   **c)** the time it takes to land on the ground again.
   **d)** the range the ball travels.
   **e)** the final velocity of the ball (with angle), using logic and calculation.

## Golf

Golf is all about projectile motion. The angle of the face of a golf club head relative to the centreline (an imaginary line perpendicular to the ground) is referred to as the **club head loft**. The number of the club iron or wood indicates the size of the club head loft. The higher the number, the larger the loft angle.

The club head loft also indicates the angle of the initial velocity of the ball. For the same force exerted on a ball, the nine-iron club will cause the golf ball to fly higher and travel a shorter distance than the three-iron club. In principle, a loft angle of 0° transfers all of the energy of the swing directly to the ball, causing the ball to travel the farthest. However, because of gravity pulling the ball down, a ball hit off a standard one-inch tee would travel only a few metres before hitting the ground. Thus, the bigger the loft angle, the greater the trajectory and the smaller the range.

3. For a driver with loft 5° and a four-wood with loft 18°, calculate
   **a)** the distance the ball travels if the initial velocity of the ball is 18.5 m/s.
   **b)** the maximum height of the ball for each club.
   **c)** the distance each ball travels if you tee off an elevated tee of height 15 m.

4. A pitching wedge causes the ball to travel 17 m for the same initial velocity as in Question 3 (18.5 m/s). What is the loft angle of the club if the ball spends 3.66 s in the air?

**Fig.3.23A**

**Fig.3.23B**

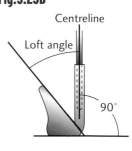

Centreline

Loft angle

90°

Iron

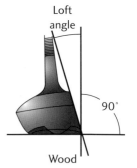

Loft angle

90°

Wood

## 3.4 Relative Velocities

Tarzan and Tarzana, brawny ape people, decide to have a race across a river. Both are excellent swimmers and have the same ability. Tarzan swims straight across, landing on shore directly across from where he started. Tarzana jumps in and points herself across the river, but ends up farther downstream when she reaches the other side. The two are pictured in Fig. 3.24.

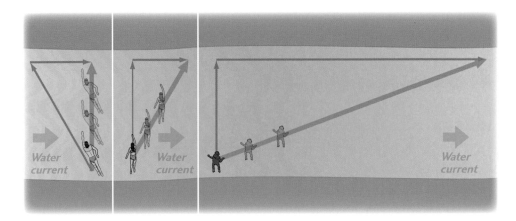

**Fig.3.24**  Family race

Who finished first? Then there was Cheetah, faithful brawny ape pet, who chose to swim across the same river, but at a time when the floods were raging and the river flowed at five times the velocity it did when Tarzan and Tarzana swam it. Cheetah too is a good swimmer and has the same ability as Tarzan and Tarzana. Did Cheetah finish the crossing in a shorter time? These questions will be answered in this section.

## Relative Motion

In trying to answer the posed problem, we need to define what **relative motion** is. Suppose you are travelling in a car and are being observed by a highway patrolman sitting by the side of the road, as shown in Fig. 3.25(a). The patrolman will measure your velocity *relative to his position*. In this case, the patrolman is not moving. Let's assume the velocity he measured is 140 km/h. Your velocity is said to be 140 km/h [E], measured relative to the ground.

Now suppose you pass the patrol car with a velocity of 140 km/h while it is moving with a velocity of 100 km/h in the same direction. This time, the velocity measured is 40 km/h *relative to the patrol car*. While the patrol car has a velocity of zero in its own reference frame, its 100 km/h velocity must be measured relative to the ground, as in Fig. 3.25(b). Notice that your velocity is the same, but the two measurements done by the patrolman are different. The bottom line is that a velocity value is measured **relative** to a **reference frame**. In everyday use, we are accustomed to using the ground as a stationary reference frame. This frame is implied in most problem situations.

Fig.3.25 Relative velocity

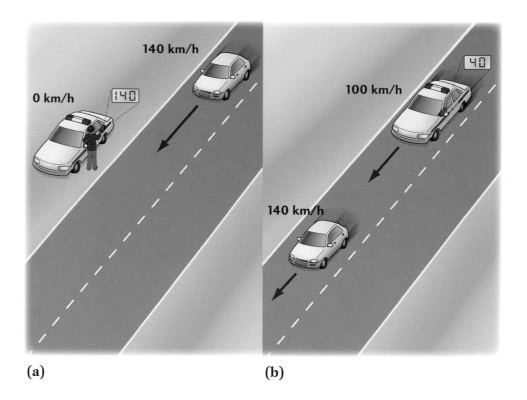

**(a)**                     **(b)**

Now we can apply this knowledge to the swimmer in the river. If Tarzana floats with the current, it will appear to her that she is not moving relative to the water. To actually measure her velocity, someone must stand on shore (relative to ground) and watch her go by. In fact, to measure the river's velocity, we also must measure it relative to the shore (relative to the ground).

In order to keep these velocities distinct, we use a series of subscripts.

---

$\vec{v}_{og}$ is the velocity of the person or **object** relative to the **ground**.

$\vec{v}_{mg}$ is the velocity of the **medium** the person or object is in relative to the **ground**.

$\vec{v}_{om}$ is the velocity of the person or **object** relative to the **medium** he/she/it is in. This velocity is not readily observed because it is affected by the medium's velocity. It can be considered the person's or object's ability without influence (such as swimming in water with no current).

You can come up with your own subscripts; choose symbols that you'll find easy to remember.

---

The relationship between the three quantities is

$$\vec{v}_{og} = \vec{v}_{om} + \vec{v}_{mg}$$

Since the vectors $\vec{v}_{om}$ and $\vec{v}_{mg}$ are being added, they must be joined head to tail. The vector $\vec{v}_{og}$ is only ever attached to other vectors tail to tail or head to head.

EXAMPLE 7    **Relative motion in one dimension**

**Fig.3.26**

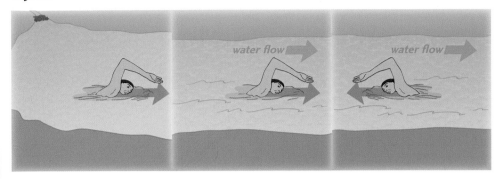

In one dimension, the river problem has the three possible cases shown in Fig. 3.26. When the river flows, its velocity is 1.0 m/s [east]. Tarzana can swim at 2.0 m/s (in still water).

Case 1. Tarzana swims in a dammed up river (no current).
Case 2. Tarzana swims with the current (dam broke).
Case 3. Tarzana swims against the current.

## Solution and Connection to Theory

### Case 1 Given

Assuming east is positive, the givens are

$$\vec{v}_{om} = 2.0 \text{ m/s} \quad \text{and} \quad \vec{v}_{mg} = 0 \text{ m/s}$$

Then

$$\vec{v}_{og} = \vec{v}_{om} + \vec{v}_{mg}.$$

Since the vectors are collinear,

$$\vec{v}_{og} = 2.0 \text{ m/s} + 0 \text{ m/s} = 2.0 \text{ m/s}.$$

Tarzana swims 2.0 m/s [E]. Without anything affecting her velocity, we see her swim at 2.0 m/s [E], as illustrated in Fig. 3.27.

**Fig.3.27**

$$\underset{\vec{v}_{om} = 2 \text{ m/s [E]}}{\longrightarrow} \quad + \quad \underset{\vec{v}_{mg} = 0}{0} \quad = \quad \underset{\vec{v}_{og} = 2 \text{ m/s [E]}}{\longrightarrow}$$

**Case 2 Given**

$$\vec{v}_{om} = 2.0 \text{ m/s [E]} \qquad \vec{v}_{mg} = 1.0 \text{ m/s [E]}$$

Since the vectors are collinear, you can add them algebraically.

$$\vec{v}_{og} = \vec{v}_{om} + \vec{v}_{mg} \qquad \vec{v}_{og} = 2.0 \text{ m/s} + 1.0 \text{ m/s} = 3.0 \text{ m/s}$$

The positive value indicates that the velocity direction is to the east. Notice in Fig. 3.28 that Tarzana is capable of swimming at 2.0 m/s, but is seen to be swimming at 3.0 m/s. This is because the current is helping her. What we see is just the resultant, $\vec{v}_{og}$.

**Fig.3.28**

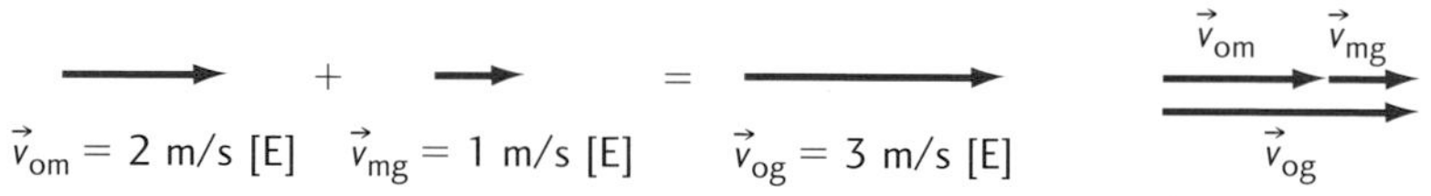

$\vec{v}_{om} = 2 \text{ m/s [E]} \quad \vec{v}_{mg} = 1 \text{ m/s [E]} \qquad \vec{v}_{og} = 3 \text{ m/s [E]}$

**Case 3 Given**

Since $\vec{v}_{om} = 2.0$ m/s [W], we write $\vec{v}_{om} = -2.0$ m/s because we have designated east as positive.

$$\vec{v}_{mg} = 1.0 \text{ m/s}$$

$$\vec{v}_{og} = \vec{v}_{om} + \vec{v}_{mg}$$

$$\vec{v}_{og} = -2.0 \text{ m/s} + 1.0 \text{ m/s} = -1.0 \text{ m/s}$$

Notice in Fig. 3.29 that even though Tarzana is capable of swimming at 2.0 m/s, she is seen to swim only at 1.0 m/s [W] because she is now fighting the current.

**Fig.3.29**

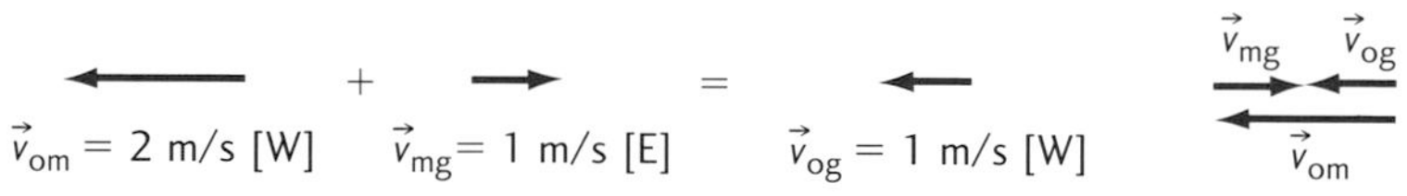

$\vec{v}_{om} = 2 \text{ m/s [W]} \quad \vec{v}_{mg} = 1 \text{ m/s [E]} \qquad \vec{v}_{og} = 1 \text{ m/s [W]}$

**Fig.3.30** Calculating Relative Velocity in One Direction

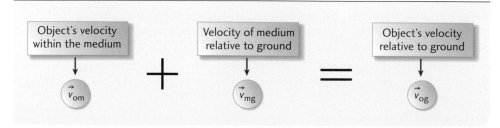

# Two-dimensional Relative Velocity

**Fig.3.31**  Determine the pattern

We have learned that when we use vector equations in two dimensions, values cannot be substituted into the equation directly. This is because the vector quantities are no longer collinear. The vector equation tells you how to draw the vector diagram. *The plus sign (+) in the equation tells you to connect the vectors **head to tail**.* By looking at the equation $\vec{v}_{og} = \vec{v}_{mg} + \vec{v}_{om}$, we can see that the vectors $\vec{v}_{mg}$ and $\vec{v}_{om}$ are the ones connected head to tail. No matter how we rearrange the equation, $\vec{v}_{og}$ is never **added** to the other two vectors. This means that $\vec{v}_{og}$ is never connected head to tail in any diagram. Figure 3.31 shows a series of vector additions. For each case, $\vec{v}_{og}$ is identified. You should notice that it is always connected either head to head or tail to tail to the other two vectors.

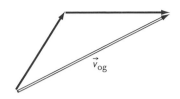

As with other 2D vector problems such as displacement and projectile motion, two methods can be used to solve them. The first is to create a scale diagram using the vector equation to guide your drawing. The final vector is then measured along with its direction. The other method is to use trigonometric formulas and Pythagoras' theorem.

We are now closer to answering the opening question.

---

**EXAMPLE 8**   **Relative motion in two dimensions**

Case 1. Assume Tarzan can swim at 2.0 m/s, the current is 1.0 m/s [E], and Tarzan is seen to swim directly across (assume north).

Case 2. Assume Tarzana can swim at 2.0 m/s, the current is 1.0 m/s [E], and Tarzana is seen to direct her body directly across (north).

Case 3. Assume Cheetah can also swim at 2.0 m/s. The water current is now 5.0 m/s [E]. Cheetah swims like Tarzana and points directly north.

Find the final velocity of each.

### *Solution and Connection to Theory*

**Fig.3.32**  Case 1

**Case 1 Given**

$\vec{v}_{og} = ?$ [N]        $\vec{v}_{om} = 2.0$ m/s [?]        $\vec{v}_{mg} = 1.0$ m/s [E]

From the vector equation $\vec{v}_{og} = \vec{v}_{om} + \vec{v}_{mg}$, construct a vector diagram. From Fig. 3.32, notice that in order for Tarzan to swim directly across the river, he must angle his body into the current while still maintaining some motion towards the far shore.

Vector $\vec{v}_{og}$, pointing directly north, will be the resultant of $\vec{v}_{mg}$ and $\vec{v}_{om}$. Note that $\vec{v}_{om}$ is the hypotenuse of the right-angle triangle. Then use Pythagoras' theorem to find $\vec{v}_{og}$.

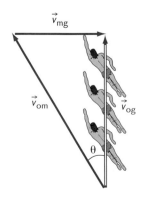

$$v_{\text{og}} = \sqrt{v^2_{\text{om}} - v^2_{\text{mg}}}$$

$$= \sqrt{(2.0 \text{ m/s})^2 - (1.0 \text{ m/s})^2} = 1.7 \text{ m/s}$$

To find the angle $\theta$ as indicated in Fig. 3.32, we can use

$$\theta = \sin^{-1}\frac{v_{\text{mg}}}{v_{\text{om}}} = \sin^{-1}\frac{1.0 \text{ m/s}}{2.0 \text{ m/s}} = 30°$$

This gives the direction as [N30°W] or [W60°N]. While Tarzan swims 2.0 m/s in that direction, his velocity relative to the ground is 1.7 m/s [N].

### Case 2 Given

$$\vec{v}_{\text{og}} = ? \text{ [?]} \qquad \vec{v}_{\text{om}} = 2.0 \text{ m/s [N]} \qquad \vec{v}_{\text{mg}} = 1.0 \text{ m/s [E]}$$

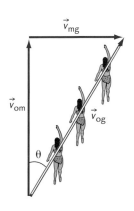

**Fig.3.33** Case 2

Construct a vector diagram. From Fig. 3.33, you can see that Tarzana is concentrating only on swimming north. In still water, you would see her moving at 2.0 m/s directly north. However, she is being pushed east by the current as she tries to move north. These two velocities act *at the same time* to create the angled motion. Notice, though, that her body position stays pointing north as she approaches the far shore at an angle. Using Pythagoras' theorem,

$$v_{\text{og}} = \sqrt{v^2_{\text{om}} + v^2_{\text{mg}}}$$

$$= \sqrt{(2.0 \text{ m/s})^2 + (1.0 \text{ m/s})^2} = 2.2 \text{ m/s}$$

The angle can be obtained from

$$\theta = \tan^{-1}\frac{v_{\text{mg}}}{v_{\text{om}}} = \tan^{-1}\frac{1.0 \text{ m/s}}{2.0 \text{ m/s}} = 27°$$

Thus, Tarzana's velocity relative to the ground is 2.2 m/s [N27°E] or [E63°N]. Because of her angled motion, she travels farther than Tarzan at a higher speed.

### Case 3 Given

$$\vec{v}_{\text{og}} = ? \text{ [?]} \qquad \vec{v}_{\text{om}} = 2.0 \text{ m/s [N]} \qquad \vec{v}_{\text{mg}} = 5.0 \text{ m/s [E]}$$

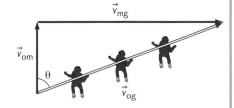

**Fig.3.34** Case 3

In the vector diagram of Fig. 3.34, you can see that Cheetah's velocity relative to the ground is $\vec{v}_{\text{og}}$. Using Pythagoras' theorem,

$$v_{\text{og}} = \sqrt{v^2_{\text{om}} + v^2_{\text{mg}}}$$

$$= \sqrt{(2.0 \text{ m/s})^2 + (5.0 \text{ m/s})^2} = 5.4 \text{ m/s}$$

The angle can be obtained by

$$\theta = \tan^{-1}\frac{v_{\text{mg}}}{v_{\text{om}}} = \tan^{-1}\frac{5.0 \text{ m/s}}{2.0 \text{ m/s}} = 68°$$

The direction is [N68°E] or [E22°N]. So Cheetah travels at 5.4 m/s in the direction 68° east of north.

In all three cases, the diagrams could have been constructed by setting a scale, using the givens, and connecting them in a manner dictated by the vector equation. The final answers could have been obtained by measuring.

## Finding the Time to Cross

So who finishes first in this race? To find out, we need to look at the three vector diagrams, which are shown together in Fig. 3.35.

The equation $\vec{v} = \frac{\Delta \vec{d}}{\Delta t}$ rearranged to find time, becomes $\Delta t = \frac{\Delta \vec{d}}{\vec{v}}$. We now need to find out which $v$ to use. If you look at the diagrams in Fig. 3.35, the velocity vector that points in the direction of the desired motion (north in our case) is the appropriate choice. The other vectors involve the motion of the current, which does nothing to help anyone cross to the other side. Tarzan swims at 1.7 m/s in the north direction. Notice that for Tarzana and Cheetah, the velocity directed north is 2.0 m/s. Thus, Tarzan finishes last, with Tarzana and Cheetah tied for first. The lesson of this story is that if you wish to cross the river quickly, then direct all your energies to do so. Tarzan used up some of his velocity in fighting the current in order to end up in a position directly across from where he started.

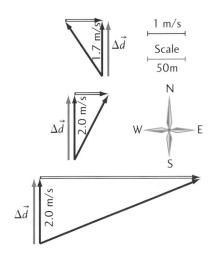

**Fig.3.35** Aligning displacement and velocity vectors

| | Magnitude | Direction |
|---|---|---|
| $\vec{v}_{pg}$ | Ground speed | Track |
| $\vec{v}_{pa}$ | Air speed | Heading |

## Airplanes

For airplanes and flight paths, the method of approaching the problem is the same as for our jungle swimmers. The velocity of the plane relative to the ground is the velocity we see. It is a combination of the plane's capability, called the velocity of the plane relative to air $(\vec{v}_{pa})$, and the velocity of the air relative to the ground $(\vec{v}_{ag})$. These two velocities continually combine throughout the flight to produce the final velocity we see.

---

**EXAMPLE 9    Relative velocity involving planes**

A pilot with a heading of [N30°E] and an airspeed of 400 km/h flies into a wind coming from the north at 110 km/h. What is the plane's velocity relative to the ground and how long would it take to complete a journey of 1000 km [N30°E]?

### *Solution and Connection to Theory*

**Given**
$\vec{v}_{pa} = 400$ km/h [N30°E]        $\vec{v}_{ag} = 110$ km/h [S]        $\vec{v}_{pg} = ?$ [?]

$\vec{v}_{pg} = \vec{v}_{pa} + \vec{v}_{ag}$

## TRIGONOMETRIC EQUATIONS

In Fig. 3.36, the angles of the triangle are labeled using capital letters, and the sides opposite them are labeled using lowercase letters. Whenever the lengths of two sides and the contained angle (the angle between them) are known, the **cosine law** is used.

$$c^2 = a^2 + b^2 - 2ab \cos C.$$

Similarly, if we know the value of an angle, the side opposite it, plus another angle or side, we can use the **sine law**.

$$\frac{\sin A}{a} = \frac{\sin B}{b} = \frac{\sin C}{c}$$

**Fig. 3.36**

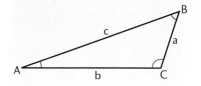

**Fig. 3.37B**

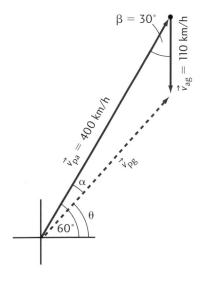

**Fig. 3.37A**

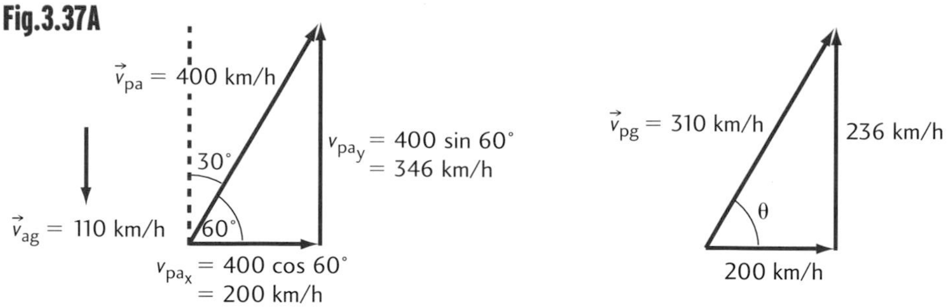

$\vec{v}_{pa} = 400$ km/h
$30°$
$v_{pa_y} = 400 \sin 60°$
$= 346$ km/h
$\vec{v}_{ag} = 110$ km/h
$60°$
$v_{pa_x} = 400 \cos 60°$
$= 200$ km/h

$\vec{v}_{pg} = 310$ km/h
$236$ km/h
$\theta$
$200$ km/h

*Component method*

**x}** $\quad v_{pg_x} = v_{pa_x} + v_{ag_x}$

$$v_{pg_x} = (400 \text{ km/h}) \cos 60° + 0 \text{ km/h} = 200 \text{ km/h}$$

**y}** $\quad v_{pg_y} = v_{pa_y} + v_{ag_y}$

$$v_{pg_y} = (400 \text{ km/h}) \sin 60° - 110 \text{ km/h} = 236 \text{ km/h}$$

$$v_{pg} = \sqrt{v_{pg_x}^2 + v_{pg_y}^2}$$

$$= \sqrt{(200 \text{ km/h})^2 + (236 \text{ km/h})^2} = 310 \text{ km/h}$$

The angle for the ground velocity is

$$\theta = \tan^{-1} \frac{v_{pg_y}}{v_{pg_x}} = \tan^{-1} \frac{236 \text{ km/h}}{200 \text{ km/h}} = 50°$$

Since both the *x* and *y* components are positive, the direction is [E50°N]. Therefore, $\vec{v}_{pg} = 310$ km/h [E50°N].

To find the time involved, we use the velocity of the plane relative to the ground. Since the distance covered is the actual displacement, the $\vec{v}_{pg}$ velocity vector is the one that lines up with the displacement direction. Therefore, the time it takes to reach the destination is

$$\Delta t = \frac{\Delta d}{v_{pg}} = \frac{1000 \text{ km}}{310 \text{ km/h}} = 3.23 \text{ h}$$

*Sine/Cosine Method*

First we construct the vector diagram, knowing that $\vec{v}_{pa}$ and $\vec{v}_{ag}$ are connected head to tail (Fig. 3.37B).

Now we use the cosine law to find $v_{pg}$:

$$v_{pg}^2 = v_{pa}^2 + v_{ag}^2 - 2v_{pa}v_{ag} \cos\beta$$

$$v_{pg} = \sqrt{(400 \text{ km/h})^2 + (110 \text{ km/h})^2 - 2(400 \text{ km/h})(110 \text{ km/h})\cos 30°}$$

$$= 310 \text{ km/h}$$

To find the angle, we use the sine law:

$$\frac{\sin\alpha}{v_{ag}} = \frac{\sin\beta}{v_{pg}}$$

$$\sin\alpha = \frac{110 \text{ km/h}}{310 \text{ km/h}} \sin 30°$$

$$\alpha = 10°$$

From the diagram, to find the angle from the horizontal,
θ = 60° − 10° = 50° (as before).

Both methods lead to the same final result. The plane's ground velocity is 310 km/h [E50°N]. It will take 3.23 h to fly 1000 km.

**Fig.3.38**  Calculating Time of Travel

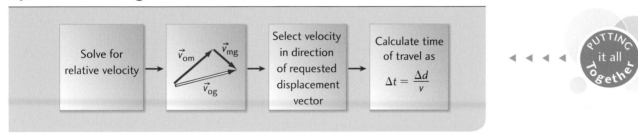

1. **a)** Clearly state the meaning of the vectors $\vec{v}_{og}$, $\vec{v}_{om}$, and $\vec{v}_{mg}$.
   **b)** Use the cases of a person swimming in a river, a plane flying in the air, and a person throwing a ball while running to illustrate the meaning of the vectors in a).
2. For the case of a wind blowing from the east at 80 km/h and a plane capable of flying at 200 km/h, find
   **a)** the velocity of the plane relative to the ground if the pilot points the plane north.
   **b)** the velocity of the plane relative to the ground and the heading the pilot must take in order to fly directly north.
   **c)** the velocity of the plane relative to the ground if the pilot points the plane [N20°W].

Make sure you state the givens for each case.

# 3.5  Average Acceleration

Consider the equation $\vec{a} = \frac{(\vec{v}_2 - \vec{v}_1)}{\Delta t}$. In two dimensions, the velocity vectors are usually in different directions. We know that if the vectors are not collinear, then we cannot substitute directly into the acceleration equation. We must use the component method of solving problems.

In the equation

$$\vec{a} = \frac{(\vec{v}_2 - \vec{v}_1)}{\Delta t},$$

time does not affect the *direction* of acceleration. Therefore, we only need to solve for

$$\Delta\vec{v} = \vec{v}_2 - \vec{v}_1.$$

Using the component method, we separate the horizontal and vertical components for $\vec{v}_1$ and $\vec{v}_2$, as we did in the previous example. We substitute the horizontal components into the equation $\Delta\vec{v} = \vec{v}_2 - \vec{v}_1$, then we do the same for the vertical components. Finally, we use Pythagoras' theorem to find the magnitude of the resultant vector. We use the function $\tan^{-1}\frac{v_y}{v_x}$ to obtain the angle.

After you obtain $\Delta\vec{v}$, divide it by the time to determine the acceleration.

**Fig.3.39A** Solving a 2D Vector Problem

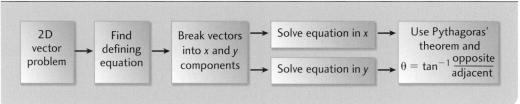

---

**EXAMPLE 10** **Finding vector acceleration**

Find the acceleration of a car moving at 30 m/s [E60°N], which then veers off and moves directly east at 25 m/s in 2.5 s.

### Solution and Connection to Theory

**Given**
$\vec{v}_1 = 30$ m/s [E60°N]     $\vec{v}_2 = 25$ m/s [E]     $\Delta t = 2.5$ s     $\vec{a} = ?$

The defining equation for the vector problem is $\Delta\vec{v} = \vec{v}_2 - \vec{v}_1$, which will be solved in both the $x$ and $y$ directions.

Next we obtain the components of each velocity.

$v_{1_x} = (30 \text{ m/s}) \cos 60° = 15$ m/s
$v_{1_y} = (30 \text{ m/s}) \sin 60° = 26$ m/s
$v_{2_x} = 25$ m/s
$v_{2_y} = 0$ m/s

Solving in the $x$ direction,

$\Delta v_x = v_{2_x} - v_{1_x} = 25 \text{ m/s} - 15 \text{ m/s} = 10$ m/s

Solving in the $y$ direction,

$\Delta v_y = v_{2_y} - v_{1_y} = 0 \text{ m/s} - 26 \text{ m/s} = -26$ m/s

Therefore, $\Delta v = \sqrt{(10 \text{ m/s})^2 + (-26 \text{ m/s})^2} = 28 \text{ m/s}.$

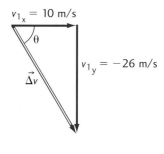

**Fig.3.39B**

Substituting the magnitudes of the velocities into the equation, the angle

$$\theta = \tan^{-1} \frac{(26 \text{ m/s})}{10 \text{m/s}} = 69°.$$

From the signs of the $x$ $(+)$ and $y$ $(-)$ values for $\Delta \vec{v}$, we can see that the direction is [E69°S]. Dividing $\Delta \vec{v}$ by 2.5 s, we obtain the acceleration, 11 m/s² [E69°S].

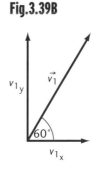

**Fig.3.39C** Finding Vector Acceleration

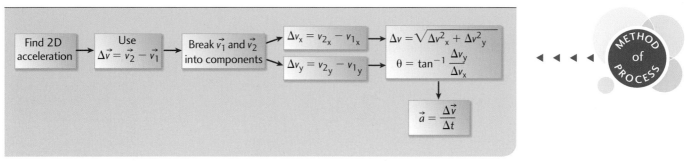

## Subtracting Vectors Using a Diagram

The component method does not require the use of a vector diagram. As long as you have a defining equation and the components of the vector quantities involved, the problem can be solved algebraically. But what does the subtraction of vectors look like?

In order to visualize vector subtraction, consider the diagram representing a plane flying north with a wind blowing east. From Fig. 3.39, we can see that the plane's actual velocity is to the northeast.

Because the defining equation is $\vec{v}_{pg} = \vec{v}_{pa} + \vec{v}_{ag}$, the vectors $\vec{v}_{pa}$ and $\vec{v}_{ag}$ are connected head to tail. This is the meaning of the plus sign in vector addition. But if the equation is rearranged to solve for either $\vec{v}_{pa}$ or $\vec{v}_{ag}$, a negative sign appears because one of these quantities must be subtracted from $\vec{v}_{pg}$ in order to solve for the missing quantity:

$$\vec{v}_{pa} = \vec{v}_{pg} - \vec{v}_{ag} \quad \text{or} \quad \vec{v}_{ag} = \vec{v}_{pg} - \vec{v}_{pa}$$

Notice from Fig. 3.40 that $\vec{v}_{pg}$ is connected either head to head or tail to tail to the other two vectors. This is the vector diagram representation for *subtraction*. We will use the tail-to-tail method of connecting vectors to illustrate subtraction.

From Example 10, we used vector subtraction, $\Delta \vec{v} = \vec{v}_2 - \vec{v}_1$. Figure 3.41 illustrates several examples of velocity vector subtraction. Notice that the resultant always points toward the head of $\vec{v}_2$.

**Fig.3.40** $\quad \vec{v}_{pa} = \vec{v}_{pg} - \vec{v}_{ag}$

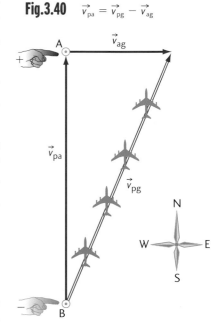

**Fig.3.41**  $\Delta\vec{v} = \vec{v}_2 - \vec{v}_1$

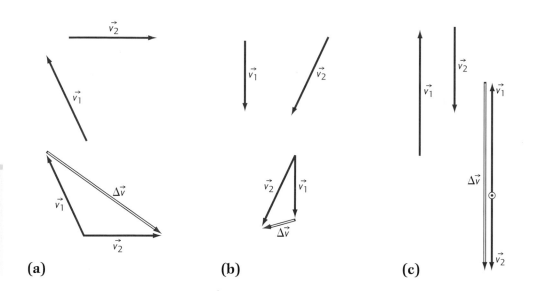

(a)　　　　　　　　　(b)　　　　　　　　　(c)

## ALTERNATIVE METHOD FOR SUBTRACTING VECTORS

$\vec{v}_2 - \vec{v}_1 = \vec{v}_2 + (-\vec{v}_1)$

$\vec{v}_1$ can be subtracted from $\vec{v}_2$ by adding $-\vec{v}_1$. $(-\vec{v}_1)$ is $\vec{v}_1$ pointing in the opposite direction. Add $\vec{v}_2 + (-\vec{v}_1)$ in the examples in Fig. 3.41 to verify that the resultant is the same.

**Fig.3.42**  General Method of Vector Subtraction

To subtract two vectors → Connect the two vectors tail to tail → Complete the triangle → The resultant points toward the first term in the subtraction

$\Delta\vec{v} = \vec{v}_2 - \vec{v}_1$

CONNECTING the Concepts ▶ ▶ ▶ ▶

## Using the Cosine and Sine Law Methods

Because we used triangles in the last example, there is an alternate approach to solving the problem. After we create a vector diagram, we can treat it like a triangle and use trigonometric equations to find the missing information.

**EXAMPLE 11**  **Sine/cosine method for solving vector problems**

Find the acceleration of a car moving at 30 m/s [E60°N], which then veers off and moves directly east at 25 m/s in 2.5 s. Solve using either the sine law or the cosine law.

**Fig.3.43A**

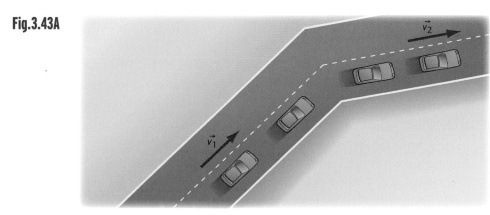

### Solution and Connection to Theory

**Given**

$\vec{v}_1 = 30$ m/s [E60°N]     $\vec{v}_2 = 25$ m/s [E]     $\Delta t = 2.5$ s     $\vec{a} = ?$

First we draw a vector diagram.

Connect the vectors tail to tail, as illustrated in Fig. 3.43B. Notice that $\Delta\vec{v}$ has its head touching $\vec{v}_2$. The angle between the two vectors is 60°. We know the size of the contained angle between two known sides. This means that we can use the cosine law.

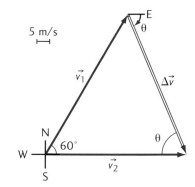

**Fig.3.43B**

$$\Delta v^2 = v_1^2 + v_2^2 - 2v_1 v_2 \cos 60°$$

$$\Delta v^2 = (30 \text{ m/s})^2 + (25 \text{ m/s})^2 - 2(30 \text{ m/s})(25 \text{ m/s}) \cos 60°$$

$$\Delta v^2 = 775 \text{ m}^2/\text{s}^2 \qquad \Delta v = 27.8 \text{ m/s}.$$

This number rounds off to 28 m/s due to significant digits.

To find the angle for this vector, we use the sine law to find $\theta$.

$$\frac{\sin\theta}{30 \text{ m/s}} = \frac{\sin 60°}{27.8 \text{ m/s}}$$

$$\sin\theta = 0.933, \ \theta = 69°$$

As before, the angle is [E69°S]. To obtain the acceleration magnitude, we divide 28 m/s by 2.5 s. Thus, the acceleration is 11 m/s$^2$ [E69°S].

The following example is done using both the component and trigonometric methods and is accompanied by a scale diagram.

---

**EXAMPLE 12**   **Comparing methods — change in velocity**

A puck is shot towards the boards at a velocity of 25.0 m/s at an angle of 30° to the boards. If the puck ricochets off the boards at an angle of 20° relative to the boards and at a speed of 20.0 m/s, find the change in velocity of the puck.

**Fig.3.44**

### Solution and Connection to Theory

**Given**

$\vec{v}_1 = 25.0$ m/s [R30°D]     $\vec{v}_2 = 20.0$ [R20°U]

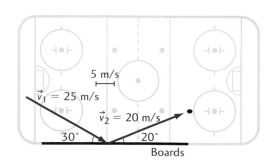

**Fig.3.45**

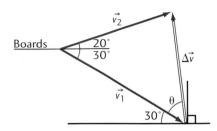

**Trigonometric Method.** We first construct a vector subtraction diagram, as in Fig. 3.45. Notice that the interior angle is 50°. Since we know the lengths of two sides and the interior angle between them, we can use the cosine law.

$$\Delta v^2 = (25.0 \text{ m/s})^2 + (20.0 \text{ m/s})^2 - 2(25.0 \text{ m/s})(20.0 \text{ m/s}) \cos 50°$$

$$\Delta v^2 = 382 \text{ m}^2/\text{s}^2$$

$$\Delta v = 19.5 \text{ m/s}$$

To find the angle for this vector, we first use the sine law to find θ.

$$\frac{\sin\theta}{20.0 \text{ m/s}} = \frac{\sin 50°}{19.5 \text{ m/s}}$$

$$\sin\theta = 0.786, \ \theta = 52°$$

Referring back to Fig. 3.45, we see that this angle is not measured from the boards. Because the angle must be given in relation to one of the cardinal directions (U, D, R, L), add 30°, as shown. 30° + 52° = 82°. The change in velocity is 19.5 m/s [L82°U] (or [U8°L]).

**Component Method.** Obtain the components of each velocity vector.

$$v_{1_x} = (25.0 \text{ m/s}) \cos 30° = 21.7 \text{ m/s}$$
$$v_{1_y} = (-25.0 \text{ m/s}) \sin 30° = -12.5 \text{ m/s}$$

The negative sign occurs because the direction of the $y$ component is down.

$$v_{2_x} = 20.0 \text{ m/s} \cos 20° = 18.8 \text{ m/s} \qquad v_{2_y} = 20.0 \text{ m/s} \sin 20° = 6.8 \text{ m/s}$$

Solving in the $x$ direction,

$$\Delta v_x = v_{2_x} - v_{1_x} = 18.8 \text{ m/s} - 21.7 \text{ m/s} = -2.9 \text{ m/s}$$

Solving in the $y$ direction,

$$\Delta v_y = v_{2_y} - v_{1_y} = 6.8 \text{ m/s} - (-12.5 \text{ m/s}) = 19.3 \text{ m/s}$$

Therefore, $\Delta v = \sqrt{(-2.9 \text{ m/s})^2 + (19.3 \text{ m/s})^2} = 19.5 \text{ m/s}$.

$$\theta = \tan^{-1} \frac{19.3 \text{ m/s}}{2.9 \text{ m/s}} = 82°$$

(We actually kept more decimal places in the calculation than are shown.) By checking the signs of the $x$ (−) and $y$ (+) values for $\Delta v$ (see Fig. 3.45), we can see that the direction is [L82°U].

In summary, we can solve relative velocity problems, total displacement problems (with two displacements), and average acceleration problems using the same two methods. The vector equations

$$\vec{v}_{pg} = \vec{v}_{pa} + \vec{v}_{ag} \qquad \Delta\vec{d}_{total} = \vec{d}_1 + \vec{d}_2 \qquad \vec{a} = \frac{\Delta\vec{v}}{\Delta t}$$

tell you how to combine the given vectors in a vector diagram. Once the triangle is formed, the appropriate trigonometric law is used. For the component method, these are the defining equations into which the components of the given vectors are substituted.

**Fig.3.46**  Solving Problems Using Vectors

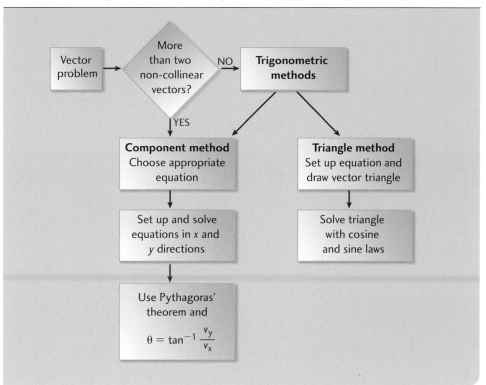

1. **a)** Given two vectors, describe the three possible methods of solving a vector equation.
   **b)** Describe the difference in meaning when two vectors are connected tail to tail and head to head.

2. **a)** For a puck travelling at 120 km/h [E], then changing its direction to [N] in 0.5 s, calculate the puck's acceleration.
   **c)** Now assume the puck changed to a direction given by [N25°W]. Calculate the acceleration using the component and cosine law methods.
   **c)** Now assume the puck changed to a new velocity of 100 km/h [N25°W]. Calculate the acceleration using the component and cosine law methods.

3. Repeat Question 2 in Section 3.4 Applying the Concepts using the sine/cosine method.

# Global Positioning System

The Global Positioning System (GPS), commissioned by the United States Department of Defense, is a navigation system that allows users to determine their location anywhere on Earth. GPS uses communications between satellites as well as a series of monitoring stations and ground-based antennas (Fig. STSE.3.1).

Triangulation calculations (Fig. STSE.3.2) between the satellites and the user make accurate results possible.

**Fig.STSE.3.1** The segments of the GPS

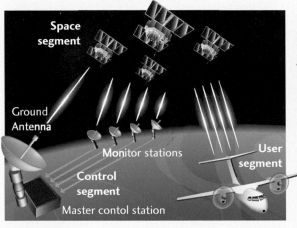

**Fig.STSE.3.2** Triangulation with satellites

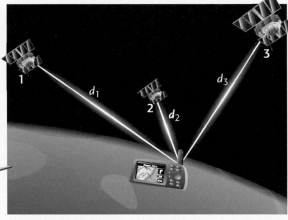

**Fig.STSE.3.3** Wherify child watch

Radio signals travelling at the speed of light are timed as they travel from the satellite to the hand unit and back to the satellite. The distances between the satellite and user can then be calculated using a simple kinematics equation.

$$d_{satellite} = \frac{ct}{2}$$

where $d_{satellite}$ is the distance between the satellite and the GPS user, $c$ is the speed of light ($3.0 \times 10^8$ m/s), and $t$ is the time it takes for the signal to descend to Earth and return to the satellite. The product, $ct$, is divided by two because we are only interested in the distance between Earth and the satellite.

Receivers on Earth have a "line of sight" that allows them to communicate with at least five GPS satellites at any one time. First widely used during the Persian Gulf War in 1991, GPS systems are now sold in many stores for personal use, and are also offered as options in some new cars. Wherify Wireless of Redwood Shores, California, is marketing a Personal Location System that uses GPS satellites and cellular phone technology to determine the location of children (Fig. STSE.3.3). Children with this watch can press a button to be directly connected to the 911 emergency system, and police can be dispatched to their exact location. As navigators in the global village, we may never need paper maps again.

## Design a Study of Societal Impact

Research GPS. What is the resolution of the system? How many satellites does it use? Are there plans to add more satellites? Think of a new application for GPS.

The evolution of GPS required the cooperation of government, science, business, and industry. Brainstorm the various fields of physics that are directly involved in developing new technology. Research other careers that are directly involved in the development of this technology. For each of these careers, examine the extent to which knowledge of physics is an asset.

Does the widespread use of GPS raise privacy issues? How should these issues be addressed?

There is only a limited amount of space "up there" in which to position satellites around Earth, and rich countries seem to have first pick. Should all countries have guaranteed access to the services the satellites provide? Which governing body would be capable of monitoring accessibility to satellites?

## Design an Activity to Evaluate

Conduct an activity to locate an object on a large, open floor or tabletop (large lab bench) using the principle of triangulation. Use the cracks between floor tiles (other marks for a tabletop) to set up a two-dimensional grid axis map. Designate three positions in this area to be used as "satellites." Using a sonic ranger (and computer interface) or tape measure, measure the distances between each "satellite" and the test object in order to locate the object on the area map. Your test object should be small and not easily discernible, such as one coin out of many that are laid out on the floor. Looking for one object among many similar objects will highlight the importance of accuracy for each measurement as well as the need for more positioning "satellites." Extend this activity to three dimensions by lifting your three satellites to different heights using retort stands or tripods.

## Build a Structure

Organize a class activity or competition similar to "capture the flag," where teams hide their "flag" (a small marker) somewhere on the school grounds, or even in the town or city in which you live. Teams must find the flag using a map that gives at least three reference points, as well as the respective distances from these points to the flag. Add more reference points if necessary. The winning team is the one that finds the flag first using a minimum number of reference points.

## SPECIFIC EXPECTATIONS

**You should be able to**

*Understand Basic Concepts:*
- Explain the difference between one-dimensional and two-dimensional vector equations.
- Add vectors in two dimensions graphically.
- Analyze uniform motion in two dimensions by creating scaled vector diagrams.
- Find the $x$ and $y$ components of any vector at any angle.
- Use the component method to find the resultant in a two-dimensional vector problem.
- Describe and solve projectile motion problems in two dimensions using kinematics equations.
- Identify the vectors involved in relative motion.
- Draw representations of problems involving relative motion.
- Solve relative velocity problems using graphical and trigonometric methods.
- Describe situations involving average acceleration in two dimensions.
- Solve average acceleration problems using graphical and trigonometric methods.

*Develop Skills of Inquiry and Communication:*
- Analyze the motion of objects using vector diagrams and two-dimensional vector equations.
- Describe why projectiles undergo parabolic motion.
- Design and carry out experiments involving projectile motion.
- Describe situations involving relative motion.

*Relate Science to Technology, Society, and the Environment:*
- Analyze the role of projectiles in sports.
- Explain how GPS works.
- Relate GPS to the transportation industry, present and future.

**Equations**

Projectile motion:
$x$ direction $\Delta d_x = v_{1x}\Delta t$
$y$ direction $\Delta d_y = v_{1y}\Delta t + \frac{1}{2}a_y\Delta t^2$

$$\Delta \vec{d}_T = \vec{d}_1 + \vec{d}_2 + \vec{d}_3 + \ldots$$

$$\vec{v}_{og} = \vec{v}_{om} + \vec{v}_{mg}$$

$$\vec{a} = \frac{\Delta \vec{v}}{\Delta t}$$

## Conceptual Questions

1. What motion would you expect if both the horizontal and vertical components of the velocity were constant? Provide instances where this can occur.

2. Find examples of motion where there is an acceleration in the horizontal direction as well.

3. Consider this possible demonstration: A student aims and shoots a peashooter at a honey pail suspended by an electromagnet (Fig. 3.47). As the pea leaves the shooter, a sensor detects its exit and sends a signal to the electromagnet, shutting it off. This causes the pail to fall. As long as the student has aimed the shooter correctly (directed at the initial position of the pail), the projectile will hit the pail. If you change the distance between the shooter and the pail, and the initial velocity of the projectile, the result will always be the same. Explain why this is so.

**Fig.3.47**

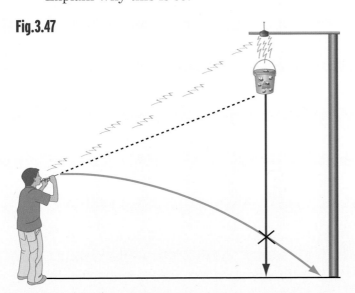

4. A batter in baseball sometimes says that the approaching baseball rises. In fact, the effect of lift is not strong enough to create this action. What motion does the ball actually undergo?

5. Does the acceleration of a projectile ever go to zero?

6. What other factors enter into projectile problems that we haven't discussed?

7. Find examples of sports that use projectile motion without spin and of sports that use projectile motion with spin. What does spin do for the projectile?

8. At what point in a projectile's path is the speed a
   **a)** maximum?
   **b)** minimum?

9. For the diagram of baseball hits (Fig. 3.48), rank the hits in order of when they land.

**Fig.3.48**

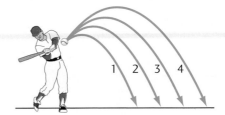

10. An airplane is moving with a constant velocity. You are sitting inside the airplane and drop a ball. Describe what the ball's path looks like to you inside the plane and to someone standing still, observing the action on the ground. Assume Superman's X-ray, telescopic vision.

11. Describe a satellite's orbit in terms of a projectile launch.

## Problems

### 3.1 Vectors in Two Dimensions

12. Copy the vectors of Fig. 3.49 into your notebook. Add them and draw in the total displacement vector. Label the start and end of the net path. No calculations are required.

## Fig.3.49

**(a)**

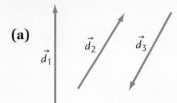

**(b)**

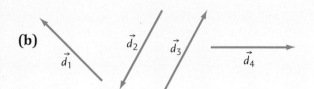

**(c)**

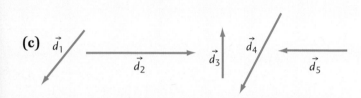

**13.** Copy the velocity vectors of Fig. 3.50 into your notebook. Add them and find the result-ant velocity. No calculations are required.

## Fig.3.50

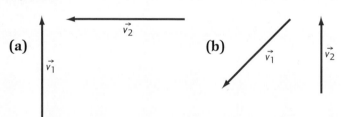

**(a)**

**(b)**

**14.** Given a velocity of 4 m/s [E] and a second velocity of magnitude 6 m/s,
   **a)** find the maximum and minimum values for the final velocity and draw a vector representation for each situation.
   **b)** Draw four more possible final velocity vec-tor diagrams.
   **c)** Using either trigonometric techniques or scaled diagrams, find the final velocity for each of your vector diagrams.

**15.** A student walking his pet duck walks 0.4 km [N], then 0.3 km [E], and then returns home. The whole walk took 0.5 hours.
   **a)** What was the total displacement for the whole walk?

**b)** Find the total displacement for the first two legs of the walk.
   **c)** What was the displacement of the final part of the walk home?
   **d)** What was the average speed for the whole walk?
   **e)** What was the average velocity for the first two parts of the walk?

## 3.2 Parabolic Motion

**16.** Copy the sketch of the soccer ball's trajectory in Fig. 3.51 into your notebook. Complete the vector diagrams at the indicated points (draw the component vectors).

### Fig.3.51

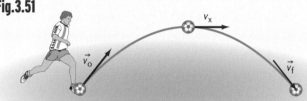

**17.** Given the trajectory in Fig. 3.52 of a baseball thrown and a baseball dropped, use the vec-tors given to create vector diagrams at the ball positions indicated.

### Fig.3.52

**18.** For a projectile thrown horizontally at 50 km/h,
   **a)** calculate the velocities in the vertical direc-tion at 1.0 s, 2.0 s, 3.0 s, and 4.0 s.
   **b)** Find the final velocity for each of these times.

**19.** For a projectile thrown at 50.0 km/h but at 45° to the horizontal, both the vertical and horizontal components are 35.4 km/h (motion is up and out).

**a)** Calculate the vertical velocities at 1.0 s, 2.0 s, 3.0 s, and 4.0 s.

**b)** What are the horizontal velocities at these times?

**c)** Find the final velocities for the four times.

**d)** Sketch the resultant trajectory.

▶ ## 3.3 Projectile Motion Calculations

**20.** A movie scene has a car fall off a cliff. If the car took 5.5 s to reach the ground, how high was the cliff?

**21.** If the car in Problem 20 had an initial horizontal velocity of 26 m/s, how far from the cliff bottom did the car land?

**22.** A bullet is shot horizontally from a gun. If the bullet's speed exiting the muzzle is 325 m/s and the height of the gun above the ground is 2.0 m,
**a)** how long was the bullet in the air?
**b)** how far did the bullet travel horizontally before it hit the ground?

**23.** A tennis player serves a tennis ball from a height of 2.5 m. If the ball leaves the racket horizontally at 160 km/h, how far away will the ball land?

**24.** A pitcher throws a baseball at 140 km/h. If the plate is 28.3 m away, how far does the ball drop if we assume the ball started travelling toward the plate horizontally?

**25.** Two pennies are sitting on a table 1.2 m high. Both fall off the table at the same time, except one is given a significant push. If the pushed penny is moving at 4.1 m/s horizontally at the time it leaves the table,
**a)** which penny lands first?
**b)** how far from the table does the pushed penny land?

**26.** For Problems 22 to 24, calculate the final velocity of each projectile.

**27.** A plane is flying horizontally with a speed of 90 m/s. If a skydiver jumps out and free falls for 10.6 s, find

**a)** how far the skydiver falls.
**b)** how far the skydiver moves horizontally.
**c)** the final vertical velocity of the skydiver.
**d)** the final velocity of the skydiver.

**28.** A plane flying level at 80 m/s releases a package from a height of 1000 m. Find
**a)** the time it takes for the package to hit the ground.
**b)** the distance it travelled horizontally.
**c)** the final velocity of the package.

**29.** The cannon in Fig. 3.53 is on the edge of a cliff 500 m above ground. The ball leaves the cannon at 100 m/s. Calculate the range for each of the three cases.
**a)** Case 1, cannon shoots horizontally, $v_x = 100$ m/s, $v_{1_y} = 0$
**b)** Case 2, cannon is elevated 60°
**c)** Case 3, cannon is depressed 60°

**Fig. 3.53**

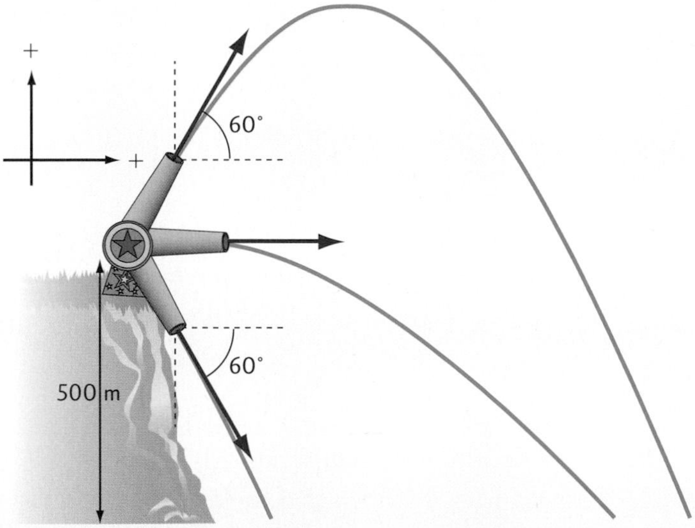

**30.** After serenading your girlfriend under her balcony window, you toss a love letter to her wrapped around a small rock (she has a baseball glove and knows how to use it). If the window is 15 m away and you toss the rock with a vertical velocity component of 13 m/s and a horizontal component of 10 m/s, how high up the wall was the balcony, assuming she caught the ball without having to reach?

31. Will a football, kicked at 14.0 m/s vertically and 9.0 m/s horizontally, clear a bar 3.0 m high and 20 m away from the kicker? Solve in two different ways.

32. Will a tennis ball served horizontally at 100 km/h from a height of 2.2 m clear a net 0.9 m high and 10 m away? Solve in two different ways.

33. Emanual Zacchini was shot over three ferris wheels, landing in a net at the same height from which he was shot (described in Fig. 3.19). Given his initial velocity of 27 m/s [R53°U] and range of 69 m, find
    a) his maximum height reached.
    b) the time spent in air, using two different methods.
    c) his final velocity, using logic and computation.

▶ 3.4 Relative Velocities

34. a) Create a series of arbitrary vector additions (two vectors) and identify the vector that could represent $\vec{v}_{pg}$.
    b) Draw a vector addition triangle where no vector can represent $\vec{v}_{pg}$.

35. A plane is flying at 100 km/h north. A passenger walks along the length of the plane. What are the maximum and minimum velocities of the passenger relative to the ground? Assume her velocity relative to the plane is 1.5 km/h.

36. Given the following conditions, what is the relative velocity of two cars if their ground speeds are 80 km/h for car A and 45 km/h for car B?
    a) Both cars are heading in the same direction, A behind B in the reference frame of A.
    b) Use the reference frame of B for part a).
    c) Both cars are heading toward each other. Take the reference frame of A.
    d) Use B's reference frame for part c).

37. A boat wishes to travel east. If there is a current of 10 km/h flowing north and the boat is capable of travelling at 30 km/h, find the heading and velocity of the boat as seen by a person on shore. Note: The term **heading** is used to describe the direction the boat must point in order to successfully travel in its desired direction.

38. A plane is seen to travel in a direction [S30°W]. If its ground velocity was 300 km/h and the wind speed is 150 km/h south, what is the plane's velocity relative to the air?

39. A boat wishes to cross a lake and end up directly south of where it started. The boat is capable of moving at 34.0 km/h. If there is a current of 8.0 km/h flowing to the west, find
    a) the heading the boat must take in order to successfully complete the trip.
    b) the velocity relative to the ground.
    c) the time (in seconds) it took the boat to cross if the lake was 21 km in the direction the boat had to travel.

40. How much faster is it to point yourself and swim directly across instead of fighting the current and swimming directly across if the width of the river is 1000 m, you are capable of swimming at 2.2 m/s, and there is a current of 1.6 m/s?

41. A large cruise boat is moving at 15 km/h east relative to the water. A person jogging on the ship moves across the ship in a northerly direction at 6 km/h. What is the velocity of the jogger relative to the water?

42. A shortstop running at 2.0 m/s toward third base catches and throws a ball toward home plate at 35 m/s. If the shortstop and catcher are lined up in a direct line of sight when the shortstop throws the ball,
    a) at what angle to his body should he throw in order for the ball to move in a straight line directly from him to the catcher?
    b) If the distance the ball travels is 20 m, how long does the ball take to get to the catcher?

43. A plane flies a square route, with each side 1500 m in length (north, west, south, then

east). If there is a wind blowing from the east at 20 km/h during the whole trip, find the total time it will take the plane to complete the journey, given that the plane is flying at 80 km/h.

## 3.5 Average Acceleration

44. Sketch the vectors $\vec{v}_1$ and $\vec{v}_2$ in Fig. 3.54 in your notebook and complete the vector diagrams for
    a) $\vec{v}_2 - \vec{v}_1$            b) $\vec{v}_1 - \vec{v}_2$
    c) $\vec{a}$, given $\Delta t = 3.0$ s    d) $\vec{v}_1 + \vec{v}_2$

**Fig.3.54**

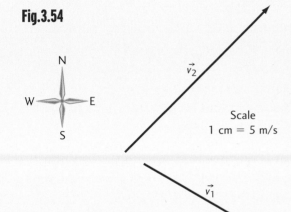

Scale
1 cm = 5 m/s

45. Sketch the parabolic trajectory of Fig. 3.55 in your notebook. Vector $\vec{v}_1$ is the initial horizontal velocity of 15 m/s. With a constant downward acceleration, the projectile follows the shape of a parabola. The marked points show its location at subsequent 1 s intervals. At points 2, 3, 4, and 5, construct the vector that represents the velocity of the projectile at

**Fig.3.55**

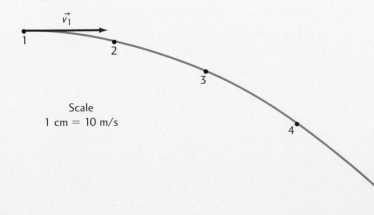

Scale
1 cm = 10 m/s

that point. Then redraw the vectors in pairs (1 & 2, 2 & 3, etc.), combining each pair in a way that shows the relation of the two velocity vectors to the acceleration vector.

46. Redraw the vectors in Fig. 3.56 into your notebook, and then draw the x and y components of each. Then *calculate* the x and y components. The vectors are
    a) $\vec{v}_1 = 54$ km/h [N33°E]
    b) $\vec{v}_2 = 70$ km/h [W71°N]
    c) $\vec{v}_3 = 43$ km/h [E18°N]
    d) $\vec{v}_4 = 50$ km/h [S45°W]
    e) $\vec{v}_5 = 27$ km/h [E40°S]

**Fig.3.56**

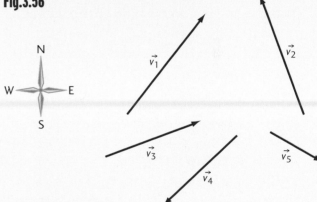

47. A boat sails at 8.0 km/h [S40°E]. What are the components of its velocity in
    a) the southward direction?
    b) the eastward direction?
    c) a direction given by [N50°E]?

48. a) A car does a slow turn. If it moves at a constant speed of 50 km/h, what is the change in velocity for the car as it moves from a direction north to west?
    b) If it took the car 5.0 s to do this, calculate its acceleration.

49. If the car in Problem 48 moved from an initial direction of [N] to one of [N20°E], what is its change in velocity and its acceleration?

50. Given that a ball moving at 30 m/s [S10°W] hits a wall and moves off at 5.0 m/s [S30°E],

find the change in the velocity of the ball. Use component and trigonometric methods.

51. a) Calculate the speed of the tip of a second hand of length 5.0 cm.
    b) Calculate the average acceleration of the tip from the moment it hits the "12" position to the moment it hits the "3" position.
    c) Calculate the average acceleration of the tip of the second hand from the moment it hits the "6" position to the moment it hits the "9" position.

52. a) Calculate the speed of the tip of a minute hand of length 25 cm.
    b) How many degrees does the hand move through when its position changes from the "12" position to the "2" position?
    c) Find the average acceleration of the tip of the minute hand in b).

53. What is the average acceleration of a car going clockwise around a circular track of radius 40 m at a constant speed if it takes the car 12.5 s to complete one lap? The angle between the positions of the car from $t_1$ to $t_2$ is 60° and the initial position of the car is at the southernmost point on the circular track.

The following questions involve the **component method** and the **trigonometric method** for total displacement and relative velocity problems. **When solving problems with two vector quantities given, use the *trigonometric method*. When three or more vectors are given, use the *component method*.**

54. Boris hops 120 km [E60°N], then 60 km [N], then 40 km [ W30°N]. Boris has big legs and is happy. Find his displacement.

55. Calculate the total displacement for a trip 12 km [N30°E], 15 km [E], 5 km [N], and 20 km [S70°E].

56. For the following path of 50 m [N47°W], 22 m [W43°N], 30 m [E60°S], 30 m [E], and 44 m [ N75°E], find
    a) the total distance travelled.
    b) the total displacement.
    c) the direction of the most direct route back to the start.

57. Remember that speed is distance divided by time and velocity is displacement divided by time. Given that the time for a complete trip is 0.15 h, find the speed and velocity in Problem 56.

58. a) An airplane has a heading east with an air speed of 120 km/h. A wind is blowing to the south at 40 km/h. Calculate its velocity relative to the ground.
    b) How long would it take to complete a flight of 1000 km?

59. A boat is moving at 15 km/h in a direction given by [N29°W]. If there is a water current of 5 km/h [S],
    a) what is the heading and speed of the boat relative to the water?
    b) If the passengers wish to get to a point 790 m away in the direction in which the boat is actually moving, how long will it take them to cover the distance?

60. A large man inhales a quantity of helium in order to fly east. If he is capable of flying at 26 km/h by waving his arms and there is a wind of 10 km/h [S20°E], find his heading and ground speed.

61. A motorized canoe is pointed [N20°W] in a river. If it has the capability to move at 5 m/s and is filmed moving at 7.6 m/s, what is the velocity of the river?

62. A plane with ground speed 380 km/h flies [N30°E]. Given a wind velocity of 80 km/h [S] during the entire flight, find the plane's heading and air speed.

## Purpose

To find the initial velocity of a projectile.

## Equipment

Steel ball, Grooved ramp, Carbon paper
Blank paper, Metre stick, Plumb line, Tape

## Procedure

1. Position the ramp a few centimetres behind the edge of the table and tape it in place.
2. Roll the steel ball down the ramp so that the ball leaves the ramp in a *horizontal* direction, and note where it hits the floor.
3. Place a blank sheet of paper on the floor and tape it down.
4. Use the plumb line to locate where the edge of the desk is projected onto the floor. Mark the point on the paper. You will be measuring the range from here.
5. Place a carbon sheet onto the paper, carbon side down.
6. Roll the ball down the ramp.
7. Remove the carbon paper and measure the distance from the mark on the paper to the point of first contact with the ball.
8. Repeat nine more times.
9. Measure the height of the table.

## Data

1. Create a chart for the 10 measured ranges.
2. Record the height of the table.

## Uncertainty (See Appendix A)

Assign a procedural and instrumental uncertainty for the measurements. Calculate the standard deviation of the mean, if that is part of your course.

## Calculations

1. Calculate the time the ball took to fall. Use $a_y = -9.8$ m/s$^2$ and $\Delta d_y = v_{1_y}\Delta t + \frac{1}{2}a_y\Delta t^2$ (you know the value for $v_{1_y}$).
2. Use the time and the average value of the range to find the initial velocity. Again, the appropriate equation is $\Delta \vec{d} = \vec{v}_1\Delta t + \frac{1}{2}\vec{a}\Delta t^2$.

## Discussion

1. What were the three values that were implied in doing this experiment?
2. Why did we use 10 trials instead of one?
3. If you calculated the standard deviation of the mean, relate its value to the confidence level you have in the obtained value for $\vec{v}_1$.
4. Why don't we need the angle of the ramp?
5. If another steel ball was used and was dropped at the same time as the moving ball left the table, which one would land first?
6. If the ramp was moved to the edge of the table, how does that change the experiment? Is the answer to Question 4 still the same?

## Conclusion

Summarize your result.

## Extension 1

Find the final velocity and compare its magnitude to the initial velocity.

## Extension 2

Redo the projectile lab, only this time put the ramp right beside the table edge. You will need to measure the angle of the ramp.

**Fig.Lab.3.1**

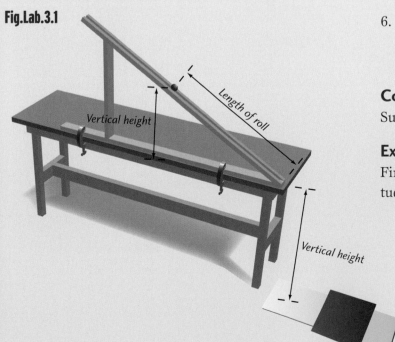

Length of roll

Vertical height

Vertical height

LABORATORY EXERCISES

# 4

# Newton's Fundamental Laws

## Chapter Outline

**By the end of this chapter, you will be able to**
- relate forces to motions
- solve problems of force and motion using free-body diagrams
- design and implement labs related to different types of motion

In previous chapters, we studied motion through observation. The five kinematics equations all describe what the object is doing. This chapter will look at what causes these motions. This is the study of *dynamics*. This chapter is based on the work of Sir Isaac Newton, who managed to bring together and explain two thousand years of motion observations.

## 4.1 The World According to Newton

In Chapter 3, we observed that an object can do the following three things in terms of its state of motion: it can be at rest, in motion with a constant velocity (constant speed in a straight line), or it can be changing its velocity.

We can summarize these concepts as follows:

$\vec{v_1} = \vec{v_2} = 0$    object at rest

$\vec{v_1} = \vec{v_2} = \vec{v}$    constant velocity (constant speed in a straight line)

$\vec{v_2} - \vec{v_1} = \Delta\vec{v}$    changing velocity (dividing by time gives the acceleration of the object)

In Fig. 4.2A, the rock happily stays in the rest position. If left alone, it will remain so forever. A rock does not move away from where it's located unless someone comes along and kicks it. The velocity, which was zero, has now become non-zero.

The second case (see Fig. 4.2B) is the same as the first, only it involves remaining in a state of constant motion rather than in a state of constant rest. Consider a satellite hurtling through space. It will do so forever unless it crashes into something or gets pulled into the gravitational field of another object. This motion is difficult to visualize because we are used to seeing the velocity of everyday objects that surround us affected by friction, air resistance, and gravity. If these forces were not present, then the objects familiar to us, such as a pitched baseball, would continue moving forever until their motion was interrupted by external forces. This concept is **Newton's first law**, also known as the **law of inertia**. More formally, it states:

> All objects will remain in a state of rest or continue to move with a constant velocity unless acted upon by an unbalanced force.

In Fig. 4.3, the velocity of the objects changes. The rock that was at rest had its state of motion altered because someone kicked it. The asteroid, hurtling through space, changed its motion by crashing into Earth. In both cases, a force was applied to the object, which caused it to change its velocity. The rate it changes its velocity depends on how much force is applied to it and how much mass the object has. The relationship between mass, force, and acceleration is given by Newton's second law. The law states:

> The acceleration of an object depends inversely on its mass and directly on the unbalanced force applied to it.

**Fig.4.1**   States of motion

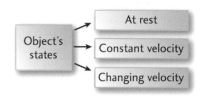

**Fig.4.2A**   At rest

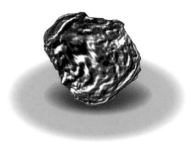

**Fig.4.2B**   Constant motion

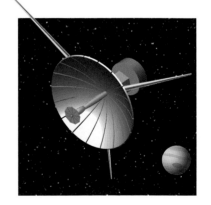

**Fig.4.3A** Ouch!

**Fig.4.3B** Force changing motion

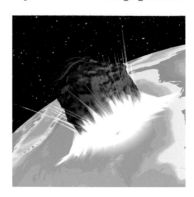

The two laws are illustrated in Figs. 4.4 and 4.5. In Fig. 4.4, the asteroid is flying without the use of rockets. It will continue on its path until a gravitational field attracts it towards the source or an object gets in the way. In Fig. 4.5, the asteroid continues along its path until it collides with Earth. The effect is obvious and drastic.

There is a connection between Newton's laws. The first law deals with an object's natural state of motion (Fig. 4.4). The second law explains what happens when the object's natural state of motion is changed (Fig. 4.5).

**Fig.4.4** Body in motion

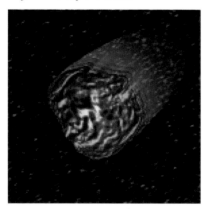

**Fig.4.5** Asteroid crash

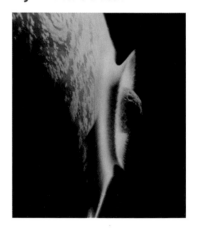

The third law describes a consequence of applying a force to an object. To understand this law we'll look at the two examples just discussed.

When you kick a rock, causing it to move, you feel a force against your toe. If you don't believe this, try kicking a rock with your bare foot! Similarly, Earth stopped the asteroid, but the asteroid created a huge crater on Earth. In other words, whenever an object A exerts a force on object B, object B resists or pushes back on object A with a force that is equal in magnitude but opposite in direction to the force object A exerted on it. This is **Newton's third law**. More formally, the law states that:

> For every action force, there is an equal and opposite reaction force.

These three statements form the basis for all classical motion in the universe and are collectively called **Newton's three laws**.

**Fig.4.6** States of Motion

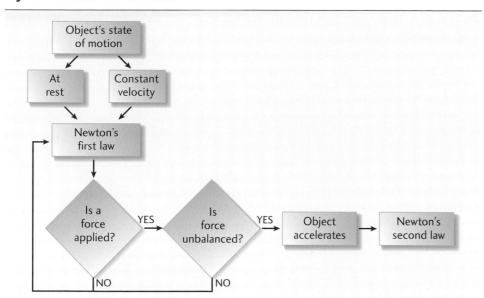

## Newton's First Law

Newton's first law describes the two possible conditions of the object if left alone: constant velocity or constant rest. The property of the object to which this law refers is called **inertia**. We can also say that inertia is the ability of the object to resist change. The object's **mass** is a measure of this property. Mass is measured in kilograms (kg) in the SI system.

To make an object change direction, a force must be applied to it. To make an object move in a circle, a force must be continuously applied toward the centre of the circle. If this force is removed, the object continues moving in the direction it was going at that instant, in a straight line tangential to the circle. When the force is being applied, Newton's second law is in effect. When the force is removed, Newton's first law applies.

The resistive nature of objects is illustrated by a series of examples of circular motion (Fig. 4.7). The water stays on the wheel until the molecular attraction between the water and the tire can no longer hold it and the water flies off in a straight line tangential to the wheel. In the hammer

### CLASSICAL PHYSICS

"Classical" often refers to ideas or things that have stood the test of time. Classical physics refers to the period in the history of physics starting with Newton (1687) and ending just before 1900. Physics since Planck and Einstein is called modern physics.

**Fig.4.7** Removing the unbalanced forces causes linear motion

throw event, the athlete hangs onto the hammer, swinging it in a circle until he releases it. The hammer then flies off in a straight line tangential to the original path of the hammer. In the third picture, the car is turning because the tires grip the road, exerting a force inward. When the car hits an icy patch, there is no more grip, so the car starts to slide forward in a straight line. Once again, the new path is straight and at a tangent to the original curve (the turn). In all three cases, once the force causing the object to move in a circular path was removed, the object's motion reverted back to that defined by Newton's first law.

## Force and Motion

Aristotle insisted that a force was needed to keep an object moving. Two thousand years later, Galileo showed that an object could continue with a constant velocity without any force being applied. He described a ball rolling on a frozen lake. In the next generation, René Descartes was closer to Aristotle than Galileo was. Descartes stated in separate laws that objects at rest remain so; and that once moving, an object would continue to do so. But Descartes considered motion and rest to be opposites.

Newton (at age 22 in 1664) wrote that an object would continue moving as long as nothing impeded it. His main interest was how to explain changes in motion. In 1673, Christian Huygens published his first hypothesis that without gravity or air, an object would continue its motion with constant speed in a straight line. Newton explicitly added "state of rest" to his first law to convince followers of Aristotle or Descartes that rest was just a constant velocity of zero.

Newton's second law was the first time anyone had explicitly stated that the action of a force was to produce a *change* in motion (or momentum) — that is, to cause acceleration. This aspect will be further explored in Chapter 6.

APPLYING the Concepts ▶ ▶ ▶ ▶

**Fig.4.8** Galileo, Descartes, and Newton

1. Research the experiments on motion that Aristotle, Galileo, and Newton designed. Find an experiment that you can duplicate. State what the philosopher was trying to prove. State also whether he was correct in his assumptions based on today's theories. Perform the experiment. Record your results and draw conclusions based on what you found. State whether or not the results confirmed your hypothesis.
2. We encounter Newton's laws of motion continuously in everyday life. Go through a typical day and select events that illustrate these laws.
3. Newton's first law states that inertia depends on mass. Newton's second law is about overcoming inertia. His third law is about feeling the effect of overcoming inertia. Choose a sports event and use

UNIT A: Motion and Forces

Newton's laws to explain an observed event. (Example: A football sits on a kicking tee (Newton's first law). A kicker's foot makes contact with the ball, causing an unbalanced force to be applied to the ball. The ball changes its velocity and accelerates in the direction of the applied force (Newton's second law). The kicker feels a force pushing against her foot because of the reaction force of the kick (Newton's third law).)

# 4.2 Newton's Second Law, $\vec{F}_{net} = m\vec{a}$

Newton's second law states that an unbalanced force causes an object to accelerate. But does this mean that a force of a certain magnitude will cause all objects to accelerate at the same rate?

Consider the two cases in Fig. 4.9. They are identical except that in Case 1, the ball is a regular baseball, whereas in Case 2, the ball is made of lead. When an equal force was applied in both cases to swing the bat and hit the ball, the ball in Case 2 achieved a much lower velocity than the ball in Case 1. The reason is because the lead ball had more inertia. Since mass is a measure of inertia, for any given force, the greater the mass, the smaller the acceleration.

In order for the lead ball to achieve the same velocity as the regular baseball, you would have to apply a much greater force. If the force changes, the acceleration also changes. The greater the force, the greater the acceleration.

We can summarise the events just described by the following proportionality statements("α" means "is proportional to"):

$$\vec{a} \; \alpha \; \vec{F}_{unbalanced} \qquad \vec{a} \; \alpha \; \frac{1}{m_{object}}$$

Combined, they produce

$$\vec{a} \; \alpha \; \frac{\vec{F}_{unbalanced}}{m_{object}}$$

or $\quad \vec{F} \; \alpha \; m\vec{a}.$

To convert the proportionality to an equality, we need to add a constant.

$$\vec{F} = km\vec{a}$$

A one-newton (1 N) force is defined as the force that gives a 1 kg mass an acceleration of 1 m/s². The equation becomes

$$1 \text{ N} = k \times 1 \text{ kg} \times 1 \text{ m/s}^2$$

## FORCE UNITS

1 newton gives 1 kg an acceleration of 1 m/s²

1 dyne gives 1 g an acceleration of 1 cm/s²

1 poundal gives 1 lb an acceleration of 1 ft/s²

1 pound-force gives 1 slug an acceleration of 1 ft/s²

(1 slug is a mass of 32 pounds)

**Fig.4.9**

A normal ball leaves the bat

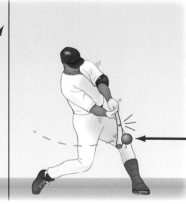

The bat is stopped by a lead ball

### YANK, TUG, SNATCH, SHAKE

From Chapter 2, we learned the progression of the rate of change: the rate of change of displacement is velocity, the rate of change of velocity is acceleration, rate of change of acceleration is jerk, and on to snap, crackle, and pop. In a similar chain of progression, we have the rate of change of force is **yank**, the rate of change of yank is **tug**, the rate of change of tug is **snatch**, and the rate of change of snatch is **shake**. Thus, it may come to pass that instead of plotting force vs. acceleration to find mass, you'll plot yank versus jerk or shake versus pop!

Solving for $k$, we find that $k = 1$, so the equation for Newton's second law is

$$\vec{F} = m\vec{a}.$$

Because acceleration is a vector quantity, force is also a vector quantity. The newton is the SI unit of force and has the symbol N. Substituting the units into $\vec{F} = m\vec{a}$, we obtain the units of force:

$$1\ N = 1\ kg \cdot m/s^2$$

One newton is approximately the force of gravity on an apple.

The force referred to in Newton's second law is a **net force**. The term *net* means the result of adding all the negative and positive forces that are acting on an object. The statement $\vec{F}_{net} = m\vec{a}$ is an identity statement, meaning that whenever we use the expression $\vec{F}_{net}$, we can always replace it with $m\vec{a}$. It is just like your first and last name. Either one can be used to identify you.

## *Car Safety*

In North America, the first car seat belts were developed in 1947. They were lap belts. The front seat belt was introduced by Ford in 1956 and became a standard feature in 1964. Rear seat belts became standard in 1966. In 1967, front seat belts became mandatory, and in 1968, shoulder belts become mandatory. By 1969, all cars had headrests. In 1973, GM installed air bags in some of its Chevy Impalas. Other air bag models followed.

1. In a car crash, the seat belt was first used to help prevent serious injuries. Then the lap-shoulder belt was introduced as an improvement to the seat belt. Use Newton's laws to explain why these safety features work and why the shoulder sash was an improvement on the seat belt design.

Pretensioners are part of the seat belt mechanism. Their purpose is to increase the tension of the seat belt during a collision.

The sash-lock mechanism stops the shoulder harness from moving during sudden starts and stops. It contains a ratchet wheel with a device similar to a pendulum that swings when there is a sudden acceleration, automatically locking the seat belt.

2. Use the diagram in Fig. 4.10 and Newton's laws to explain how this mechanism works.

Air bags are the latest devices used in trying to prevent serious injury in collisions. They provide energy-absorbing buffers between passengers and the dashboard and windshield. They are usually mounted in the steering wheel and the front instrument panel (on the passenger side). It is important that the lap-shoulder belt be used in conjunction with the air bag. It prevents people from being thrown out of cars and

**Fig.4.10**

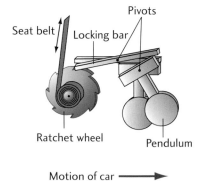

adds an extra degree of braking for the person. It also keeps the person back about 25 cm, the minimum distance needed to ensure safe deployment of the air bag.

3. a) Build a small cart that can hold an egg. Use a pulley, a mass, and a string to accelerate the cart across a table when the mass is dropped. Have a wall or obstacle in place to stop the cart suddenly. Observe what happens to the egg.

   b) Now construct a seat belt with a shoulder harness to hold the egg securely in the cart. Repeat Step a).

Use Newton's laws to explain how the lap-sash belt works in preventing accidents.

4. a) Find statistics that relate the number of car accidents involving fatalities to the number of people not wearing a seat belt.

   b) People have argued that making seat belts mandatory is an infringement of their rights. Hold a class debate where one side argues in favour of the individual's right to take responsibility for his or her safety, and the other side argues in favour of the state's right to legislate safety.

## 4.3 Free-body Diagrams

A powerful tool for analyzing force problems is the **free-body diagram** or **FBD**. The FBD simplifies the problem by isolating the studied object from its environment. On this diagram, we draw *only the forces acting on the object*. Any force generated by the object itself is excluded. The forces on the diagram are always drawn pointing away from the object we are studying.

Figure 4.11A shows an FBD. Notice that we have isolated the duck and the sled by drawing a circle around them. We then draw the forces acting on the duck and the sled, projecting them *outward* or away from the circle. Even the push of the person on the sled is drawn coming out of the diagram.

**Fig.4.11A** A free-body diagram

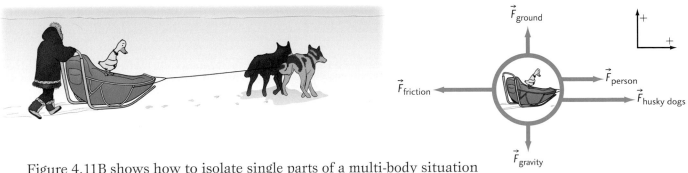

Figure 4.11B shows how to isolate single parts of a multi-body situation — the *duck* sits on the *book* resting on the head of the *person* who sits on a *chair* resting on the ground.

**Fig.4.11B** Free-body diagrams

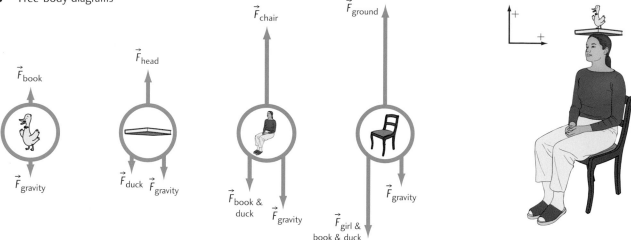

## FREE-BODY DIAGRAMS

In more formal physics, the object in a free-body diagram is reduced to a dot representing the object's centre of mass. The forces are shown pointing away from the dot, as in Fig. 4.11 C(top). Notice that side-by-side forces are drawn slightly offset. An alternative is to place parallel forces head to tail in a line (Fig. 4.11 C(bottom)).

**Fig.4.11C**

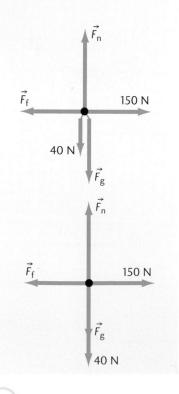

If the problem involves more than simply drawing an FBD, we write an $\vec{F}_{net}$ statement after the FBD. This statement has the general form

$$\vec{F}_{net} = \Sigma \vec{F}_{acting \, on \, object}$$

The symbol "Σ" means "sum of" and is used to indicate all the forces on the diagram. Remember to keep track of the negative signs of forces! If the solution to the problem requires acceleration, replace the $\vec{F}_{net}$ in the equation with $m\vec{a}$ and solve.

Figure 4.12 illustrates the steps just outlined. The car is circled, thereby isolating it from its environment. Both forces acting on the car are drawn projecting out from the circle. The $\vec{F}_{net}$ statement then sums up what the diagram is showing you. Designating up as positive, we find that $\vec{F}_{net}$ is the vector addition of the crane's force and the force of gravity. Since the problem is in one dimension only, we add signs to the forces to specify their

**Fig.4.12** FBD for upward acceleration

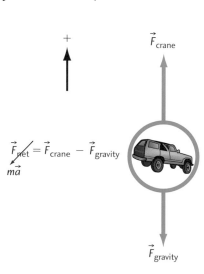

**Fig.4.13** Applying Newton's Laws

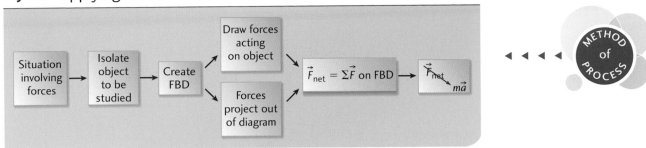

direction. Finally, we replace $\vec{F}_{net}$ with its alternate expression, $m\vec{a}$. If we know the mass of the object, we can now find its acceleration.

## Using the FBD Process

Consider the following situation. A movie sequel to *Tarzan* is being made, called *Tarzana, Brawny Ape Woman, Meets the Beast*. In one of the scenes, Tarzan is being pulled in one direction by Tarzana and in the other direction by a ferocious beast.

   If the two forces are equal in magnitude but opposite in direction, they will cancel and produce a net force of zero. Thus, Tarzan will not change his velocity and Newton's first law applies. However, if one of the forces is slightly larger, Tarzan will move in the direction of the unbalanced force, thereby making Newton's second law applicable. We will study two possible scenes (assume Tarzan has a mass of 90 kg, the beast—130 kg, and Tarzana—100 kg).

---

**EXAMPLE 1**   **Scene 1, the beast is stronger**

The beast pulls on Tarzan with a force of 180 N and Tarzana pulls with a force of 150 N. What is Tarzan's acceleration?

**Fig.4.14**

*Solution and Connection to Theory*

**Given**
Assume the standard reference system.

$$\vec{F}_T = +150 \text{ N} \qquad \vec{F}_B = -180 \text{ N} \qquad m_{\text{Tarzan}} = 90 \text{ kg}$$

Construct a free-body diagram (consider the horizontal direction only).

$$\vec{F}_{net} = \vec{F}_T + \vec{F}_B$$

$$m\vec{a} = 150 \text{ N} - 180 \text{ N} = -30 \text{ N}$$

$$\vec{a} = \frac{-30 \text{ N}}{90 \text{ kg}} = -0.33 \frac{\text{N}}{\text{kg}} = -0.33 \text{ m/s}^2$$

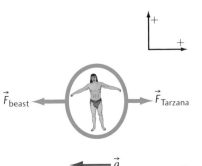

Notice that Tarzan was circled in the FBD because he was the object being studied. Similarly, to calculate Tarzan's acceleration, we only needed to use Tarzan's mass because he was the object studied. The negative acceleration indicates that Tarzan's motion will be towards the beast, given a stationary start.

EXAMPLE 2 **Scene 2, Tarzana is stronger**

## UNIT ANALYSIS

$$\vec{a} = \frac{\vec{F}}{m} \rightarrow \frac{N}{kg}$$

$$\frac{N}{kg} = \frac{kg \cdot m/s^2}{kg} = \frac{m}{s^2}$$

Tarzana pulls with 200 N and the beast, who is weakening, pulls with 90 N. What is Tarzan's acceleration now?

### Solution and Connection to Theory

**Given**

Assume the standard reference system.

$$\vec{F}_T = +200 \text{ N} \qquad \vec{F}_B = -90 \text{ N} \qquad m_{\text{Tarzan}} = 90 \text{ kg}$$

Construct the free-body diagram in Fig. 4.15A (consider the horizontal direction only).

**Fig.4.15A**

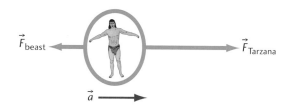

$$\vec{F}_{\text{net}} = \vec{F}_T + \vec{F}_B \qquad m\vec{a} = 200 \text{ N} - 90 \text{ N} = 110 \text{ N}$$

$$\vec{a} = \frac{110 \text{ N}}{90 \text{ kg}} = 1.2 \frac{N}{kg} = 1.2 \text{ m/s}^2$$

In this case, the acceleration is positive. Given a stationary start, Tarzan moves towards Tarzana and they live happily ever after.

Now that we have a value for acceleration, we can go back and use our kinematics equations to find any other aspect of the motion.

EXAMPLE 3    **Combining kinematics and free-body diagrams**

Assume from the last scene that Tarzana pulled for 2.7 s before the beast let go. Assume that this time, all the characters started from rest and that Tarzana's average pull was 150 N while the beast was pulling with a force of 90 N. Find Tarzan's velocity and the distance he moved before the beast let go.

### Solution and Connection to Theory

**Given**

Assume the standard reference system.

$m_{\text{Tarzan}} = 90 \text{ kg}$ $\qquad \vec{F}_T = 150 \text{ N}$ $\qquad \vec{F}_B = -90 \text{ N}$ $\qquad \vec{v}_1 = 0 \text{ m/s}$

$\Delta t = 2.7 \text{ s}$ $\qquad\qquad \vec{a} = ?$ $\qquad\qquad \vec{v}_2 = ?$ $\qquad\qquad \Delta \vec{d} = ?$

**Fig.4.15B**

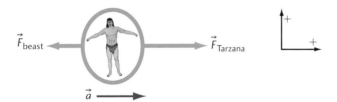

$\vec{F}_{\text{net}} = 150 \text{ N} - 90 \text{ N}$

$m\vec{a} = 60 \text{ N}$

$\vec{a} = \dfrac{60 \text{ N}}{90 \text{ kg}} = 0.67 \text{ m/s}^2$

To find $\vec{v}_2$, we can use $\vec{a} = \dfrac{\Delta \vec{v}}{\Delta t} = \dfrac{\vec{v}_2 - \vec{v}_1}{\Delta t}$

Rearrange for $\vec{v}_2$:

$\vec{v}_2 = \vec{v}_1 + \vec{a}\,\Delta t$

$\vec{v}_2 = 0 \text{ m/s} + (0.67 \text{ m/s}^2)2.7 \text{ s} = 1.8 \text{ m/s}$

Solve for $\Delta \vec{d}$ by using one of the kinematics equations. There are several to choose from.

$\Delta \vec{d} = \vec{v}_1 \Delta t + \left(\tfrac{1}{2}\right)\vec{a}\,\Delta t^2$

$\Delta \vec{d} = 0 + \tfrac{1}{2}(0.67 \text{ m/s}^2)(2.7 \text{ s})^2 = 2.4 \text{ m}$

We summarize the possible scenarios associated with linear motion and $\vec{F}_{\text{net}}$ using a terrific toy for all ages (Fig. 4.16) and Table 4.1. All the possible acceleration values are covered. Figure 4.17 summarizes the steps for solving FBD problems.

**Fig.4.16** Ducks in a row

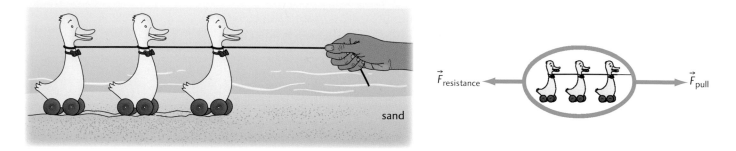

**Table 4.1**
**Possible values of $\vec{F}_{net}$**

| Case | Relation of forces (pull/resistance) | Net force | Acceleration | Motion | Action |
|------|--------------------------------------|-----------|--------------|--------|--------|
| 1 | $\vec{F}_p = \vec{F}_r$ | $\vec{F}_{net} = 0$ | $\vec{a} = 0$ | No motion | Sand resists pull |
| 2 | $\vec{F}_p > \vec{F}_r$ | $\vec{F}_{net} > 0$ | $\vec{a} > 0$ | Ducks accelerate in direction of pull | Person increases force and gets the ducks rolling |
| 3 | $\vec{F}_p = \vec{F}_r$ | $\vec{F}_{net} = 0$ | $\vec{a} = 0$ | Ducks move with constant speed in a straight line | Person exerts only enough force to maintain motion (Newton's first law) |
| 4 | $\vec{F}_p < \vec{F}_r$ | $\vec{F}_{net} < 0$ | $\vec{a} < 0$ | Ducks accelerate negatively (slow down) | String breaks, leaving only the resistive force. |

**Fig.4.17**   Solving Problems in One Dimension

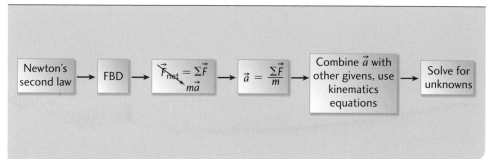

1. For the following situations, draw an FBD around the bike and the person and include $\vec{F}_{net}$ statements in both the $x$ and $y$ directions. For each $\vec{F}_{net}$ statement, state if the acceleration is positive, negative, or zero.
   a) A person sits on a bicycle, not moving.
   b) The person is moving with a constant velocity on the bicycle.
   c) The person is speeding up on the bicycle.
   d) The person is coasting to a stop.
   e) The person is turning.

2. For a person on a toboggan being pulled by three friends, find the acceleration for the following situations. The mass of the person and the toboggan is 60 kg. Each friend can pull 20 N. Draw an FBD for each case.

a) All three friends pull in the same direction.

b) Two friends pull forward and one pulls backward.

c) One friend pulls forward and two pull backward.

d) There is a 30 N force of friction acting on the toboggan. All three friends pull in one direction.

# 4.4 Free-body Diagrams in Two Dimensions

When dealing with objects being pulled or pushed in the $x$ and $y$ directions simultaneously, the free-body diagram requires two $\vec{F}_{net}$ statements, one for each direction. Once the components of each $\vec{F}_{net}$ statement are found, they can be combined using a scaled diagram or Pythagoras' theorem and trigonometric equations. We learned these methods in Chapter 3.

**Fig.4.18** Solving Force Problems in Two Dimensions

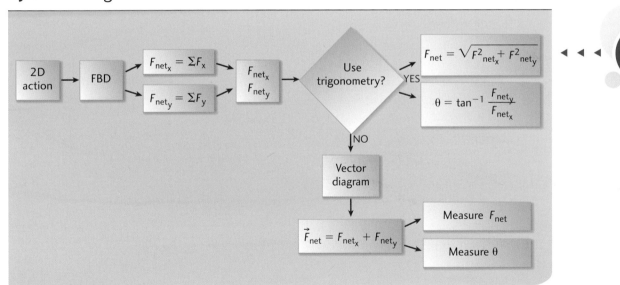

## EXAMPLE 4    Forces in two dimensions

Figure 4.19A illustrates four students playing a board game. They all have their hands on a puck and are pushing it simultaneously. The students are labelled 1 to 4 and the force with which each student pushes is given. The mass of the puck is 0.2 kg. The four forces are $\vec{F}_1 = 2.0$ N to the left, $\vec{F}_2 = 1.2$ N to the right, $\vec{F}_3 = 0.8$ N down, and $\vec{F}_4 = 1.4$ N up. Find the net force on the puck and its acceleration.

**Fig.4.19A**

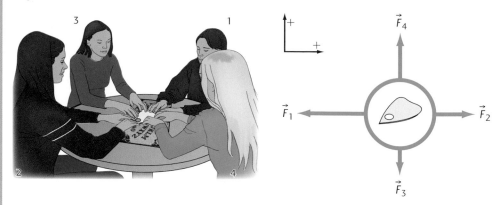

## Solution and Connection to Theory

**Given**

Assume the standard reference system.

$$\vec{F}_1 = -2.0 \text{ N} \quad \vec{F}_2 = +1.2 \text{ N} \quad \vec{F}_3 = -0.8\text{N} \quad \vec{F}_4 = +1.4 \text{ N} \quad m = 0.2 \text{ kg}$$

$x$} $\quad F_{net_x} = 1.2 \text{ N} - 2.0 \text{ N} = -0.8 \text{ N}$
$y$} $\quad F_{net_y} = 1.4 \text{ N} - 0.8 \text{ N} = 0.6 \text{ N}$

These two vectors make a right-angle triangle, with $\vec{F}_{net}$ as the hypotenuse. Using Pythagoras' theorem,

$$F^2_{net} = (-0.8 \text{ N})^2 + (0.6 \text{ N})^2 \qquad F_{net} = 1.0 \text{ N}$$

**Fig.4.19B**

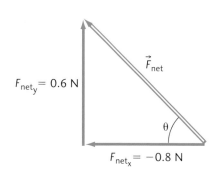

To find the angle, we can either construct a scale diagram and measure the angle or use trigonometry.

Using trigonometry, we substitute the magnitudes of the component forces.

$$\theta = \tan^{-1}\left(\frac{0.6}{0.8}\right) = 37°.$$

Checking the directions of the component forces, we find that the direction is [L37°U]. The complementary angle, 53°, can also be used [U53°L].

## More Complicated Scenarios

When all the forces do not act along the $x$ and $y$ axes, we use the component or trigonometric methods of solving vector problems. If there are only two vectors involved, then either method can be used. However, if there are more than two forces, then the component method is the easiest to use.

EXAMPLE 5  **Two forces at different angles acting on an object**

A person of mass 70 kg is sitting on a 20 kg toboggan. If two people are pulling her with two different ropes, find the person's acceleration. The force of person 1 is 50 N [E40°N], and the force of person 2 is 60 N [E25°S] as seen from the top. (See Fig. 4.20A.)

**Fig.4.20A**

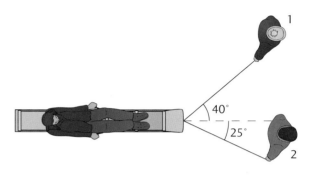

*Solution and Connection to Theory*

**Given**

$\vec{F}_1 = 50 \text{ N [E40°N]}$    $\vec{F}_2 = 60 \text{ N [E25°S]}$    $m_{\text{total}} = 90 \text{ kg}$

**Trigonometric Method**

We first construct a triangle based on the defining equation, $\vec{F}_{\text{net}} = \vec{F}_1 + \vec{F}_2$, and the FBD. The "+" sign indicates that the two vectors will be connected head to tail. This is illustrated in Fig. 4.20B.

**Fig.4.20B**

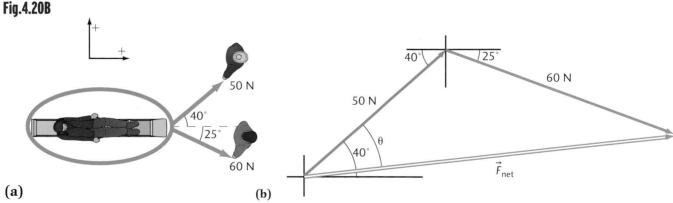

**(a)**          **(b)**

From the diagram, the interior angle between the two forces is $180° - (40° + 25°) = 115°$. To solve for $\vec{F}_{\text{net}}$, use the cosine law.

$$F^2_{\text{net}} = (50 \text{ N})^2 + (60 \text{ N})^2 - 2(50 \text{ N})(60 \text{ N})\cos 115°$$

$$F^2_{\text{net}} = 8636 \text{ N} \qquad F_{\text{net}} = 93 \text{ N}$$

To find the angle, use the sine law.

$$\frac{\sin\theta}{60\ \text{N}} = \frac{\sin 115°}{93\ \text{N}}$$

$$\theta = \sin^{-1}(0.585), \theta = 36°$$

The angle representing the $\vec{F}_{\text{net}}$ vector is $40° - 36° = 4.0°$. From the diagram, we can see that the direction of $\vec{F}_{\text{net}}$ is [E4°N]. Thus, the acceleration is

$$\frac{\vec{F}_{\text{net}}}{m_{\text{total}}} = \frac{93\ \text{N [E4°N]}}{90\ \text{kg}} = 1.0\ \text{m/s}^2\ \text{[E4.0°N]}.$$

**Component Method**

We draw the original FBD followed by the component FBD (see Fig. 4.20C).

**Fig.4.20C**

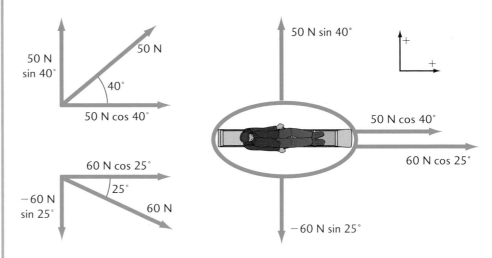

The components of the force vectors are

$\boldsymbol{x}\}$   $F_{1_x} = 50\ \text{N} \cos 40° = 38.3\ \text{N}$

      $F_{2_x} = 60\ \text{N} \cos 25° = 54.4\ \text{N}$

$\boldsymbol{y}\}$   $F_{1_y} = 50\ \text{N} \sin 40° = 32.1\ \text{N}$

      $F_{2_y} = -60\ \text{N} \sin 25° = -25.4\ \text{N}$

The defining equation is

$$\vec{F}_{\text{net}} = \vec{F}_1 + \vec{F}_2$$

This is the equation we use to add the components in the $x$ and $y$ directions.

Solving in the $x$ direction, $F_{\text{net}_x} = 38.3\ \text{N} + 54.4\ \text{N} = 92.7\ \text{N}$

Solving in the $y$ direction, $F_{\text{net}_y} = 32.1\ \text{N} - 25.4\ \text{N} = 6.7\ \text{N}$

Therefore, $F_{\text{net}} = \sqrt{(92.7\ \text{N})^2 + (6.7\ \text{N})^2} = 92.9\ \text{N} = 93\ \text{N}$

$$\theta = \tan^{-1} \frac{F_{net_y}}{F_{net_x}} = \tan^{-1} \frac{6.7 \text{ N}}{92.7 \text{ N}} = 4.0°.$$

Fig.4.20D

6.7 N

92.7 N

$\theta$

Because both the $x$ and $y$ components of $\vec{F}_{net}$ are positive, the angle 4.0° is in the first quadrant and is expressed as [E4.0°N]. Thus, the acceleration is

$$\frac{\vec{F}_{net}}{m_{total}} = \frac{93 \text{ N}}{90 \text{ kg}} = 1.0 \text{ m/s}^2 \text{ [E4.0°N]}.$$

This answer agrees with the previous one, arrived at using the trigono-metric method.

If a third person was added to the problem, then the method of choice would be the component method. In this example, if person 3 was pulling straight back with a force of 10.0 N, then the solution in the $x$ direction would read

$$F_{net_x} = 38.3 \text{ N} + 54.4 \text{ N} - \mathbf{10.0 \text{ N}} = 82.7 \text{ N}.$$

Now Pythagoras' theorem and the $\tan^{-1}$ function can be used to obtain the new value for $\vec{F}_{net}$.

1. Two tugboats are pulling a freighter. Find the net force and direc-tion of the acceleration for the following cases. Assume that each tugboat pulls with a force of $1.2 \times 10^5$ N. Assume no resistive force at this time.

   **a)** Tugboat 1 pulls north and tugboat 2 pulls east.

   **b)** Tugboat 1 pulls in a direction given by [N60°E] and tugboat 2 pulls in a direction given by [S60°E].

   **c)** Tugboat 1 pulls [N70°E] and tugboat 2 pulls [S80°E].

   **d)** Repeat parts a), b), and c), adding a resistive force of $5.0 \times 10^4$ N on the freighter.

   Note: For part c), solve the problem using components and the trigonometric method.

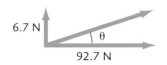

◄ ◄ ◄ ◄

APPLYING the Concepts

## SUVs, ATVs, and Space Rovers

These vehicles have one property in common. They must remain sta-ble while traversing rugged and diverse terrain. Sport utility vehicles (SUVs) are four-wheel-drive vehicles built on a truck platform and weighing less than 4500 kg. Their heavy-duty suspension contributes to the extra ground clearance they require.

The Hummer is a military-based utility vehicle that is gaining pop-ularity as a recreational vehicle.

It is capable of maintaining positive traction up a 60° grade for extended periods of time. It can go shorter distances at higher grades. If the mass of the vehicle is 3090 kg,

**Fig.4.21A** The Hummer

**a)** draw an FBD for a Hummer going up a 60° hill.

**b)** break the force of gravity into components along the incline (hill) and perpendicular to the hill.

**c)** write the $\vec{F}_{net}$ statements associated with these two directions.

**d)** If the vehicle rolls down the hill, what is its acceleration if the friction is negligible?

**Fig.4.21B**   Sojourner

All-terrain vehicles (ATVs) are small, 500–700 kg vehicles that can seat one to four people. They are not normally licensed for the road. Different tires or tracks allow ATVs to be specialized for different types of terrain (mud, snow, swamps, etc.). They are similar in design and appearance to Lunar and Martian space rovers.

"Sojourner," the Martian rover, is a six-wheel vehicle that uses a rocker-bogie suspension system. This system gives each wheel its own suspension, allowing it to move up and down independently of the other wheels depending on terrain. It also minimizes the change in orientation of the vehicle body when moving. The Sojourner is only 28.0 cm high, 63.0 cm long, and 48.0 cm wide. Its wheels are 13 cm in diameter. Its maximum speed is 1.0 cm/s, but its distance of travel from the lander is no more than 10 m.

**2.** Why is the Martian vehicle so small?

**3.** Compare the six-wheel independent suspension system to that of a track system. Speculate as to why NASA chose not to use tracks.

**4.** The Moon rover was 210 kg. Why did it have to be so large? (Compare the Moon mission's goal to that of the Martian mission.)

**5.** Would rocker-bogie suspension work for ATV designs? What might be a drawback to using the system?

## 4.5  Newton's Third Law and Free-body Diagrams

**Fig.4.22**   The glass pushes back

If you are pushed by a person, you react by moving in the direction of the push. Now consider Fig. 4.22, where a person standing on ice pushes against the glass. Notice that the person moves away from the glass as though the glass pushed him. The effect of moving away is the same as in the case of the person pushing you.

Consider the process of swimming in Fig. 4.23A. You move your arms backward, pushing on the water. As you do so, you move forward. The water reacts in the opposite direction to your push and drives you in the forward direction.

When you walk, you put your foot down and push backward, but you move forward. The action of pushing back on the ground causes you to be

**Fig.4.23A** Equal and opposite forces when swimming

Force on swimmer

Force on water

**Fig.4.23B** Walking requires a forward force from the ground

Equal and opposite forces

pushed in the forward direction by the ground. Notice in Fig. 4.23B that the force of the ground is directed forward.

According to Newton's third law, the wall, the water, and the ground are all inanimate objects that respond to your initiating force with a reaction force.

*Action forces cause equal and opposite reaction forces.* If this is true, why does anything move at all? It sounds as though each time a force is produced, an equal and opposite force cancels it.

Using FBD diagrams to study the events will clarify the situation. In the case of a person pushing the wall, we isolate the wall, then mark on the FBD the forces acting only on the wall (Fig. 4.24). From the FBD, we can write an $\vec{F}_{net}$ statement.

Since the forces are balanced (i.e., they are equal in magnitude and opposite in direction, so they cancel each other out), $\vec{F}_{net} = 0$ and the wall does not move.

Figure 4.25A is an FBD of the person pushing against the wall. It shows that the forces acting on the person are unbalanced, i.e., they don't cancel each other out. There is no equal and opposite force pushing from behind the person to keep him in place. The $\vec{F}_{net}$ value is not zero for this case, so the person moves backwards.

Compare this situation to Fig. 4.25B, where one person was pushed by another person while both people were standing on ice. Notice from the FBDs that both people must move because the forces acting on them are unbalanced.

**Fig.4.24** No net force on the glass

$\vec{F}_{push}$       $\vec{F}_{structure}$

**Fig.4.25A** An unbalanced force on the person

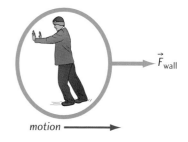

$\vec{F}_{wall}$

*motion*

**Fig.4.25B** Action–reaction pairs require two FBDs

A    B

$\vec{F}_B$       $\vec{F}_A$

Do action–reaction forces cancel each other out? We can see from the example that *action–reaction forces act on different objects*. For this reason, they can never cancel each other out. Other external forces must be present in order for the forces to cancel and create an $\vec{F}_{net}$ of zero.

If you were to push on a wall while standing on firm ground rather than on ice, then the force of friction would counteract the reaction force of the wall on you. This force is equal and opposite but acting on the same body. It produces an $\vec{F}_{net}$ of zero; therefore, you do not move.

In other words, action–reaction pairs can never be drawn on the same FBD, thus they cannot be added to give a net force of zero.

Figure 4.26 is another example of action–reaction pairs of forces. Launching a shuttle is similar to releasing a balloon with a weighted neck filled with air. After reading through this example, you can create the two FBDs for the balloon case.

When a shuttle is launched, violent combustion forces burning exhaust gases out of the boosters. The action force is the rockets forcing the gases downward and out of the boosters. The reaction force is the gases pushing back and up against the boosters. The force on the boosters in the upward direction is greater than the force of gravity and air resistance acting downward. $\vec{F}_{net}$ is not zero and the shuttle accelerates upward.

**Fig.4.26**  Forces on the shuttle

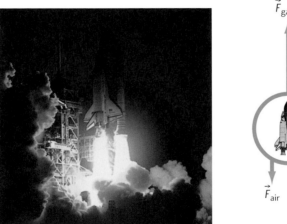

UNIT A: Motion and Forces

**Fig.4.27**  Applying Newton's Laws

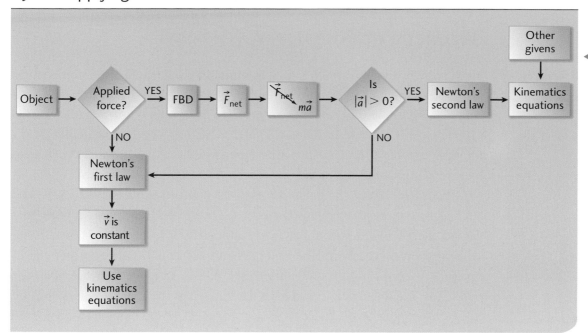

PUTTING it all Together

1. A person sits on a chair with another person pressing down on her shoulders. Draw FBDs for the person on the chair, for the chair, and for the ground. For each FBD, list the forces on the diagram and explain what is happening according to Newton's third law.

2. How does the situation in Question 1 change if it takes place in a moving vehicle when
   **a)** the vehicle is moving at a constant speed?
   **b)** the vehicle is speeding up?

APPLYING the Concepts

## Supplemental Restraint Systems

**Fig.STSE.4.1** A crash test dummy

Newton's first law outlines the most important safety hazards in the transportation industry: objects keep doing what they have been doing. Objects stay at rest or move with constant velocity unless they are made to do otherwise by an external unbalanced force. Once passengers in a vehicle are moving, it takes a force to stop them. During a collision, a car is decelerated by a large force and the passengers tend to keep moving forward. The body continues moving at the same velocity until it hits some object in the car, such as the steering wheel or dashboard, and comes to a stop. Injuries from car accidents result when the force applied to the passenger from these objects is very large. Supplemental restraint systems (S.R.S.) protect you by applying a restraining force to the body that is smaller than the force the body would experience if it hit the dashboard or steering wheel suddenly. S.R.S. refers to the technology used to provide these external unbalanced forces safely to passengers in motor vehicles. The crash test dummy in Fig. STSE.4.1 will need to be restrained from hitting the steering wheel by an unbalanced force to stop it from moving with respect to the car.

The first S.R.S. technology was the seat belt, intended to limit body movement in a vehicle during sudden acceleration. Lap belts, the first type of seat belt restraint, proved inadequate because they applied the large restraining forces required during a collision over a small surface area. The result was high pressures that often caused severe injuries. Shoulder belts use a three-point anchorage system that provides a drastic improvement in terms of safety and crash survivability by increasing the surface area over which the restraining force is applied.

**Fig.STSE.4.2** An air bag spreads the restraining force over a larger surface area

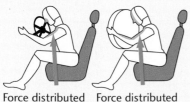

Force distributed over small area.    Force distributed over large area.

The latest development in S.R.S. technology is the air bag. An air bag applies a restraining force to the body by spreading this force over a larger surface area, as illustrated in Fig. STSE.4.2. Here is how an air bag works. Sudden deceleration when moving above 22 km/h triggers the air bag. Electrical signals from two separate sensors confirm the crash event. Electric current sent to a detonator ignites pellets made of the rocket fuel sodium azide. Combustion of the rocket fuel produces a rapidly expanding nitrogen gas cloud that inflates the air bag and cushions the rapid deceleration of the passenger in the vehicle in about $\frac{1}{25}$ s.

Although air bags have saved lives, Fig. STSE.4.3 shows the need to combine them with the use of standard shoulder belts to be even more effective.

Despite the obvious safety benefits of air bags, there have been many problems with them that pose a significant risk to car passengers. Some young children, possibly in a child car seat, as in Fig. STSE.4.4, have been injured or killed from the rapidly expanding air bag that was designed for an adult.

**Fig.STSE.4.3**

**Percentage Reduction in Driver Deaths Attributed to Air Bags Among Drivers Using Seat Belts**

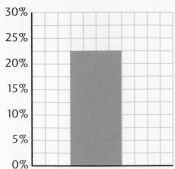

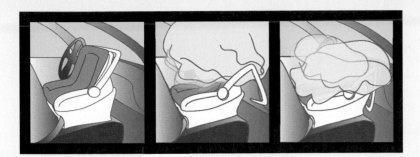

**Fig.STSE.4.4** Deploying air bags pose a risk to small children

Other problems with air bags include minor burns from release of the combustion by-product sodium hydroxide, along with eye damage, and face lacerations. Air bags are also very expensive to repair or replace, making more extensive use of side air bags even more cost prohibitive for the average driver.

## Design a Study of Societal Impact

Research accident statistics to determine the effectiveness of S.R.S. products such as seat belts and air bags.

Are the safety benefits worth the added cost of air bags? Does the misfiring of air bags cause more problems than it solves?

Surprisingly, some people still choose not to wear a seat belt. Design a billboard advertisement to convince people of the value of seat belts. Use your knowledge of physics (Newton's laws of motion and other concepts) along with an eye-catching slogan, drawing, or photograph to communicate your message.

## Design an Activity to Evaluate

Design an experiment to measure the restraining forces required during various impact situations. Construct a device that records the force exerted on this device during an impact. For example, relate the overall stretch of a spring to the maximum braking force that would be required to stop an object connected to it. Use different materials to correlate the "elasticity" of impact materials with maximum braking force.

Design an experiment to measure distance travelled, velocity, and time data for a car. Use a video camera aimed at the speedometer/odometer with a stopwatch running beside it. A frame-by-frame review of the videotape will reveal the d, v, and t information you require.

## Build a Structure

Design and build a box that will restrain an egg and prevent it from breaking when the container is dropped from various heights.

SPECIFIC EXPECTATIONS

## You should be able to

*Understand Basic Concepts:*
- State the conditions surrounding Newton's first law.
- State Newton's three laws of motion and give examples of each.
- Use FBDs to isolate and analyze objects and the external forces acting on them.
- Solve problems involving Newton's second law using FBDs.
- Solve problems involving Newton's second law using FBDs and kinematics equations.
- Solve FBD and $\vec{F}_{net}$ problems in two dimensions using trigonometric methods.

*Develop Skills of Inquiry and Communication:*
- Carry out experiments to verify Newton's second law of motion.
- Analyze the motion of objects using FBDs.
- Combine FBDs with the equations of motion in order to calculate and explain specific variables that affect motion.

*Relate Science to Technology, Society, and the Environment:*
- Explain how the contributions of Aristotle, Galileo, and Newton changed the way people looked at the world around them and laid the foundations for the classical physics understood today.
- Evaluate the design and workings of seat belts and air bags in terms of Newton's laws, and their effect on drivers and passengers during collisions.
- Analyze and explain the role of gravity, friction, and cost in the development of the Martian space vehicle.
- Compare the design of various space vehicles to their mission objectives and program cost.
- Compare recreation vehicles to space vehicles in terms of maneuverability, traction, suspension, stability, and durability.
- Analyze and explain the relationship between an understanding of forces and motion and an understanding of political, economic, environmental, and safety issues in the development and use of transportation technologies (terrestrial and space) and recreation and sports equipment.

## Equations

$$\vec{F}_{net} = m\vec{a}$$

## Conceptual Questions

1. If you pull a tablecloth very fast from underneath a table setting, given minimal friction, the dishes will not move from their original position. Describe this trick in terms of Newton's first law.

2. Are there any conditions you could impose on the demonstration in Question 1 to make it more difficult? Describe them in terms of Newton's second law.

3. a) Use Newton's laws to explain why you feel the same in a motionless car as you do in a car moving with a constant velocity.
   b) Explain the effect of being pressed back in your seat when accelerating forward and pushed forward when coming to a sudden stop.

4. Dingle balls, furry dice, and air fresheners hanging from the rearview mirror of your car indicate all the possible motions of the car because of their hanging position. For the following motions, indicate which way the above articles will move.
   a) Constant velocity forward
   b) Constant velocity backward
   c) Speeding up backward
   d) Slowing down forward
   e) Coming to sudden stop while going forward

5. While driving your car, you make a sharp turn. Explain what happens to you in terms of Newton's laws of motion. What happens to the dingle balls hanging from the rearview mirror? Is a turning motion an example of Newton's first law?

6. Whiplash is a consequence of many car accidents. Use Newton's laws to explain why whiplash occurs.

7. What do the propulsion system of rockets, balloons, and squids have in common?

8. As a rocket accelerates upward, its thrust remains constant but its acceleration increases. Given that $\vec{F} = m\vec{a}$, what could cause an increase in acceleration? (Hint: It's a major contributor to space junk.)

9. When you are standing on the floor, you push down on the floor and the floor pushes back on you. Why doesn't the floor make you rise up?

10. A person steps onto a dock off a boat that is tied securely and close to the dock. In another case, a person steps off a boat not attached to the dock. Use Newton's laws to explain what happens in each case.

11. In Fig. 4.28, explain why this method of propelling a boat will not work. Suggest three modifications to the diagram that would allow the boat to move forward.

**Fig.4.28**

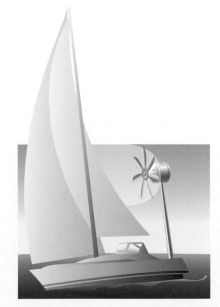

12. If Earth pulls you down, then, according to Newton's third law, you pull Earth up. Is this possible? (Remember that $\vec{F} = m\vec{a}$ for each object.)

**13.** A particle is moving with a constant speed in a corkscrew tunnel (i.e., it is moving in a circle as it moves forward). When it exits the tunnel, what path will it follow?

**14.** A car driving too fast hits an icy patch where the steering becomes useless. It then drives into a bale of hay. Use all of Newton's laws to explain this event.

**15.** A three-stage rocket is launched from Earth to travel to Pluto. After the rocket stages are jettisoned, the rocket continues on its way. For each part of the journey, state which of Newton's laws is applicable.

**16.** Explain how Newton's first law applies to air bags, seat belts, and head rests.

**17.** Riding a roller coaster is a great way to experience Newton's laws. Relate each law to an aspect of the ride. (Don't forget about the butterflies in your stomach!)

**18.** The back of a loaded pickup truck is open. A car rear-ends the pickup truck, causing its load to spill. Explain the event in terms of Newton's laws.

## Problems

▶ ### 4.2 Newton's Second Law, $\vec{F}_{net} = m\vec{a}$

**19.** Calculate the net force acting on a 20 kg object if the acceleration is
   **a)** 9.8 m/s$^2$.
   **b)** 0.28 m/s$^2$.
   **c)** 5669 km/h$^2$.
   **d)** (50 km/h)/s.

**20.** What is the acceleration when an unbalanced force of 50 N is applied to
   **a)** a 40 kg person?
   **b)** a 3 g penny?
   **c)** a 1.6 x 10$^8$ kg supertanker?
   **d)** a 2.2 x 10$^6$ g car?

**21.** On the Superman roller coaster, you are able to experience an acceleration of 4.5 $g$s. If one $g$ is 9.8 m/s$^2$, find the net force acting on a person of mass 65 kg.

**22. a)** A Sikorsky freight helicopter can easily lift a 5000 kg truck. If the acceleration of the truck is 1.5 m/s$^2$ up, what is the net force being applied by the helicopter?
   **b)** Calculate the acceleration on a 2.5 × 10$^6$ kg rocket if the net thrust of the rocket is 2.8 × 10$^7$ N.

**23.** A person accelerating at 9.80 m/s$^2$ as she falls out of a plane experiences a net force of 1000 N. What is her mass?

**24.** A skateboarder of mass 60 000 g undergoes an acceleration of 12.6 m/s$^2$. What is the unbalanced force acting on him?

**25.** A jet reaches a takeoff speed of 95 m/s in 50 s, while a jet fighter reaches 60 m/s in 3.0 s. If each plane is 8.0 × 10$^4$ kg, find the net force applied to each.

**26.** A supertanker of mass 1.0 × 10$^8$ kg travels 3.5 km, reaching a speed of 4.1 km/h from rest. What was the magnitude of the unbalanced force acting on it?

**27.** If it takes a human cannonball 1.5 s to exit a 1.6 m long cannon, what is the average net force acting on the performer if his mass is 65 kg?

**28.** A net force of 200 N is applied to an object, causing its velocity to change from 30 km/h to 20 km/h in 2.3 s. What is the object's acceleration? What is its mass?

**29.** A car changes its velocity from 20 m/s [N] to 20 m/s [S] in 5.5 s. If the mass of the car is 1500 kg, what is the net force acting on it?

**30.** A bicycle of mass 14.6 kg and a rider of mass 50 kg generate a net force of 12 N. How fast are they going after 2.0 s?

1. A batter of mass 100 kg uses a bat of mass 2.0 kg to hit a 140 g ball. If the impact time is 0.010 s and the ball reaches a speed of 60 km/h from rest, what was the average force applied to the ball?

2. Repeat Problem 31, for a bat of mass 3.0 kg hitting a 140 g pitched ball moving at 60 km/h, causing it to fly off at 60 km/h along the same line as the pitch.

## 4.3 Free-body Diagrams

3. For the following situations, draw a properly labelled FBD and include an $\vec{F}_{net}$ statement.
   a) A fishing lure descends slowly into the water.
   b) A parachute slows the shuttle after touch-down.
   c) A gorilla holds barbells equivalent to the mass of two cars above its head (no steroids).
   d) An apple is hanging on a tree branch.
   e) A car is moving with a constant velocity on a level road.

34. Draw all possible FBD combinations for three people on sleds attached by ropes, being pulled in a straight line along the ice. (Draw FBDs for all the people individually, then in combinations.)

35. Find the acceleration in the following FBDs (Fig. 4.29):

**Fig.4.29**

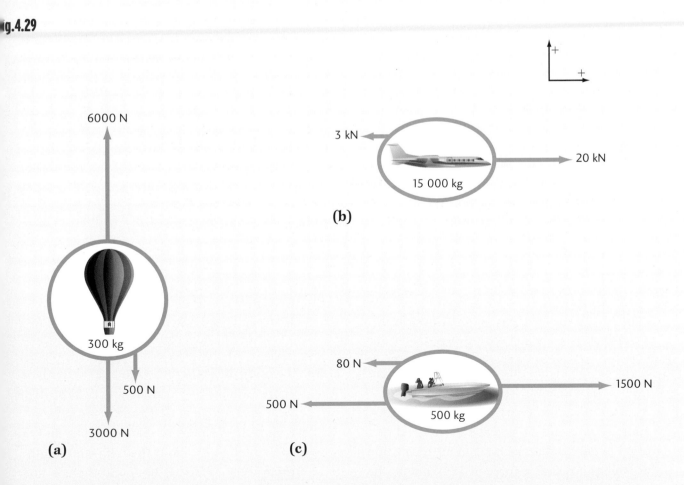

(a)

(b)

(c)

**36.** Fill in the missing quantity for the following:

**Fig.4.30**

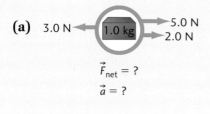

**(a)** 3.0 N ← 1.0 kg → 5.0 N, 2.0 N

$\vec{F}_{net} = ?$
$\vec{a} = ?$

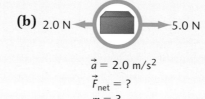

**(b)** 2.0 N ← ■ → 5.0 N

$\vec{a} = 2.0 \ m/s^2$
$\vec{F}_{net} = ?$
$m = ?$

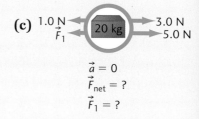

**(c)** 1.0 N $\vec{F}_1$ ← 20 kg → 3.0 N, 5.0 N

$\vec{a} = 0$
$\vec{F}_{net} = ?$
$\vec{F}_1 = ?$

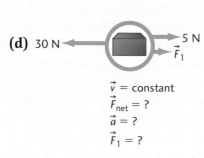

**(d)** 30 N ← ■ → 5 N, $\vec{F}_1$

$\vec{v} = constant$
$\vec{F}_{net} = ?$
$\vec{a} = ?$
$\vec{F}_1 = ?$

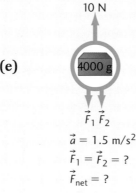

**(e)** 10 N ↑ 4000 g ↓↓ $\vec{F}_1$ $\vec{F}_2$

$\vec{a} = 1.5 \ m/s^2$
$\vec{F}_1 = \vec{F}_2 = ?$
$\vec{F}_{net} = ?$

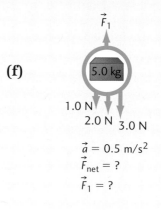

**(f)** $\vec{F}_1$ ↑ 5.0 kg ↓↓↓ 1.0 N, 2.0 N, 3.0 N

$\vec{a} = 0.5 \ m/s^2$
$\vec{F}_{net} = ?$
$\vec{F}_1 = ?$

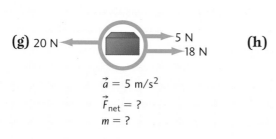

**(g)** 20 N ← ■ → 5 N, 18 N

$\vec{a} = 5 \ m/s^2$
$\vec{F}_{net} = ?$
$m = ?$

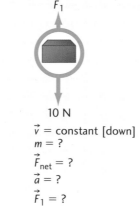

**(h)** $\vec{F}_1$ ↑ ■ ↓ 10 N

$\vec{v} = constant \ [down]$
$m = ?$
$\vec{F}_{net} = ?$
$\vec{a} = ?$
$\vec{F}_1 = ?$

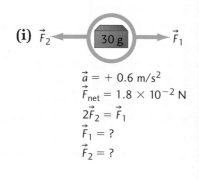

**(i)** $\vec{F}_2$ ← 30 g → $\vec{F}_1$

$\vec{a} = +0.6 \ m/s^2$
$\vec{F}_{net} = 1.8 \times 10^{-2} \ N$
$2\vec{F}_2 = \vec{F}_1$
$\vec{F}_1 = ?$
$\vec{F}_2 = ?$

**37.** A car of mass 2000 kg has a driving force of 4500 N and experiences an air resistance of 1500 N. What is the car's acceleration?

**38.** Being the good daughter you are, you are cutting the estate lawn with a push mower of mass 12.6 kg. You exert a force of 117 N horizontally, and you experience a frictional force of 45 N due to the mechanism of the machine as well as a resistive force of 58 N due to the grass itself.

**a)** What is your acceleration?
**b)** What speed do you reach after 7.0 s of pushing from rest?

**39.** Two toy ducks, attached to each other by a string, are being pulled by a very happy guy who just got them as a graduation present (Fig. 4.31). The front duck is 5.0 kg and the back duck is 2.0 kg. If the happy guy pulls them with a force of 10 N and there is no friction, calculate

**a)** the acceleration of both ducks.

**b)** the tension in the string connecting duck 1 and duck 2.

Fig.4.31

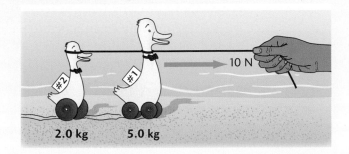

**2.0 kg          5.0 kg**

**40.** If the student in Problem 39 receives another duck of mass 1.0 kg from his grandma (he now has three ducks), and he puts the new duck at the front of the row, find
  **a)** the acceleration of the three ducks.
  **b)** the tension in the string connecting ducks 1 and 2.
  **c)** The tension in the string connecting ducks 2 and 3.
  **d)** Repeat b) and c) with different FBDs.

**41.** A puck of mass 30 g slides across rough ice, experiencing a frictional force of 0.2 N. If it was moving at 10 km/h when it hit the ice patch,
  **a)** how long did it take to stop?
  **b)** how long was the ice patch?

**42.** A dragster reaches 350 km/h from rest in 6.2 s. If the car is 800 kg and generates a driving force of 14 000 N, find the force of friction acting on the car.

**43.** A parachutist of mass 70 kg, in free fall at 136 km/h, opens a parachute. If the chute creates a 895 N air resistive force and the parachutist is being pulled down by a force of gravity of 686 N,
  **a)** find the acceleration of the parachutist.
  **b)** In which direction is the parachutist travelling just after the chute opens?
  **c)** How far does she fall in 5.0 s?

## ▶ 4.4 FBDs in Two Dimensions

**44.** For the following FBDs, create two separate $\vec{F}_{net}$ statements, one for each direction.

Fig.4.32

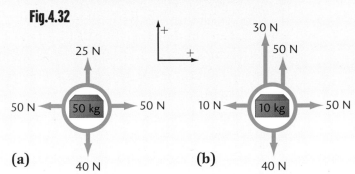

**(a)**          **(b)**

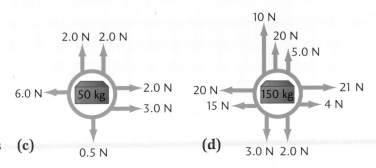

**(c)**          **(d)**

**45.** Calculate the net force of the objects in Problem 44. Use Pythagoras' theorem and the $\tan^{-1}$ function, or use Pythagoras' theorem and state the quadrant where the total net force is acting.

**46.** Two people are pushing a car of mass 2000 kg. If they each push with a force of 320 N at an angle of 15° to each side of the car, calculate the acceleration of the car, assuming no resistance. Use the component and trigonometric methods.

**47.** Repeat Problem 46, adding a resistive force of 425 N due to friction acting on the car. Use the component method only.

**48.** A canoe of mass 70 kg with a paddler of mass 55 kg are in a river. If the river's current exerts a force of 15 N [E] while the paddler is paddling with an average force of 22 N [N38°W], find the acceleration of the canoe and paddler. Use both the component and trigonometric methods.

**49. a)** Two people are lifting a small motor using ropes attached to the top of the motor. The motor hangs straight down and has a force of gravity of 1600 N acting on it. If one person lifts at 800 N [L80°U] and the other person on the other side of the motor lifts at 830 N [R85°U], find the acceleration of the motor if its mass is 163 kg. Use the component method.

**b)** How far have the people moved the motor if they lift for 1.2 s?

**50. a)** A person is sitting on a sled. The sled and person have a mass of 110 kg. If they are being pulled with a force of 40 N [U20°R] and pushed from behind with a force 44 N [D75°R], calculate the acceleration of the person in the horizontal direction.

**b)** If the person and sled experience a force of gravity of 1078 N, how much more lifting force is required by the person pulling at the front to balance the weight of the sled and person?

**51. a)** Two tugboats are towing a tanker of mass $3.30 \times 10^7$ kg. If one tug is pulling at $2.40 \times 10^4$ N [E16°N] and the other is pulling at $2.40 \times 10^4$ N [E9°S], calculate the acceleration of the tanker, assuming no resistance. Use both vector methods to solve this part of the problem.

**b)** If the tanker has a resistive force on it of $5.60 \times 10^3$ N, find its acceleration using the component method.

**c)** Calculate the speed reached in each of the two cases after 2.0 minutes. Convert it to km/h.

**d)** Calculate the distance required in each case to reach a speed of 5.0 km/h.

**52. a)** A balloon with person A in it has a force of gravity of 3000 N acting on it. The balloon has an upward force of 3800 N due to the hot air in it. Two people are keeping the balloon hovering just above their head by holding onto ropes attached to each side of the balloon. If person B exerts a force of 540 N [L40°D] and person C can exert a force of 700 N, what is the minimum angle, measured from the horizontal, at which person C should hold the rope in order for the balloon to not fly away?

**b)** What happens in the horizontal direction for this case?

**c)** If person C exerts the 700 N force straight down, how long will it take to bring the balloon to the ground if the rope held by person B is 30 m long? Remember, he is pulling at an angle of [L40°D].

## 4.5 Newton's Third Law and FBDs

**53.** Two hockey players are standing on the ice. One is a Maple Leaf (mass 100 kg) and the other is a Canuck (mass 112 kg). If the Canuck drives the Leaf with a force of 50 N,

**a)** what are the action–reaction forces involved in this situation?

**b)** calculate the acceleration of each player.

**54.** Would your answer to Problem 53 change if the players drive each other with 50 N forces?

**55.** Repeat Problem 54, adding a 5.0 N force of friction acting on each player.

# LAB 4.1  Newton's Second Law

## Purpose

To study the different aspects of Newton's second law ($\vec{F} = m\vec{a}$).

## Equipment

Tickertape setup

Cart that can accept masses of known mass (you may have to find the mass of the cart before you start the experiment)

Pulley plus clamp, Strong string

Various masses—make sure that three of them are 200 g

## Safety Note

The cart is carrying a number of large loose masses. If the cart is not cushioned properly by someone in the group before it hits the pulley, it may hurt someone.

## A. Constant Total Mass

### Fig.Lab.4.1

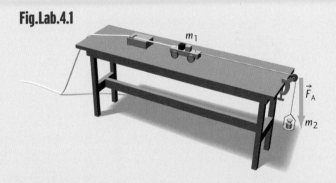

Note: Before starting the lab, copy the table in the Data section into your notebook.

1. Refer to the diagram when setting up this experiment. Attach the pulley to the table using the clamp.
2. Tie a string to one end of the cart. Make sure that the string is no longer than the height of the worktable.
3. To the other end of the cart, attach a length of tickertape no longer than the string, and thread it through the clacker/sparker.
4. Hang three 200 g masses (for a total of 600 g) from the pulley.

5. Start the clacker/sparker and release the cart. Make sure that someone is ready to catch the cart before it hits the pulley.
6. Repeat the experiment, only this time transfer 200 g to the top of the cart (leaving 400 g hanging from the pulley).
7. Repeat the experiment again, only this time transfer another 200 g to the top of the cart (leaving 200 g hanging from the pulley).

## B. Constant Force

We will repeat the experiment two more times.

8. Repeat the experiment, but first increase the hanging mass to 600 g (as in Step 4) and place 1.2 kg on the cart.
9. Repeat the experiment, but first increase the mass on the cart to 3.5 kg (the hanging mass stays the same).

## Data

1. In your notebook, construct a chart as follows:

| Trial | $m_1$ (kg) | $m_2$ (kg) | $m_{total}$ (kg) | number of dots | $\Delta t$ | $\vec{\Delta d}$ (m) |
|---|---|---|---|---|---|---|
| 1 | cart | 0.600 | 0.600 + cart | | | |
| 2 | cart + 0.200 | 0.400 | 0.600 + cart | | | |
| 3 | cart + 0.400 | 0.200 | 0.600 + cart | | | |
| 4 | cart + 1.200 | 0.600 | 1.800 + cart | | | |
| 5 | cart + 3.500 | 0.600 | 4.100 + cart | | | |

$m_1 = m_{cart} + m_{masses\ on\ cart}$, $m_2$ is the total mass of the hanging masses

2. Measure the distance from the first dot to the last dot for each tape. Record it in the chart under $\vec{\Delta d}$.
3. Count all the dots and subtract one to get the total number of time intervals. Record this number in the chart.
4. Calculate the time by multiplying the period of the clacker/sparker ($T$) by the number of dots on the tickertape ($\Delta t$ = number of dots $\times$ $T$).

Uncertainty: For this lab, record all possible instances when the measured value may have an uncertainty.

## Calculations

1. Construct the following chart in your notebook:

| Trial | $m_{total}$ (kg) | $m_2$ (kg) | $\vec{F}_A$ (N) | $\vec{a}$ (m/s²) |
|---|---|---|---|---|
| | | | | |

2. Calculate $\vec{F}_A$ by using $\vec{F}_A = m_2(9.8 \text{ m/s}^2)$ and record it in the chart.

3. Calculate acceleration by using the equation $\Delta\vec{d} = \frac{1}{2}\vec{a}\Delta t^2$.

4. a) Construct the following subchart using the values from the chart you have just completed.

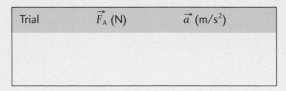

| Trial | $\vec{F}_A$ (N) | $\vec{a}$ (m/s²) |
|---|---|---|
| | | |

For trials 1, 2, and 3,

b) graph $\vec{F}$ vs. $\vec{a}$ for the three points and find the slope.

5. a) Construct the following subchart in your notebook:

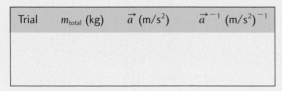

| Trial | $m_{total}$ (kg) | $\vec{a}$ (m/s²) | $\vec{a}^{-1}$ (m/s²)⁻¹ |
|---|---|---|---|
| | | | |

(Note! $\vec{a}^{-1}$ is just $\frac{1}{\vec{a}}$.)

For trials 1, 4, and 5,

b) Graph a $m_{total}$ vs. $\vec{a}$ (draw a curve of best fit) and $m_{total}$ vs. $\vec{a}^{-1}$ (draw a line of best fit). Find the slope for the $m_{total}$ vs. $\vec{a}$ graph only.

6. Construct the following chart in your notebook and complete it for all the trials:

| Trial | $(m_{total})\vec{a}$ (kg m/s²) | $\vec{F}_A$ (N) | % deviation (use $\vec{F}_A$ as the accepted value) |
|---|---|---|---|
| | | | |

## Discussion

1. For the $\vec{F}$ vs. $\vec{a}$ graph, what was the expected shape of the graph? What does it mean?
2. For the $\vec{F}$ vs. $\vec{a}$ graph, what was the expected value of the slope? How close was your value?
3. Why did you expect a curve for the $m$ vs. $\vec{a}$ graph?
4. Why did you expect a straight line for the $m$ vs. $\frac{1}{\vec{a}}$ graph?
5. What was the expected value for the slope of the $m$ vs. $\frac{1}{\vec{a}}$ graph? How close was your value?
6. How close were your $m\vec{a}$ values to $\vec{F}_A$?
7. Account for any differences between obtained and expected values by using the uncertainty possibilities you came up with in the uncertainty section.

## Conclusion

Which aspects of Newton's laws were seen or proven in this lab?

# 5 Applying Newton's Laws

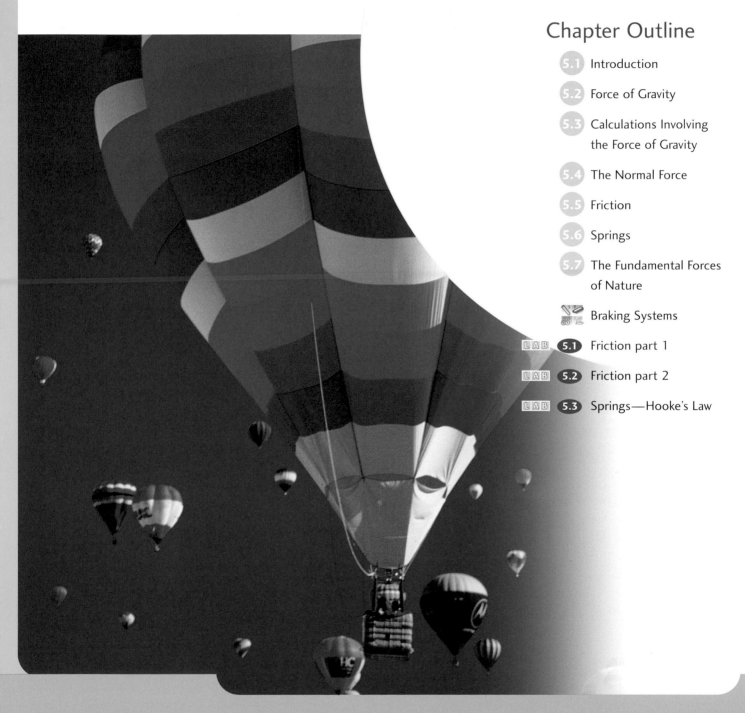

## Chapter Outline

**At the end of this chapter, you will be able to**
- define gravity, normal force, friction, and tension
- solve problems involving gravity, normal force, friction, and springs

# 5.1  Introduction

The previous chapter established a process for analyzing forces and motions in general. The method for solving force-motion problems is twofold. First, to simplify the situation, we isolate the object from its environment and create a free-body diagram for the forces. From the free-body diagram, we derive an expression for $\vec{F}_{net}$ and calculate the acceleration of the object being analyzed. Once we know the acceleration, we can combine it with other known variables and use the kinematics equations to obtain a complete picture of the event.

Now we can apply this process to a series of common everyday forces, other than direct pushing or pulling. We start with the force that's a real downer, gravity; we progress to the not-so-slippery concept of friction, and then we bounce back to springs.

**Fig.5.1**  Steps to Solving Force Problems

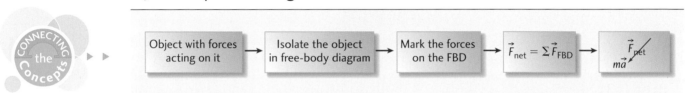

**Fig.5.2**  Real forces

# 5.2  Force of Gravity

Gravity is one of the fundamental forces of the universe. Acting through the property **mass**, it binds the universe together, keeps Earth orbiting the Sun, keeps us on the planet and, with time, makes some of us pear-shaped, and all of us shorter.

## Mass

Mass is stuff. It is the matter an object is composed of and is unchanging, regardless of position relative to Earth. After all, an astronaut orbiting Earth

**Fig.5.3** Effects of gravity

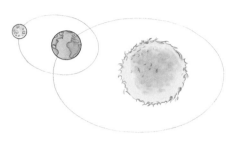

**Fig.5.4** Mass determines inertia

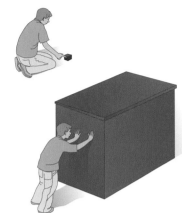

in the space shuttle doesn't vanish, even though she becomes weightless. Mass can also be considered in the context of Newton's first law. An object such as a large, completely filled dumpster has a greater ability to remain at rest than a child's building block. This ability to resist force is called **inertia**, and mass is a measure of it. The standard SI unit for mass is the kilogram (kg).

## Weight

**Weight**, on the other hand, is the gravitational pull on an object towards the centre of Earth. Without this force, you would become weightless, not massless, and would not be able to exert a force down on any scale. According to Newton's third law, the scale would not be able to press back and measure your weight. Weight, therefore, is a force, and it is measured in newtons (N). The downward weight or force acting on us is caused by the large mass of Earth. Other celestial objects have different masses, and would therefore exert different forces on us. For example, our weight on the Moon is less than our weight on Earth because the Moon is less massive than Earth. Our weight will change, depending on which celestial object we're visiting, whereas our mass doesn't change.

**Fig.5.5** Weight depends on gravitational pull

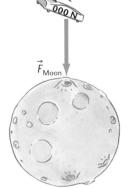

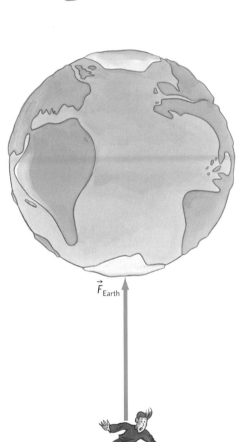

## 5.3 Calculations Involving the Force of Gravity

### Factors Affecting the Force of Gravity on an Object

We know that the mass of the object causes the force of gravity to act on it. But how does the distance between objects affect this force? To answer this question, consider a series of weight measurements of a person as he moves away from Earth.

**Fig.5.6** Change in weight with distance from Earth

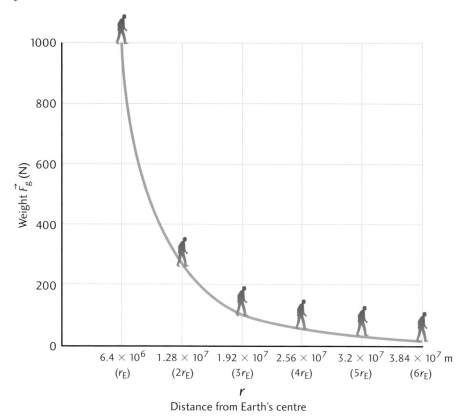

Distance from Earth's centre

**WEIGHT VS. MASS**

When you weigh yourself, you are interested in how much there is of you, i.e., your mass. However, you often measure yourself on a spring scale, which actually measures the force of gravity on you. So, in everyday usage, you often say that you *weigh* 60 kg. Even though the spring scale measures the force of gravity (588 N), the manufacturer calibrated it in kilograms (assuming $g = 9.8$ N/kg). It works fine on the surface of Earth, but would not give a correct reading on the Moon.

The graph indicates that as you move away from Earth, your weight decreases rapidly. In fact, the decrease in weight is so rapid that it is related to the square of the distance between you and Earth's centre. We are going to use $r$ to mean the distance between the centres of two objects. Written mathematically, this statement is

$$\text{weight} \propto \frac{1}{r^2}$$

Since weight is the force of gravity on an object,

$$\vec{F}_g \propto \frac{1}{r^2}$$

This is called an **inverse-square relationship**. The symbol $\propto$ means "is proportional to."

UNIT A: Motion and Forces

We now know the factors that affect weight. They are the mass of the object causing the gravitational pull toward its centre ($m_1$), the mass of the object on which gravity is acting ($m_2$), and the distance separating the centres of the two objects ($r$). When we combine these three aspects of weight, we produce the following proportionality statement:

$$\vec{F}_g \propto \frac{m_1 m_2}{r^2}$$

We must make two assumptions when using this relationship: (1) the objects are spheres, and (2) the distance between the objects is measured from their centres.

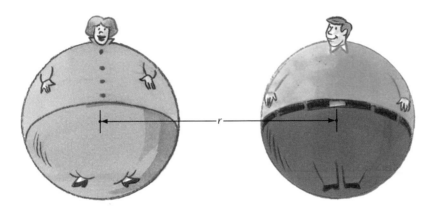

**Fig.5.7** When measuring the force of gravity, all objects can be considered spheres

To convert the proportionality to an equality, we need to introduce a constant. The constant is called the **universal gravitational constant**, with symbol $G$. The value of $G$ provides a measure of the strength of the force of gravity between any two objects anywhere in the universe. It has been determined to be $6.67 \times 10^{-11}$ Nm$^2$/kg$^2$. When substituted into the proportionality statement, the units cancel to leave newtons (N), the unit for force.

$$\frac{N m^2}{kg^2} \times \frac{kg^2}{m^2} = N$$

With this last piece in place, the full equation is

$$\vec{F}_g = \frac{G m_1 m_2}{r^2}$$

We have all heard the story of the apple hitting Newton on the head. This event started him thinking about the force that had made it fall. Newton realized that all objects exert a gravitational force on each other, and that the size of the force depends directly on the masses of the objects and inversely on the square of the distance between their centres. This relationship is called Newton's **universal law of gravity**.

If $m_1$ is a 1.0 kg mass, then the force of gravity per kilogram at any distance from Earth is

**Fig.5.8** Earth's gravitational field

$$\frac{\vec{F}_g}{1.0 \text{ kg}} = \frac{Gm_{Earth}}{r^2} = g$$

This equation gives the **gravitational field strength**, $g$, around Earth. **Field theory** explains why you do not have to be in contact with an object in order to feel the effects of a force. Gravitational fields are represented by **field lines** going directly to the centre of an object. They are the paths along which an object travels when it is affected by a gravitational force. Thus, no matter where we are on Earth, we will fall directly toward the planet's centre.

**EXAMPLE 1**  **The force of attraction between two objects**

Find the force of gravity between a large sumo wrestler of mass 300 kg and a small gymnast of mass 40 kg if they are separated by 1.5 m.

*Solution and Connection to Theory*

**Given**

$m_1 = 300 \text{ kg}$     $m_2 = 40 \text{ kg}$     $r = 1.5 \text{ m}$     $G = 6.67 \times 10^{-11} \text{ Nm}^2/\text{kg}^2$

$$\vec{F}_g = \frac{Gm_1 m_2}{r^2} = \frac{6.67 \times 10^{-11} \text{ Nm}^2/\text{kg}^2 \, (300 \text{ kg})(40 \text{ kg})}{(1.5 \text{ m})^2} = 3.6 \times 10^{-7} \text{ N}$$

**Fig. 5.9**

**UNIT CHECK**

$$\frac{\frac{\text{Nm}^2}{\text{kg}^2} \times \text{kg} \times \text{kg}}{\text{m}^2} = \text{N}$$

**SI REVIEW**

m (milli)  1 mN = $10^{-3}$ N
M (mega) 1 MN = $10^6$ N
t (tonne)  1 t   = $10^3$ kg

There is not much gravitational attraction. You therefore need not worry about finding yourself drawn irresistibly to heavy objects.

While the equation

$$\vec{F}_g = \frac{Gm_1m_2}{r^2}$$

works well, it is somewhat awkward to use. In the next example, we will use an easier version of this equation.

**EXAMPLE 2**   **Using the formula for universal gravitation**

Calculate the force of attraction between a 1.0 kg melon and Earth of mass $5.98 \times 10^{24}$ kg if the object is sitting on the surface of Earth.

**Solution and Connection to Theory**

**Given**

$m_1 = 5.98 \times 10^{24}$ kg       $m_2 = 1.0$ kg

The melon's radius is negligible compared to Earth's. Therefore, we consider the distance from the melon's centre to Earth's centre to be equal to Earth's radius,

$r = 6.38 \times 10^6$ m

$$\vec{F}_g = \frac{Gm_1m_2}{r^2} = \frac{6.67 \times 10^{-11} \text{ Nm}^2/\text{kg}^2 \, (5.98 \times 10^{24} \text{ kg})(1.0 \text{ kg})}{(6.38 \times 10^6 \text{ m})^2} = 9.8 \text{ N}$$

Thus, the force of attraction between the 1.0 kg melon and Earth is 9.8 N.

**UNIT CHECK**

Substituting units on each side of the equation,

$$\frac{\text{m}}{\text{s}^2} = \frac{\frac{\text{Nm}^2}{\text{kg}^2} \cdot \text{kg}}{\text{m}^2} = \frac{\text{N}}{\text{kg}}$$

The number 9.8 is familiar. It is the SI value in m/s$^2$ of the acceleration due to gravity ($g$) at Earth's surface, which you saw in earlier chapters.

Therefore, at Earth's surface, we can write

$$\vec{F}_g = \frac{Gm_{\text{Earth}}m_{\text{object}}}{r_{\text{Earth}}^2} = m_{\text{object}}\frac{Gm_{\text{Earth}}}{r_{\text{Earth}}^2} = mg$$

$$g = \frac{Gm_{\text{Earth}}}{r_{\text{Earth}}^2}, \text{ the } \textbf{gravitational field strength}.$$

$g$ is the gravitational field strength at a given distance from the centre of a celestial object.

As long as an object is at or near the surface of a celestial object, and we know the value of $g$, the gravitational field strength at the surface of the celestial body, we can use $\vec{F}_g = mg$ to find the weight of the object.

EXAMPLE 3   **Two methods of calculating weight**

Find the weight of a 100 kg rugby player using both forms of the equation for weight.

### Solution and Connection to Theory

Let's first try the long version for calculating weight.

**Given**

$m_1 = 5.98 \times 10^{24}$ kg          $m_2 = 100$ kg          $r = 6.38 \times 10^6$ m

$$\vec{F_g} = \frac{Gm_1m_2}{r^2} = \frac{6.67 \times 10^{-11} \text{ Nm}^2/\text{kg}^2(5.98 \times 10^{24} \text{ kg})(100 \text{ kg})}{(6.38 \times 10^6 \text{ m})^2} = 980 \text{ N}$$

Now the shorter version.

**Given**

$m = 100$ kg          $g = 9.8$ m/s$^2$

$$\vec{F} = mg = 100 \text{ kg} \times 9.8 \text{ m/s}^2 = 980 \text{ N}$$

As long as you are near the surface of Earth, this latter method is the easier one to use.

The value of $g$ is not constant over the surface of Earth. From the formula, you can see that it depends on Earth's radius. Because Earth is flattened at the poles, the North Pole is closer to the centre of Earth than the equator is. The force of gravity is also slightly reduced by the effect of Earth's rotation. At the equator of a perfectly spherical Earth, the spin would reduce your weight by about 0.33%. The effect of these factors is shown in Table 5.1.

When astronauts and cosmonauts land on other planets of our solar system, their weights will be different than on Earth. Their weight will depend on the radius of the planet and its mass. Table 5.2 shows the value of $g$ and the weight of a 60 kg person on the surfaces of some of the other planets.

| Table 5.1 Acceleration Due to Gravity | | | |
|---|---|---|---|
| Place | Latitude (°) | Altitude (m) | $g$ (m/s$^2$) |
| Quito, EQ | 0 | 2850 | 9.78023 |
| Kingston, ON | 44.5 | 75 | 9.8057 |
| Nelson, BC | 49.5 | 532 | 9.8102 |
| Winnipeg, MB | 59.8 | 200 | 9.8105 |
| Banff, AB | 51.2 | 1390 | 9.8116 |
| Moosonee, ON | 51.3 | 0 | 9.8118 |
| North Pole | 90 | 0 | 9.8321 |

| Table 5.2 How much does a 60 kg earthling weigh? | | |
|---|---|---|
| Place | $g$ (N/kg) | Weight (N) |
| Earth's moon | 1.62 | 97 |
| Mercury | 3.61 | 217 |
| Mars | 3.75 | 225 |
| Venus | 8.83 | 530 |
| Earth | 9.81 | 589 |

**Fig.5.10** Finding the Force of Gravity Using the Correct Distance

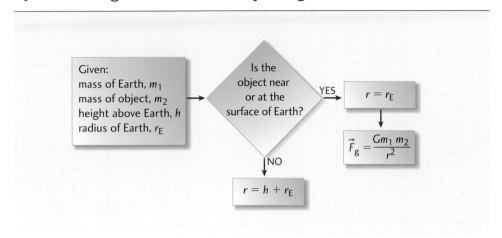

---

**EXAMPLE 4** **Comparing weights at different distances from the Earth**

A 1000 kg satellite is the payload on a planned shuttle launch. What is its weight 32 000 km from Earth's surface?

### Solution and Connection to Theory

It is not always necessary to use the universal formula for gravitation to obtain a weight value of an object significantly above a planet's surface.

For a satellite first sitting on the surface of Earth, then 32 000 km away, we can solve the problem by finding the ratio between the two forces at the two different locations. The following variables remain the same: $G$, $m_{Earth}$, $m_{satellite}$. The radius $r$ can also be simplified for the second case. $r_2$, the distance of the satellite from Earth, is 32 000 km + 6400 km = 38 400 km above the centre of Earth. (Remember, we always use distances from the centre of the object.) $r_2$ as a ratio of $r_1$ is $\frac{38\ 400\ km}{6400\ km} = 6$. Therefore, $r_2 = 6r_1$. Similarly, we can take a ratio of the weights, $\vec{F}_1$ and $\vec{F}_2$. The common factors cancel out.

$$\frac{\vec{F}_2}{\vec{F}_1} = \frac{\frac{Gm_1 m_2}{r_2^2}}{\frac{Gm_1 m_2}{r_1^2}} = \frac{\frac{1}{r_2^2}}{\frac{1}{r_1^2}}$$

$$= \frac{r_1^2}{r_2^2}$$

$$= \frac{r_1^2}{(6r_1)^2}$$

This relationship produces the simple ratio

$$\frac{F_2}{F_1} = \frac{1}{36}$$

We can find $\vec{F_1}$ easily by using $\vec{F} = mg$. Therefore, the weight of the satellite on Earth is

1000 kg $\times$ 9.8 m/s$^2$ = 9800 N.

From our ratio, $F_2 = \frac{F_1}{36} = 272$ N. At its orbital height, the satellite's weight is 272 N. That is the force of Earth's gravity on it at that location.

In general, you can do problems like this very quickly by using some fundamental logic. If the object is farther away from the planet, its weight will decrease. If the object moves closer, its weight increases. The factor used to relate the two weights is the square of the ratio of the distances from the centre of the planet.

EXAMPLE 5     **Logical method of solving problems**

For the satellite in Example 4, what is its weight at a distance of 12 800 km from the centre of Earth?

### Solution and Connection to Theory

For this problem, we know that the satellite's weight decreases because its distance from Earth increases. Taking the square of the ratio of the distances from centres, we find that the factor by which the weight decreases is

$$\left(\frac{12\ 800\ \text{km}}{6400\ \text{km}}\right)^2 = 2^2 = 4.$$

Therefore, the weight of the satellite 12 800 km away from Earth's centre is $\frac{9800\ \text{N}}{4} = 2450$ N.

As an offshoot of this answer, we can find the local $g$ value as well. We know that $\vec{F} = mg$;

therefore, $g = \dfrac{\vec{F}}{m}$

so $g = \dfrac{2450\ \text{N}}{1000\ \text{kg}} = 2.45$ N/kg $= 2.45$ m/s$^2$

**Fig.5.11** Finding the Force of Gravity

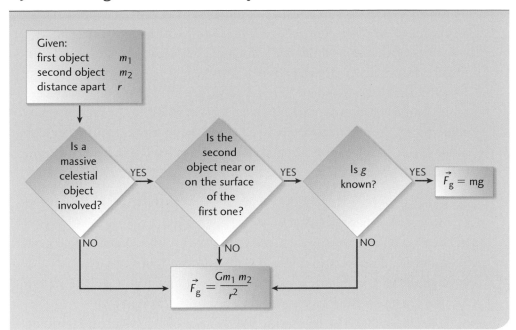

Given:
first object    $m_1$
second object   $m_2$
distance apart  $r$

Is a massive celestial object involved? — YES → Is the second object near or on the surface of the first one? — YES → Is $g$ known? — YES → $\vec{F}_g = mg$

NO ↓ ... NO ↓ ... NO ↓

$$\vec{F}_g = \frac{Gm_1\,m_2}{r^2}$$

**1.** The force of gravity on an object causes the object to exert a force on a scale. This is what we call weight.

a) Calculate the weight on Earth of the Hubble Telescope, which has a mass of about 12 000 kg.

b) What is the weight of the Hubble Telescope at an orbit of radius $6.98 \times 10^6$ m as measured from Earth's centre?

c) What is the distance of the orbit as measured from the surface of Earth? Why don't we use this value in the calculation?

d) What would the Hubble Telescope weigh on the Moon?

e) Why would testing a lunar or Martian exploration vehicle on Earth be unreliable in predicting how it would react to the terrain on different planets and moons? How could researchers compensate for the effect of variations in gravitational force on other celestial objects?

## Surviving for Long Periods of Time in Space

The effect of weightlessness on the human body causes body fluids to shift towards the head. The reason for this effect is that gravity no longer pulls body fluids down towards the feet and hands, and the heart doesn't have to work as hard in pumping the blood back up against gravity. The heart therefore shrinks in size, thus decreasing the volume of blood being pumped at any time.

Over time, muscles also atrophy. The lack of use, compounded by radiation damage, poorer circulation, and stress, all contribute to muscle loss and nerve damage.

**Fig.5.12A** Four crew members inside the space shuttle

**Fig.5.12B**

The body regulates the production of bone tissue. If the bones are no longer needed to support the person against gravity, less bone tissue is produced and the bones weaken. This weakening occurs in the weight-bearing parts of the body, such as the leg bones. The skull and fingers do not show deterioration.

Other effects include puffiness of the face, and sweat accumulating around areas of high production, such as the armpits. One very noticeable change is an increase in height of two to three centimetres or more. This effect causes problems in clothes and space suits fitting properly over time.

2. What possible things can an astronaut do to slow down these processes of deterioration?
3. What would an astronaut feel when he or she returned to Earth again and had to move around under the influence of gravity?
4. Would the astronaut experience any serious adverse effects in the short term and the long term after returning to Earth?
5. Speculate what a human being would look like if he or she spent his or her entire life in a weightless environment in outer space (see Fig. 5.12B).

# 5.4 The Normal Force

Newton's third law of action-reaction forces deals with situations involving two bodies. An initiating body creates the action force and the receiving body creates the reaction force. From this situation, we generate *two free-body diagrams,* one for each object. The action-reaction pair of forces is split up, each going to one diagram.

**Fig.5.13** Action-reaction forces

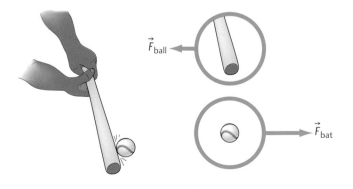

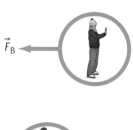

When the body receiving the action force is a surface, the reaction force of the surface pressing back is called the **normal force**. For example, if your feet are pressing down on the floor, the normal force is the reaction force of

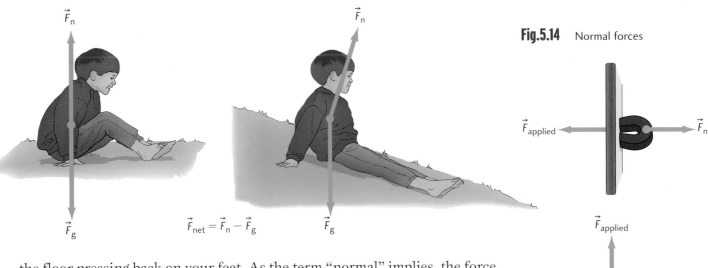

Fig.5.14    Normal forces

the floor pressing back on your feet. As the term "normal" implies, the force is always perpendicular to the surface. If the reaction force is acting at an angle to the surface, the normal force is the part of this force that acts perpendicular to the surface.

## Calculating the Normal Force, $\vec{F}_n$

The next series of examples illustrates the nature of the normal force.

**EXAMPLE 6**    **Finding the normal force for a person sitting down**

**Fig.5.15**

For a person of mass 40 kg sitting on a box, what is the value of the normal force?

### Solution and Connection to Theory

First create a free-body diagram, using the standard reference system for sign convention. The next step is always an $\vec{F}_{net}$ statement:

$$\vec{F}_{net} = \vec{F}_n - \vec{F}_g$$

But, $\vec{F}_{net} = m\vec{a}$. Since the person is motionless (i.e., seated), $\vec{a} = 0$. Therefore, $\vec{F}_{net} = 0$ and $\vec{F}_g = mg$.

$$\vec{F}_{net} = \vec{F}_n - \vec{F}_g$$

$$0 = \vec{F}_n - mg$$

$$\vec{F}_n = mg$$

Solving for the normal force gives

$$\vec{F}_n = mg = 40 \text{ kg} \times 9.8 \text{ m/s}^2 = 392 \text{ N}.$$

In this case, the pressing of the person's seat on the crate's surface caused the normal force, which was found to be equal to her weight.

**EXAMPLE 7** **An uplifting problem**

A friend is now trying to lift the person sitting on the box using a crane that exerts a force of 92 N.

**Fig. 5.16A**

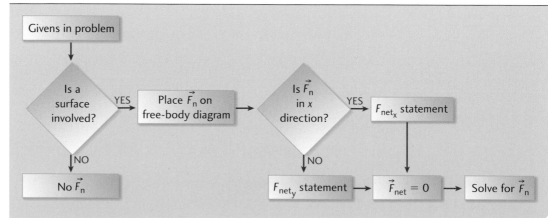

**Fig.5.16B**

## Solution and Connection to Theory

Create a free-body diagram, using the standard system for sign convention.

$$\vec{F}_{net} = \vec{F}_n + 92 \text{ N} - \vec{F}_g$$

$$\underset{0}{\underset{\downarrow}{m\vec{a}}} \qquad \qquad \underset{mg}{\underset{\downarrow}{}}$$

$$0 = \vec{F}_n + 92 \text{ N} - mg$$

$$\therefore \vec{F}_n = mg - 92 \text{ N} \qquad \vec{F}_n = 40 \text{ kg}(9.8 \text{ m/s}^2) - 92 \text{ N} = 300 \text{ N}$$

Because of the crane, you are not exerting as great a force down on the surface of the box; therefore, the box does not press back as much. In fact, if the crane were to lift with a force of 392 N, the normal force would go to zero and you would be unable to register a weight on a scale.

**Fig.5.17** Finding the Normal Force

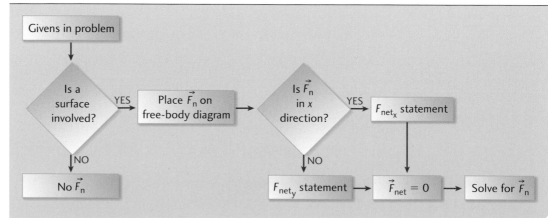

1. If you were standing on a bathroom scale in an elevator, the normal force acting on you would be the reading on the bathroom scale. This number is called your **apparent weight**. For the following cases, use FBDs and $\vec{F}_{net}$ statements to calculate the reading on the bathroom scale. The mass of the person is 70 kg.

   a) The elevator is at rest.

   b) The elevator is moving up at a constant speed of 10 km/h.

   c) The elevator is moving down with an acceleration of 2.0 m/s².

   d) The elevator cable broke and the elevator is free-falling.

2. a) Using the $\vec{v}$-t graph for a roller coaster that you generated in section 2.1 and the acceleration values for each section of the ride, calculate the person's apparent weight for all the different sections of the roller coaster ride. An FBD must be included with the corresponding $\vec{F}_{net}$ statements.

   b) In Section 1.7, you described the sensations associated with each section of the ride. Explain those sensations using the results from part a).

◀ ◀ ◀ ◀

*Astronaut Training*

The "Vomit Comet," a nickname given the aircraft used in training astronauts, uses the result in 1.d). The real effect of weightlessness is hard to produce on Earth. It is simulated by training under water, where buoyancy allows the astronaut to move in a manner similar to the way he/she would move in outer space.

The sensation of weightlessness is produced when the plane carrying the astronauts goes into free fall (Fig. 5.18A), causing the normal force to become zero and hence create apparent weightlessness. The plane (a KC-135, which is a predecessor of the Boeing 707, a plane used to refuel airforce jets in flight) rises to about 9800 m and free falls to 7300 m. Its path is parabolic, with a pitch angle of 45–50 degrees. For periods of 25 s, the person feels weightless. For 55 s periods, the person experiences double gravity and a sensation of being encased in lead.

The trainees go through last-minute safety discussions and videos. The observers (researchers) don their flight suits along with heavy boots and are issued an allotment of "barf bags." The flight lasts about two hours, during which time the plane makes about 40 parabolas, and sometimes as many as 100! The main limitation is the plane. The structure itself needs to take a break.

NASA runs a program designed to take students up for this experience. A period of training and in-class work is done beforehand. Typically, only about 20 parabolic sequences are flown.

**Fig.5.18A**

**Fig.5.18B** Astronaut Jeffrey S. Ashby aboard NASA's KC-135 "zero-gravity" aircraft

**3. a)** Using the position of the plane in the roller-coaster-type flight pattern, explain the sensations experienced by the trainees. Indicate where the person would feel heavy and where he or she would feel light.

**b)** Use a free-body diagram and $\vec{F}_{net}$ statement to show why a person feels heavier on the climb up.

**c)** Research the NASA Web site to find information on the student weightlessness experience program.

# 5.5 Friction

Friction is the Jekyll and Hyde of forces. On the one hand, we need friction to move. Without friction, a car would sit in one spot spinning its tires, and a person wouldn't be able to take a step forward. But on the other hand, the motion of an object along a surface with friction causes the production of heat, a loss of mechanical energy, and general wear and tear on the object.

**Fig.5.19**  Surface friction

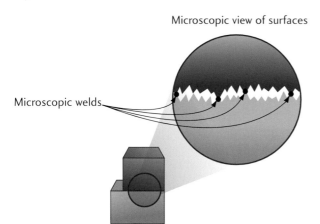

Microscopic view of surfaces

Microscopic welds

The microscopic details of the force of friction are still not properly understood. We believe that the two objects in contact make microscopic connections at various points on their surfaces. Even highly polished surfaces are rough and ridged microscopically. Because the contact points are so close to each other, intermolecular forces form **microscopic welds** that must be broken in order for the object to move. As the object moves, these welds form and break along the length of the path.

> The magnitude of the frictional force is determined by the types of materials in contact, and by the normal force exerted by one object on the other.

Combining the two components that make up the frictional force, we obtain the following equation:

$$\vec{F}_f = \mu \vec{F}_n$$

The Greek letter $\mu$ (mu) is called the **coefficient of friction**. It depends only on the kinds of surfaces in contact. The coefficient of friction has no units because it is a ratio of two forces, $\frac{\vec{F}_f}{\vec{F}_n}$.

There are two types of frictional forces. Friction is **kinetic** when the object is moving and **static** when the object is not moving. The theory of frictional forces states that an object at rest experiences more friction than when it is already moving. That is because it is harder to form microscopic welds when the object is moving across a surface than when it is stationary.

Since there are two types of friction, there are also two types of coefficients for friction. The **coefficient of static friction ($\mu_s$)** is larger than the **coefficient of kinetic friction ($\mu_k$)**. Although both $\mu_s$ and $\mu_k$ can be substituted in the same equation, $\vec{F}_f = \mu \vec{F}_n$, they must be calculated separately.

**Fig.5.20** Finding the Force of Friction

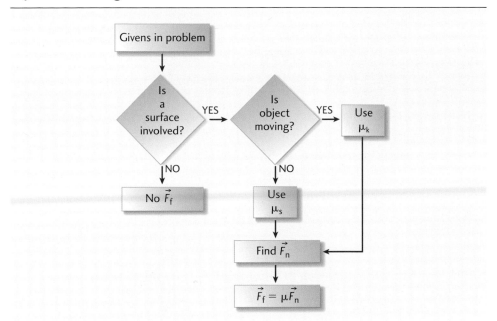

## Calculating Friction

A force of friction is involved if there is (1) a coefficient of friction, (2) a normal force between the two surfaces, and (3) an applied force trying to move the object. In general, the force of friction acts opposite to the direction of the object's motion. If you know the direction the object is moving in, then you can confidently put the frictional force on your free-body diagram with its direction opposite to the direction of motion.

**EXAMPLE 8** **Calculating the force of friction for a lawnmower being pushed**

A lawnmower of mass 12 kg is being pushed by a force of 150 N horizontally and 40 N down. If the kinetic coefficient of friction between wheels and grass is 0.9, find the force of friction acting on the lawnmower.

**Fig.5.21**

**(a)**

**(b)**

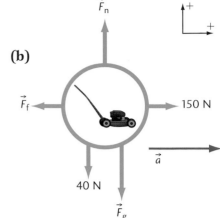

*Solution and Connection to Theory*

Assume the standard reference system and that motion is to the right.

**Given**

$m = 12$ kg      $g = 9.8$ m/s$^2$      $\mu_k = 0.9$      $\vec{F}_h = 150$ N, $\vec{F}_v = 40$ N

Notice that we have isolated the lawnmower and not the person and lawnmower. If we did that, the two given forces would not be marked on the diagram because they act on the lawnmower only. Because the force of friction involves the normal force, we chose the direction of the normal force first when solving for $\vec{F}_{net}$. We designate $\vec{F}_n$ as positive.

Vertically,

$$\vec{F}_{net} = \vec{F}_n - \vec{F}_g - 40 \text{ N}$$

There is no vertical motion. Therefore, $\vec{F}_{net} = 0$ and $\vec{F}_g = mg$.

$$\therefore \vec{F}_n = mg + 40 \text{ N} \qquad \vec{F}_n = 12 \text{ kg}(9.8 \text{m/s}^2) + 40 \text{ N} = 158 \text{ N}$$

Horizontally, because the lawnmower is moving,

$$\vec{F}_f = \mu_k \vec{F}_n \qquad \vec{F}_f = 0.9(158 \text{ N}) = 142 \text{ N}$$

The force of friction acting on the lawnmower is 142 N.

Because the question asked for the force of friction only, the 150 N applied force was not used.

---

**EXAMPLE 9**    **Finding the acceleration of the lawnmower**

*Solution and Connection to Theory*

In the free-body diagram, assume the standard reference frame and that the motion is to the right.

Having solved for $\vec{F}_{net}$ in the $y$ (vertical) direction, we now solve for $\vec{F}_{net}$ in the direction of motion (horizontal, $x$).

$$\vec{F}_{net} = 150 \text{ N} - \vec{F}_f$$

Notice how the direction of friction was chosen to be opposite to the direction of motion. In this case,

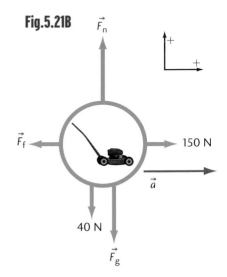

Fig.5.21B $\vec{F}_n$

$$\vec{F}_{net} = m\vec{a} \qquad m\vec{a} = 150 \text{ N} - 142 \text{ N} = 8.0 \text{ N}$$

$$\vec{a} = \frac{8.0 \text{ N}}{12 \text{ kg}} = 0.7 \text{ m/s}^2$$

The applied force accelerates the mower at 0.7 m/s² [E].

The following flow chart explains the method of solving for the acceleration (combining Examples 8 and 9).

## Fig.5.22  Steps to Solving a Friction Problem

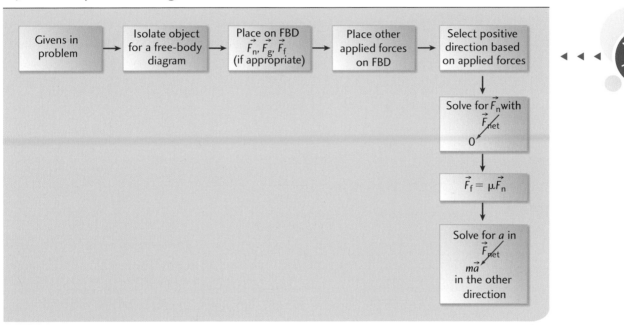

### EXAMPLE 10  Practising the full friction calculation

Be alert. The answer is twisted!

Two people are pushing horizontally on a crate of mass 50 kg. One person is pushing from the right with a force of 50 N, and the other person is pushing from the left with a force of 80 N. The coefficient of kinetic friction is 0.3. Find the acceleration of the crate.

### *Solution and Connection to Theory*

**Given**

$m = 50 \text{ kg} \qquad g = 9.8 \text{ m/s}^2 \qquad \mu_k = 0.30 \qquad \vec{F}_1 = -50 \text{ N}, \vec{F}_2 = 80 \text{ N}$

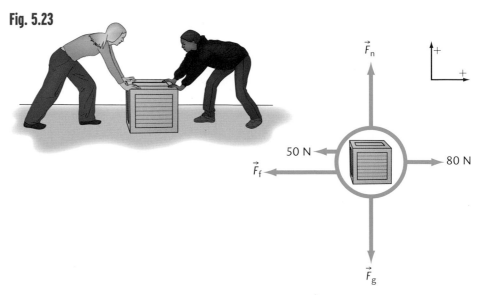

**Fig. 5.23**

Assume the standard reference system and motion to the right because the applied force to the right is larger than the applied force to the left. Because the crate is not accelerating upwards or downwards, $F_{net_y} = 0$.

$$F_{net_y} = \vec{F}_n - mg \qquad \therefore \vec{F}_n = mg \qquad \vec{F}_n = 50 \text{ kg}(9.8 \text{ m/s}^2) = 490 \text{ N}$$

$$F_{net_y} = 0$$

$$\vec{F}_f = \mu_k \vec{F}_n \qquad F_f = 0.30(490 \text{ N}) = 147 \text{ N}$$

$$F_{net_x} = 80 \text{ N} - 50 \text{ N} - 147 \text{ N}$$

$$m\vec{a} = -117 \text{ N} \approx -120 \text{ N}$$

It's time to pause here. The acceleration sign is *negative*, indicating that the acceleration is to the *left*. But everything indicates that the acceleration should be to the *right*. After all, the applied force to the right is larger than the applied force to the left. However, the force of friction is so large that the applied force in either direction cannot overcome it. The logical answer to this problem, therefore, is that ***the crate does not move at all***.

## FINDING FORCE OF FRICTION

Since object is not moving,

$\vec{F}_f \leq \mu_s \vec{F}_n$ and

$\vec{F}_{net} = 0$

$\therefore \vec{F}_{net} = 80 \text{ N} - 50 \text{ N} - \vec{F}_f$

$0 \quad \vec{F}_f = -30 \text{ N}$

A good time to check if any acceleration is possible is as soon as you have calculated a value for friction and placed it on the free-body diagram. At a glance, you will be able to see whether the applied forces are great enough to cause an acceleration.

**EXAMPLE 11** **A problem involving a slight change in orientation**

A 0.5 kg block is being slid up a chalkboard with an applied force of 6.0 N upward and 2.0 N inward towards the board. If the coefficient of kinetic friction is 0.4, calculate the acceleration of the block.

**Solution and Connection to Theory**  **Fig.5.24**

**Given**

Using the standard reference system,
$m = 0.5$ kg   $g = 9.8$ m/s$^2$

$F_y = 6.0$ N, $F_x = 2.0$ N      $\mu_k = 0.4$

$F_{net_x} = F_n - 2.0$ N

Notice that the normal force is now in the $x$ direction, so we solve for $\vec{F}_{net}$ in that direction first.

$\vec{F}_n = 2.0$ N      $\vec{F}_f = 0.4(2.0$ N$) = 0.8$ N

$F_{net_y} = 6.0$ N $- mg - F_f = 6.0$ N $- 4.9$ N $- 0.8$ N $= 0.3$ N

$$\vec{a} = \frac{F_{net_y}}{m}$$

$$= \frac{0.3 \text{ N}}{0.5 \text{ kg}} = 0.6 \text{ m/s}^2$$

The acceleration of the block is 0.6 m/s$^2$ upward.

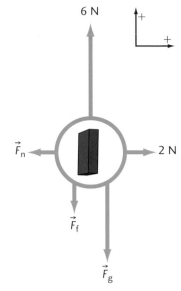

---

**EXAMPLE  12**    **Connecting motion and force**

**Fig.5.25**

A puck of mass 0.30 kg is sliding along an essentially frictionless patch of ice at 6.0 m/s. It encounters a rough patch of ice with a coefficient of kinetic friction of 0.10. How long will it take for the puck to stop and how far will it travel?

**Solution and Connection to Theory**

**Given**

Using the standard reference system and assuming the puck is sliding to the right,

$\vec{v}_1 = 6.0$ m/s,     $\vec{v}_2 = 0$ m/s     $m = 0.30$ kg     $\mu_k = 0.10$

First set up the free-body diagram.

Since the puck is moving in the horizontal direction only, $F_{net_y} = 0$.

$F_{net_y} = \vec{F}_n - \vec{F}_g$      $F_n = F_g = 0.30$ kg$(9.8$ m/s$^2) = 2.9$ N

$\therefore F_f = 0.10(2.9$ N$) = 0.29$ N

$F_{net_x} = -\vec{F}_f$

Notice that in the standard reference system, the force of friction is pointing to the left, hence it is negative. In this case, it is also the only applied force.

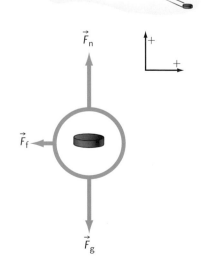

$$F_{\text{net}_x} = -0.29 \text{ N} \qquad \vec{a} = \frac{F_{\text{net}_x}}{m} = \frac{-0.29 \text{ N}}{0.30 \text{ kg}} = -0.97 \text{ m/s}^2$$

Now we can solve for time using

$$\vec{a} = \frac{\vec{v}_2 - \vec{v}_1}{\Delta t}$$

$$\Delta t = \frac{0 \text{ m/s} - 6.0 \text{ m/s}}{-0.97 \text{ m/s}^2} = 6.2 \text{ s}$$

Notice how the negatives have cancelled to produce a positive time. To find the distance travelled, we can use any equation with $\Delta \vec{d}$ in it.

$$\Delta \vec{d} = \tfrac{1}{2}(\vec{v}_1 + \vec{v}_2)\Delta t \quad \Delta \vec{d} = \tfrac{1}{2}(6.0 \text{ m/s} + 0 \text{ m/s})6.2 \text{ s} = 19 \text{ m}$$

The puck will stop in 6.2 s, after travelling 19 m.

**Fig.5.26  Combining Kinematics with Forces**

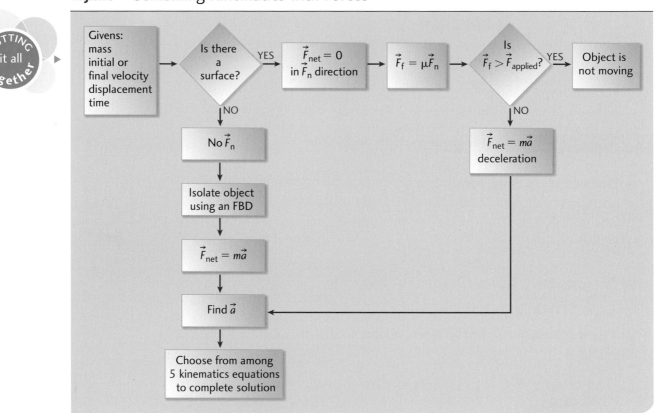

PUTTING it all Together

*Force or Property?*

Friction plays an important role in our world. Aristotle considered it to be natural and thus a property of material rather than a force. Galileo, on the other hand, called friction a force and treated it as such. It is interesting to note that the force of gravity is now discussed in the same manner. We are accustomed to thinking of it as a force. Yet, in some theories, it is considered a property of space. In Section 5.7, we will describe the fundamental forces of nature. The Theory of Everything (TOE) tries to unify the force of gravity with the other fundamental forces. So far, the theory has failed to do so. Thus, the idea that gravity is really the effect of mass on what Einstein termed "space-time" becomes plausible.

1. Tread designs play an important role in maintaining friction between a tire and the road under various conditions. Use Newton's laws to explain why tread designs are used.

2. A car is turning a corner when it encounters an icy patch and loses traction. Use Newton's first and second laws as well as friction to explain how the car was turning and the subsequent action of the car when it hit the icy patch.

3. Calculate the force of friction for the following cases. Use an FBD for each case.
   a) A 30 kg crate is pushed at constant speed across a surface with a coefficient of friction of 0.5.
   b) The same crate is being pushed with a force of 100 N, but it does not move.
   c) For the case in part b), what is the value for the coefficient of friction? What is the value of $\frac{\vec{F_f}}{\vec{F_n}}$?
   d) A person is now pushing down on the crate with a force of 20 N. Using this information, repeat parts a) to c).
   e) The person is now lifting the crate up with a force of 20 N. Using this information, repeat parts a) to c).

# 5.6 Springs

We have already discussed springs implicitly in our discussion of gravity. This is because the bathroom scale you use to measure your weight operates by compressing a spring attached to a dial. When you measure that prize salmon you hooked, you also use a Newton spring scale.

Whether you pull down on an expansion spring or press in on a compression spring, the effect is always the same: the spring tries to restore itself to its original length (Fig. 5.27).

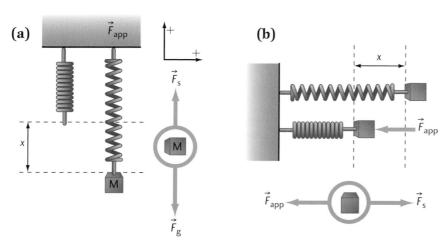

**Fig.5.27** Extension and compression of springs

**Fig.5.28** Balanced forces using springs

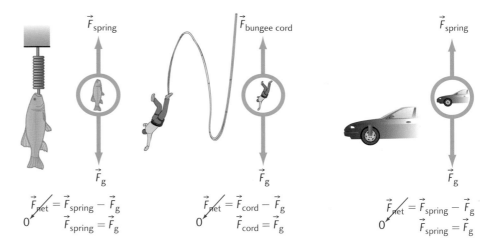

$$\vec{F}_{net} = \vec{F}_{spring} - \vec{F}_g$$
$$0 \qquad \vec{F}_{spring} = \vec{F}_g$$

$$\vec{F}_{net} = \vec{F}_{cord} - \vec{F}_g$$
$$0 \qquad \vec{F}_{cord} = \vec{F}_g$$

$$\vec{F}_{net} = \vec{F}_{spring} - \vec{F}_g$$
$$0 \qquad \vec{F}_{spring} = \vec{F}_g$$

**Fig.5.29** Graph of force used to stretch the spring vs. the amount the spring stretched from rest position

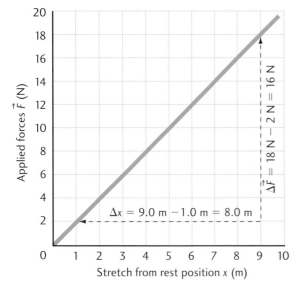

$$k = \frac{16\ N}{8.0\ m} = 2.0\ N/m$$

For all the examples in Fig. 5.28, $\vec{F}_{net}$ is zero because the spring is at rest (in equilibrium).

Providing you do not stretch a spring to the point where you turn it into a wire, a graph of the *force* needed to stretch the spring versus the *stretch* of the spring from its rest position produces a straight line.

The slope from the $\vec{F}$-$x$ graph in Fig. 5.29 has the units N/m and is an indicator of how stiff the spring is. This indicator is called the **spring constant** and has the symbol $k$.

To find the spring equation, use the general straight-line equation, $y = mx + b$. Replace $m$ by $k$, setting $b = 0$ (no force, therefore no stretch). Then $x$ becomes the stretch or compression of the spring from its natural position. Replace $y$ with $\vec{F}$.

---

**Hooke's law** The restoring force of a spring is $\vec{F} = kx$, where $k$ is the spring constant.

---

**EXAMPLE 13** Tire pressure gauge

**Fig. 5.30**

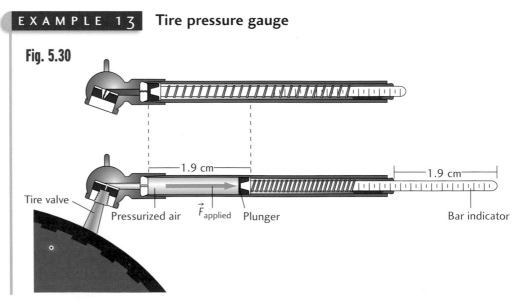

UNIT A: Motion and Forces

For the given tire gauge, the spring constant is 300 N/m. When the tire gauge is pushed onto the valve stem of the tire, the bar indicator extends 1.9 cm. What force does the air in the tire apply to the spring?

### *Solution and Connection to Theory*

**Given**

$k = 300$ N/m     $x = 1.9$ cm $= 1.9 \times 10^{-2}$ m

$\vec{F} = kx$     $F = 300$ N/m$(1.9 \times 10^{-2}$ m$) = 5.7$ N

The force applied by the air is 5.7 N.

If a spring stretches beyond the linear region of the graph (Fig. 5.28), distortion will occur. In many cases, you can substitute another value of $k$ for the region where the spring characteristics change. This can be done only if you keep the region of non-linearity small.

**Fig.5.31   The Total Picture**

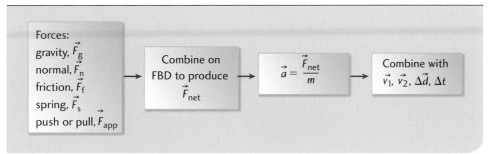

1. How could you find the $k$ value of a spring using a known mass?
2. Find the unknown for the following, using $\vec{F} = kx$:
   a) $\vec{F} = 10$ N and $x = 1.2$ cm
   b) $k = 3.0$ N/m and $x = 550$ mm
   c) $\vec{F} = 20$ N and $k = 3.0$ N/m
   d) A mass of 2.0 kg is hanging on a spring stretched 4.0 cm from its rest position.

## 5.7   The Fundamental Forces of Nature

### What are they?

When studied at the fundamental level, all the forces we have learned about so far—weight, gravity, the normal force, friction, springs, tension, pushes and pulls—fall into one of four types of forces. They are *gravity, the electromagnetic force, the strong force,* and *the weak force.*

**Fig.5.32**
(a) Push
(b) Tension
(c) Weight

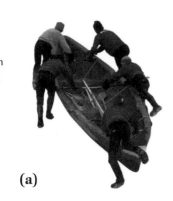
**(a)**

**(b)**

**(c)**

All the contact forces we have dealt with (the normal force, friction, springs, tension, pushes and pulls (see Fig. 5.32)) are considered to be electromagnetic forces. The movement of a spring is caused by the electromagnetic forces acting between the atoms in the spring. Friction is the bonding at the molecular level of two surfaces in contact. We will explore the electromagnetic force further in later chapters.

The strong and weak forces are short range, i.e., they are found only within an atom's nucleus. The **strong force** is responsible for binding the nucleus of an atom (composed of neutrons and protons). The range of the strong force is about $10^{-15}$ m, which is the size of an atom's nucleus. It is called the strong force because it must overcome the repulsive electromagnetic force between two protons. (Remember that protons are positively charged and that likes repel.)

The **weak force** is responsible for nuclear decay. The weak force causes instability in the atom's nucleus, which creates some of the change seen in the universe, such as the transmutation of elements.

## Beginning of Time

**Fig.5.33**

The Big Bang

According to the **Big Bang Theory**, which explores the origin of the universe (discussed in Chapter 12), all four of the fundamental forces of nature were once a single unified force. The **Theory of Everything (TOE)**, which would describe this force, is currently one of the most sought-after theorems in physics. The person or persons who formulate it will win the Nobel Prize (see Fig. 5.35).

It is postulated that this force existed from the beginning of the universe until a scant $10^{-43}$ s after the Big Bang (Fig. 5.33). At this time, gravity separated from the main force. This force is described by the **Grand Unified Theorem (GUT)**, which proved mathematically that the electromagnetic force, the weak force, and the strong force were initially unified. At about $10^{-35}$ s after the Big Bang, when the temperature of the universe had cooled to $10^{28}$ K, the strong nuclear force separated by taking on its own characteristics. The remaining force (consisting of the weak and electromagnetic forces) is termed the **electroweak force**. Finally, at about $10^{-10}$ s from the beginning of time, the electromagnetic force and the weak force separated from each other. By this time, the universe had cooled to a temperature of $10^{15}$ K.

When the universe was about three minutes old, protons and neutrons came into existence. The rest is "history." Helium appeared, then hydrogen, lithium, and so on. Gases formed and were drawn together by the force of gravity, creating stars, star systems, galaxies, and other celestial objects. It is currently believed that our universe is about $10^{+10}$ years old, give or take a power, and its temperature has now reached a frigid 2.7 K.

The current debate is whether the universe will continue to expand and cool, eventually ending in a uniformity at 0 K (absolute zero), or whether there is enough mass in the universe that gravity will slow and then reverse its expansion, causing the universe to collapse into nothingness in an event termed the **Big Crunch**.

**Fig.5.34**

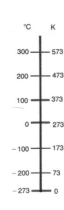

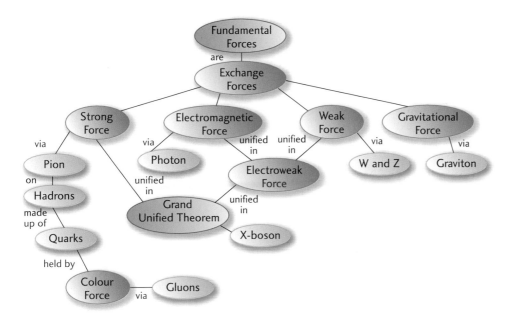

**Fig.5.35**   The connections among the fundamental forces and the fundamental particles

1. According to the Big Bang Theory, the universe started out from a single point. Find out the size of the universe at significant stages during the first three minutes of its existence.
2. The Hubble constant is used to determine the age of the universe. Research how this constant is calculated and how it is used to find the universe's age.
3. Discuss the following implications of the Big Bang:
   a) How is it possibile that all the matter and energy in the universe were once contained in something smaller than the nucleus of an atom?
   b) What will be the state of the universe if it keeps expanding?
   c) How does the universe create "space" as it expands?
   d) What was before the Big Bang?
   e) What is the universe expanding into?
4. Human beings have only five senses and a finite life span. How can they find answers to these questions?

◄ ◄ ◄ ◄ ◄   APPLYING the Concepts

**Fig.5.36**   The Horsehead Nebula

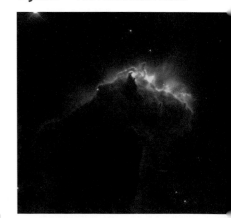

## Braking Systems

In the simplest terms, Newton's first law states that once we are moving, we must apply an external unbalanced force in order to stop. The braking system is probably the single most important safety feature of any vehicle. Many different systems have been used over many generations of automobiles, but in principle, they all provide a resistant force (through friction) to stop a car's motion. The two most enduring systems are the drum and the disc systems.

Figure STSE.5.1 illustrates how a generic (disk-drum) brake system works. Pressure on the brake pedal increases brake fluid pressure in the master cylinder, which is multiplied by the brake booster. The pressurized brake fluid is then passed through the brake lines to each wheel's respective hydraulic mechanical component: the caliper (usually at the front) or the wheel cylinder (usually at the rear).

With drum brakes (usually at the rear), the wheel cylinder applies pressure to the inside of two semicircular shoes, pushing them outwards to the inside of a rotating wheel drum. With disk brakes (usually at the front), the

**Fig.STSE.5.1A** How a generic brake system works

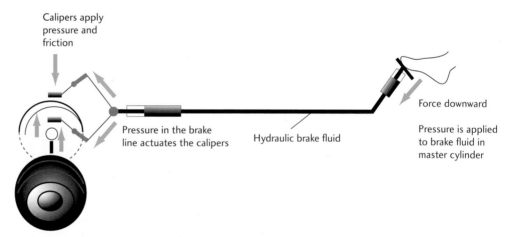

Calipers apply pressure and friction

Pressure in the brake line actuates the calipers

Hydraulic brake fluid

Force downward

Pressure is applied to brake fluid in master cylinder

**Fig.STSE.5.1B**

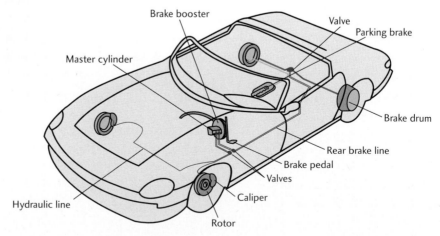

Brake booster

Valve

Parking brake

Master cylinder

Brake drum

Rear brake line

Brake pedal

Valves

Caliper

Hydraulic line

Rotor

brake caliper squeezes two opposing pads against either side of a disk (rotor) that rotates the wheel (Fig. STSE.5.2). The disks are easily cooled, which prevents brake pedal fade (boiling of the brake fluid that creates a compressible gas in the fluid and a loss of fluid pressure).

Many cars have anti-lock braking systems (ABS), which use computer-controlled valves to limit the pressure delivered to each brake cylinder. When pressure is applied to the brake, the ABS turns the pressure on and off at a much higher frequency than humans could. This braking frequency ensures that the wheels don't lock (anti-lock), giving the driver maximum steering control when it is most needed.

**Fig.STSE.5.2**  A disk brake system

## Design a Study of Societal Impact

What is the social and environmental impact of taking asbestos fibres out of brake pads? How well do the new metal fibre brake pads work compared with the asbestos pads? What problems are caused by poor maintenance of metal fibre brake pads?

What are the risks and/or benefits of anti-lock brakes? Does the increased cost of ABS provide a significant improvement in brake safety?

## Design an Activity to Evaluate

How could you use the braking system of a bicycle to investigate various braking parameters?

Modify the hand brake of a bicycle to include a newton spring scale or a pulley system to which you can apply varying forces by adding calibrated masses. Measure the effectiveness of the braking force by counting the number of wheel rotations before stopping. Videotape the rotations along with a stopwatch for later analysis. Apply the variables of braking force, friction contact area, brake material, etc. Examine brake fade by adding water or another coating material to the brake pads.

## Build a Structure

Design and build a braking system for a stationary bicycle that uses the "drag" of an electric generator, such as those used to power bicycle lights. Research the theory behind electromagnetic generators (see Chapter 18) and build your own adjustable electromagnetic brake.

## SPECIFIC EXPECTATIONS

**You should be able to**

*Understand Basic Concepts:*
- State the factors affecting the force of gravity.
- Solve problems involving the universal gravitational force equation.
- Define weight and calculate the weight of an object on different planets.
- Calculate the gravitational field constant for various celestial objects.
- Define the normal force and represent it on FBDs.
- Relate Newton's third law to the normal force.
- Define, describe, and calculate the force of friction (kinetic and static).
- Solve problems in two dimensions involving friction by using FBDs and trigonometric methods.
- Define and describe the equation associated with Hooke's law (springs).
- Use FBDs to solve problems involving springs as well as other forces.
- Describe the four fundamental forces of nature.

*Develop Skills of Inquiry and Communication:*
- Design and carry out experiments to identify specific variables that affect the motion of a sliding object.
- Describe events in terms of kinematics and dynamics.
- Analyze the motion of objects using an FBD, Newton's laws, and the motion equations.

*Relate Science to Technology, Society, and the Environment:*
- Evaluate the need for humans to be in space in a weightless environment given the effects of extended weightlessness on the human body.
- Evaluate the design and explain the operation of braking systems using scientific principles.

**Equations**

$$\vec{F} = mg$$

$$\vec{F}_g = \frac{Gm_1m_2}{r^2}$$

$$\frac{\vec{F}_1^2}{\vec{F}_2^2} = \frac{r_2^2}{r_1^2}$$

$$\vec{F}_s = kx$$

$$\vec{F}_f = \mu\vec{F}_n$$

## EXERCISES

## Conceptual Questions

1. The force of gravity extends out a long way. If you and your best friend were the only two entities left in the universe, would you move together if you were separated by a distance of many light years?

2. In free fall, why are you apparently weightless?

3. When you're standing on a bathroom scale and it reads 50 kg, is this a reading of weight or mass? What would your bathroom scale read in outer space?

4. Cartoon characters standing in elevators find themselves pasted to the ceiling after the cables are cut. Is this good humour or good physics?

5. Give examples of actions (such as running, jumping, etc.) that would be easier to perform on the Moon rather than on Earth. Which actions would be more difficult?

6. Mass is the producer of gravity. What complications are there in finding the force of gravity as you go deeper into Earth? What would your weight be at its centre?

7. Why do animals living on land require a skeleton? What happens to astronauts who spend a long time in a weightless environment?

8. Rank the planets in our solar system according to their gravitational field constants.

9. Can the elevation at which athletes compete be a factor in world and Olympic records in events where the value of $g$ matters?

10. If a black hole is actually a collapsed star, why is the gravitational field of this type of star so large?

11. If friction is present, is it easier to push or pull an object if the force is at an angle to the object? Use an FBD to help in the explanation.

12. What is the implication of either a zero or negative normal force in the case of an object having multiple forces applied to it?

13. List the benefits of friction in
    a) sports.
    b) the transportation industry.

14. List the drawbacks of friction in the same fields as Question 13.

15. Why is friction so necessary when you are riding inside a subway?

16. Ground effects on racing cars cause a large downward force on the car. What are the benefits of this force?

17. Can a normal force cause an object to lift off a surface?

18. For the following toys or equipment, what would happen if the spring constant was changed dramatically (made greater or smaller): bungee cord, pogo stick, sling shot, slinky toy?

19. You have two springs with identical $k$ values. Will the combination spring be stronger if the two springs are attached in series (end to end) or in parallel (beside each other)?

## Problems

### 5.3 Calculations Involving the Force of Gravity

(Common constants: $m_{Earth} = 5.98 \times 10^{24}$ kg, $r_{Earth} = 6.38 \times 10^6$ m, $G = 6.67 \times 10^{-11}$ Nm$^2$/kg$^2$)

20. Find the force of attraction between a 60 kg student and
    a) another student of mass 80 kg, 1.4 m away.
    b) a 130 t blue whale, 10 m away.
    c) the Great Pyramid in Egypt, with an estimated mass of $5.22 \times 10^9$ kg, 1.0 km away.
    d) a 45 g golf ball, 95 cm away.

**21.** What is the distance between the Moon and Earth if the mass of the Moon is $7.34 \times 10^{22}$ kg, and the force of attraction between the two is $2.00 \times 10^{20}$ N?

**22.** Two tankers of equal mass attract each other with a force of $3.5 \times 10^3$ N. If their centres are 85 m apart, what is the mass of each tanker?

**23.** Find a 68.0 kg person's weight
   **a)** on the surface of Earth.
   **b)** on top of Mt. Everest (8 848 m above sea level).
   **c)** at $2\frac{1}{2}$ times the radius of Earth.

**24.** Calculate the gravitational field constants for the following planets: Mars ($r = 3.43 \times 10^6$ m, $m = 6.37 \times 10^{24}$ kg), Jupiter ($r = 7.18 \times 10^7$ m, $m = 1.90 \times 10^{27}$ kg), Mercury ($m = 3.28 \times 10\ \text{kg}^{23}$, $r = 2.57 \times 10^6$ m).

**25.** If the two 10 t freighters shown below are 20 m apart, find the gravitational attraction between them.

**Fig.5.37**

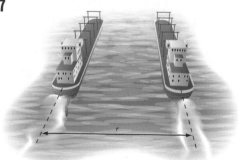

**26.** On or near the surface of Earth, $g$ is 9.80 m/s². At what distance from Earth's centre is the value of $g = 9.70$ m/s²? At what height above the surface of Earth does this occur?

**27.** Repeat Problem 26 for a $g$ value of 0.1 m/s².

**28.** For this problem, use ratios only to obtain the weight of a person at the following distances. Assume the person weighs 980 N on the surface of Earth.
   **a)** Three times the distance from the centre of Earth

**b)** Seven times the distance from the centre of Earth
   **c)** 128 000 km above the surface of Earth
   **d)** 4.5 times the distance from the centre of Earth
   **e)** 745 500 km from Earth's centre.

**29.** The weight of an object in space is 500 N. Use ratios to obtain the object's new weight
   **a)** at half as great a distance from the centre of Earth.
   **b)** at $\frac{1}{8}$ as great a distance from Earth's centre.
   **c)** at 0.66 as great a distance from Earth's centre.

**30.** Use the values of $g$ obtained in Problem 24 to compare the time it takes for an object dropped from the CN Tower (height 553 m) to reach the ground. Include the time it would take on Earth.

**31.** Use an FBD and data from Problem 21 to calculate the net force acting on a satellite at $\frac{2}{3}$ the distance to the Moon from Earth. Given that the satellite is 1200 kg, what is the net gravitational field constant here?

▶ **5.4 The Normal Force**

## Note: FBDs are a must!

**32.** A person of mass 40 kg stands on a bathroom scale. What is the normal force (the reading on the scale)?

**33.** How would the reading on the scale in Problem 32 change if the person was standing in an elevator on the scale and
   **a)** the elevator was moving up with a constant speed?
   **b)** the elevator was accelerating upwards and moving upwards?
   **c)** the elevator was moving down with a constant speed?
   **d)** the elevator was accelerating in a downward direction and moving downwards?
   Use FBDs and $\vec{F}_{net}$ statements.

**34.** A person of mass 70 kg jumps up and lands on a bathroom scale, causing the scale to read 750 N. Find the person's weight and acceleration.

**35. a)** Calculate the normal force on person A of mass 84 kg standing on the ground while balancing person B of mass 50 kg on his head.
   **b)** What would the normal force be if someone handed person B a helium balloon capable of generating a lift force of 300 N?

**36.** A 20 g fridge magnet is being held onto the fridge by a 0.9 N force. What is the normal force?

**37.** You're holding up a light fixture of mass 1.4 kg with a force of 21 N against the ceiling. What is the normal force?

**38.** A sled of mass 26 kg has an 18 kg child on it. If big brother is pulling with a force 30 N to the right and 10 N up and big sister is pushing at 40 N right and 16 N down, what is the normal force?

### 5.5 Friction

Include FBDs for all questions.

**39.** For Problem 36, $\mu_k = 0.3$. Calculate
   **a)** the force of friction acting on the magnet.
   **b)** the weight of the magnet.
   **c)** the acceleration of the magnet.

**40.** For Problem 38, $\mu_k = 0.12$. Calculate
   **a)** the force of friction.
   **b)** the acceleration of the sled and child.

**41.** An ox exerts a force of 7100 N in the horizontal direction without slipping. If the ox has a weight of 8000 N, what is the minimum coefficient of static friction?

**42.** A crate of mass 20 kg is being pushed by a person with a horizontal force of 63 N, moving with a constant velocity. Find the coefficient of kinetic friction.

**43.** For Problem 42, your good friend watching you do all the work comes over and sits on the crate. His mass is 60 kg. What happens? Justify using values.

**44.** Compare forces required to push a fridge across a floor if, in one case, friction exists and in the other case, friction does not exist. Fridge mass is 100 kg and $\mu_k = 0.4$.

**45.** Calculate the force required to start pushing the fridge in Problem 44 if $\mu_s = 0.46$.

**46.** A box of mass 5.7 kg slides across a floor and comes to a complete stop. If its initial speed was 10 km/h and $\mu_k = 0.34$, find
   **a)** the friction acting on the box.
   **b)** the acceleration of the box.
   **c)** the distance travelled by the box before stopping.
   **d)** the time it took to stop.

**47. a)** What force is required to accelerate a lawnmower of mass 12 kg to 4.5 km/h from rest in 3.0 s (neglecting friction)?
   **b)** If there is friction present and $\mu_k = 0.8$, what force is required now?

**48.** A racing car has a mass of 1500 kg, is accelerating at 5.0 m/s², is experiencing a lift force of 600 N up (due to its streamlined shape) and ground effects of 1000 N down (due to airdams and spoilers). Find the driving force needed to keep the car going given that $\mu_k = 1.0$ for the car.

**49.** In the last chapter, we had a very happy fellow pulling two ducks on wheels around his room. The ducks were 2.0 kg and 5.0 kg (front duck) and the guy was pulling them with a force of 10 N.
   **a)** Calculate the new acceleration if $\mu_k = 0.10$.
   **b)** Calculate the tension in the rope between the ducks.

**50.** Now Grandma gave the guy from Problem 49 another duck of mass 1.0 kg, which he attached to the front of the line. Calculate the acceleration of all the ducks and the tension of the ropes joining them.

## ▶ 5.6 Springs

**51.** For the following graph,
   **a)** find the spring constant.
   **b)** find the units of the area under the graph.

**Fig.5.38**

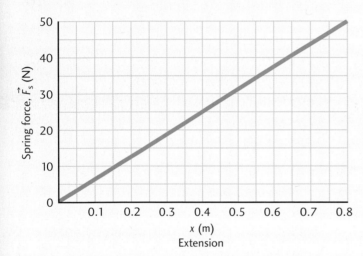

x (m)
Extension

**52.** Given that a spring has a spring constant of 58 N/m, how much force is required to stretch the spring
   **a)** 0.30 m?
   **b)** 56 cm?
   **c)** 1023 mm?

**53.** When exercising using a spring, you pull the spring 0.30 m with a force of 365 N. What distance will the spring stretch from its zero position if you applied a force of
   **a)** 400 N?
   **b)** 223 N?
   **c)** 2.0 N?

**54.** A fishing rod has an effect spring coefficient of 25 N/m. The rod bends 0.3 m. Given that 2.2 lb = 1 kg, how many pounds was the fish on the end of the line?

**55.** A 50 kg student rides a pogo stick to school. If she compresses the spring 0.25 m on an average bounce and the spring's $k = 2200$ N/m, find her acceleration on the bounce moving upward. Use an FBD for this problem.

**56.** What spring constant is required to balance your weight if the spring compresses 17 cm? Use an FBD.

**57.** Find the normal force for a crate of mass 670 kg being pulled up by a spring with $k = 900$ N/m if the spring is stretched 1.55 m. Use an FBD.

**58.** A 12 kg object accelerates at 3.0 m/s² when being pulled by a spring with $k = 40$ N/m. How far does the spring stretch?

**59.** A duck of mass 40 kg (wow!) is being pulled by a spring with $k = 900$ N/m. If $\mu_k = 0.6$ between the duck and the road, find the acceleration of the duck given that the spring stretches 0.4 m. Use an FBD.

## Purpose

To find the coefficient of kinetic friction.

## Equipment

Wooden slider with string attached (of known mass)

Newton spring scale

Various masses

Wooden board

**Fig.Lab.5.1**

## Procedure

1. Attach the spring scale to the wooden slider.
2. Using the Newton scale, pull the slider at a constant speed across the wooden plank. Note the reading on the scale. Record it in the data table outlined in the data section. Make sure the pull is horizontal and the scale does not touch the board.
3. Add a mass to the slider and repeat Step 2. Record the total mass in the chart (slider + mass).
4. Repeat Steps 2 and 3 using more mass combinations.

## Data

1. Construct the following chart:

   $m_{slider}$ (kg)     $m_{added}$ (kg)     $m_{total}$ (kg)
   $\vec{F}_{Applied}$ (N)
2. Fill the chart in as you proceed through the lab.

## Uncertainty

Assign a value for the uncertainty in reading the spring scale.

## Analysis

1. Construct and complete the following chart. Note: To calculate the normal force, use $\vec{F} = mg$.
2. $m_{total}$ (kg)     $\vec{F}_{normal}$ (N)     $\vec{F}_{Applied}$ (N)
3. Graph $\vec{F}_{Applied}$ vs. $\vec{F}_{normal}$.
4. Calculate the slope of the graph.

## Discussion

1. Why is the normal force equal to $mg$? Explain using an FBD.
2. What does the slope represent? Prove it.
3. Look up the expected value for the slope and comment on how close the values are.

## Conclusion

Summarize your results.

**LABORATORY EXERCISES**

## Purpose
To find the value of the coefficient of static friction.

## Equipment
Slider
Board
Protractor (You can use a ruler and calculate the angles.)

**Fig.Lab.5.2**

## Procedure
1. Place the slider plus an attached mass on the board. If you tape the mass on, make sure the tape is not on the bottom of the slider. Carefully lift the board until the slider just starts to move.
2. Record the interior angle (relative to the base) at which the slider started to move.
3. Repeat this procedure 10 times.
4. Repeat Steps 1 to 3 for two more mass combinations.

## Data
Record the total mass used and the lift angles.

## Uncertainty
Note any parts in the experiment where the procedural part of the uncertainty may become large.

## Analysis
To calculate the static coefficient of friction, use the equation $\tan\theta = \mu_s$ and the average angle.

## Discussion
1. Use FBDs to derive the equation $\tan\theta = \mu_s$.
2. From your data, does mass affect the value of the coefficient?
3. Is the coefficient of static friction larger or smaller than the coefficient of kinetic friction from the previous lab? What would you expect?
4. What is the effect of the uncertainties you thought of on the value obtained?

## Conclusion
Summarize your results.

## Extension: Other Factors Affecting the Motion of a Sliding Object
1. Design and implement a lab that will test how the motions of two sliding objects are affected by the surface contact area between them. Make sure you keep all other factors in the experiment constant. These factors should be stated in the lab write-up.
2. Design and test how the shape of the surface that is in contact with the sliding object's surface affects the object's motion. Which factors must be kept constant in this case?
3. What other factors can affect the motion of the sliding object? Suggest methods of testing these factors.

## Purpose

To study the characteristics of a spring.

## Equipment

Light spring
Dense spring
Masses
Ruler

### Fig.Lab.5.3

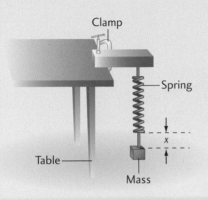

## Procedure

1. Hang the spring in a place where it is free to stretch. Mark the end of the spring in neutral position, or measure the length of the spring.
2. Hang a mass on the spring and measure the stretch from the neutral position, or measure the length of the spring and subtract the relaxed length from it.

3. Repeat Step 2 for four more different masses.
4. Repeat the experiment for the other spring.

## Data

Record the mass (m) and the net stretch of the spring from the relaxed position ($x$) in a table.

## Uncertainty

Assign an uncertainty for the measurements.

## Analysis

1. Create a new chart for weight ($\vec{F}$) and stretch ($x$).
2. Plot a graph of $\vec{F}$ vs. $x$ for each spring.
3. Calculate the slopes.

## Discussion

1. What shape of graph did you expect? Did you obtain this shape?
2. What does the slope represent?
3. Compare the appearance of the springs with their slopes.
4. How would you redo the experiment for a compression spring?

## Conclusion

Summarize your findings.

# Momentum

## Chapter Outline

**By the end of this chapter, you will be able to**

- solve problems using impulse and momentum
- use the principle of momentum conservation to solve collision problems

**Fig.6.1** Change in motion

# 6.1 Introduction

Many people have a vague idea of what momentum is. It is often associated with a change in the flow of support for a candidate in an election. Or it may be a sports team gaining an advantage by changing the flow of action and pace in a game. The idea of momentum contains some notion of a change in motion.

Newton's second law from his work, *Principia, Lex II*, translates from the Latin as:

"Change of motion is proportional to the moving force impressed, and takes place in the direction of the straight line in which that force is impressed." Expressed in more modern terms,

> The **momentum** of an object is changed when an unbalanced force is applied over a given period of time. The resulting change occurs in the direction of the force.

The physics definition of momentum is mass times velocity, or

$$\vec{p} = m\vec{v}$$

where $\vec{p}$ is the momentum. Notice that momentum is a vector quantity and has a direction associated with it. The SI units for momentum are kg·m/s and have no special name assigned to them. Perhaps you will become a famous physicist and these units will be named after you.

**EXAMPLE 1**    **Calculating momentum**

Calculate the momentum of a 1.0 kg duck moving at 28 m/s (a new biotech superperformance duck) and of a sumo wrestler with mass 200 kg, moving slowly at 0.5 km/h, as shown in Fig. 6.2.

**Fig.6.2**

### *Solution and Connection to Theory*

**Given**

$m_{duck} = 1.0$ kg, $\vec{v}_{duck} = 28$ m/s

$m_{sumo} = 200$ kg, $\vec{v}_{sumo} = 0.5$ km/h $= 0.14$ m/s

$\vec{p} = m\vec{v}$      $p_{duck} = 1.0$ kg(28 m/s) $= 28$ kg·m/s

and $p_{sumo} = 200$ kg(0.14 m/s) $= 28$ kg·m/s

0.5 km/h                                              28 m/s

Notice that the two momenta are similar, even though the objects are not.

**Fig.6.3** Mass and velocity determine momentum

When someone asks you whether you would rather be hit by a piece of chalk or tackled by a serious football player, at first, the answer seems to be the chalk. But if the chalk were moving at 250 m/s, then you're basically dealing with a bullet, and the choice becomes obvious.

Momentum is an important concept when considering impacts, collisions, and how objects in general interact. It is not just an object's mass that is important; it is the product of its mass and velocity.

APPLYING the Concepts

▸ ▸ ▸ ▸

1. Calculate the momentum of the following objects:
   **a)** A 100 kg football player running at 12 km/h
   **b)** A blue whale of mass 150 tonnes moving at 30 km/h
   **c)** The Saturn V rocket with mass $8.7 \times 10^6$ kg and velocity 28 000 km/h
2. How does momentum relate to Newton's first law?

## ▶ 6.2  Momentum and Newton's Second Law

**Fig.6.4**  A rocket undergoes a large change in momentum

From Newton's second law,

$$\vec{F} = m\vec{a} = \frac{m\Delta\vec{v}}{\Delta t}.$$

Multiplying both sides by $\Delta t$,

$$\vec{F}\Delta t = m\Delta\vec{v}$$

$m\vec{v}$ is called the **momentum**, $\vec{p}$, of an object, so $m\Delta\vec{v}$ is the change in momentum of an object.

$\vec{F}\Delta t$, the force multiplied by the time it acts, is called the **impulse** of the force, and is equal to the change in momentum of the object.

The equation for Newton's second law may be written

$$\vec{F} = m\vec{a} \qquad \text{or} \qquad \vec{F}\Delta t = \Delta(m\vec{v})$$

The second law equation

$$\vec{F}\Delta t = \Delta \vec{p}$$

is a statement illustrating *cause* and *effect*. An object just sitting around, minding its own business (Newton's first law), has a force applied to it for a period of time, $\Delta t$. We will call this part the "cause." Now the object has moved and its velocity has changed. Because velocity changes, so does momentum. This part is the "effect." In general, it is easier to see the "effect" side of an action rather than the "cause" side. The left side of the equation is called impulse (units N·s and symbol $\vec{J}$), and the right side is the change in momentum (units kg·m/s).

**The case of $\Delta m \neq 0$**
In most momentum problems, we expect the mass to be constant. Rockets are an important exception. Most of the mass of a rocket standing on its launch pad comprises fuel. As the rocket lifts off (Fig. 6.4), the burning fuel provides the thrust to move the rocket (following Newton's third law). While the rate of burning (determining the thrust) does not change, the mass being pushed is decreasing because fuel is being used up. With a decreasing mass and constant thrust, you get an increasing acceleration.

**Fig.6.5** Cause and Effect from Newton's Second Law

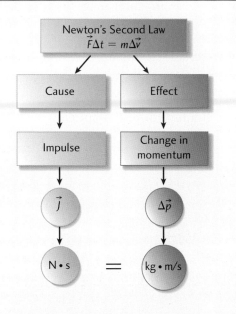

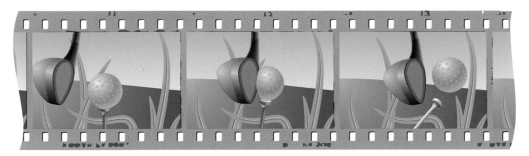

**Fig 6.6** Impulse from a club changes the momentum of a golf ball

Note that since the vectors $\vec{J} = \Delta \vec{p}$ are in the same direction, we can perform calculations using their magnitudes only. However, you should always be conscious of the effect direction may have on the solution to a problem.

EXAMPLE 2    Calculating impulse and change in momentum

A golfer hits a ball of mass 45 g, causing it to leave the tee at 40 m/s. Find the impulse imparted by the club to the ball and the change in momentum of the ball.

### Solution and Connection to Theory

**Given**

$m = 45$ g $= 0.045$ kg $\qquad \vec{v}_1 = 0$ m/s $\qquad \vec{v}_2 = 40$ m/s

We know that impulse is $\vec{F}\Delta t$, but neither $\vec{F}$ nor $t$ is given. However, we also know that $\vec{F}\Delta t = \Delta \vec{p}$, where $\Delta \vec{p} = m(\vec{v}_2 - \vec{v}_1)$, which we can calculate.

$\Delta \vec{p} = 0.045$ kg$(40$ m/s $- 0$ m/s$) = 1.8$ kg·m/s

Therefore, the impulse is also 1.8 N·s. Notice that the sign of the velocity and the sign of the impulse are the same. The direction of the impulse was acting in the direction of the golf swing.

In sports involving something hitting a projectile, we watch the *effect* part of the equation (change in momentum). If we were to watch the impulse part, our eyes would need to see and interpret events much faster than they can. Times in the tens of milliseconds would be involved.

**Fig 6.7**   Impulse in sports

## Impulse

The role impulse plays in sports is often subtle. When a goalie catches a puck or an outfielder catches a ball in their gloves, the gloves do more than protect the hand and provide a larger catching surface. The glove is made of a soft material with a webbing stitched into the catching part of the glove. When the puck or ball hits the glove, the puck or ball is cushioned and brought to rest. Why not use a piece of wood instead? It would seem to protect your hand much better.

Let's apply the impulse equation to this situation.

**Fig.6.8** Calculating Impulse and Momentum

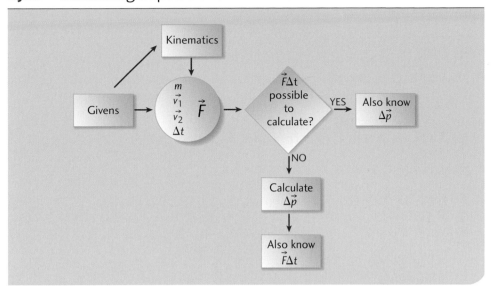

$$\vec{F} \Delta t = \Delta \vec{p}$$

In both cases, the ball is brought to rest at some point. Assuming that the ball was travelling at the same initial velocity each time, the change in momentum is the same for both cases. However, in the case of the wooden glove, the time of interaction between ball and glove is much shorter than for the normal glove. This means that the force imparted to the ball caught with the wooden glove is greater. This in turn gives the ball a greater recoil velocity, which creates the tendency for it to fly out of the glove.

For the normal glove, the time of interaction between ball and glove is longer. Therefore, the average force imparted to the ball is smaller. This means that the ball's rebounding ability is decreased, allowing the catcher more time to close the glove. The more time you have in contact with the ball, the more control you gain over it. To help with the complete stopping of a puck, the goalie moves his or her hand back, in the direction of motion of the puck as it hits the glove. This increases the time of interaction with puck and glove, and ensures that the puck stays in the glove. The reflexes of the player are now fast enough to close the glove before the puck bounces out of it.

**Fig.6.9** How well would a wooden glove work?

**Fig.6.10** Moving the glove back increases the time of interaction

**Fig.6.11** Increasing impulse time decreases force

> **EXAMPLE 3** **Force of impact on landing for a parachutist**

A parachutist lands, flexes her knees, and rolls in order to stop. Calculate the impact force on a 70 kg parachutist falling at 10 m/s if the time to stop was 0.8 s. Compare the force of impact if a soldier lands in a rigid position, standing at attention. The time of stopping is 0.05 s.

### *Solution and Connection to Theory*

Assume the standard reference system.

**Given**

$m = 70$ kg      $\vec{v}_1 = 10$ m/s      $\vec{v}_2 = 0$ m/s

$\Delta t = 0.8$ s for first case and $\Delta t = 0.05$ s for the second case.

$$\vec{F}\Delta t = \Delta \vec{p}$$

$$\vec{F} = \frac{\Delta \vec{p}}{\Delta t} = \frac{70 \text{ kg } (0 \text{ m/s} - 10 \text{ m/s})}{0.8 \text{ s}} = -875 \text{ N}$$

For the stiff-legged case,

$$\vec{F} = \frac{\Delta \vec{p}}{\Delta t} = \frac{70 \text{ kg } (0 \text{ m/s} - 10 \text{ m/s})}{0.05 \text{ s}} = -14\ 000 \text{ N}$$

The negative sign indicates that the stopping action is in the opposite direction to the initial velocity. Notice also, that for the small change of 0.75 s, the force has increased by 13 125 N, enough to cause serious injury!

In Example 3, where the soldier did not roll and bend his knees, the stopping force required to produce the necessary change in momentum was disastrously high. However, there are many cases, like the actions in Fig. 6.12, where keeping the time of interaction low and the force high is desirable.

**Fig.6.12** A small interaction time means a large force

**Fig.6.13** A larger interaction time means a smaller force

UNIT A: Motion and Forces

These events require a violent change in momentum. In events where control is important, like in Fig. 6.13, you increase the time of interaction to yield a smaller force.

In most cases, the force acting on an object during the collision process is a complicated one. It increases as the colliding objects are compressed together and decreases as the objects move away from each other. All this may be on a microscopic level (for hard objects). We will use average force when dealing with such interactions. We can still get a value for the impulse if we have a graph of force vs. time available to us. Analysis of the graph in Fig. 6.14 shows that the area under the graph produces the desired units of impulse, N·s.

> To find impulse using $\vec{F}$-$t$ graphs, calculate the area under the curve.

**Fig.6.14A** Area under the $\vec{F}$-$t$ graph is equal to the impulse

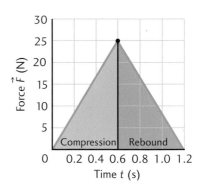

**Fig.6.14B**

### IMPULSE FROM AN $\vec{F}$-$t$ GRAPH

The graph in Fig. 6.14 shows the impulse involved in a collision. Imagine it to be a ball being kicked. During the first 0.6 s, the ball compressed as it was kicked. The force of compression increased from 0 to 25 N. After the ball reached its maximum compression, it began to rebound. During the next 0.6 s, the force diminished to zero. The graph shows the whole interaction over 1.2 s.

The area under the $\vec{F}$-$t$ graph is

$\frac{1}{2}$(25 N)(1.2 s) = 15 N·s

The impulse between the ball and the foot is 15 N·s.

## Fig.6.15 Solving Problems Using Momentum

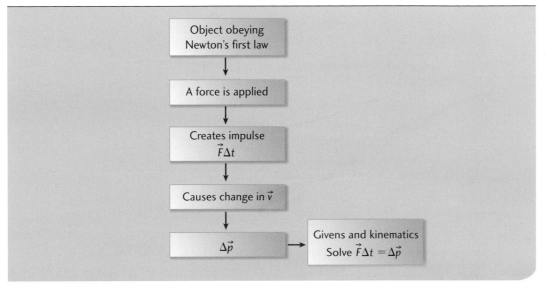

1. Impulse causes a change in momentum. Explain this change in terms of Newton's second law.

2. In sports, follow-through is the continuation of the motion (e.g., continued swing) after contact with the ball has been made. It is an important factor in performance. Use the fact that impulse involves $\Delta t$ to explain why follow-through is important. Which sports are most affected by this concept?

3. Use the graph in Fig. 6.14 to calculate impulse at 0.4 s and 1.0 s.

4. Find the impulse for the following situations. Each case involves a 20 kg object.

   **a)** The object changes its velocity from 0 to 3.0 m/s.

   **b)** The object slows down from 3.0 m/s to 0 m/s.

   **c)** The object hits a surface at 3.0 m/s and rebounds with the same speed.

### Rockets

When a rocket blasts off, the burning of fuel causes gases to be expelled from it, so the rocket is pushed upward, away from Earth. The total momentum of the system is zero because the momentum of the gases moving down and the momentum of the rocket moving up add up to zero. As fuel is used up, the mass of the rocket decreases, causing its velocity to increase. But the velocity of the ejected gas with respect to the rocket remains constant. The impulse force driving the rocket upward is called *thrust*.

5. **a)** From Newton's second law, $\vec{F} = \frac{\Delta \vec{p}}{\Delta t}$. Derive the formula for thrust:

$$\vec{F}_{thrust} = \vec{v}_{gas}\left(\frac{\Delta m}{\Delta t}\right),$$

where $\vec{v}_{gas}$ is the speed of the gas relative to the rocket and $\frac{\Delta m}{\Delta t}$ is the rate at which the rocket burns fuel.

   **b)** A rocket of mass 780 kg wishes to attain a speed of 1000 m/s from rest. If the rate at which the rocket consumes fuel is 2.0 kg/s and the speed of the exhaust gas relative to the rocket is 2500 m/s, find the acceleration of the rocket and the time the rocket takes to reach a speed of 1000 m/s.

## 6.3 Conservation of Momentum

Most of us have heard the expression "energy cannot be created or destroyed." This is called a **conservation law**. Translated, it means that in a closed system, no matter what the event, the total energy before the event will equal the total energy after the event. It implies that energy can change its form or be distributed, but its total quantity remains the same. This concept will be explained further in the energy unit.

**Fig.6.16**

The conservation of linear momentum is very similar. The total momentum of a system before a collision is the same as after a collision. It also implies that the object's motions will change and the momentum will be distributed, but the sum total of momentum for the system remains the same.

In mathematical form, the conservation of momentum is

$$\vec{p}_{\text{total}_{\text{initial}}} = \vec{p}_{\text{total}_{\text{final}}}$$

$$\text{or } \vec{p}_{t_0} = \vec{p}_{t_f}$$

For clarity in calculations involving two or more objects in a collision process, we use "0" to denote "initial" and the "f" to denote "final." We use the numbers 1 and 2 to denote the colliding objects. When two objects collide, the values of their momenta can be related by the equation

$$m_1\vec{v}_{1_0} + m_2\vec{v}_{2_0} = m_1\vec{v}_{1_f} + m_2\vec{v}_{2_f}$$

**Fig.6.17** Momentum is Conserved in All Situations

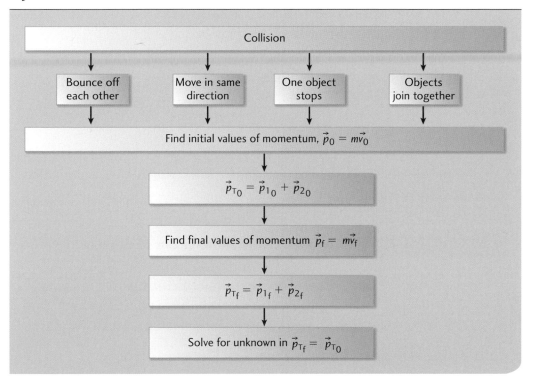

**EXAMPLE 4**    **Calculating the momentum of objects initially at rest (recoil situations)**

Consider two hockey players, both at rest on the ice. The 90 kg Montreal Canadiens player pushes the 105 kg Ottawa Senators' player. Find the velocity of the Senator if the Canadien moves back at 10 km/h after the push.

**Fig.6.18**

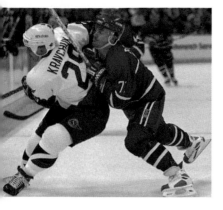

### Solution and Connection to Theory

**Given**

$$m_1 = 90 \text{ kg} \qquad m_2 = 105 \text{ kg} \qquad \vec{v}_{1_0} = 0 \text{ m/s} \qquad \vec{v}_{2_0} = 0 \text{ m/s}$$
$$\vec{v}_{1_f} = -10 \text{ km/h} = -2.8 \text{ m/s} \qquad \vec{v}_{2_f} = ?$$

We are using the standard reference system and are assuming that the Canadien went to the left after the push.

Conservation of momentum gives

$$m_1\vec{v}_{1_0} + m_2\vec{v}_{2_0} = m_1\vec{v}_{1_f} + m_2\vec{v}_{2_f}$$

$$90 \text{ kg}(0 \text{ m/s}) + 105 \text{ kg}(0 \text{ m/s}) = 90 \text{ kg}(-2.8 \text{ m/s}) + 105 \text{ kg}(\vec{v}_{2_f})$$

Now solve for $\vec{v}_{2_f}$:

$$(0 \text{ kg} \cdot \text{m/s}) = -252 \text{ kg} \cdot \text{m/s} + 105 \text{ kg}(\vec{v}_{2_f})$$

$$\vec{v}_{2_f} = \frac{252 \text{ kg} \cdot \text{m/s}}{105 \text{ kg}} = 2.4 \text{ m/s}$$

The Senator moves to the right at 2.4 m/s. Notice how the equation produced the expected direction of the Senator.

In Example 4, both the initial and final total momenta are zero. Checking the final momentum, you get

$$\vec{p}_{t_0} = \vec{p}_{t_f} = 90 \text{ kg}(-2.8 \text{ m/s}) + 105 \text{ kg}(2.4 \text{ m/s})$$
$$= -252 \text{ kg} \cdot \text{m/s} + 252 \text{ kg} \cdot \text{m/s} = 0$$

This example shows that you must be careful not to automatically assume there is no motion when the total momentum is zero.

---

**EXAMPLE 5** — **Calculating the momentum of objects in motion**

**Fig.6.19**

Calculate the initial velocity of the American rugby player if she tackles a stationary Canadian player, causing both of them to move off with a velocity of 5 km/h. Both rugby players have a mass of 75 kg.

### Solution and Connection to Theory

**Given**

$$m_1 = 75 \text{ kg} \qquad m_2 = 75 \text{ kg} \qquad \vec{v}_{1_0} = ? \qquad \vec{v}_{2_0} = 0 \text{ m/s}$$
$$\vec{v}_{1_f} = 5 \text{ km/h} = 1.4 \text{ m/s} \qquad \vec{v}_{2_f} = 5 \text{ km/h} = 1.4 \text{ m/s}$$

$$m_1\vec{v}_{1_0} + m_2\vec{v}_{2_0} = m_1\vec{v}_{1_f} + m_2\vec{v}_{2_f}$$

$$75 \text{ kg}(\vec{v}_{1_0}) + 0 \text{ kg} \cdot \text{m/s} = 75 \text{ kg}(1.4 \text{ m/s}) + 75 \text{ kg}(1.4 \text{ m/s})$$

$$\vec{v}_{1_0} = 2.8 \text{ m/s}$$

Therefore, the American rugby player's initial velocity is 2.8 m/s.

Example 5 shows a collision where two separate bodies join and become one body. Car crashes, where the cars do not spring apart, are another example of this case (see Fig. 6.20).

**Fig.6.20**

| EXAMPLE 6 | **A poor excuse for a pool game, but a valuable insight into solving momentum problems** |

Two pool balls are shot towards each other at the same time (Fig. 6.21). They hit and recoil. If the velocity of ball 1 is 2.0 m/s to the right, and the velocity of ball 2 is 1.2 m/s to the left, find the velocity of ball 2 after the collision if ball 1 recoils with a velocity of 0.4 m/s.

**Fig.6.21**

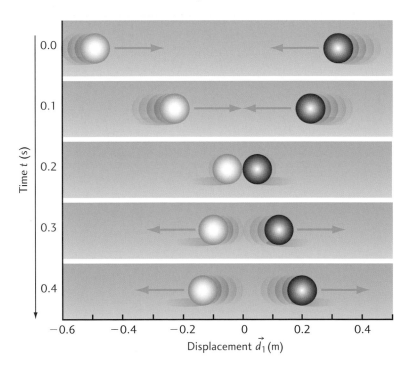

### Solution and Connection to Theory

**Given**

For this example, the masses were not given. However, we can assume that the masses are equal given the nature of the game.

$$m_1 = m_2 = m \quad \vec{v}_{1_0} = 2.0 \text{ m/s} \quad \vec{v}_{2_0} = -0.4 \text{ m/s} \quad \vec{v}_{1_f} = 0 \text{ m/s} \quad \vec{v}_{2_f} = ?$$

$$m_1\vec{v}_{1_0} + m_2\vec{v}_{2_0} = m_1\vec{v}_{1_f} + m_2\vec{v}_{2_f}$$
$$m(2.0 \text{ m/s}) + m(-1.2 \text{ m/s}) = m(-0.4 \text{ m/s}) + m\vec{v}_{2_f}$$

Since the $m$s are common, they cancel.

$$\vec{v}_{2_f} = 1.2 \text{ m/s}$$

The velocity of the second ball after the collision is 1.2 m/s [right].

Another way to solve a problem involving equal masses is to assign your own value for the masses. A useful choice is 1.0 kg, thereby eliminating an extra calculation.

The conservation of momentum is applicable to all interactions among objects, and is one of the most important laws in the universe. It deals with all possible situations and any number of participants. For example, if two stars collide, exploding into a million pieces, the total momentum of the system before the collision would still equal the total momentum after the collision.

**Fig.6.22** Collision Overview

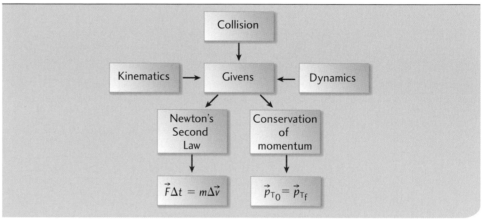

1. For the following cases, assume that object 1 has a mass of 1.5 kg and object 2 has a mass of 2.0 kg. Use the conservation of momentum to find the unknown velocity.
   a) $m_1$ moves toward $m_2$ with a velocity of 3.0 m/s, $m_2$ is at rest, and $m_1$ bounces back at 1.0 m/s.
   b) $m_1$ moves at 3.0 m/s while $m_2$ moves at 1.0 m/s in the same direction, then moves off at 2.0 m/s.
   c) $m_1$ moves at 3.0 m/s while $m_2$ moves at 1.0 m/s in the opposite direction. After collision, $m_1$ moves at 0.5 m/s in its original direction.
   d) The same as part c) except that both objects stick together after collision.
2. In a car accident, conservation of momentum plays a large role in determining what happens during the collision. What factors would affect the final position of a two-vehicle crash?

UNIT A: Motion and Forces

## Rubber Bullets

To enforce the law, police occasionally need to use force, especially during riots. The trick is to control a violent mob without causing fatal injuries by firing real bullets. The invention of rubber bullets has provided a solution.

Consider the case of two bullets with the same mass, fired with the same velocity. One is a rubber bullet, the other is a metal one. Which bullet will knock over a wooden test dummy more easily?

The answer is the rubber bullet. Because of its elastic material, when a rubber bullet rebounds off a test dummy, it gains twice the impulse it had when it was fired, and hence twice the momentum. The dummy provides the necessary force to stop the bullet and then to cause it to fly in the opposite direction with an equal velocity. According to Newton's third law, the bullet applies an equal and opposite force (hence impulse) to the dummy, thereby knocking it over (Fig. 6.23(a)). In contrast, the metal bullet merely penetrates the dummy and remains embedded in it, so it only transfers its original momentum to the dummy. The equal and opposite force (impulse) applied only stops the bullet, so the dummy remains standing (Fig. 6.23(b)).

**Fig.6.23**

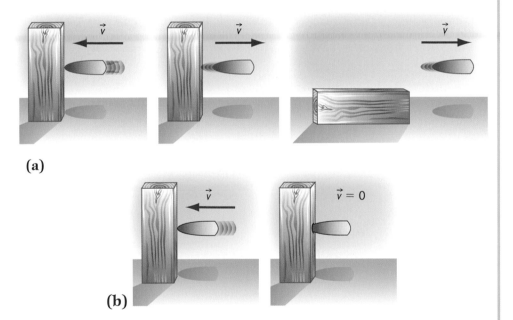

**(a)**

**(b)**

When solving problems in the conservation of linear momentum, it is extremely important to designate a system. Consider the case of a falling ball. As the ball falls towards the ground, its velocity increases. If we consider the ball only, conservation of momentum is not true because the initial and final momenta of the ball are not the same. However, if we include Earth (which causes the ball to fall) in the system, then the total momentum of the system remains constant. We are now implying that Earth is moving up to meet the ball. Because of Earth's enormous mass, its motion is not observed. In general, if the net force of the system is zero, then momentum is conserved.

# Police Analysis of Car Accidents

After a car accident, one of the tasks of a police officer is crash reconstruction and computer modelling of the event. Many of the analysis techniques used in accident investigation are based on the principle of conservation of momentum.

When two cars approach each other at an intersection, each car possesses a portion of the total momentum of a what can be considered a closed system. The law of conservation of momentum states that the total momentum after an interaction is the same as the total momentum before the interaction. Figure STSE.6.1 shows the collision between two cars. If the colliding vehicles stick together after the crash, the skid marks are like momentum vectors drawn on the ground. Working backwards, the total momentum of the system and the initial skid marks can be used, along with eyewitness accounts, to estimate the direction and speeds of the cars before the collision. Other clues, such as the collision position, are obtained from the location of debris on the road, such as glass or dried mud that was knocked free from underneath the cars during impact. Much of the information from a crash site may be analyzed using crash simulation software. Information from actual or staged crashes may also be used by automobile manufacturers to improve the safe operation of motor vehicles.

**Fig.STSE.6.1**   Conservation of momentum in an inelastic car collision

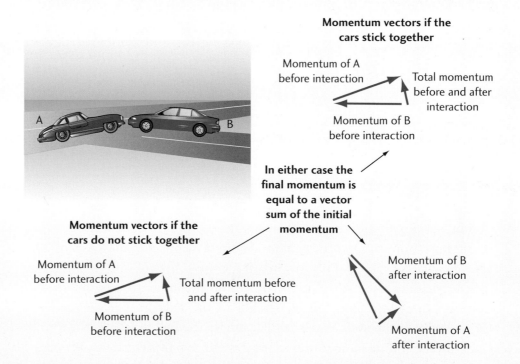

Momentum vectors if the cars stick together

Momentum of A before interaction

Total momentum before and after interaction

Momentum of B before interaction

In either case the final momentum is equal to a vector sum of the initial momentum

Momentum vectors if the cars do not stick together

Momentum of A before interaction

Total momentum before and after interaction

Momentum of B before interaction

Momentum of B after interaction

Momentum of A after interaction

## Design a Study of Societal Impact

Many provinces in Canada now have a "no fault" system of auto insurance coverage. According to this system, the insurance company pays for its client's car repairs, regardless of who was at fault during the accident. Fault is still assessed in car accidents to determine possible criminal charges and civil lawsuits, as well as driver insurance rates.

Research the insurance rates of various driver groups. Consider variables such as gender, driving record, and type of vehicle.

What other types of police work use math and physics?

## Design an Activity to Evaluate

You are a police officer who is investigating the scene of an automobile collision on a dry, sunny day. Car B approached an intersection on a minor road, while Car A approached the intersection from a major road (see Fig. STSE.6.2). Your responsibility as an accident investigator is to assign blame to one or both drivers.

**Fig.STSE.6.2**  A sample accident scene

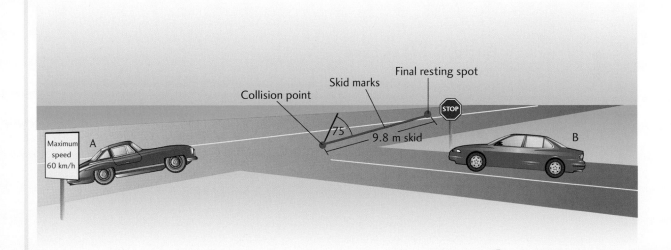

From your investigation, you have come up with the following facts:

1. The angle and length of the skid marks (shown in the Fig. STSE.6.2) of both cars indicate that they moved together from the point of impact to their final resting spot.
2. The minor road has a stop sign at the intersection and the major road has a speed limit of 60 km/h (see Fig. STSE.6.2).
3 According to manufacturers' specs, Car B of mass 1400 kg can accelerate from 0 to 80 km/h in 7.9 seconds. Car A has a mass of 1075 kg.
4. You have a table of frictional road forces for different masses of cars and road conditions (Table STSE.6.1).

| Table STSE.6.1 Frictional Force (N) | | | |
|---|---|---|---|
| Road conditions | Mass of skidding body (kg) | | |
| | 2400 | 2500 | 2600 |
| Dry asphalt | 25166 | 26215 | 27264 |
| Wet asphalt | 22344 | 23275 | 24206 |
| Dry concrete | 23990 | 24990 | 25990 |
| Wet concrete | 22814 | 23765 | 24716 |
| Icy | 118 | 123 | 127 |

## Build a Structure

Design an event (accident or otherwise) that is amenable to a physics-based post-collision forensic analysis.

**Design Project:** Design a spring-powered billiard ball launcher that can be angled to "sink" the ball in a predetermined pocket from an assigned spot on a billiard table. The shot may involve one or more "bank" shots before entering the pocket of choice.

SPECIFIC EXPECTATIONS

## You should be able to

*Understand Basic Concepts:*
- Describe and define momentum using real-life examples.
- Relate momentum to Newton's first law.
- Solve problems involving impulse and the change in momentum.
- Explain the conservation of momentum using different two-body collision situations.
- Solve problems in one dimension using conservation of momentum.

*Develop Skills of Inquiry and Communication:*
- Relate the change in momentum to Newton's second law.
- Define and relate impulse using real-life examples.
- Describe events in terms of impulse and momentum.

*Relate Science to Technology, Society, and the Environment:*
- Relate job aspects, such as a police officer recording the events of a traffic accident, in terms of the concepts studied to date.
- Suggest other careers in which momentum plays a significant role.
- Explain why rubber bullets are used in crowd control.
- Explain the principles of rocketry.

## Equations

$$\vec{p} = m\vec{v}$$

$$\vec{F}\Delta t = \Delta\vec{p}$$

$$\vec{p}_{t\ initial} = \vec{p}_{t\ final}$$

## Conceptual Questions

1. Can there be any motion in a system where the total momentum is zero? Explain.

2. Which of Newton's laws is applicable to Question 1?

3. You step out of a canoe, but instead of landing on shore, you miss and fall into the lake. How does this situation involve conservation of momentum?

4. When a novice fires a high-powered rifle, his/her shoulder hurts afterwards. An experienced handler does not have this problem. Explain this effect in terms of conservation of momentum and the impulse experienced by the person.

5. Create a chart of various types of collisions (example: two objects hit and move off in different directions, two objects hit and stick together, etc.). Find two examples of each case from real life.

6. During mating season, a lemming falls off a cliff and into a net. As the lemming is falling, it is gaining momentum because its velocity is increasing. Explain how this increase is possible using conservation of momentum.

7. Explain in terms of momentum how a rocket moves up.

8. An astronaut in space manoeuvres by using little jets. Assume you're an astronaut working for a cheap country that has provided you with an aerosol can as an emergency propellant. How do you cause yourself to move using the spray can?

9. Air bags can save lives. They can also cause great harm to individuals. Use impulse to explain these statements.

10. A person can apply a force through a push. That same force applied by a martial arts expert can cause great damage. Explain why.

11. In football, each position requires a different type of individual. Which positions require a large impulse due to a short time period? Which positions require a slow transfer of momentum?

12. Superman is standing on the highway, ready to stop a runaway cement truck. By simply standing there,
    a) will Superman stop the truck in a reasonable distance?
    b) What is he relying on to stop the truck?
    c) What could Superman do or be doing to stop the truck faster?
    d) If the truck is stopped suddenly, impulse predicts that a large force is generated. What can Superman do to lessen the effect of the force on the truck?

13. A duck walks along a long, thin raft in the water. What does the raft try to do? What hinders this action?

14. On a cruise, all the passengers are at the stern of the ship for a dance. After the dance, they all move towards the bow of the ship. If the ship is also moving forward, does this action affect its velocity?

15. Two objects with a coiled spring between them are forced apart when the spring releases. If one object is on ice and the other is on 60 grit sandpaper, then one object moves away quickly, while the other stops quickly. How is the total momentum conserved in this situation?

## Problems

### ▶ 6.2 Momentum and Newton's Second Law

16. Calculate the momentum for the following:
    a) A 120 kg rugby player running at 4.0 m/s
    b) The Statue of Liberty ($m = 2.04 \times 10^5$ kg) moving forward at 0.2 m/s
    c) A 60 g tennis ball moving at 140 km/h
    d) A blue whale ($m = 130$ tonnes) swimming at 20 km/h
    e) A dragonfly of mass 0.900 g flying at 29 km/h

17. A golf ball is hit with an average force of 2200 N. If the impact lasts $1.30 \times 10^{-3}$ s,
    a) what is the impulse imparted to the ball?
    b) what is the ball's change in momentum?

18. A car travelling at 22 m/s changes its velocity to 26 m/s in the same direction. If the car's mass is 1750 kg,
    a) what is the change in momentum of the car?
    b) what is the impulse applied to the car?

19. Repeat Problem 18, assuming that the car changed its velocity to 26 m/s in the opposite direction.

20. Find the impulse on the object from the following graphs:

**Fig.6.24**

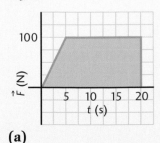

(a)

(b)

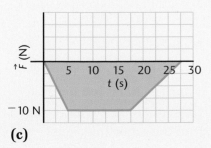

(c)

21. A car of mass 2200 kg is travelling at 50 km/h [west]. Using the graph provided, find the car's final velocity. Use the standard reference system.

**Fig.6.25**

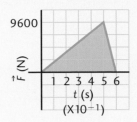

22. If the mass of a golf ball is 45 g, use the result from Problem 17 to find the ball's final velocity if it was driven off a tee.

23. A pilot experiences an acceleration of 125 m/s² for 0.20 s when she ejects out of a fighter plane. If her mass is 60 kg,
    a) what impulse is applied to her?
    b) what is her change in velocity?

24. One of the dangers of space walks is that there are numerous small particles moving at great speeds in space. Calculate the speed a golf ball of mass 45 g must have in order to have the same momentum as a 2 mm piece of paint of mass 4.0 g moving at $8.1 \times 10^3$ m/s. Convert your answer to km/h.

25. When the astronauts are doing space walks, the shuttle is oriented such that it protects them from the small, high-speed particles. However, there are numerous other larger pieces of space junk out there that could cause great harm to the shuttle itself. What speed would a 2000 kg car need to have in order to have the same momentum as a 2.0 lb object moving at 4.5 miles/s? (1 kg = 2.2 lbs, 1 mile = 5280 feet, 1 foot = 12 inches, 1 inch = 2.54 cm)

26. What force is exerted on a catcher's glove if a 142 g baseball is thrown at 160 km/h and takes
    a) 20 ms to stop?
    b) 0.20 s to stop?

**27.** A person of mass 80 kg falling at 100 km/h opens a parachute, which slows him down to 33 km/h in 4.0 s. He then lands on the ground and comes to a complete stop. Find the force in each of the following cases:

   **a)** The force of the parachute exerted to slow the person down

   **b)** The force exerted by the ground if he bends his legs, rolls, and takes 0.500 s to come to a stop

   **c)** If he lands stiff-legged in 0.0150 s

**28.** A bullet of mass 0.0600 kg is fired into a block of wood. If the bullet is moving at 330 m/s as it enters the block and takes 0.15 m to stop, find

   **a)** the average force required to stop the bullet.

   **b)** the impulse exerted by the wood on the bullet.

   **c)** the change in momentum of the bullet.

**29.** A tennis ball travelling at 30 m/s is hit back with a racket at 40 m/s. If the ball has a mass of 60 g and is in contact with the racket for 0.025 s,

   **a)** what is the average force on the ball?

   **b)** what is the acceleration of the ball?

**30.** A football player of mass 120 kg is moving at 15 km/h. If he is stopped by a tackle lasting 1.10 s, find

   **a)** the change in momentum of the football player.

   **b)** the impulse imparted to the football player.

   **c)** the average force needed to stop the player.

   **d)** the distance he moved during the stopping time.

▶ **6.3 Conservation of Momentum**

Problems 31-35 involve two identical pool balls.

**31.** A pool ball of mass 0.165 kg, moving at 8.2 m/s, hits another pool ball, which is at rest. If the first ball continues to move at 3.0 m/s in the forward direction, find the velocity of the second ball.

**32.** Find the velocity of the second ball if the ball in Problem 31 rebounds at 1.2 m/s.

**33.** If the second ball is moving at 2.0 m/s in the same direction as the original ball, find its final velocity after being hit by ball 1 in Problem 31.

**34.** If the second ball attains a velocity of 4.5 m/s from a velocity of 2.2 m/s, what is the initial velocity of the first ball if its final velocity is 0.8 m/s? Both balls move in the same direction after collision.

**35.** Ball 1 is moving at 7.6 m/s to the right. Ball 2 is moving at 4.5 m/s to the left. If ball 2 moves at 2.5 m/s to the right after the collision, find ball 1's final velocity.

**36.** A lump of clay of mass 40 g moving at 25 cm/s collides with another lump of clay of mass 50 g at rest. What is the final velocity of the two lumps if they are joined together after the collision?

**37.** A 2200 kg car moving at 40 km/h collides head on with an 1800 kg car moving at 20 km/h. Find the velocity of the combined cars after the collision.

**38. a)** A large meteor hits Earth with a velocity of 70 000 km/h. If the mass of the meteor is $5.5 \times 10^{10}$ kg and the mass of Earth is $5.98 \times 10^{24}$ kg, calculate the recoil velocity of Earth (assume Earth's velocity in the direction of the hit is zero).

   To get an idea of how fast Earth moves around the Sun, use the average radius of Earth's orbit ($r = 1.49 \times 10^{11}$ m) and the fact that it takes one year to complete one rotation. ($C = 2\pi r$ and $\vec{v} = \frac{\Delta \vec{d}}{\Delta t}$)

   **b)** Prove that the asteroid has no effect on Earth's speed if it collides with Earth in the direction of Earth's motion.

**39.** A grenade of mass 300 g at rest blows up into two fragments. If one fragment has a mass of 120 g and is moving at 220 m/s, what is the mass and velocity of the other fragment?

**40.** A 250 g bullet moving at 330 m/s hits and travels through a 1.2 kg block of wood, 0.30 m long. If the bullet's speed upon leaving the block is 120 m/s, find
  **a)** the block's velocity after the bullet exits.
  **b)** the impulse applied to the block.
  **c)** the impulse applied to the bullet. (Which of Newton's laws does this instance remind you of?)
  **d)** the time the bullet spent in the wood.
  **e)** the force applied to the bullet.
  **f)** the acceleration of the bullet.

**41.** A 10 000 kg loaded truck is moving at 30 km/h. Superman, with mass 100 kg, stands waiting to stop it. When the truck hits him, the only force available to stop the truck is that of friction. Assume that the coefficient of kinetic friction between his suit and the ground is 1.4, and calculate
  **a)** the change in momentum of the truck.
  **b)** the impulse applied to the truck by Superman.
  **c)** the force of friction available.
  **d)** the time it takes to bring the truck to rest.
  **e)** the distance the truck and Superman travel before they stop.

# Conservation of Linear Momentum

## Purpose

To show conservation of momentum in a one-dimensional collision.

## Equipment

Air track and carts
Modelling clay
Video camera and tripod
Overhead transparency and marker
TV and VCR

Note: If you have photo gates that can measure the speed of the air track carts before and after collision, they may be used instead of the procedure given here.

**Fig.Lab.6.1**  Air track

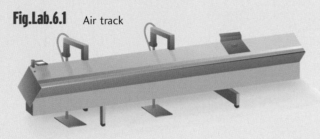

## Procedure

1. Set up the video camera on the tripod so that most of the air track is visible in the viewfinder. Increasing the shutter speed will make individual frame pictures sharper.
2. Record the mass of the two carts. Tape a pencil vertically to the back of the first cart to act as a marker. Place the second cart in the middle of the track and stick a piece of modelling clay to the back of it so that the two carts will stick together when they collide.
3. Record the motion of the first cart moving in, hitting the second cart (initially at rest), and the two carts continuing forward after collision.
4. Repeat the procedure four times using carts of different masses.
5. Set the VCR to run at standard speed. Place an overhead transparency over the TV screen. The static charge will cause the transparency to stick to the screen.
6. Move through the video one frame at a time and mark the position of the pencil in each

frame on the transparency. Repeat for each collision, using a different transparency each time.
7. Measure the length of the first cart (the cart with the pencil). Then measure the length of the corresponding cart's image on the TV screen in a stopped frame. Divide the actual length of the cart by the image length to obtain a scaling factor for distances on the TV screen.

## Data

1. The time between video frames is $\frac{1}{30}$ s. Find the average distance between pencil images before the collision and record them. Find the velocity of the cart before the collision and record it. Use the same method to find the speed of the two carts after the collision.
2. In a chart, record the masses and velocities of the carts.

## Analysis

1. Calculate the total momentum, $\vec{p}$, before and after each collision and record it in your chart.
2. Compare the initial and final momenta of the carts using percent deviation.

## Discussion

1. What type of motion do the carts have before and after the collision?
2. What is the major difference between this experiment and two objects sliding into each other on a surface?
3. What could cause a difference in your answers for initial and final momenta?

## Conclusion

Was momentum conserved, within experimental error?

## Extension

Design and carry out an experiment to determine if momentum is conserved when both objects are moving before the collision and/or they bounce off one another.

# Work, Energy, and Power

# UNIT B: Work, Energy, and Power

What do you have in common with molecules, cars, rivers, and wind? One answer is that all these things move because of energy. What is energy? How does energy cause motion? You know that "what goes up must come down," but can you explain why? These are some of the questions you will find answered in this unit.

This unit addresses a wide range of topics. Exploration of these topics will enable you to understand the subtle but important difference between force, work, energy, and power. You will also learn why heat and temperature are not the same thing, why sand on the beach is hotter than water on a hot summer day, and why your physics teacher would not consider the quiet reading you are now doing to be work.

This unit will also give you the opportunity to view the universe through Einstein's eyes, a perspective that will allow you to see how the universe would appear at speeds much greater than we have previously considered. On our journey, time, mass, and dimensions will no longer be constant, and we will see how energy and matter are different manifestations of the same thing. It sounds like the plot of a science fiction movie!

## Timeline: The History of Work, Energy, and Power

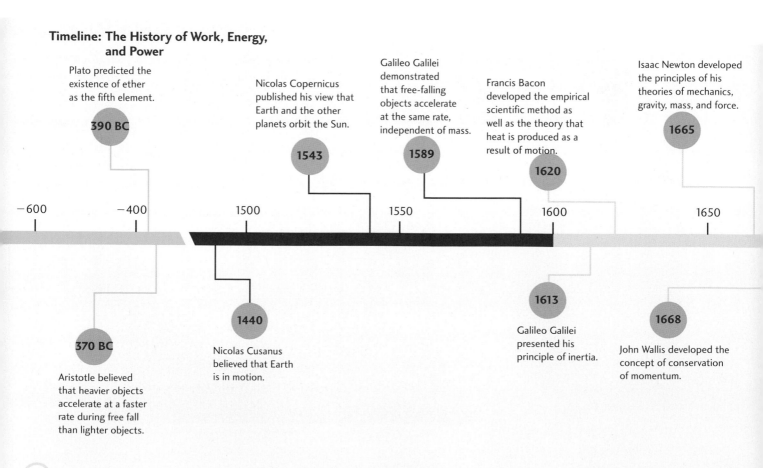

Plato predicted the existence of ether as the fifth element.
**390 BC**

Aristotle believed that heavier objects accelerate at a faster rate during free fall than lighter objects.
**370 BC**

Nicolas Cusanus believed that Earth is in motion.
**1440**

Nicolas Copernicus published his view that Earth and the other planets orbit the Sun.
**1543**

Galileo Galilei demonstrated that free-falling objects accelerate at the same rate, independent of mass.
**1589**

Francis Bacon developed the empirical scientific method as well as the theory that heat is produced as a result of motion.
**1620**

Galileo Galilei presented his principle of inertia.
**1613**

Isaac Newton developed the principles of his theories of mechanics, gravity, mass, and force.
**1665**

John Wallis developed the concept of conservation of momentum.
**1668**

−600  −400  1500  1550  1600  1650

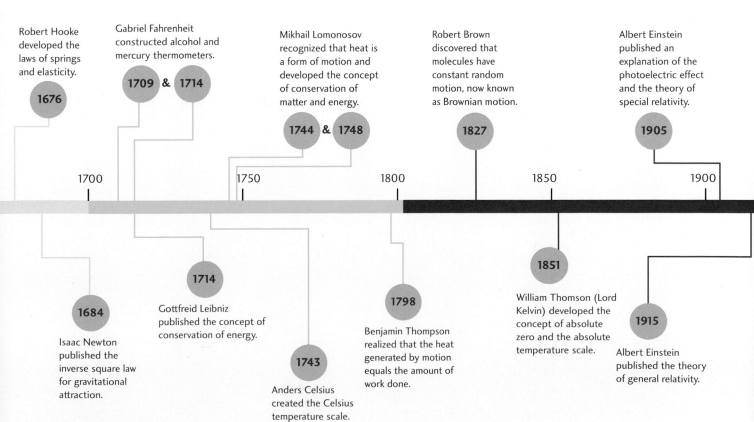

Robert Hooke developed the laws of springs and elasticity.

**1676**

Gabriel Fahrenheit constructed alcohol and mercury thermometers.

**1709** & **1714**

Mikhail Lomonosov recognized that heat is a form of motion and developed the concept of conservation of matter and energy.

**1744** & **1748**

Robert Brown discovered that molecules have constant random motion, now known as Brownian motion.

**1827**

Albert Einstein published an explanation of the photoelectric effect and the theory of special relativity.

**1905**

1700

1750

1800

1850

1900

**1684**

Isaac Newton published the inverse square law for gravitational attraction.

**1714**

Gottfreid Leibniz published the concept of conservation of energy.

**1743**

Anders Celsius created the Celsius temperature scale.

**1798**

Benjamin Thompson realized that the heat generated by motion equals the amount of work done.

**1851**

William Thomson (Lord Kelvin) developed the concept of absolute zero and the absolute temperature scale.

**1915**

Albert Einstein published the theory of general relativity.

# 7

# Mechanical Energy and Its Transfer

## Chapter Outline

**By the end of this chapter, you will be able to**

- describe how energy is transferred from one form to another by doing work
- apply the concept of power to changes in gravitational potential and kinetic energies
- outline how the law of conservation of energy applies during an energy transfer

# 7.1 Introduction to Energy

In the broadest possible terms, physics is the study of the relationship between matter and energy. **Matter** is the "stuff" of the universe, everything around us that has mass and takes up space. Unlike the matter that we experience every day with our five senses, **energy** has no body or substance. Rather, it is the fuel that makes matter go. Without energy, matter would be "lifeless." There would be no motion, no heat, no light, and no "get up and go."

In physics, **energy** is defined as the ability to do work. In order for matter to become more energetic, work needs to be done on it. Fig. 7.1 illustrates the close yet strange relationship between work and energy. In it, we see that the definition for work involves energy, and the description for energy also links to work. **Work** is the process of transferring energy from one of its many forms to another. Quite often, the only time we know that any energy transformation has occurred is by observing the effects on the matter involved in the transformation. In Fig. 7.2, the energy or "fuel" that is making car A "go" is expressed in the car's motion.

**Fig.7.1**

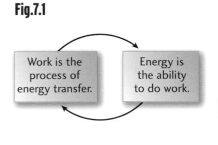

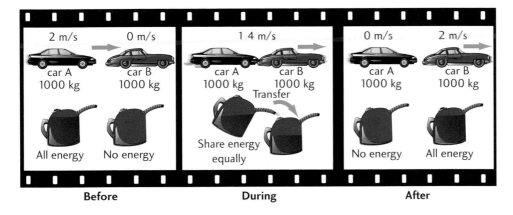

**Fig.7.2**   Work transfers energy

| Before | During | After |
|---|---|---|

When one car bumps another car, car A does work on car B by transferring all of its energy of motion to car B. In effect, the energy or "fuel" was moved from car A to car B. Using money as an analogy, energy could be represented by the amount of money in a person's wallet, while work would be the process of paying someone for a job done. The amount of money in the employee's wallet will increase by the same amount he or she received in payment.

The difficulty in understanding the relationship between work and energy arises from the fact that energy can be expressed in so many different ways. In the next section, we will define the various types of energy more clearly.

## Types of Energy

Energy is the *fuel* of an object. When work is being done on the object, the amount of *fuel* the object has changes (see Fig. 7.2). This *fuel* can be expressed in many different ways.

Energy comes in many different forms, like different flavours of ice cream. The two main "flavours" of energy are kinetic energy and potential energy.

| | |
|---|---|
| **Kinetic energy** | is the energy of motion, the energy that we know exists because we observe a piece of matter moving. The faster an object is moving, the more kinetic energy it has. |
| **Thermal** or **heat energy** | is the energy that makes objects hot. It is a form of kinetic energy at the molecular level. When we boil water in a kettle, we are increasing the kinetic energy of every particle of water in the kettle. The collective kinetic energy of all these particles is called thermal energy. The familiar "whistling" of a tea kettle illustrates how the thermal energy of the expanding steam could be put to use to do work. |
| **Potential energy** | is energy that is stored or energy that is not actually in use at the present moment. There are seven types of potential energy: |
| **Gravitational potential energy** | is the energy stored in an object due to its height in an area where the force of gravity can act on it to make it fall. Water at the top of Niagara Falls can be said to have gravitational potential energy that can be used to do work as it "falls." |
| **Elastic potential energy** | is the energy stored by the bending, stretching, or compressing of matter. If you stretch an elastic band over someone's leg, the person will make it clear that he or she is aware of the energy that might be released from the band. |
| **Chemical potential energy** | is energy that is stored in the chemical bonds of matter and can be released by way of a chemical reaction. An unlit match, a sandwich, and gasoline are examples of chemical potential energy. |
| **Electric potential energy** | is the energy stored when static electric charges are held a certain distance apart. A sock stuck to a towel, coming out of the dryer with an electrostatic charge, will return to the towel if it is lifted away. |
| **Magnetic potential energy,** | like electric potential energy, is stored in the space between two magnets. Lift a fridge magnet a small distance and it too will fall back to the fridge. |
| **Radiant energy** | is a complicated form of potential energy that is carried by electromagnetic waves (we will discuss it in Chapter 10). As one of these radiant energy waves travels, the stored energy is being shifted between a form of electric and magnetic potential energy. Both visible and invisible forms of radiant energy come from sources such as the Sun. Radiant energy can do work on matter by transferring its energy to other forms, such as heat. It melts snow and can be used to power your calculator. |
| **Nuclear potential energy** | is the energy stored in an atom's nucleus that is waiting to be released in a nuclear reaction. |

**Fig.7.3** Types of Energy

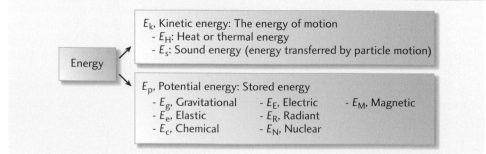

Energy

$E_k$, Kinetic energy: The energy of motion
- $E_H$: Heat or thermal energy
- $E_S$: Sound energy (energy transferred by particle motion)

$E_p$, Potential energy: Stored energy
- $E_g$, Gravitational    - $E_E$, Electric    - $E_M$, Magnetic
- $E_e$, Elastic    - $E_R$, Radiant
- $E_c$, Chemical    - $E_N$, Nuclear

CONNECTING the Concepts ▶ ▶ ▶ ▶ ▶

UNIT B: Work, Energy, and Power

# 7.2 Work, the Transfer of Energy

How does an object transfer energy from one form to another? Thermal energy forces a radiator cap off, chemical energy forces a car engine piston downward, and gravity forces a stalled car down a hill (Fig. 7.4). The common element is that for work to be done, a force must be applied. In other words, energy is transferred by applying a force to the object receiving the energy.

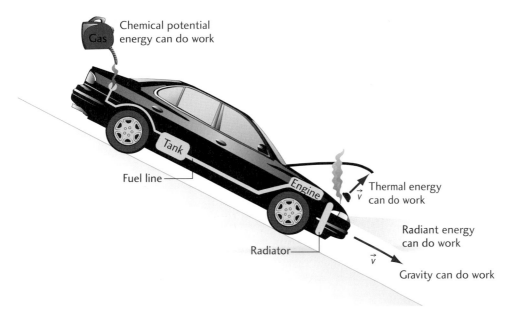

Chemical potential energy can do work

Fuel line

Tank

Engine

Radiator

Thermal energy can do work

Radiant energy can do work

Gravity can do work

**Fig.7.4** Work is the transfer of energy. Work can be done in many ways.

Figure 7.5 shows that if force is applied over a greater displacement, then the amount of energy transferred or the work done will be greater. We can quantitatively calculate the amount of work done by using the formula

$$W = \vec{F}_{app} \Delta \vec{d}$$

where $\vec{F}_{app}$ is the applied force in newtons (N), $\Delta \vec{d}$ is the displacement in metres (m), and $W$ is work in newton-metres (N·m). 1 N·m is given the derived unit name of the joule (J).

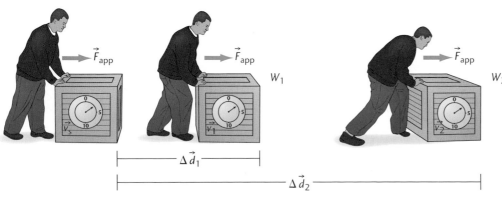

**Fig.7.5** The larger the distance, the more work is done

# Work is a Scalar Quantity

**Fig.7.6**

$W = (F_{app}\cos\theta)\Delta d$

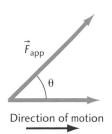

$\vec{F}_{app}$

$\theta$

Direction of motion

Work is independent of direction. When a car accelerates, work is being done, regardless of the direction of the car's motion. Whether you push a car from behind to speed it up or stand in front of a car and push on it to slow it down, you are still transferring energy to the car. Therefore, even though it is the product of two vectors, force ($\vec{F}$) and displacement ($\Delta\vec{d}$), work is a scalar quantity.

We can then simplify our treatment of work in calculations by not specifying the direction of force and displacement. If you make this simplification, however, make sure that the force you use in your calculations is the component of the applied force in that direction. This component can be calculated using the formula

$$F_{app}\cos\theta$$

## Table 7.1
### Force and/or Displacement but No Work

| Case | Example | Diagram |
|---|---|---|
| Force and displacement must be in the same direction or no work is being done. | You carry a knapsack to school. You exert a force of 50 N [up] against the force of gravity, but your displacement is in the forward direction and perpendicular to the force. Because force and displacement are not in the same direction, the work that is done on the knapsack is not due to the 50 N force. The knapsack doesn't gain or lose energy, so **no work is done**. | |
| A force is being applied, but there is no displacement. The formula predicts that no work is being done. | You are breaking your back trying to pull a tree stump out of the ground. But the tree stump is not moving (no displacement); therefore, you are not doing any work on the tree stump, despite your efforts. The stump's energy doesn't change, so no work is done. | |
| No force is being applied, but an object is being displaced. Once again, no work is being done. | A paper airplane glides through the air at constant speed. Launching the plane involved work because a force is applied in the direction of motion. Now that the plane is gliding, no force is being applied and there is no change in energy; therefore, no work is being done on the plane. | |

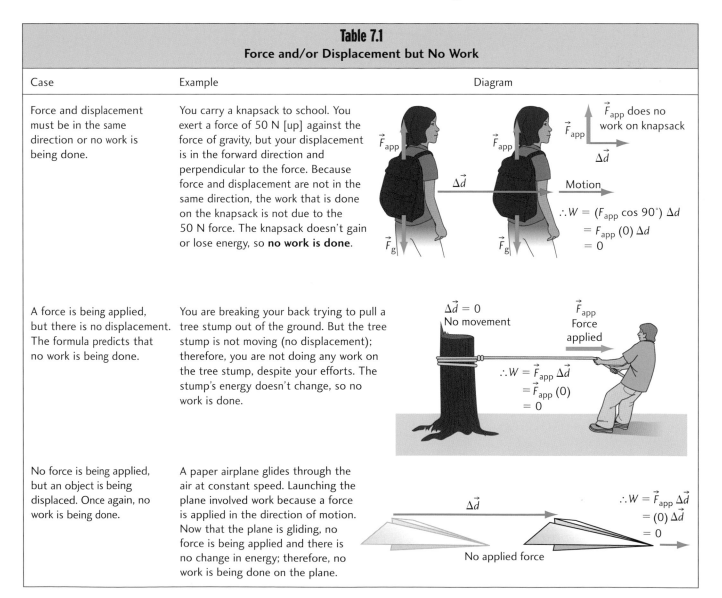

$\vec{F}_{app}$ does no work on knapsack

$\therefore W = (F_{app}\cos 90°)\,\Delta d$
$= F_{app}(0)\,\Delta d$
$= 0$

$\Delta\vec{d} = 0$
No movement

$\vec{F}_{app}$
Force applied

$\therefore W = \vec{F}_{app}\,\Delta\vec{d}$
$= \vec{F}_{app}(0)$
$= 0$

$\therefore W = \vec{F}_{app}\,\Delta\vec{d}$
$= (0)\,\Delta\vec{d}$
$= 0$

No applied force

## EXAMPLE 1    Calculating work

How much work is done by a boy pulling a wagon with a horizontal force of 50 N for a distance of 5.4 m?

### *Solution and Connection to Theory*

**Given**

$\vec{F}_{app} = 50$ N    $\Delta \vec{d} = 5.4$ m    $W = ?$

$W = \vec{F}_{app}\Delta \vec{d} = (50$ N$)(5.4$ m$) = 2.7 \times 10^2$ J

The boy does $2.7 \times 10^2$ J of work.

## EXAMPLE 2    Working against friction

A man is pushing a box across the floor with a force of 250 N, as shown in Fig. 7.7. The box moves at a constant speed for 12.75 m. How much work has the man done to move the box?

### *Solution and Connection to Theory*

**Given**

$\vec{F}_{app} = 250$ N    $\Delta \vec{d} = 12.75$ m    $W = ?$

**Fig.7.7**

$\vec{F}_f$    $\vec{F}_{app}$
250 N

—— 12.75 m ——

Since the box is not accelerating, the net force on it must be zero. The force of friction is therefore equal and opposite to the applied force. Once the box starts moving, it continues at a constant speed.

$W = \vec{F}_{app}\Delta \vec{d} = (250$ N$) (12.75$ m$) = 3.19 \times 10^3$ J

Therefore, the man would do $3.19 \times 10^3$ J of work to move the box. You will see later that the kinetic energy of the box hasn't changed. The work done was all transferred to heat energy by friction.

## EXAMPLE 3    Work done with force at an angle

A student is pulling a toboggan at a constant velocity with a force of 50 N. The rope handle of the toboggan is angled at 37° above the horizontal, as shown in Fig. 7.8. How much work is done by the student if he must walk 0.50 km to the toboggan hill?

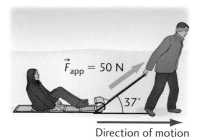

**Fig.7.8** Force applied at an angle to the direction of motion

$\vec{F}_{app} = 50$ N

37°

Direction of motion

**Fig.7.9**

$\vec{F}_{app}$

$\vec{F}_g$

$\vec{F}_{app}$

## Solution and Connection to Theory

**Given**

$\vec{F}_{app} = 50$ N     $\Delta \vec{d} = 0.50$ km     $\theta = 37°$     $W = ?$

First, convert the displacement to metres.

$$\Delta d = 0.50 \text{ km} \left( \frac{1000 \text{ m}}{1 \text{ km}} \right) = 500 \text{ m}$$

The force used in this calculation must be the component of the applied force in the direction of motion.

$$W = F_{app}(\cos\theta)\Delta d$$
$$= 50 \text{ N}(\cos 37°)500 \text{ m}$$
$$= 2.0 \times 10^4 \text{ J}$$

The work done by the student pulling the toboggan is $2.0 \times 10^4$ J.

| EXAMPLE 4 | **Raising a flag** |

Every morning, a boy scout raises a flag with a mass of 1.5 kg to the top of a 15.0 m flag pole. How much work is done by the scout?

## Solution and Connection to Theory

**Given**

$m = 1.5$ kg     $\Delta \vec{d} = 15.0$ m     $W = ?$

The force that the scout applies to the flag to raise it at a constant rate is equal in magnitude but opposite in direction to the force of gravity on the flag, as shown in Fig. 7.9. Therefore,

$$W = \vec{F}_g \Delta \vec{d}$$
$$= mg\Delta \vec{d}$$
$$= (1.5 \text{ kg})(9.8 \text{ m/s}^2)(15.0 \text{ m})$$
$$= 2.2 \times 10^2 \text{ J}$$

The scout does $2.2 \times 10^2$ J of work.

**Fig.7.10  Calculating Work Done**

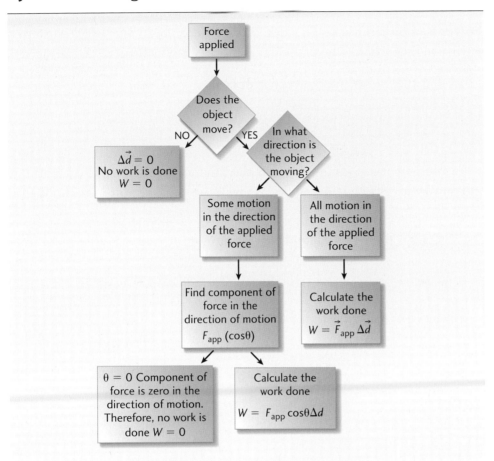

If a person pushes a refrigerator across a floor at a constant speed, the work he does is given by $\vec{F}_{app}\Delta\vec{d}$. But the refrigerator is not gaining energy because its speed is not increasing. The energy expended by the person is all converted to heat by the force of friction.

1. Use Newton's laws to explain
   a) why the fridge is moving if there is an equal force of friction acting on it.
   b) how you know that there is an equal and opposite force of friction acting on the fridge.
   c) why the net work on the fridge is zero (include an FBD).
2. How much work is done on an object moving in a circle with constant speed? Use Newton's first law, momentum (if you have studied this section), and Newton's second law in your explanation.
3. Calculate the work done for the following:
   a) A person pushes a 5.0 kg box with a force of 40 N for 2.0 m.
   b) A person pushes a 5.0 kg box with a force of 40 N for 2.0 s at a constant speed of 1.2 m/s.
   c) A person with mass 55 kg walks at a constant speed up a set of stairs with 20 steps, each 20 cm high.

# 7.3 Power, the Rate of Energy Transfer

**Power** is often confused with work. Work is the amount of energy transferred during an interaction, whereas power is the rate at which energy is transferred.

> Power is the rate at which work is done.

$$P = \frac{W}{\Delta t}$$

where $W$ is work in joules (J), $\Delta t$ is the time taken in seconds (s), and $P$ is the power measured in J/s, which is given the derived unit of watt (W).

---

**EXAMPLE 5**    Calculating power

What is the power of a crane that does $6.7 \times 10^4$ J of work in 1.7 s?

*Solution and Connection to Theory*

**Given**
$W = 6.7 \times 10^4$ J     $\Delta t = 1.7$ s     $P = ?$

$$P = \frac{W}{\Delta t}$$

$$P = \frac{6.7 \times 10^4 \text{ J}}{1.7 \text{ s}}$$

$$P = 3.9 \times 10^4 \text{ W}$$

Therefore, the crane will develop $3.9 \times 10^4$ W of power.

---

**EXAMPLE 6**    The power of a crane

How much power would the crane in Example 4 develop if it lifts a 1.25 t bucket of concrete a vertical distance of 57.4 m in 3.5 s?

*Solution and Connection to Theory*

**Given**
$m = 1.25$ t     $\Delta d = 57.4$ m     $\Delta t = 3.5$ s     $P = ?$

The mass in this example is given in tonnes and must be converted to kilograms.

$$m = 1.25 \, t \left( \frac{1000 \text{ kg}}{1 \, t} \right) = 1.25 \times 10^3 \text{ kg}$$

The work is being done by applying a force equal to the force of gravity on the bucket of concrete for the vertical distance.

$$W = \vec{F}_g \Delta d = mg\Delta d$$

So the power becomes

$$P = \frac{W}{\Delta t}$$

$$P = \frac{mg\Delta d}{\Delta t} = \frac{(1.25 \times 10^3 \text{ kg})(9.8 \text{ m/s}^2)(57.4 \text{ m})}{3.5 \text{ s}}$$

$$P = 2.0 \times 10^5 \text{ W}$$

The power developed by the crane in this case would be $2.0 \times 10^5$ W.

Power plays an important role in determining how energy is delivered. For the same work done in a shorter period of time, the energy delivered has a greater impact on the situation. For an elevator to take 10 people to the top of the CN Tower, a given amount of energy is required. If the elevator took the people up in half the time, the amount of energy required would be the same, but the power of the elevator would have to be doubled.

1. For a person of mass 70 kg moving up 30 steps, each 20 cm high, calculate the work and power developed if the process took 8.6 s at constant speed.
2. For the person in Problem 1, what would happen to the work and power if there was a landing half way up the stairs, causing the person to move sideways before starting up again? Consider the work against gravity for this case.
3. Consider the total power generated in lifting weights. Compare the total work and power for someone who does more repetitions with less weight to someone who lifts more weight with fewer repetitions. Find which workout works best for strength development, muscle tone, muscle bulk, and endurance.

 ◄ ◄ ◄ ◄ **APPLYING the Concepts**

## 7.4 Kinetic Energy

One connection between work and energy can be illustrated when work is done on an object while it is being displaced. As expected, the object picks up speed or becomes more energetic due to its change in motion. In other words, doing work on an object increases its energy of motion, or kinetic energy.

Mathematically, kinetic energy is described by the equation

$$E_k = \tfrac{1}{2} mv^2$$

where $m$ is the mass in kg, $v$ is the velocity of the object in m/s, and $E_k$ is the kinetic energy in J.

**DERIVING FORMULA FOR KINETIC ENERGY**

$$E_k = W = F\Delta d = ma\Delta d$$

If $v_1 = 0$,

$$a = \frac{v_2 - v_1}{t_2 - t_1} = \frac{v - 0}{\Delta t} = \frac{v}{\Delta t}$$

$$\text{and } \Delta d = \left(\frac{v_1 + v_2}{2}\right)\Delta t$$

$$\Delta d = \left(\frac{0 + v}{2}\right)\Delta t = \frac{v}{2}\Delta t$$

$$\therefore E_k = ma\Delta d$$

$$= m\left(\frac{v}{\Delta t}\right)\left(\frac{v}{2}\Delta t\right) = \tfrac{1}{2}mv^2$$

## AN ALTERNATIVE DERIVATION

A force $F$ acts on an object of mass $m$ to increase its speed from 0 to $v$ over a distance of $\Delta d$. Substitute in the kinematic equation

$$v_2^2 = v_1^2 + 2a\Delta d, \text{ but } v_1 = 0$$

$$v^2 = 2a\Delta d$$

$$\tfrac{1}{2}mv^2 = ma\Delta d$$

$$\Delta E_k = W = F\Delta d = ma\Delta d$$

$$= m(a\Delta d)$$

$$= \tfrac{1}{2}mv^2$$

**EXAMPLE 7**   Calculations involving kinetic energy

What is the kinetic energy of a 250 g softball that has been thrown at a velocity of 160 m/s?

### *Solution and Connection to Theory*

**Given**

$$m = 250 \text{ g} \qquad v = 160 \text{ m/s} \qquad E_k = ?$$

The mass is given in grams and must be converted to kg.

$$250 \text{ g}\left(\frac{1 \text{ kg}}{1000 \text{ g}}\right) = 2.50 \times 10^{-1} \text{ kg}$$

$$E_k = \tfrac{1}{2}mv^2$$

$$E_k = \tfrac{1}{2}(2.50 \times 10^{-1} \text{ kg})(160 \text{ m/s})^2$$

$$E_k = 3.20 \times 10^3 \text{ J}$$

The kinetic energy of the softball is $3.20 \times 10^3$ J.

**EXAMPLE 8**   The kinetic energy of a bale of hay

What would be the velocity of a 17.0 kg bale of hay if it had a kinetic energy of 212 J?

### *Solution and Connection to Theory*

**Given**

$$m = 17.0 \text{ kg} \qquad E_k = 212 \text{ J} \qquad v = ?$$

$$E_k = \tfrac{1}{2}mv^2 \Rightarrow v^2 = \frac{2E_k}{m}$$

$$v = \sqrt{\frac{2E_k}{m}}$$

$$v = \sqrt{\frac{2(212 \text{ J})}{17.0 \text{ kg}}}$$

$$v = 5.0 \text{ m/s}$$

The velocity of the hay would be 5.0 m/s.

# Work, Power, Force, and Energy — What is the Difference?

Sometimes it is easy to confuse the terms "work," "power," "force," and "energy." We will illustrate these terms once again, using karate as an example.

Karate began as a weaponless form of combat in 17th century Japan; hence its name, which means "open hand." Karate is a martial art that has become popular among people wanting to combine fitness and self-defence. It has also been glamourized by Hollywood as involving superhuman strength and endurance. The techniques used in karate are complicated and should be practised with appropriate instruction, but the physics of karate may be used to illustrate the topics covered in this chapter.

Work is the transfer of energy. In karate, the karateka (karate participant) does work when he or she applies a force through a distance to strike a target, thereby transferring kinetic energy from his or her moving fist to the target, as shown in Fig. 7.11. The goal is to maximize the amount of kinetic energy transferred to the target. This is done by using the appropriate technique, which is perfected through practice to make it as efficient as possible.

Fig. 7.12 illustrates the transfer of kinetic energy in karate. Since work depends on force and distance, to maximize the amount of work done, the force applied and the distance covered should be as large as possible. The karateka maximizes the distance by aiming at the target as though it were past the point of impact.

Because of the limits of the human body, we cannot apply large forces for long periods of time. Power is the rate at which work is done, or the amount of work done per unit time. In karate, to maximize the power of the strike, the karateka tries to execute it in the shortest time possible because he or she cannot maintain a large force for very long. Ideally, for maximum power, the athlete tries to deliver the greatest possible force over the greatest possible distance in the shortest possible time. That's why a well-executed strike is painful.

**Fig.7.11** Transfer of energy

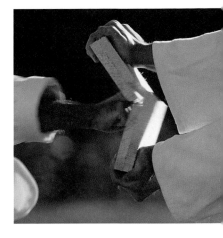

**Fig.7.12** Analysis of a karate strike

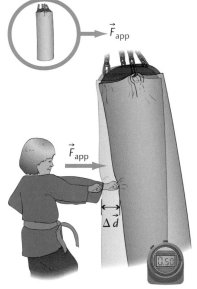

**Fig.7.13** How Force, Distance, and Time Affect Power

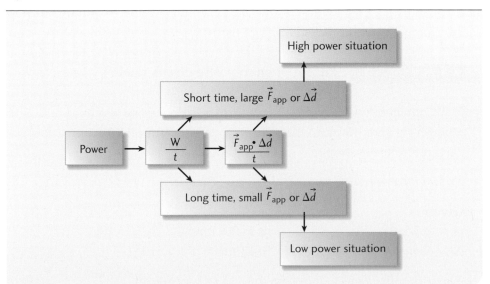

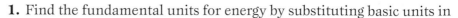

APPLYING the Concepts

1. Find the fundamental units for energy by substituting basic units in
   a) the kinetic energy formula.
   b) the work formula.
2. What happens to the kinetic energy of an object when work is done on it?
3. Calculate the kinetic energy or the change in kinetic energy for the following cases involving a mass of 2.0 kg:
   a) The mass moves at 4.0 m/s.
   b) The mass moves at 20 km/h.
   c) The mass increases its speed from 2.0 m/s to 5.5 m/s.
   d) A force of 50 N is applied to the object for a distance of 2.0 m.
   e) For Part d), assume that the object was at rest at the beginning. What speed did it achieve because of the work done on it?
4. Explain the process of a tackle in football or rugby in terms of impulse and momentum (if you have studied Chapter 6), force, work, power, and kinetic energy.

## 7.5 Gravitational Potential Energy

When an object is lifted, work is done on it by applying a force against the force of gravity. Because work is being done, the energy of the object increases as it is lifted. This form of stored energy is called gravitational potential energy.

Figure 7.14 shows a weightlifter increasing the gravitational potential energy of a barbell by lifting it up. If you lift an object at a constant velocity, the applied force that does the work balances the force of gravity. Thus, the applied force is equal in magnitude but opposite in direction to the force of gravity.

Mathematically, gravitational potential energy is described as

$$\Delta E_g = mg\Delta h$$

where $\Delta E_g$ is the change in gravitational potential energy in joules, $m$ is the mass of the object in kilograms, $g$ is the acceleration due to gravity, and $\Delta h$ is the change in the object's height in metres.

To derive the equation for gravitational potential energy,

$\Delta E_g = W = F\Delta d$
But $F = mg$ and $\Delta d = \Delta h$
$\therefore \Delta E_g = F\Delta d = mg\Delta h$

**Fig.7.14** Increasing gravitational potential energy

$\vec{F}_{app} = -\vec{F}_g$

$\Delta \vec{h}$

$\vec{F}_g$

### EXAMPLE 9    Potential energy of a circus duck

How much potential energy does Projecto, a 2.5 kg circus duck, gain when he is shot 45 m up into the air from the ground? Assume the standard reference system.

### *Solution and Connection to Theory*

**Given**
$m = 2.5$ kg     $\Delta h = 45$ m     $g = 9.8$ m/s²     $\Delta E_g = ?$
$\Delta E_g = mg\Delta h = 2.5$ kg$(9.8$ m/s²$)(45$ m$) = 1.1 \times 10^3$ J

Therefore, Projecto would gain $1.1 \times 10^3$ J of energy.

EXAMPLE 10 **Transferring potential energy at the circus**

How much gravitational potential energy does Projecto lose as he falls back down from a height of 45 m onto a net that is suspended 5.0 m above the ground? Assume the standard reference system.

### *Solution and Connection to Theory*

**Given**

$m = 2.5$ kg     $h_1 = 45.0$ m     $h_2 = 5.0$ m     $g = 9.8$ m/s$^2$     $\Delta E_g = ?$

This time, the object *loses* height, so
$\Delta h = h_2 - h_1 = 5.0$ m $- 45.0$ m $= -40.0$ m
$\Delta E_g = mg\Delta h = 2.5$ kg$(9.8$ m/s$^2)(-40.0$ m$) = -9.8 \times 10^2$ J

Therefore, the gravitational potential energy transferred by Projecto is $9.8 \times 10^2$ J.

## Relative Potential Energy

The problem with calculating gravitational potential energy is that we have no designated spot on Earth that everyone accepts as a reference point with zero height. When calculating the gravitational potential energy of an object, the value of the height, $h$, depends on your frame of reference. For example, if you were to measure your own gravitational potential energy from your current position (seated at your desk) and designate the floor as your frame of reference, $h$ is your distance from the floor. If you were to use the basement as your reference point instead, then $h$ would be the distance between the seat of your chair and the basement floor.

To calculate the gravitational potential energy lost or gained, you can use the formula

$$E_g = mgh$$

where $h$ represents the vertical distance above or below your reference point.

EXAMPLE 11 **The gravitational potential energy of a watermelon**

A 2.0 kg watermelon rolls off a 0.75 m high table on to a chair that is 0.45 m high before it finally hits the floor. While it is still on the table, what is the gravitational potential energy of the watermelon relative to
(a) the table?     (b) the chair?     (c) the floor?

### *Solution and Connection to Theory*

(a) The reference point is the table top, so $h$ is zero.
$\quad E_g = mgh = 2.0$ kg$(9.8$ m/s$^2)(0$ m$)$
$\quad E_g = 0$ J relative to the table top.

(b) The reference point here is the chair, which is $(0.75 \text{ m} - 0.45 \text{ m})$ or 0.30 m below the watermelon.

$E_g = mgh = 2.0 \text{ kg}(9.8 \text{ m/s}^2)(0.30 \text{ m})$

$E_g = 5.9 \text{ J}$ relative to the chair top.

(c) The reference point here is the floor, which is 0.75 m below the table top.

$E_g = mgh = 2.0 \text{ kg}(9.8 \text{ m/s}^2)(0.75 \text{ m})$

$E_g = 15 \text{ J}$ relative to the floor.

▶ ▶ ▶ ▶

1. Calculate the potential energy for the following cases:
   **a)** A 10 kg mass moves up 2.4 m.
   **b)** A 589 mg mass moves up 325 cm.
   **c)** A 10 kg mass sits on top of a roof that is 15 m above the top of a 120 m high cliff.
2. What role does gravitational potential energy play in the production of electricity by Ontario Power Generation?
3. Ontario Power Generation at Niagara Falls operates under a normal head of about 55 m (height from which water falls). If about $4.54 \times 10^8$ kg of water falls every minute, how many megajoules of energy are created by the falling water?

## ▶ 7.6 The Law of Conservation of Energy

The last two sections have shown how energy can manifest itself in many forms, such as chemical, gravitational potential, thermal, and kinetic energy. A car skidding to a stop is doing work on the road and therefore transferring thermal energy to it by heating it up. Some energy is transferred to air in the form of sound energy, as witnessed by the "screech," and also to kinetic energy of the air molecules around the car as the once still air is disturbed. Where did the energy come from to heat the road, make the sounds, and move the air? This energy was not just created; it came from the original kinetic energy of the car (Fig. 7.15). By transferring some of its kinetic energy to its surroundings, the car now has less kinetic energy. The total amount of energy in the system is still the same.

**Fig.7.15** A car losing its kinetic energy

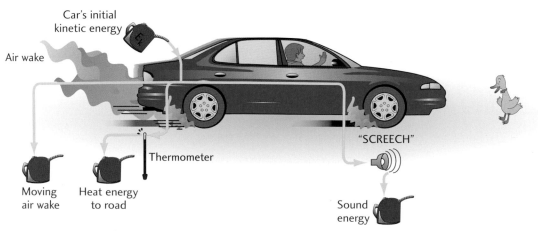

Car's initial kinetic energy

Air wake

Moving air wake

Heat energy to road

Thermometer

"SCREECH"

Sound energy

UNIT B: Work, Energy, and Power

The car example illustrates one of the most famous laws of physics: **the law of conservation of energy**. Three possible ways of stating the law are

1. Energy cannot be created or destroyed, but only transferred from one form to another without any loss.

2. The total energy of any closed system always remains the same.

3. Energy can change from one form to another, but the total amount of energy always remains the same as long as the system being considered is a closed one.

The total amount of usable energy that we can access is constantly decreasing. The ball in Fig. 7.16 begins with an amount of gravitational potential energy, $E_g$, that is useful energy. When the ball falls and bounces on the floor, a series of energy transfers occurs. $E_g$ is converted to $E_k$ as the ball falls, $E_k$ is converted to elastic potential energy when the ball deforms, and then the process occurs in reverse as the ball rises. The fact that the ball loses height after each subsequent bounce means that unrecoverable energy has been transferred to the surroundings. The floor and ball are hotter, sound was produced at each bounce, and the air is disturbed by the ball's motion. The law of conservation of energy is not being violated. No energy is being destroyed — it is transferred elsewhere. But for all practical purposes, it is lost to us.

## A CLOSED SYSTEM

Think of a system as some section of the universe. It is a closed system if you can isolate it from the rest of the universe so that no matter or energy can move in or out. It is like sealing a section of the universe inside a room and closing the door.

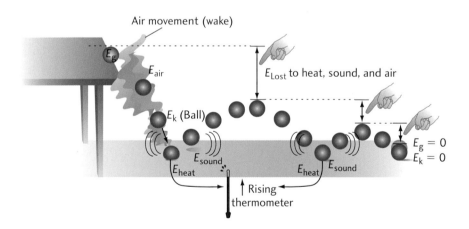

**Fig.7.16** Energy from a bouncing ball is not destroyed but converted into other forms

# 7.7 Conservation of Mechanical Energy

In the physics lab, it is extremely difficult to show that energy is totally conserved during all the transformations shown in Fig. 7.16 because they are subtle and numerous. We can get some sense of conservation by considering a small system, such as the changes between gravitational potential and kinetic energies of an object that is rising or falling.

In Fig. 7.17, we see a roller coaster of mass 1000 kg that is about to travel from the top of a hill at position A, down into a valley, then over one more hill before returning to the platform. For this system, the total mechanical energy (the sum of gravitational potential energy and the kinetic energy) always remains the same, as shown in Table 7.2.

**Fig.7.17** Path of a roller coaster

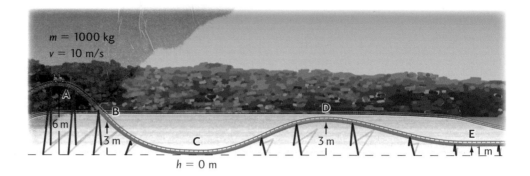

| Table 7.2 Roller Coaster Energy ($m = 1000$ kg) | | | | | |
|---|---|---|---|---|---|
| Time interval | Height of coaster ($h$ in m) | Speed of coaster ($v$ in m/s) | $E_k$ (in J) | $E_g$ (in J) | Total mechanical energy ($E_T$ in J) |
| A | 6 | 10.00 | 50 000 | 58 800 | 108 800 |
| B | 3 | 12.60 | 79 400 | 29 400 | 108 800 |
| C | 0 | 14.75 | 108 800 | 0 | 108 800 |
| D | 3 | 12.60 | 79 400 | 29 400 | 108 800 |
| E | 1 | 14.07 | 99 000 | 9 800 | 108 800 |

As the coaster falls, the *decrease* of gravitational potential energy is compensated by an *increase* in kinetic energy, so the coaster picks up speed. Once the conditions of velocity and height are known, the total mechanical energy can be calculated. The total mechanical energy can then be used to evaluate $E_g$ (given the velocity) or $E_k$ (given the height) for any point along the trip. Note that once we have found $E_g$, we can easily find height. Similarly, we can find the velocity at any point if the $E_k$ value is known.

---

**EXAMPLE 12**   **A roller coaster's kinetic energy**

(a) What is the kinetic energy ($E_k$) of the roller coaster described in Table 7.2, when the roller coaster has an $E_g$ of 19 600 J?

(b) How high is the roller coaster at this point?

(c) What is the velocity of the roller coaster at that moment?

UNIT B: Work, Energy, and Power

## Solution and Connection to Theory

**Given**

$E_g = 19\ 600$ J     Table 7.2 shows $E_T = 108\ 800$ J

a)   $E_k = E_T - E_g = 108\ 800$ J $- 19\ 600$J $= 89\ 200$ J

b)   $E_g = mgh$

$$h = \frac{E_g}{mg} = \frac{19\ 600\ \text{J}}{(1000\ \text{kg})(9.8\ \text{N/kg})} = 2.0\ \text{m}$$

c)   $E_k = \frac{1}{2}mv^2; v = \sqrt{\dfrac{2E_k}{m}} = \sqrt{\dfrac{2(89\ 200\ \text{J})}{1000\ \text{kg}}} = 13.35$ m/s

---

## EXAMPLE 13   Energy of a stone

An inquisitive boy throws a 0.50 kg stone at 1.0 m/s towards the ground from the top of his roof, which is 3.2 m high.

(a) What is the gravitational potential energy and the kinetic energy of the stone at the beginning of the throw?

(b) What is the total mechanical energy of the stone at the beginning of its trip?

(c) What is the total mechanical energy as the stone hits the ground?

(d) With what speed would the stone hit the ground?

### Solution and Connection to Theory

**Given**

$m = 0.50$ kg     $v = 1.0$ m/s     $h = 3.2$ m     $g = 9.8$ m/s$^2$

(a) To calculate the gravitational potential energy,

$E_g = mgh = 0.50$ kg$(9.8$ m/s$^2)(3.2$ m$) = 15.68$ J

The stone has a gravitational potential energy of 16 J at the start of the throw.

To calculate the kinetic energy,

$E_k = \frac{1}{2}mv^2 = \frac{1}{2}(0.50$ kg$)(1.0$ m/s$)^2 = 0.25$ J

The stone has a kinetic energy of 0.25 J at the start of the trip.

(b) The total mechanical energy, $E_T$, is the sum of the gravitational potential energy and the kinetic energy at any time.

$E_T = E_g + E_k = 15.68$ J $+ 0.25$ J $= 15.93$ J

The total mechanical energy at the start of the trip is 16 J.

> 15.68 J
> +  0.25 J
> 15.93 J
> → 16 J, rounded to
> two significant digits

(c) In a closed system, the total mechanical energy of the stone should remain the same throughout the entire trip. This would be true except if there were considerable air resistance or friction.

Therefore, the total mechanical energy of the stone when it hits the ground is still 16.0 J.

(d) Although the total mechanical energy remains the same, the stone will lose all of its height and therefore all of its gravitational potential energy. As the stone falls, its gravitational potential energy will be transferred to kinetic energy, causing the stone's velocity to increase as it nears the ground.

To calculate the stone's velocity,

$$E_T = E_g + E_k = mgh + \tfrac{1}{2}mv^2 = 0.50 \text{ kg}(9.8 \text{ m/s}^2)(0 \text{ m}) + \tfrac{1}{2}(0.50 \text{ kg})v^2$$
$$= 15.9 \text{ J}$$

$$v = \sqrt{\frac{2(15.9 \text{ J})}{0.50 \text{ kg}}}$$

$$v = 8.0 \text{ m/s}$$

The speed of the stone as it reaches ground level is 8.0 m/s.

**EXAMPLE 14**   **Archery class**

A high school student shoots a 0.040 kg arrow straight up in the air at 30.0 m/s during an archery class in the school gym.

(a) Assuming no air resistance, what is the maximum height that the arrow could reach?

(b) How fast is the arrow going when it hits the ceiling at a height of 15.0 m?

*Solution and Connection to Theory*

**Given**
$m = 0.040 \text{ kg} \quad v = 30.0 \text{ m/s}$

First we need to determine the total mechanical energy.

At ground level, where $h = 0$, $E_g = 0$. Therefore, at ground level, the total mechanical energy, $E_T$, is expressed as kinetic energy.

$$E_T = E_g + E_k = 0 \text{ J} + \tfrac{1}{2}mv^2 = \tfrac{1}{2}(0.040 \text{ kg})(30.0 \text{ m/s})^2 = 18 \text{ J}$$

Now that we know the total mechanical energy, we know the total mechanical energy at maximum height.

(a) At maximum height, the speed of the arrow is zero. Therefore, kinetic energy is also zero. At this point, the total mechanical energy is entirely expressed as gravitational potential energy.

$$E_T = E_g + E_k = mgh + 0 \text{ J}$$

$$18 \text{ J} = (0.040 \text{ kg})(9.8 \text{ m/s}^2)h$$

$$h = \frac{18 \text{ J}}{0.392 \text{ kg} \cdot \text{m/s}^2} = 45.9 \text{ m}$$

The maximum height that this arrow could reach is 46 m.

(b) At the 15.0 m mark,

$$E_T = E_g + E_k = mgh + \tfrac{1}{2}mv^2$$

$$18 \text{ J} = 0.040 \text{ kg}(9.8 \text{ m/s}^2)(15.0 \text{ m}) + \tfrac{1}{2}(0.040 \text{ kg})v^2$$

$$18 \text{ J} = 5.88 \text{ J} + \tfrac{1}{2}(0.040 \text{ kg})v^2$$

$$v = \sqrt{\frac{18 \text{ J} - 5.88 \text{ J}}{0.020 \text{ kg}}} = 24 \text{ m/s}$$

At the ceiling, the arrow is travelling at 24 m/s, not much slower than it began.

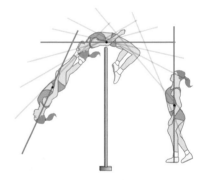

**Fig.7.18A**  Body motion over the high bar

## Olympic Athletics and the Conservation of Mechanical Energy

The athletics field at the XXVII Olympiad in Sydney, Australia saw many examples of the application of the law of conservation of energy. The high jump is an event in which the kinetic energy of the competitor's run is converted to gravitational potential energy. Figure 7.18 illustrates how physics can be used to analyze the complex motion of an athlete.

From a pure physics point of view, the high jump involves an athlete maximizing his or her speed so that he/she can maximize his/her horizontal kinetic energy. When a jump is executed, ideally most of the kinetic energy should be transferred to gravitational potential energy to give the athlete maximum height. Olympic athletes train extensively to make the transfer from kinetic to gravitational potential energy as efficient as possible (see Fig. 7.18). In the next section, we will learn that no energy transfer is perfect.

**Fig.7.18B**

**Fig.7.19**  Summary of the Conservation of Mechanical Energy

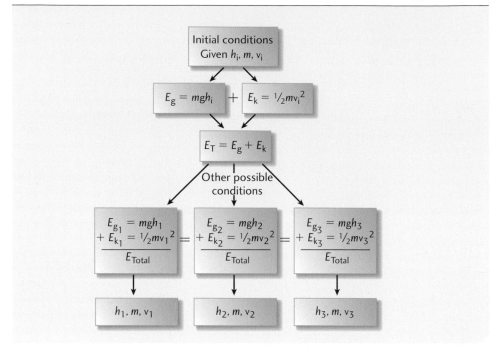

1. For the case of a rock thrown down from a cliff, calculate the following. Assume the rock is 6.5 kg and moving at 18 m/s down at the time it was thrown from a 120 m high cliff.
   a) The kinetic energy at the top of the cliff
   b) The potential energy at the top of the cliff
   c) The total mechanical energy at the top of the cliff
   d) The kinetic energy of the rock halfway down
   e) The speed of the rock halfway down
   f) The speed of the rock just as it hits the ground
   g) What height will the rock reach if thrown upwards with the velocity you found in Part f)?
2. Recalculate Part 1. g) using kinematics techniques.
3. Use your answer in 1. g) to find the speed of the rock as it falls back down to the cliff top. Use kinematics techniques first, then conservation of energy.

## Extreme Sports

Extreme sports are usually traditional sports taken to new danger levels. These sports have not only developed "new tricks for old dogs," but also a different attitude and dress. Skateboarding, BMX cycling (terrain, street, vert or $\frac{1}{2}$ pipe), rock climbing, air surfing, bungee jumping, heli-skiing, snowboarding, wakeboarding, and extreme skiing are a few extreme sports that have gained major followings.

**Fig.7.20**

**4.** Use the transfer of energy (from gravitational potential energy to kinetic energy and vice versa) along with the law of conservation of energy to describe three extreme sports. Discuss where energy is lost and what form this energy takes (heat, sound, shape changes, etc.).

## 7.8 Efficiency of Energy Transfer Processes

When energy is transferred from one form to another, according to the law of conservation of energy, none of the energy is destroyed. However, some of it is transferred to a form that is not useful for its intended purpose. Figure 7.21 shows how the electrical energy of two different types of light bulbs is transferred into useful light energy, but some of it is also transferred to heat energy.

Even though the newer technology of the compact fluorescent light bulb produces a greater proportion of light than the standard light bulb, there is still some energy lost to heat. Recall from Fig. 7.16 that our ball bounce was never 100% efficient because some energy was transferred elsewhere. Very few energy transfers are perfect or 100% efficient, so physicists have developed a simple way of ranking exactly how complete an energy transfer is. This ranking is called **efficiency** and is based on a percentage scale.

$$\text{Efficiency} = \frac{\text{useful output energy}}{\text{total input energy}} \times 100\%$$

We transfer energy either to generate a useful form of energy, such as electricity, or to do useful and productive things, like lighting our houses or running our cars. Cars are extremely inefficient: only about 10% of a car's fuel energy is used to move the car. Engineers have turned some of this waste heat energy into "useful energy" for heating the passenger compartment during the winter months. Unfortunately, this does nothing to improve the efficiency of the car. Later in the text, we will discuss in greater detail how energy is transferred in generating electrical energy.

**Fig.7.21** Energy comparison between light bulbs

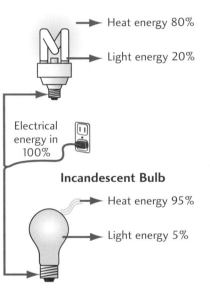

**Compact Fluorescent Bulb**

Heat energy 80%
Light energy 20%

Electrical energy in 100%

**Incandescent Bulb**

Heat energy 95%
Light energy 5%

**Fig.7.22**

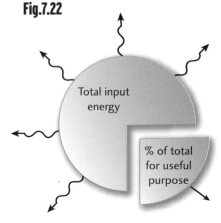

Total input energy

% of total for useful purpose

---

**EXAMPLE 15** **Efficiency of a crane**

What is the efficiency of a crane that uses $5.10 \times 10^5$ J of energy to lift 1000 kg a vertical height of 32.0 m?

### *Solution and Connection to Theory*

**Given**

$E_{\text{input}} = 5.10 \times 10^5 \text{ J}$    $m = 1000 \text{ kg}$    $h = 32.0 \text{ m}$    $g = 9.8 \text{ m/s}^2$

The useful energy can be found by the gain in gravitational potential energy, $E_g$.

$$E_g = mgh = 1000 \text{ kg}(9.8 \text{ m/s}^2)(32.0 \text{ m}) = 3.14 \times 10^5 \text{ J}$$

Then the efficiency is

$$\text{Efficiency} = \frac{E_{\text{useful output}}}{E_{\text{input}}} \times 100\%$$

$$\text{Efficiency} = \frac{3.14 \times 10^5 \text{ J}}{5.10 \times 10^5 \text{ J}} \times 100\%$$

$$\text{Efficiency} = 61.6\%$$

Therefore, the crane is 61.6% efficient.

---

### EXAMPLE 16  Lighting efficiency

A particular light bulb is known to be 7.5% efficient.

(a) How much light energy would actually be provided by a 100 W light bulb in one minute of operation?

(b) What would be the effective "light power" from this 100 W bulb?

Example 16 (b) illustrates that the efficiency equation can also be applied to power, not just energy.

### Solution and Connection to Theory

**Given**

Efficiency = 7.5%     $P_{\text{input}} = 100$ W

$$t = 1 \text{ min}\left(\frac{60 \text{ s}}{1 \text{ min}}\right) = 60 \text{ s}$$

(a) The energy input, $E_{\text{input}}$, can be calculated. Recall $P = \dfrac{E}{t}$.

$$E_{\text{input}} = Pt = (100 \text{ W})(60 \text{ s}) = 6000 \text{ J}$$

$$E_{\text{useful output}} = \frac{\text{Efficiency} \times E_{\text{input}}}{100\%}$$

$$E_{\text{useful output}} = \frac{7.5\% \times 6000 \text{ J}}{100\%}$$

$$E_{\text{useful output}} = 450 \text{ J}$$

(b) $P = \dfrac{E}{t}$

$$= \frac{450 \text{ J}}{60 \text{ s}}$$

$$= 7.5 \text{ W}$$

Therefore, the actual light energy provided would be 450 J/min.

**Fig.7.23** Efficiency of Energy Transfer

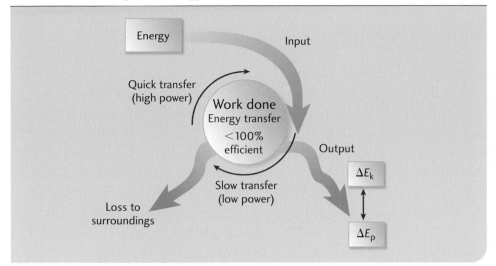

◀ ◀ ◀ ◀ ◀  PUTTING it all Together

1. In general terms, compare the efficiency of producing energy from waterfalls to that of burning wood or fossil fuels (remember the fuel must be obtained somehow). How does using a windmill or solar panels compare to burning wood or fossil fuels? What benefits are there to using methods other than burning materials?

2. In general, the greater the number of steps in transferring energy, the less efficient the process. Why is this so?

◀ ◀ ◀ ◀ ◀  APPLYING the Concepts

## Heat Pumps

A conventional way to heat a house is to use a heating source inside the house (burning gas or oil, or heating a wire using electricity). The heat is then distributed throughout the house through a blower-duct system. Ideally, the energy that powers the heating system (electrical or chemical) is all converted to heat energy.

**Heat pumps** are units that sit outside the house. They are essentially refrigerators in reverse. They cool on one side of the pump and heat on the other side. (The refrigerator gives off a lot of energy in the form of heat, usually by way of cooling coils at the back of the fridge.) The heat pump *uses the heat available outside the house to transfer heat from outside to inside*, thereby decreasing the total amount of energy used to heat a house. For example, if we heat our house strictly from the inside using conventional sources like propane, gas, or oil, we use about 3500 J of energy per day. Using a heat pump, we would use only about 2500 J. The heat pump extracts the remaining 1000 J, from outside the house. As well as being more energy efficient, the heat pump can be run in reverse, acting like an air conditioner in the summer.

3. If the heat pump is so much more efficient, why doesn't everyone use it? Research to find the answer.

4. Research the Carnot engine. Compare it to the heat pump. What are the differences in terms of efficiency?

**Fig.STSE.7.1**   Extreme sports use
extreme physics

# Bungee Jumping

Bungee jumping is one of a new breed of activities called "extreme sports." The bungee jumper jumps from a high structure and free falls for a few seconds before being snatched from impact by an elastic "bungee" cord tethered to his or her ankles. The photo (Fig. STSE.7.1) illustrates how dangerous this activity can be without the correct safety measures in place. Much of these safety parameters are based on classical mechanics and the conservation of energy. The first graph (Fig. STSE.7.2) profiles the forces that are exerted on the jumper at different stages of the fall. The green arrows represent the force of gravity, which is constant throughout. The brown arrows represent the force exerted upward on the person by the bungee. As it becomes taut, it stretches, resulting in a constant increase of its upward force.

Figure STSE.7.3 illustrates how energy is conserved during the jump. As the gravitational potential energy drops during the first part of the free fall, the kinetic energy, and therefore the speed of the participant, increases. As the bungee becomes taut, the loss in gravitational potential energy is compensated for by a corresponding increase in the elastic potential energy of the bungee. At any point in the activity, the sum of the kinetic and elastic potential energies of the bungee is equal to the gravitational potential energy lost during the fall.

**Fig.STSE.7.2**   A force profile

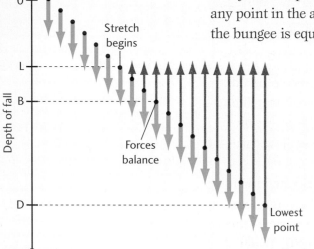

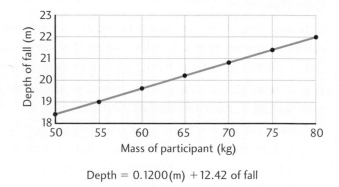

Depth = 0.1200(m) + 12.42 of fall

**Fig.STSE.7.3**

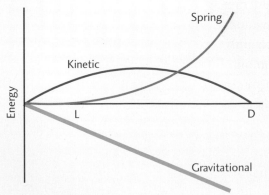

The jumper's kinetic energy becomes zero when he or she has stopped falling. The work done to stop the fall is related to the stiffness of the bungee cord. The cord acts like a spring that obeys Hooke's law. Table STSE.7.1 and the graph show the acceptable mass range for a cord with a moderate force constant of 204 N/m for a 22 m fall. Anyone over 80 kg won't stop in time to avoid hitting the ground.

| Medium Cord Range (length of 9.0 metres) | | | | | |
|---|---|---|---|---|---|
| Mass of person (kg) | Force of gravity $\vec{F}_g$ (N) | Length of bungee L (m) | Bungee spring constant k (N/m) | Bungee stretch d (m) | Depth of fall d + L (m) |
| 50 | 490 | 9 | 204 | 9.40 | 18.40 |
| 55 | 539 | 9 | 204 | 10.03 | 19.03 |
| 60 | 588 | 9 | 204 | 10.64 | 19.64 |
| 65 | 637 | 9 | 204 | 11.24 | 20.24 |
| 70 | 686 | 9 | 204 | 11.84 | 20.84 |
| 75 | 735 | 9 | 204 | 12.43 | 21.43 |
| 80 | 784 | 9 | 204 | 13.01 | 22.01 |

## Design a Study of Societal Impact

Thrill seekers often depend on others to ensure their safety when taking part in extreme sports such as bungie jumping, sky-diving, or white-water rafting.

- What was the original purpose of bungee cords?
- Do bungee cord manufacturers make their product with the high level of quality control needed to ensure safety when jumping?

## Design an Activity to Evaluate

Simulate a bungee cord using elastic bands or surgical or rubber tubing. Attach masses to the elastic and analyze their motion using a video camera, video point software, a sonic ranger motion detector, and a computer interface.

Evaluate a video tape of actual bungee jumps with video point software or using frame-by-frame advance. Plot the data and analyze the velocity, the kinetic energy, and the gravitational potential energy throughout the jump.

## Build a Structure

Design and build a small adjustable bungee jumping platform. Release a "test mass" attached to a "bungee" from a certain height such that it just touches the ground with a velocity close to zero. Use a "floor" made of smooth and pliable putty to test the results of the impact.

Hold a competition in which, given a certain mass and platform height, you have to select a length and stiffness of "bungee" to keep the mass from striking the ground, or to reach a specific height.

## SPECIFIC EXPECTATIONS

**You should be able to**

*Understand Basic Concepts:*
- Describe the relationship between matter and energy.
- Compare and contrast the concepts of work and energy with respect to their relationship with each other and their units.
- Define energy and describe how it manifests itself in different forms.
- Identify the conditions required for work to be done and calculate the work done when displacement occurs along the line of force.
- Define and describe the concept of power and apply the quantitative relationships among power, energy, and time.
- Derive the formula for kinetic energy from work and kinematics formulas and use it to solve problems involving energy transformations.
- Define the law of conservation of energy and apply it to solve problems involving a closed system of conservation of mechanical energy.
- Analyze in quantitative terms the relationship between percent efficiency, input energy, and useful output energy for different energy transformations.

*Develop Skills of Inquiry and Communication:*
- Design and carry out experiments related to the energy transformations involved in a swinging pendulum.
- Verify the law of conservation of mechanical energy for a car as it rolls down a track by analyzing experimental data taken using an electronic photo gate or video camera.
- Perform an experiment to determine the power produced by a student and present this data to the class in graphical and tabulated form.

*Relate Science to Technology, Society, and the Environment:*
- Describe how work and the law of conservation of energy are involved in various sports activities such as high jump.
- Relate the improvement of performance in a sport such as karate to the knowledge and application of the concepts of force, work, and power.
- Use the law of conservation of energy and the concept of elastic potential energy to analyze the role of physics in safety measures for extreme sports such as bungee jumping.

### Equations

$$W = \vec{F}\Delta\vec{d}$$

$$W = F(\cos\theta)\Delta d$$

$$W = mg\Delta\vec{d}$$

$$E_g = mg\Delta h \text{ or } E_g = mgh$$

$$P = \frac{W}{t} = \frac{E}{t}$$

$$E_k = \tfrac{1}{2}mv^2$$

$$mg\Delta h_1 + \tfrac{1}{2}mv_1^2 = mg\Delta h_2 + \tfrac{1}{2}mv_2^2$$

$$\text{Efficiency} = \left(\frac{\text{Useful output energy}}{\text{Input energy}}\right)100\,\%$$

## Conceptual Questions

1. After pushing against a brick wall for a long time, you are feeling extremely tired, but you have not done any work on the wall. Explain.

2. Using the law of conservation of energy, explain what is going on in the motion of a simple pendulum.

3. You now can appreciate that the energy required to make your morning coffee has taken part in many transformations along its "lifetime." Create a list of at least three energy transformations that the energy has undergone, in the appropriate order.

4. Give three examples in which a force is exerted but no work is done.

5. A tennis ball and a squash ball are dropped from the same height, but the tennis ball returns to a higher height than the squash ball after the first bounce. What is happening with the kinetic energy in each case to explain the difference? Which ball has the most efficient bounce?

6. By what factor does the kinetic energy of an object change if its speed is doubled?

7. Describe the energy changes that take place when a small spring-driven toy vehicle is wound up and then released.

8. A billiard player transfers energy to the cue ball to set it in motion. In terms of energy, describe what happens when the ball bounces straight back off the side cushion.

9. A baseball and a car can have the same kinetic energy. If this is true, what must be different about them? What else can be the same?

10. Although energy is conserved in the sense that none of it really disappears, why should we be concerned about conserving energy in our daily lives?

11. Many Canadians "count calories" or Joules of energy that they consume while on a diet. The human body is only about 25% efficient in converting stored energy from body fat to actual mechanical energy, such as the gravitational potential energy ($mg\Delta h$) required to lift weights during a workout. Where does the other 75% of the stored energy go?

## Problems

### 7.2 Work, the Transfer of Energy

12. A toddler pushes a chair at a constant speed with a force of 25.0 N for a distance of 2.5 m. How much work is the child doing on the chair?

13. A businesswoman is applying a force of 12.0 N [upwards] to carry her briefcase for a horizontal distance of 200.0 m. How much work is she doing on the briefcase?

14. Some physicists with nothing better to do measured the force that teachers were applying to a rope during a staff-student tug of war. The force that was applied by the teachers was 6 000 N. How much work did they do on the other team during the two minutes in which they did not move at all?

15. 4 050 J of work was done on a pile of snow to move it 3.4 m. What force must have been applied by the snow plow to do this work?

16. How far is an arrow drawn horizontally in a bow if 1 020 J of work was done on it by an average applied force of 2525 N?

17. The toddler in Problem 12 still applies the same 25.0 N force to the chair over a distance of 2.5 m, but this time the chair is being pushed across a smooth floor against a force of friction (resistance of 10.0 N). How much work is being done now?

18. A father is pulling his two girls in their toboggan with a force of 500 N for a distance of 22 m. Calculate the work that would be done by the father in each of the following cases.
    a) The snow provides no friction.
    b) One of the children drags her hands in the snow, producing a frictional force of 500 N.
    c) What visible difference would you see in the motion between a) and b)?

19. How much work is done on a 750 kg load of bricks by a bricklayer if he carried the bricks upward to a height of 8.2 m to repair a chimney?

20. If the bricklayer in Problem 19 decided to use a motor-driven rope lift that can do 2 000 J of work, what mass of bricks could be lifted to the 8.2 m height?

21. A woman pushes a shopping cart with a force of 75 N at a constant speed of 0.75 m/s for an hour around a grocery store. How much work does she do on the cart?

22. The school caretaker is applying a 200 N force 45° to the horizontal to push a lawn mower a horizontal distance of 20.0 m, as shown in Fig. 7.24. How much work does he do on the lawn mower, assuming no friction?

**Fig. 7.24**

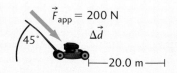

$\vec{F}_{app}$ = 200 N
$\vec{\Delta d}$
45°
—20.0 m—

## ▷ 7.3 Power, the Rate of Energy Transfer

23. If a hair dryer does 3 000 J of work to heat the air every two seconds, what is its power?

24. How much electrical energy is used by a 100 W light bulb if it was accidentally left on for eight hours?

25. A snow blower does $1.8 \times 10^6$ J of work in 0.600 h. What is its power?

26. How long would it take a 1.00 kW electric motor on a conveyor belt to do 750 J of work?

27. A 613.0 kg mass is placed on a forklift that can generate 950 W of power. What is the constant speed of the forklift while lifting this load?

28. Water is pumped up to a water tower, which is 92.0 m high. The flow rate up to the top of the tower is 75 L/s and each litre of water has a mass of 1.00 kg. What power is required to keep up this flow rate to the tower?

## ▷ 7.4 Kinetic Energy

29. What is the kinetic energy of a 60.0 g tennis ball that is travelling at
    a) 10.0 m/s?      b) 25.0 m/s?

30. What is the mass of an object that is travelling at 10.0 m/s with a kinetic energy of 370 J?

31. A 37.0 g arrow is shot from a crossbow at 234.0 km/h. What is the arrow's kinetic energy?

32. A 2000 kg truck is travelling at 80 km/h. What is the kinetic energy of the truck?

33. What speed would the truck in Problem 32 have if its kinetic energy was cut in half by applying the brakes?

**34.** How much work is done by an Olympic triathlete who accelerates herself on her bicycle (a combined mass of 105 kg) from 5.0 m/s to 10.0 m/s?

**35.** At what speed must a 250.0 kg motorcycle be travelling to have a kinetic energy of
**a)** $2.8 \times 10^4$ J?    **b)** $1.12 \times 10^5$ J?

## 7.5 Gravitational Potential Energy

**36.** How much gravitational potential energy would a 275.0 g book have if it was placed on a shelf
**a)** 2.60 m high?    **b)** 1.80 m high?
**c)** 0.30 m high?

**37.** A man decides to climb an office tower using the stairs. If the floors are 3.8 m apart, how much gravitational potential energy would the man have relative to the ground floor if he made it to the
**a)** fifth floor?    **b)** tenth floor?
**c)** the first basement level?

**38.** What percentage of its gravitational potential energy does a squash ball lose if it falls from 3.0 m and returns to a height of 0.76 m after bouncing once?

**39.** A cliff at the Elora Gorge is 19.6 m above the surface of the Grand River, which is 5.34 m deep. What is a 70.0 kg cliff diver's gravitational potential energy from the top of the cliff with respect to the water's surface and with respect to the bottom of the river?

**40.** A 1.00 kg book falls 0.75 m from a desk to the floor. How much potential energy did the book lose?

## 7.7 Conservation of Mechanical Energy

**41.** A 5.0 kg rock is dropped from a height of 92.0 m. What is the kinetic energy and the gravitational potential energy when the rock is 40.0 m from the ground?

**42.** A ball of mass 240 g is moving through the air at 20.0 m/s with a gravitational potential energy of 70 J. With what speed will the ball hit the ground?

**43.** A basketball rolls off the rim and falls to the floor from a height of 3.05 m. Then it bounces up and loses 15 % of its kinetic energy. To what height will it rise this time?

**44.** The Jetscream amusement park ride at Paramount Canada's Wonderland is shown in Fig. 7.25. It starts off by swinging like a simple pendulum until its amplitude becomes so great that it swings completely around. If the diameter of the circle is 30.0 m, what speed must the ship have at the very bottom to just make it to the highest point and sit there with no residual speed?

**Fig.7.25**

## 7.8 Efficiency of Energy Transfer Processes

45. A water pump is run by an electric motor with a power rating of 750 W. It is used to pump water from a reservoir up to a height of 37.0 m and into a water tower at a rate of 1.48 kg of water per second.
    a) What is the useful energy output, $E_{useful\ output}$?
    b) How much energy does the water pump actually use?
    c) What is the efficiency of the water pump?

46. If a karate blow that can transfer 35.0 J of energy is only 25 % efficient, what maximum velocity can the 70.0 kg target ever reach?

47. Several students in an auto shop class need to lift an engine out of a car using a rope and pulley system. The mass of the engine is 170.0 kg. By pulling as a team, the students can exert a force of about $1.72 \times 10^3$ N to lift the engine to the necessary height of 2.20 m.
    a) How much "useful work" was done by the students?
    b) How much work was done in total to lift the engine?
    c) What was the overall efficiency of the students in lifting the engine?
    d) One of the students recommends that all of her friends who helped lift the engine should receive a final grade equal to their percent efficiency. The shop teacher claims that this would be unfair to the students because none of them could ever achieve 100 % efficiency. Explain.

## Purpose

To examine if the total mechanical energy of a pendulum is conserved when it swings.

## Equipment

Metre stick
One large mass (1 kg)
String
Support/ceiling hook
Timing device (photogate and millisecond timer or Computer interface, video camera, or spark timer and tickertape)

## Procedure

1. Read all of the procedures and make a quick list of all measurements that you need to take. Create a table for recording all your data.
2. Construct the apparatus, as shown in the diagram.
3. Set up your timing apparatus so that the speed of the pendulum bob can be measured at the bottom of a swing.
4. Perform all initial data measurements (see data section).
5. Pull the pendulum bob aside and measure the bob's height once again, above your reference level (floor or table).
6. Release the bob. With the photogate and millisecond timer (or other method specific to your school equipment), measure the speed with which the bob passes the rest position at the very bottom of the swing (Fig. Lab.7.1).
7. Stop the pendulum before it swings back for another cycle.

## Data

1. With the pendulum at rest, measure its height from the table or floor above which it is suspended.
2. Measure the height above the same reference level after pulling the bob aside.
3. Measure the speed of the pendulum at its lowest point during a swing. Use a photogate and millisecond timer or computer interface.

## Uncertainty

Assign both instrumental and procedural uncertainties for each time you used the ruler.

You should have a combined instrumental and procedural uncertainty for each of the two heights measured as well as for the speed of the pendulum. Check with your teacher about the uncertainty in the speed because it may be complicated by the timing/speed measurement method that you use in your school.

**Fig.Lab.7.1**

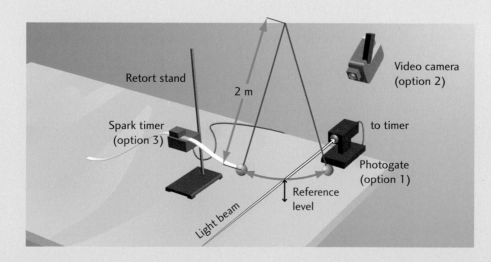

Retort stand
2 m
Video camera (option 2)
Spark timer (option 3)
to timer
Photogate (option 1)
Reference level
Light beam

## Analysis

1. If you have not already done so, calculate the speed of the pendulum at the lowest point in the swing.
2. Find the difference in height between the rest position of the bob and the position when the bob was pulled sideways.
3. Calculate the gravitational potential energy when the pendulum was pulled aside and when it passed the lowest point in the swing.
4. Using the concept of the conservation of mechanical energy, calculate the expected speed of the pendulum at the bottom of the swing. Be sure to use uncertainty analysis for all calculations.

## Discussion

1. Within the margins of experimental uncertainty, was the total mechanical energy conserved during the swing?

2. If your activity used a spark timer or any other system that placed a "drag" on the pendulum, you would not expect it to show the conservation of energy. If conservation of energy was not demonstrated in your activity, calculate the percentage of the original gravitational potential energy that was transferred to the kinetic energy of the pendulum.
3. Explain where the mechanical energy is lost as the amplitude of the swinging pendulum decreases.

## Conclusion

Did your activity show that the total mechanical energy was conserved? Use the percentage calculation of your original value for $E_g$ to prove your point.

# LAB 7.2 Conservation of Mechanical Energy: Motion of a Rolling Object

## Purpose

To examine how gravitational potential energy, kinetic energy, and total mechanical energy are related as an object rolls down a ramp.

## Equipment

Toy car track or three different planks of wood and support (see the diagram)

Steel ball bearing or toy car

Metre stick

Video camera and tripod

VCR and T.V. for video playback

Overhead transparency

Overhead transparency marker

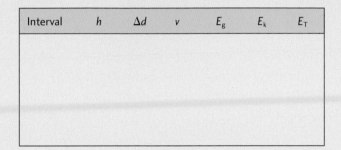

| Interval | $h$ | $\Delta d$ | $v$ | $E_g$ | $E_k$ | $E_T$ |
|----------|-----|------------|-----|-------|-------|-------|
|          |     |            |     |       |       |       |
|          |     |            |     |       |       |       |
|          |     |            |     |       |       |       |
|          |     |            |     |       |       |       |

## Procedure

1. Prepare a data table to record measurements for 10 or more intervals. For each data point, you will measure height and displacement, and calculate speed, gravitational potential energy, kinetic energy, and total energy.

2. Set up the track as shown in the Fig. Lab.7.2, using either the toy track or the three planks.

3. Set the video camera on the tripod so that the entire track is visible from the side. (The track should appear as in the diagram through the camera's view finder.)

4. Be sure that the metre stick is in full view of the camera during the activity.

5. Set the camera to record on SP mode and release the cart or ball. Using a faster shutter speed will make individual frame pictures sharper.

6. After the run is done, rewind the video tape and replay the scene on a television screen.

7. Place an overhead transparency on the television screen (static will make it stick).

**Fig.Lab.7.2**

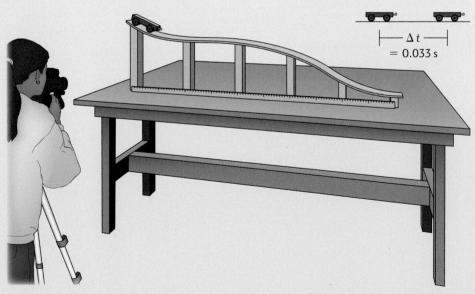

$$\vdash \Delta t \dashv$$
$$= 0.033\,s$$

8. With the camera playing frame by frame, place a dot on the overhead transparency, marking the image of the moving object at each frame with an overhead marker.

9. Place a dot at both ends of the visible metre stick to mark your scale. Finally, draw a horizontal base line along the bottom of the scene, as shown in the diagram.

## Uncertainty

Assign an instrumental and a procedural uncertainty for every measurement that you take.

## Analysis

1. Take the transparency back to your desk. With a ruler, draw a connecting line between each consecutive dot. With another colour of marker, place another dot halfway through the interval.

2. Number these new dots consecutively from the top of the trip to the bottom of the trip.

3. Measure the height from the baseline to the numbered dots and correct for scale. Enter these values in the data table as $h$.

4. Measure the distance travelled between the original dots on each side of the numbered ones, correct for scale, and record this value as $\Delta d$.

5. Find $v$ by dividing the $\Delta d$ value by $\frac{1}{30}$ of a second. This is the time interval between each frame on a VHS video tape that has been recorded at SP speed.

6. Calculate the $E_g$, the $E_k$, and the total energy, $E_T$, using the mass that you measured.

7. On one set of axes, plot a graph of the three forms of energy found in this lab. The time axis can be calibrated in intervals instead of seconds.

## Discussion

1. Look at the data in the total energy column. What should this data look like on a graph if the total energy is conserved over the entire trip?

2. It is very difficult to show that energy was conserved because it is transferred to other forms of energy. Into what other forms could the mechanical energy in this lab be transferred?

## Conclusion

Make a final summary statement about your lab data and the way that it either verified or did not verify the law of conservation of energy. If you didn't verify it, then suggest reasons why.

## Purpose

To calculate the efficiency of an inclined plane when it is used to do work to raise a cart.

## Equipment

Inclined plane
Bricks or books for propping
Skateboard or lab cart
Newton spring scale
Metre stick

## Fig.Lab.7.3

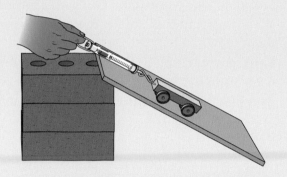

## Procedure

1. Set up the lab apparatus as shown in Fig. Lab.7.3.
2. Prepare a data table for all of your measured values, their uncertainty, and any analysis calculations. This should be of your own design and should be done after you have read the lab to see what is required.
3. Measure both the vertical height ($h$) and the length ($l$) of the inclined plane.
4. Use the newton spring scale to measure the weight of the cart (or skateboard) by hanging the cart freely on the spring scale.
5. Hook the spring scale on to the cart and slowly pull the cart up the ramp, taking note of the average force that is required.
6. Repeat Steps 3–5 for two more heights of incline and two more masses.

## Data

Be sure that you have measured the vertical height ($h$), the length of the ramp ($l$), the force of gravity on the cart ($\vec{F}_g$), and the force applied ($\vec{F}_{app}$) to pull it up the ramp.

## Uncertainty

Be sure that the newton spring scale is calibrated to zero before you take any measurements. Assign both instrumental and procedural uncertainty for each time you used the ruler and the newton spring scale (usually $\pm 0.5$ mm for a metre stick).

## Analysis

1. If the weight of the cart exceeds the capacity of the spring scale, then you may calculate $\vec{F}_g$ by finding the mass of the cart and using $\vec{F}_g = mg$.
2. Calculate the useful energy output (work that would be required to just lift the cart vertically through the distance $h$).
3. Calculate the energy input (actual work done to raise the cart vertically along the length ($l$) using the inclined plane).
4. Finally, calculate the efficiency of the inclined plane using the relationship

$$\text{Efficiency} = \frac{\text{(useful energy output)}}{\text{(energy input)}} \times 100\%$$

## Discussion

1. What is the efficiency and its uncertainty for the inclined plane and your cart?
2. Find one lab group that achieved an efficiency that was either higher or lower than yours. What adjustment to your lab setup could be done to increase the efficiency of your task?
3. Based on your answer to Question 2 above, what would be the maximum possible efficiency that could be achieved?

## Conclusion

In a concise format, state your results for this lab.

Power Output of a Typical Student

## Purpose

To examine which physical characteristics of students affect how much power they can generate when performing an activity such as running up a flight of stairs.

## Equipment

Metre stick
Balance/scale calibrated in kilograms
Stopwatch
Students*
*Caution: Students who have health problems or are wearing inappropriate or unsafe footwear should not participate in this activity.

## Procedure

1. Prepare a data chart that has the following headings: Student Name, Mass (kg), Weight (N), Vertical Height (m), Work Done (J), Time (s), Power (W), Ranking.
2. Measure the mass of each participant in kilograms.
3. One student in the class should measure the height of one of the steps in the stairwell that you are using and count the total number of these steps.
4. Time each student to see how long it takes him or her to run from the bottom step to the top step from a standing start (Fig. Lab.7.4).

## Data

1. Record all of the data in the chart that was previously prepared.
2. Calculate the weight of each student using the formula $\vec{F}_g = mg$.
3. Find the total height of the flight of stairs and record it in metres.

## Uncertainty

For this activity, assign both instrumental and procedural uncertainties for all measured quantities, including the mass and the time for each trip. Be sure to take a few step measurements to decide if each step is in fact a consistent height. As a class or in groups, decide what uncertainty margins should be left for the total height of the stairs.

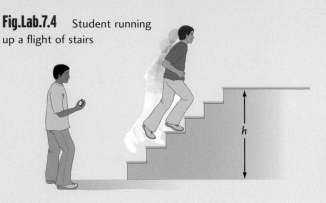

**Fig.Lab.7.4** Student running up a flight of stairs

## Analysis

1. Calculate the work done using the formula $W = mgh$, and calculate the power using $P = \frac{W}{\Delta t}$.
2. Rank the students in the "Ranking" column using numbers, assigning a "1" to the student who had the greatest power, and so on.

## Discussion

1. For this activity, is the uncertainty analysis of key importance?
2. Review the power ranking for the various students and prepare a list of the five most powerful students. Next to each student's name, choose at least three words from the following list (or come up with your own words) to describe the reason why these students had the most power: tall/short, strong, agile, heavy/light, thin, athletic, alert, fast, etc.
3. Review the power equation from a mathematical standpoint. Because the formula is a fraction, to maximize the power, a participant could be heavy (large mass) or run up the stairs the fastest (less time). Either one of these factors could increase a participant's power. Explain why the power output of two students of the same mass could be very different.

## Conclusion

In a short sentence or paragraph, summarize the characteristics of the students in your class who achieved maximum power output.

# Thermal Energy and Heat Transfer

## By the end of this chapter, you will be able to

- describe how heat is transferred between substances
- quantitatively account for the heat energy involved in a change of state
- apply the principles of heat transfer to calorimetry to explain certain phenomena

# 8.1 Introduction to Thermal Energy —Kinetic Molecular Theory

How do you feel right now? If you are ill, you may be running a fever, i.e., your body temperature may be higher than normal. You may not be able to concentrate while reading this text because the temperature of the room is too hot or too cold. You may also be reading this book waiting for your hot chocolate to cool. All of these cases show how important heat and temperature are to us.

**Heat** is the energy of motion or the kinetic energy of matter at the atomic and molecular levels. In 1827, Robert Brown observed the vibration of pollen grains bombarded by air particles. He concluded that all matter at the molecular level moves constantly in a random and erratic fashion. We call this motion **Brownian motion**. Since that time, other scientists, including Albert Einstein, have further developed what is now called the kinetic molecular theory and have used its ideas to solidify current ideas of atomic theory. The main postulates of the **kinetic molecular** theory are:

- All matter is made up of small, constantly moving particles called atoms and groups of atoms called molecules.
- These atoms and molecules exert forces on one another that keep them a certain distance apart. If they move too close to each other, a repulsive force pushes them apart. Likewise, if they move too far apart, an attractive force brings them together.
- The distances between molecules and the strength of force between them is responsible for the three physical states of matter: solid, liquid, and gas. The major features of the three states of matter are outlined in Table 8.1.

## Table 8.1
### The States of Matter

| Solids | Liquids | Gases |
|---|---|---|
| In solids, strong forces hold the vibrating atoms and molecules so closely that they remain in a fixed position, giving solids their rigid nature. | In liquids, vibrating atoms are still bound together, but with greater speeds, these particles may move from place to place in the liquid. Liquids clump together, but they are less rigid than solids and can take the shape of the container they are in without changing volume. | The particles that make up gases are held by even weaker forces of attraction. These faster-moving particles tend to "get as far away from each other as possible." Gases expand in volume to take the shape of the container they are in. |

**Fig.8.1**

**Fig.8.2**

**Fig.8.3**

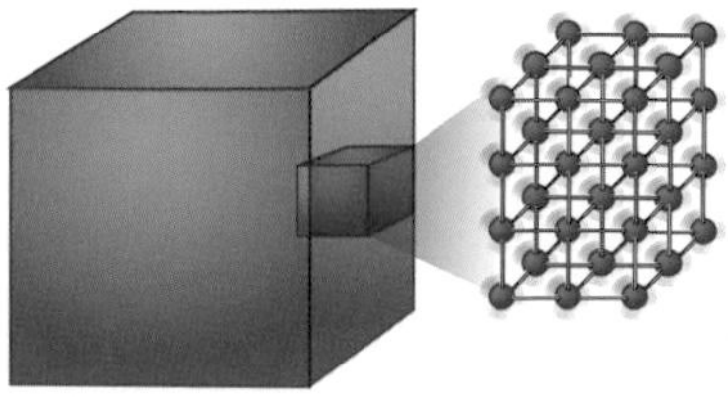

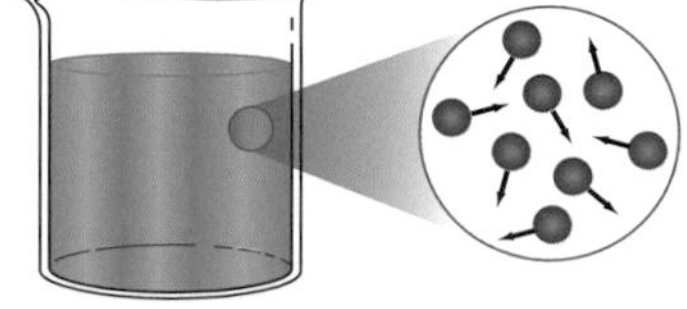

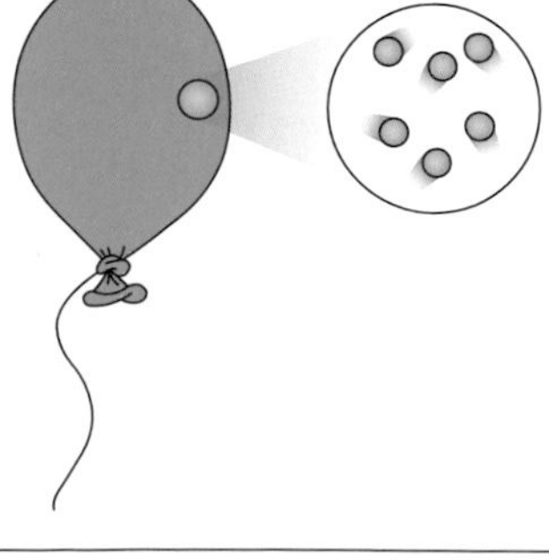

UNIT B: Work, Energy, and Power

The motion of these molecules is due to energy transformations between electrostatic potential energy and particle kinetic energy. The total thermal energy must take into account both of these energies.

In the next few sections, we will be discussing heat or thermal energy and the impact that it has on our lives.

1. Use the kinetic molecular theory to describe the differences in molecular motion in the three states of matter.
2. Describe what heat is in terms of kinetic energy.

## 8.2 Thermal Energy and Temperature

As all particles of matter are constantly moving and interacting in a random fashion, the actual amount of energy that they possess is too difficult to quantify because it is constantly fluctuating. **Temperature** is simply a way to measure the *average* kinetic energy of all of the particles in a quantity of matter. There are various ways of measuring the temperature of a substance. All of them show a visible change when the average kinetic energy of the substance they are measuring changes.

**Thermal expansion** is the increase in volume of a substance when it is heated. Thermal energy increases the atomic and molecular kinetic energies of the particles that make up the substance, causing an increase in the average distance between them.

A **thermometer**, a device for measuring temperature, operates according to the principle of thermal expansion. Table 8.2 describes different kinds of thermometers.

Before you can use a thermometer to measure temperature, you first need to *calibrate* it using reference points and a scale or unit of measure. Several different temperature scales have been used since thermometers were invented. Figure 8.4 shows the relationship between three common scales.

**Fahrenheit.** Daniel Fahrenheit used the lowest temperature of an ice-salt bath and body temperature to calibrate his thermometers. On this scale, freezing and boiling points appeared at 32°F and 212°F, respectively.

**Celsius.** Anders Celsius used the freezing and boiling points of water for his two calibration points of reference. He then divided this range into 100 degrees. *A lowercase t represents Celsius temperature.*

**Kelvin.** William Thomson (Lord Kelvin) devised a scale to put zero at the lowest possible temperature, when all molecular

**Fig.8.4** A comparison of three different temperature scales

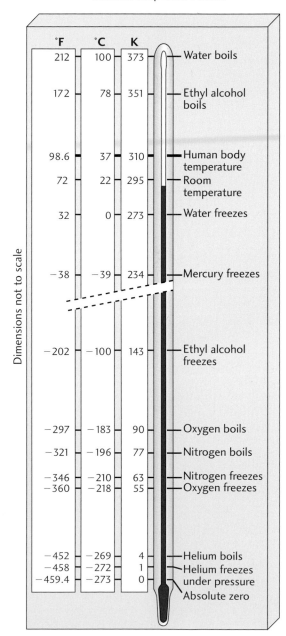

Physical chemists use Charles' law $\left(\frac{V_1}{T_1} = \frac{V_2}{T_2}\right)$ to describe the relationship between the volume (*V*) and the temperature (*T*) of gases at constant pressure. If we use the Celsius scale for temperature, at 0°C, the ratio $\frac{V}{T}$ is undefined, so instead they use the Kelvin scale.

motion stops. The size of a degree Kelvin is the same as that of a degree Celsius. The lowest temperature is called absolute zero and is determined experimentally to be −273°C. The SI unit of temperature is the kelvin (K) without a ° symbol. The freezing point of water is 273 K and the boiling point of water is 373 K.

The Celsius scale was used in the original metric system. The Kelvin scale is required in many branches of science with calculations involving temperature. *An uppercase* T *represents Kelvin temperature.*

| Table 8.2 Types of Thermometers | |
|---|---|
| Thermometer | Construction |
| **Liquid Filled Thermometer** A trapped liquid expands when heated and contracts when cooled. In a long thin tube, a liquid column moves up and down in relation to the temperature. | 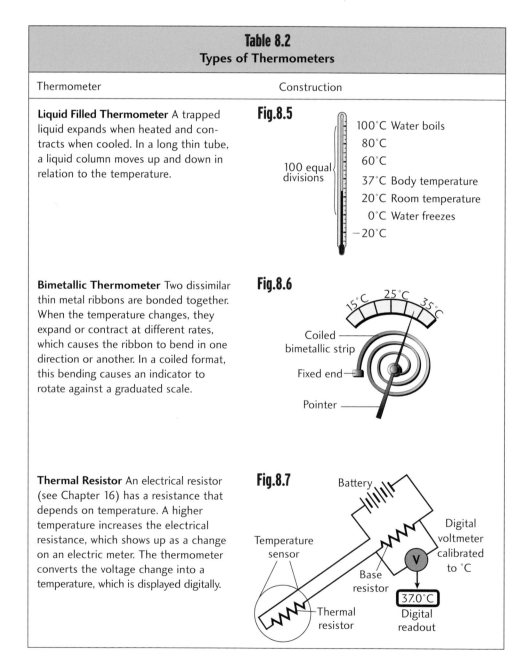 |
| **Bimetallic Thermometer** Two dissimilar thin metal ribbons are bonded together. When the temperature changes, they expand or contract at different rates, which causes the ribbon to bend in one direction or another. In a coiled format, this bending causes an indicator to rotate against a graduated scale. | |
| **Thermal Resistor** An electrical resistor (see Chapter 16) has a resistance that depends on temperature. A higher temperature increases the electrical resistance, which shows up as a change on an electric meter. The thermometer converts the voltage change into a temperature, which is displayed digitally. | |

**Fig.8.5**
100 equal divisions
100°C Water boils
80°C
60°C
37°C Body temperature
20°C Room temperature
0°C Water freezes
−20°C

**Fig.8.6**
15°C   25°C   35°C
Coiled bimetallic strip
Fixed end
Pointer

**Fig.8.7**
Battery
Temperature sensor
Base resistor
Digital voltmeter calibrated to °C
V
37.0°C
Digital readout
Thermal resistor

1. Adding heat increases molecular motion and causes materials to expand. How are temperature and heat related?
2. What are the three different temperature scales and where are they used?

# 8.3 Heat—Thermal Energy Transfer

Place your hand on a piece of wood, perhaps your desktop. Take note of the warmth of the material. With the same hand, grasp something that is metal, such as the leg of your chair or a metal table leg. You are sure to have noticed a difference in the perceived temperature between the wooden and the metal object. In actual fact, if they have been in the same room for a while, they are at the same temperature. Our body doesn't measure temperature. Instead, it registers thermal energy flow or the movement of thermal energy into or out of the body. When we feel cold, we are actually registering heat flowing out of our body. According to our bodies, there is no such thing as cold or hot, only a deficit or excess of heat.

In Chapter 7, we studied the law of conservation of energy. We found that when energy is transferred from one form to another in a closed mechanical system, none of it is lost. But we did not measure any conversions to heat energy.

In 1847, James Joule showed that energy is conserved when it is converted from gravitational potential energy to heat energy. He used an apparatus like the one shown in Fig. 8.8. As the falling masses lose gravitational potential energy, the vanes (or paddles) stir the water, which results in a notable rise in temperature of the water. This temperature rise signifies an increase in the water's thermal energy. Joule was able to show quantitatively that the decrease in gravitational potential energy caused the increase in the thermal energy of the system.

**Heat** is the flow of thermal energy from an object of high temperature to an object of low temperature.

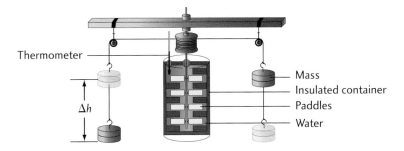

**Fig.8.8** Conversion of mechanical energy to heat

## Methods of Heat Energy Transfer

Heat is transferred from one point to another by three possible methods: conduction, convection, and radiation.

**Conduction** is the process of transferring heat by particle collision. Figure 8.9 shows how heat conducts along the length of a piece of metal

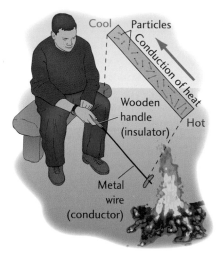

**Fig.8.9** Conduction of thermal energy

Cool Particles

Conduction of heat

Hot

Wooden handle (insulator)

Metal wire (conductor)

| Table 8.3 Thermal Conductivities | |
|---|---|
| Material | Relative conductivity |
| Air | 1.0 |
| Down | 1.1 |
| Cork | 1.8 |
| Asbestos | 6.7 |
| Human tissue | 8.7 |
| Water | 25 |
| Glass | 35 |
| Brick | 37 |
| Concrete | 37 |
| Lead | 1 400 |
| Iron | 2 800 |
| Brass | 4 600 |
| Aluminum | 8 800 |
| Copper | 16 000 |
| Silver | 17 000 |

from the hot end to the cooler end. Kinetic molecular theory helps to explain this process. The hot molecules have more kinetic energy than the cool molecules, so they vibrate more violently, colliding with nearby molecules and transferring some of their energy to them. Like some sort of chain reaction, the energy of the hot molecules is transferred down to the cooler end of the metal by molecules bumping into each other.

A heat **conductor** is a material that allows heat to transfer easily through it. Good conductors of heat are able to quickly pass the kinetic energy of their particles from one end of the material to the other. Metals are particularly good conductors because their atoms have very mobile electrons that easily transfer the thermal energy that is applied to the metal.

A heat **insulator**, such as wood, doesn't allow easy heat transfer between its molecules, which makes it practical for holding hot things such as the hotdog rod in Fig. 8.9. Table 8.3 shows the relative conductivity for various substances compared to air. The higher the number in the chart, the more conductive the material.

**Convection** is the process of transferring heat by a circulating path of fluid. The circulating path of fluid is called a convection current. As the particles of the fluid are heated, their increased kinetic energy causes them to move apart, making the fluid less dense. The decrease in density of the hot fluids makes them rise, taking their thermal energy with them. The colder fluid then flows in to take the place of the displaced hot fluid and the process continues. Figure 8.10 shows how electric baseboard heaters use the process of convection to heat homes.

**Fig.8.10** Convection of heat

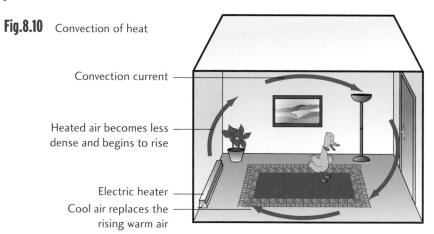

Convection current

Heated air becomes less dense and begins to rise

Electric heater

Cool air replaces the rising warm air

Air is a poor *conductor* of heat, so it is far more efficient to heat the air in buildings and circulate it around by *convection* currents. Convection currents also play a prominent role in weather patterns. Figure 8.11 illustrates how a **sea breeze** along a shoreline is a convection current. Because land heats up faster than water, the cooler, more dense air over the water flows in to replace the air that has been heated by the land. At night, the land cools faster than the water and a convection current in the reverse direction, called a **land breeze**, is created (Fig. 8.11).

UNIT B: Work, Energy, and Power

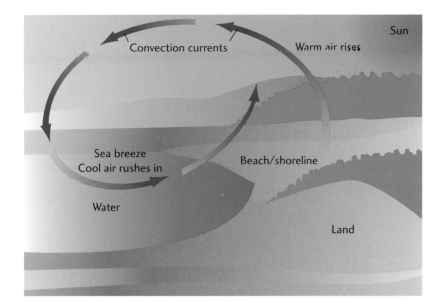

**Fig.8.11** A sea breeze is a natural convection current

**Radiation** transfers heat energy through a wave form of electromagnetic radiant energy. Electromagnetic radiant energy comes in many forms, which include visible light, X-rays, radar, microwaves, radio waves, and infrared radiation (we will study these electromagnetic waves in greater detail in later chapters). Radiant energy travels in straight lines from its source at the speed of light ($3.0 \times 10^8$ m/s). This form of heat transfer doesn't require the interaction of particles of matter and can travel through a vacuum where no matter exists. The transfer of heat energy in this way is very similar to what occurs when you listen to the radio. The radio transmitter emits radio waves (electromagnetic waves similar to radiant heat waves) by oscillating (vibrating) electrons in the antenna. These waves travel through the atmosphere or empty space to a receiver. The radio receiver picks up the signal, which causes the electrons in the antenna to oscillate with the same frequency as they did in the transmitter. These oscillations are then decoded by a radio into sound that we can recognize.

Warm substances radiate infrared radiation (a longer length of waves than visible light) because of oscillating electrons in them and the radiant energy travels outward. When the waves hit matter, the energy is either absorbed by, reflected from, or transmitted through the material.

If the radiant energy is absorbed, the particles of the medium increase their movement and the thermal energy of the material increases, which is exactly what you experience when the Sun beats down on your black shirt in the summertime.

If radiant energy is reflected or transmitted, the energy either bounces off the object or continues to pass through it the way that your image is reflected in a mirror or light passes through a transparent window.

Figure 8.12 shows a radiant heater, which is a marvellous example of how the radiant transmission of heat energy can be used. The heater's red-hot element "broadcasts" its heat energy and some things in the room act like receivers.

Hot upward air currents, called *thermals,* are used by some migrating birds to increase their flight time and cover large distances. Glider pilots have taken a cue from these birds and jump from thermal to thermal so they can stay in flight much longer.

Fig.8.12 A radiant electric heater

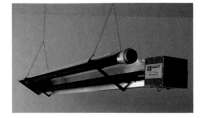

A thermometer in the room may not even register that the room is any warmer because only some surfaces can receive the radiant heat effectively (some surfaces reflect it). Black-coloured materials are good at picking up radiant heat energy, which is one reason why it is not advisable to wear black in the summertime.

Your skin is much more effective at absorbing radiant heat energy when it is bare than when it is covered, so much so that you may feel warmer in front of a radiant heater if you are naked.

## Controlling Heat Transfer

There are many cases when we want to control whether heat is transferred away from a hot object or kept in to maintain its temperature. A Thermos® travel mug (Fig. 8.13) illustrates how materials can be designed and manipulated, using all three processes of conduction, convection, and radiation, to minimize heat transfer.

**Fig.8.13** Thermos® travel mug

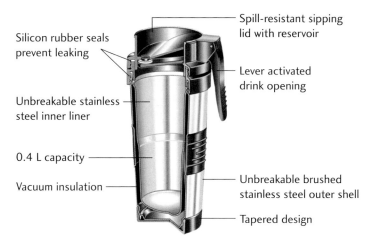

Silicon rubber seals prevent leaking

Spill-resistant sipping lid with reservoir

Lever activated drink opening

Unbreakable stainless steel inner liner

0.4 L capacity

Vacuum insulation

Unbreakable brushed stainless steel outer shell

Tapered design

**Fig.8.14** Windows are designed to prevent heat loss

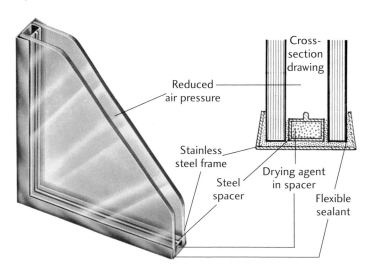

Reduced air pressure

Cross-section drawing

Stainless steel frame

Steel spacer

Drying agent in spacer

Flexible sealant

In the Thermos®, this is accomplished by using a double-walled container with a vacuum between the walls, which reduces the amount of heat flow by conduction. The vacuum also reduces convection, and the shiny, reflective surfaces both inside and out of the container work to reflect radiant energy back inside the container. Other practical applications of these principles is in window design. Figure 8.14 shows that air pressure is reduced between each layer of glass, which helps to prevent both conduction and convection of heat from one side to the other.

Insulated mittens (Fig. 8.15) take advantage of the insulative value of dead air trapped in the foam layer.

Shiny metal surfaces reflect radiant heat. The aluminum reflector in the back of the electric arena heater in Fig. 8.12 reflects radiant heat toward the the spectators. Food wrapped in aluminum foil stays warmer longer because the foil reflects heat back into the food. Fast-food restaurants employ this technique to keep hamburgers warm. Figure 8.16 shows how the gases in the atmosphere, such as carbon dioxide ($CO_2$) and methane ($CH_4$), act like a greenhouse for Earth. These gases cause the Sun's radiant energy to be re-reflected back down to Earth, resulting in an increase in Earth's temperature.

The average levels of carbon dioxide in our atmosphere have been steadily increasing because of the increased amount of hydrocarbons such as oil, coal, and natural gas that have been burned since the onset of the Industrial Revolution. An increase in global temperatures will produce drastic changes in life on this planet as ecosystems are re-aligned because of the increased temperatures.

**Fig.8.15**  Reduction of heat transfer in a mitten

**Fur-lined mitten**

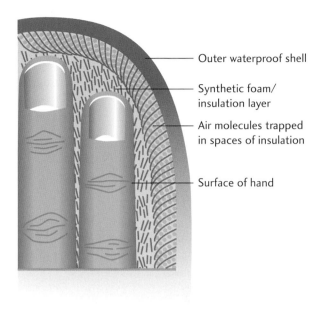

- Outer waterproof shell
- Synthetic foam/ insulation layer
- Air molecules trapped in spaces of insulation
- Surface of hand

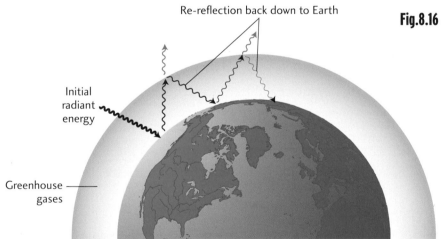

Re-reflection back down to Earth

Initial radiant energy

Greenhouse gases

**Fig.8.16**  The greenhouse effect

1. Relate the terms "heat," "thermal energy," and "temperature."
2. Why does your bare hand feel cold when you grab a metal pole as opposed to a wooden one, given that both were outside in –20°C weather? (This principle applies when using the outhouse in the winter. Instead of a painted toilet seat, a foam (polystyrene) ring can be used.)
3. Compare the methods of heat transfer (conduction, convection, and radiation). How are these methods used to heat a home?
4. Would a person dressed in black feel hotter or cooler than a person dressed in white? Why?

◀ ◀ ◀ ◀ ◀

**Fig.8.17**

Set-back timer/thermostat for home heating and air conditioning minimizes the temperature difference between inside and outside the home, reducing heat flow inside or out, which can save you money.

| Table 8.4 Specific Heat Capacities | |
|---|---|
| Material | Specific heat capacity (J/kg°C) |
| Liquid nitrogen | $1.1 \times 10^2$ |
| Gold | $1.3 \times 10^2$ |
| Lead | $1.3 \times 10^2$ |
| Mercury | $1.4 \times 10^2$ |
| Steam | $2.0 \times 10^2$ |
| Silver | $2.3 \times 10^2$ |
| Ethyl alcohol | $2.4 \times 10^2$ |
| Glycerine | $2.4 \times 10^2$ |
| Methyl alcohol | $2.5 \times 10^2$ |
| Brass | $3.8 \times 10^2$ |
| Copper | $3.9 \times 10^2$ |
| Iron | $4.6 \times 10^2$ |
| Crown glass | $6.7 \times 10^2$ |
| Pyrex® | $7.8 \times 10^2$ |
| Granite | $8.0 \times 10^2$ |
| Sand | $8.0 \times 10^2$ |
| Aluminium | $9.1 \times 10^2$ |
| Air | $1.0 \times 10^3$ |
| Wood | $1.8 \times 10^3$ |
| Ice | $2.1 \times 10^3$ |
| Concrete | $2.9 \times 10^3$ |
| Water | $4.2 \times 10^3$ |

The robes worn by Bedouins in the Sinai desert are black. This fact seems to contradict the concepts you have learned. However, upon closer examination of the situation, we see that even though the black robe is 4–6° higher in temperature than the white robe, the black robe causes more convection under it by warming the air to a higher temperature than the white robe. The warmer air rises faster and leaves through the pores and openings of the material. This causes external air to be drawn in from the large, open end at the bottom of the robe. The increased circulation keeps the person cool.

# 8.4 Specific Heat Capacity

Heat transfer to any substance depends on three things:

**Temperature difference**. The greater the temperature difference between the hot and cold substance, the greater the heat flow.

**Mass of substance**. The more mass a substance has, the more molecules need to have thermal energy transferred to or from them.

**Type of substance**. Different substances are held together by their own specific intermolecular forces and accept the transfer of heat to different extents.

Two separate pots are heated on a stove under the same conditions, one pot containing water and the other containing vegetable oil. The temperature of the oil rises at a faster rate than the water temperature, but the water starts to boil at a lower temperature. This phenomenom is a property of matter that describes the thermal differences between materials, called the **specific heat capacity**.

Specific heat capacity is the amount of heat energy that is needed to increase the temperature of 1 kg of a particular substance by 1°C.

The units of heat capacity are J/kg°C and its symbol is given as $c$. The specific heat capacities ($c$) for water and several other common substances are given in Table 8.4.

The greater the value of the specific heat capacity, $c$, the more heat energy must be transferred to the substance to change its temperature by one degree Celsius.

The mathematical formula for calculating heat transfer is

$$\Delta E_\mathrm{H} = mc\Delta t$$

where $\Delta E_\mathrm{H}$ is the heat energy transferred to or from a substance in joules (J), $m$ is the mass of the substance in kilograms (kg), $\Delta t$ is the temperature change of the substance in °C, and $c$ is the specific heat capacity of the substance in J/kg°C.

EXAMPLE 1 **Heating copper**

How much heat energy is required to heat a 1.0 kg piece of copper pipe from 25.0°C to 66.0°C?

## Solution and Connection to Theory

### Given

$m = 1.0$ kg    $t_1 = 25.0°C$    $t_2 = 66.0°C$    material is copper    $\Delta E_H = ?$

We can find the specific heat capacity ($c$) of copper in Table 8.4.

$c_{copper} = 3.9 \times 10^2$ J/kg°C

Substituting into the equation,

$\Delta E_H = mc\Delta t = mc(t_2 - t_1) = 1.0$ kg$(3.9 \times 10^2$ J/kg°C$)(66.0°C - 25.0°C)$
$= 1.0$ kg$(3.9 \times 10^2$ J/kg°C$)(41.0°C)$

$\Delta E_H = 1.6 \times 10^4$ J

Therefore, the heat energy $E_H$ required to heat a 1.0 kg piece of copper pipe from 25.0°C to 66.0°C is $1.6 \times 10^4$ J.

If the copper was cooled instead of heated, the value for $E_H$ would be negative because the two temperature values would be reversed, making $\Delta t$ negative. This means that for a substance, a positive $\Delta E_H$ means it is warming and a negative $\Delta E_H$ means that it is cooling.

EXAMPLE 2 **Cooling iron**

A 0.50 kg block of iron at 80.0°C is cooled by removing $2.28 \times 10^4$ J of heat energy. What will the final temperature of the metal be?

## Solution and Connection to Theory

### Given

$m = 0.50$ kg  $t_1 = 80.0°C$   $\Delta E_H = -2.28 \times 10^4$ J   material is iron  $t_2 = ?$

The word "removing" indicates that $E_H$ is negative. From Table 8.4, the specific heat capacity for iron is $4.6 \times 10^2$ J/kg°C.

$\Delta E_H = mc\Delta t = mc(t_2 - t_1)$

$t_2 = \dfrac{E_H}{mc} + t_1$

$t_2 = \dfrac{-2.28 \times 10^4 \text{ J}}{(0.50 \text{ kg})\left(4.6 \times 10^2 \frac{J}{kg \cdot °C}\right)} + 80.0°C$

$t_2 = -99.13°C + 80.0°C = -19°C$

Therefore, the final temperature for this piece of iron is $-19°C$.

APPLYING
the
Concepts
▶ ▶ ▶ ▶

1. What three things does heat transfer depend on?
2. Answer Question 2 at the end of Section 8.3 (holding onto a metal pole in the cold as opposed to a wooden one) by using the values for specific heat capacity in Table 8.4.
3. Compare the heat required to heat 1.5 kg pieces of gold (we wish), iron, and silver from 12°C to 40°C. How does the solution change when these materials are cooled?

# 8.5 Heat Exchange — The Law of Conservation of Heat Energy

In the previous section, we examined what happens to the temperature of a specific substance when heat is either added or taken away. According to the law of conservation of energy, the total amount of heat energy must be constant as long as none of it is lost to the surroundings. If we think of heat energy as moving from a hot object to a cold object, then we can simplify the law of conservation of heat energy to be

$$|E_{H_{lost}}| = |E_{H_{gained}}| \text{ or}$$

$$\Delta E_{H_1} = -\Delta E_{H_2}$$

Because this application of the law of conservation of energy specifically involves the exchange of heat energy, this principle is also called the **principle of heat exchange**. The negative sign represents the direction in which heat is flowing. It shows that the values of $E_H$ are the same, but one material is losing heat while the other one is gaining heat.

### EXAMPLE 3   A spot of tea?

A 0.500 kg pot of hot water for tea has cooled to 40.0°C. How much freshly boiled water must be added (at 100.0°C, of course) to raise the temperature of the tea water to a respectable 65.0°C?

*Solution and Connection to Theory*

**Given**

| **cool water** | **hot water** |
| --- | --- |
| $m_c = 0.500$ kg | $m_h = ?$ |
| $c_w = 4.2 \times 10^3$ J/kg°C | $c_w = 4.2 \times 10^3$ J/kg°C |
| $t_1 = 40.0°C,\ t_2 = 65.0°C$ | $t_1 = 100.0°C,\ t_2 = 65.0°C$ |
| $\Delta t_c = (65.0°C - 40.0°C) = 25.0°C$ | $\Delta t_h = (65.0°C - 100.0°C) = -35.0°C$ |

The fact that one $\Delta t$ value is negative and the other is positive shows that one material is losing heat while the other is gaining heat.

According to the law of conservation of heat energy,

$$E_{H_c} = -E_{H_h}$$
$$m_c c_w \Delta t_c = -m_h c_w \Delta t_h$$

As both materials are water, $c_w$ from each side can cancel.

$$0.500 \text{ kg}(25.0°C) = -m_h(-35.0°C)$$
$$m_h (35.0°C) = 12.5 \text{ kg°C}$$
$$m_h = 0.357 \text{ kg}$$

Therefore, 0.357 kg of water is required to increase the temperature of the tea water to 65.0°C.

## EXAMPLE 4 Cooling an egg

A hard-boiled egg with a heat capacity of $2.4 \times 10^3$ J/kg°C and a mass of 50.0 g is cooled from 100.0°C by 1.0 L of water at 5.0°C. What will be the final temperature of the water and egg after they have been allowed to sit for a few moments?

$$m_{egg} = 50.0 \text{ g} = 50.0 \times 10^{-3} \text{ kg} = 5.00 \times 10^{-2} \text{ kg} \quad m_{water} = 1.0 \text{ kg}$$

### Solution and Connection to Theory

**Given**

**egg**
$$c_{egg} = 2.4 \times 10^3 \text{ J/kg°C}$$
$$t_{1_{egg}} = 100.0°C$$
$$t_{2_{egg}} = ? °C$$

**water**
$$c_{water} = 4.2 \times 10^3 \text{ J/kg°C (see Table 8.4)}$$
$$t_{1_{water}} = 5.0°C$$
$$t_{2_{water}} = ? °C$$

The heat lost from the egg will be used to warm up the water as long as we assume that none of the heat is lost to the surroundings. Both the water and the egg will end up at the same temperature, which is our missing quantity ($t_2$).

Metric conversions can easily be done using the exponent multiplier. In this case, a gram is $\frac{1}{1000}$ of a kilogram, so the multiplier "$\times 10^{-3}$" can be added to make a quick conversion. See Appendix C for other multipliers.

Recall that by definition, 1 mL of water was assigned a mass of 1 g. Therefore, 1.0 L has a mass of 1.0 kg (see Fig. 8.18).

**Fig.8.18** The relationship between mass and volume of water

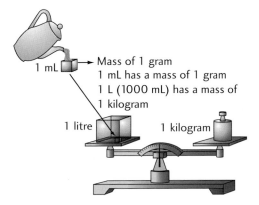

1 mL → Mass of 1 gram
1 mL has a mass of 1 gram
1 L (1000 mL) has a mass of 1 kilogram

1 litre    1 kilogram

Therefore,

$$\Delta t_{egg} = t_{2_{egg}} - t_{1_{egg}} \qquad \text{and} \qquad \Delta t_{water} = t_{2_{water}} - t_{1_{water}}$$

$$E_{H_1} = -E_{H_2}$$

$$m_{egg}c_{egg}\Delta t_{egg} = -m_{water}c_{water}\Delta t_{water}$$

$$50.0 \times 10^{-3}\,kg(2.4 \times 10^3\,J/kg°C)(t_2 - 100°C)$$
$$= -1.0\,kg(4.2 \times 10^3\,J/kg°C)(t_2 - 5°C)$$

$$120\,J/°C(t_2) - 12000\,J = -4.2 \times 10^3\,J/°C(t_2) - (-21000\,J)$$

$$4320\,J/°C(t_2) = 33000\,J$$

$$t_2 = 7.6°C$$

Both the water and the egg end up at an intermediate temperature (between 5°C and 100°C) of about 8°C.

▶ ▶ ▶ ▶

1. State examples of the law of conservation of energy that you have seen throughout the various units you have studied.
2. In western movies, the cowboy or cowgirl takes a bath by adding hot water to a partially filled tub or barrel to warm it up. If the person is sitting in 100 kg of lukewarm water (15°C), how much boiling water must be added to the bath water in order to raise the temperature to a modest 35°C? Note: If you wish to calculate the volume of water needed, use the equation $\rho = \frac{m}{V}$, where $\rho$ is the density of water (1000 kg/m³), $m$ is the mass, and $V$ is the volume.

### Seasonal Turnover of Lakes

For fishing enthusiasts, the end of summer and the beginning of fall is ushered in when the lake "turns over." In this process, the colder temperatures cool the water at the surface of the lake, causing it to become more dense and sink under the warm water layer under the surface. This sinking causes convection currents, which mix the different temperature layers. As a result, the water at the bottom of the lake comes to the surface and the water at the surface of the lake moves to the bottom.

This process continues until the water reaches its maximum density at a temperature of 4°C. Below this temperature, the water at the surface cools further, eventually turning to ice. Because water is at its maximum density in its liquid state, the ice, which is less dense than water, floats on the surface and acts as an insulating blanket for the lake water and inhabitants below.

**Fig.8.19** Convection in a cooling lake

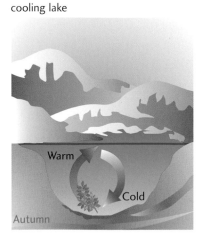

**Fig.8.20**

3. Summarize the conduction of heat in the water system during each season. Use the kinetic molecular theory to explain how heat is transferred.
4. Explain the conduction of heat in water in terms of the conservation of energy.
5. How does this process benefit the lake and its ecosystem?
6. Water's unusual property of density allows life in the water to survive the winter. Explain.

## 8.6 Changes of State and Latent Heat

In Section 8.2, we learned that when heat is added or removed from a substance, the change in thermal energy affects the temperature of the substance. If the change in thermal energy is great enough, it will cause a change of state in the substance. Figure 8.21 shows a cooling-warming curve for water as a consistent amount of heat is added or removed. As the water is heated or cooled, it goes through all three states of matter: vapour/gas, liquid, and solid.

As steam cools, its temperature drops, as expected. But at 100°C, the temperature remains constant. Thermal energy is still being removed from the vapour, but it doesn't register on the thermometer as a drop in temperature.

**Fig.8.21**   Changes of state for water

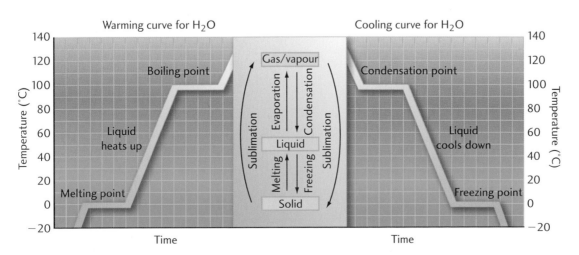

This extra or stored amount of energy is associated with a change of state and is called latent heat. From Fig. 8.21, we see that **latent heat** seems to be released during condensation and freezing, and stored when heat is added during melting and vapourization. The two types of latent heat are the latent heat of fusion and the latent heat of vapourization.

## Latent Heats of Fusion and Vaporization

The **latent heat of fusion** ($L_f$) is the amount of energy needed to melt 1.0 kg of ice. The word "latent" means "hidden." It refers to the fact that during melting, the added heat does not cause a rise in temperature and will lay hidden until it is released in the freezing process. The greater the mass of melting material, the more energy is required. Latent heat is defined as the amount of heat required per unit of mass to change state. The latent heat of fusion (melting) is given by the equation

$$L_f = \frac{E_H}{m}$$

where $E_H$ is the heat in joules and $m$ is the mass in kilograms.
Latent heat is measured in joules per kilogram (J/kg)

The **latent heat of vapourization**, $L_v$, is the heat required per unit mass to vapourize a liquid.

$$L_v = \frac{E_H}{m}$$

Like $L_f$, $L_v$ is measured in joules per kilogram (J/kg).

Table 8.5 lists the latent heats of fusion and vapourization for some common substances.

### Table 8.5
#### Latent Heats of Fusion and Vapourization

| Substance | $L_f$ (J/kg) | Melting/ freezing point (°C) | $L_v$ (J/kg) | Boiling/ condensation point (°C) |
|---|---|---|---|---|
| Aluminum | $9.0 \times 10^4$ | 659 | $1.1 \times 10^7$ | 1509 |
| Ethyl alcohol | $1.1 \times 10^5$ | −130 | $8.6 \times 10^5$ | 78 |
| Methyl alcohol | $6.8 \times 10^4$ | −97.8 | $1.1 \times 10^6$ | 64.7 |
| Iron | $2.5 \times 10^5$ | 1530 | $6.3 \times 10^6$ | 1820 |
| Lead | $2.3 \times 10^4$ | 327 | $8.7 \times 10^5$ | 1780 |
| Nitrogen | $2.5 \times 10^4$ | −209.9 | $2.0 \times 10^5$ | −196.8 |
| Oxygen | $1.4 \times 10^4$ | −218.9 | $2.1 \times 10^5$ | −183 |
| Silver | $1.1 \times 10^5$ | 960 | $2.3 \times 10^6$ | 1950 |
| Water | $3.3 \times 10^5$ | 0 | $2.3 \times 10^6$ | 100 |

These values were found experimentally by measuring the amount of heat required to melt or vapourize a certain amount of mass of material, as described in the following example.

**EXAMPLE 5** Calculating the latent heat of fusion

A 0.27 kg sample of a material requires $8.91 \times 10^4$ J of energy to melt it without raising its temperature. What is the latent heat of fusion for this material?

**Given**

$m = 0.27$ kg      $E_H = 8.91 \times 10^4$ J      $L_f = ?$

***Solution and Connection to Theory***

$$L_f = \frac{E_H}{m}$$

$$= \frac{8.91 \times 10^4 \text{J}}{0.27 \text{ kg}}$$

$$= 3.3 \times 10^5 \text{J/kg}$$

Therefore, the latent heat of fusion is $3.3 \times 10^5$ J/kg.

Referring to Table 8.5, we see that this substance is most likely water.

**EXAMPLE 6** Calculating the heat of vapourization

One danger of leaving a tea kettle unattended on the stove is having it boil dry. How much heat is required to change 0.20 kg of water (about the amount for a good cup of tea) from a liquid state to vapour?

**Given**

$m = 0.20$ kg      $L_v = 2.3 \times 10^6$ J/kg      $E_H = ?$

***Solution and Connection to Theory***

$L_v = \dfrac{E_H}{m}$ Rearrange the equation.

$E_H = (m)L_v$

$$= (0.20 \text{ kg})\left(2.3 \times 10^6 \frac{\text{J}}{\text{kg}}\right)$$

$$= 4.6 \times 10^5 \text{ J}$$

Therefore, the amount of heat required to vapourize 0.20 kg of water is $4.6 \times 10^5$ J.

Note: The addition or subtraction of heat will change the temperature of a substance up until it reaches the critical temperature at which a change in state occurs. At this temperature, any heat transfer is used to facilitate the phase change.

---

**EXAMPLE 7** — **The heat required to carry a substance through a change of state**

What would be the total amount of heat required to warm a 0.100 kg solid sample of water from $-30°C$, through melting at $0°C$, to a final liquid temperature of $80°C$?

**Given**

$t_{1 \text{ (solid)}} = -30°C$ $\quad$ $t_{2 \text{ (solid)}} = 0°C$ $\quad$ $t_{1 \text{ (liquid)}} = 0°C$

$t_{2 \text{ (liquid)}} = 80°C$ $\quad$ $m = 0.100$ kg

$L_{f \text{ (water)}} = 3.3 \times 10^5$ J/kg $\quad$ $c_{ice} = 2.1 \times 10^3$ J/kg°C

$c_{water} = 4.2 \times 10^3$ J/kg°C

$E_T = ?$

**Solution and Connection to Theory**

The total heat would be the sum of the heat required to warm the solid to the melting point, cause the melting, and then the final warming of the liquid from the melting to the final temperature.

$E_T = E_{\text{warming of ice}} + E_{\text{melting of ice}} + E_{\text{warming of water}}$

$$= m\Delta t_{\text{warming}_1} c_{ice} + L_f (m) + m\Delta t_{\text{warming}_2} c_{water}$$

$= (0.100 \text{ kg})(0°C - (-30°C))2.1 \times 10^3 \text{ J/kg°C} + (3.3 \times 10^5 \text{ J/kg})(0.100 \text{ kg}) + (0.100 \text{ kg})(80°C - 0°C)4.2 \times 10^3 \text{ J/kg°C}$

$= 6.3 \times 10^3 \text{ J} + 3.3 \times 10^4 \text{ J} + 3.4 \times 10^4 \text{ J}$

$= 7.3 \times 10^4 \text{ J}$

Therefore, the total heat energy required to heat 0.100 kg of water from $-30°C$ to $80°C$ is $7.3 \times 10^4$ J.

## Effects of Latent Heat

Any heat that is added during a "warming cycle" to raise the temperature of a substance can be recovered later when the substance cools. The heat used to affect the phase changes of melting and vapourization is stored as latent heat. It can be recovered only when the substance undergoes the reverse phase changes of condensation and freezing. Our formulas from the above examples can also be used to calculate the heat that must be removed from the system.

The "extra" amount of heat required to cause a change in state is responsible for the moderate climates near large bodies of water. In the spring, melting the ice on these bodies of water draws some of the heat from the atmosphere, which makes the air temperature lower than normal. This heat that we miss during the cool spring months is stored as the latent heat of fusion. During the winter freeze, this latent heat of fusion is released as heat into the atmosphere and the result is higher temperatures.

In many Canadian backyards, tomato plants are protected from frost in spring and fall by spraying the foliage with water. During a frost, the water on the plants freezes, releasing the latent heat of fusion. This extra energy can protect the plants from temperatures as low as $-2°C$.

Orange growers in Florida spray their crops with water if there is a threat of freezing. Explain how this procedure could provide enough heat to save their crops.

1. **a)** Which latent heat value, fusion or vapourization, is larger for any given substance?

   **b)** Use the kinetic molecular theory to explain what is going on at the molecular level during these two changes of state.

2. How much heat does a freezer remove from 0.25 kg of water in an ice cube tray if the temperature of the water is $0°C$?

3. A 0.54 kg sample of material requires $1.782 \times 10^5$ J of energy to melt it. What is the latent heat of fusion for this material?

4. A tank containing 740 kg of water cools from $15°C$ to $0°C$ and completely freezes. How many hours would a 1.2 kW electric heater have to work to provide the equivalent heat the water gives off? (The heater provides $1.2 \times 10^3$ J/s of heat.)

# 8.7 Calorimetry—Some Practical Applications

One practical application of the physics of heat energy is the careful and precise measurement of heat transfer in the process of **calorimetry**.

During calorimetry, a calorimeter measures the heat flow into a supply of water by tracking the temperature increase as the process continues. Knowing the specific heat capacity, mass, and the initial and final temperatures of the water allows us to calculate the heat flow by applying the formula $E_H = mc\Delta t$. Calorimetry may be used to find specific heat capacities of materials or to find the energy content of foods.

The old unit for the measure of heat energy was the calorie. We now use the joule as the unit of measure for heat energy, but the term "calorimetry," or "measuring heat," is still used today. The conversion factor between these units is 4.18 J/C, where C represents calories.

## Calorimetry and Specific Heat Capacity

**Fig.8.22** A simple calorimeter

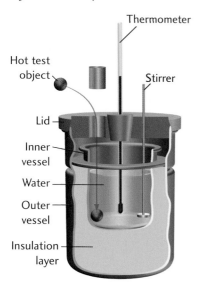

- Thermometer
- Hot test object
- Stirrer
- Lid
- Inner vessel
- Water
- Outer vessel
- Insulation layer

The specific heat capacities of some selected substances are given in Table 8.4. These are all found experimentally using a simple calorimeter, such as the one shown in Fig. 8.22, and the law of conservation of heat energy (heat lost by a material is equal to the heat gained by the calorimeter).

The specific heat capacity is found by heating a material in question to a known high temperature and placing it into the calorimeter. Since heat energy is conserved, the specific heat capacity of the sample may be found using

$$m_s c_s(t_2 - t_{1_s}) = -m_w c_w(t_2 - t_{1_w})$$

or

$$c_s = -\left(\frac{m_w \times c_w}{m_s}\right)\frac{t_2 - (t_{1_w})}{t_2 - (t_{1_s})}$$

The items in the brackets are all known quantities, so the key measurement that is required is the final temperature of the calorimeter.

### EXAMPLE 8 Specific heat capacity of aluminum

A 0.700 kg piece of aluminum is heated to 100°C in boiling water and quickly placed into a calorimeter that contains 0.200 kg of water at 20.0°C. The final temperature of the calorimeter was determined to be 54.4°C. What is the specific heat capacity, $c_{Al}$, for aluminum?

#### Solution and Connection to Theory

**Given**

**aluminum**
$m_{Al} = 0.700$ kg
$c_{Al} = ?$
$t_{1_{Al}} = 100°C$
$t_{2_{Al}} = 54.4°C$
$m_{Al}c_{Al}\Delta t_{Al} = -m_w c_w \Delta t_w$

**water**
$m_w = 0.200$ kg
$c_w = 4.2 \times 10^3$ J/kg°C
$t_{1_w} = 20.0°C$
$t_2 = 54.4°C$

Rearranged, the equation becomes

$$c_{Al} = -\left(\frac{m_w c_w}{m_{Al}}\right)\frac{t_{2_w} - (t_{1_w})}{t_{2_{Al}} - (t_{1_{Al}})}$$

$$c_{Al} = -\left(\frac{0.200 \text{ kg} \times 4.2 \times 10^3 \text{ J/kg°C}}{0.700 \text{ kg}}\right)\frac{54.4°C - 20.0°C}{54.4°C - 100°C}$$

$$c_{Al} = 9.05 \times 10^2 \text{ J/kg°C}$$

The specific heat capacity for aluminium is $9.05 \times 10^2$ J/kg°C, which may be compared to the value in Table 8.4.

# Calorimetry and Food Energy

In food calorimetry, a bomb calorimeter like the one in Fig. 8.23 is used to burn electrically ignited food. The heat that is liberated is transferred to the water in the calorimeter, which registers a temperature rise. The entire apparatus is insulated from the surroundings and the water is stirred to ensure precise results. The energy content of the food is then determined by the equation

$$\Delta E_H = m_w c_w \Delta t_w$$

where $m_w$ is the mass of the water in the calorimeter, $c_w$ is the specific heat capacity of water ($4.2 \times 10^3$ J/kg°C), and $\Delta t_w$ is the temperature change of the water in the calorimeter.

**Fig.8.23** A bomb calorimeter

Thermometer
Ignition terminals
Stirrer
Water
Insulation
Sealed reaction chamber containing food item and oxygen
Ignition wire
Potato chip

---

**EXAMPLE 9** **How well balanced is that breakfast?**

A 30 g sample of Kellogg's Corn Pops cereal is burned inside a bomb calorimeter and the 2.00 kg of water warms from 24.0°C to 81.1°C. What is the amount of energy that is stored in the cereal?

### *Solution and Connection to Theory*

**Given**

$m_c = 30.0$ g     $m_w = 2.00$ kg     $c_w = 4.2 \times 10^3$ J/kg°C

$\Delta t_w = t_2 - t_1 = 81.1°C - 24.0°C = 57.1°C$

$\Delta E = mc\Delta t$

$\Delta E = 2.00$ kg$(4.2 \times 10^3$ J/kg°C$)(57.1°C)$

$\Delta E = 480\ 000$ J or 480 kJ for 30.0 g of cereal.

The Corn Pops cereal has 480 kJ of energy in every 30.0 g, or 16 kJ/g.

## Fig.8.24  Methods of Heat Transfer

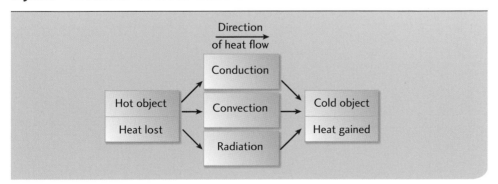

Direction of heat flow

Hot object → Conduction → Cold object
Heat lost → Convection → Heat gained
→ Radiation →

PUTTING it all Together ◄ ◄ ◄ ◄

1. How is calorimetry related to the conservation of energy?
2. A 1.200 kg piece of iron is heated to 95°C. It is placed into a calorimeter that contains 0.430 kg of water at 10.0°C. Find the final temperature of the calorimeter.

APPLYING the Concepts ◄ ◄ ◄ ◄

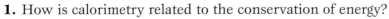

# Global Warming: Heating Ourselves to Death

**Fig.STSE.8.1**

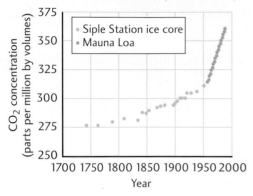

**Atmospheric Concentration of Carbon Dioxide (1744–1992)**

**Fig.STSE.8.2**

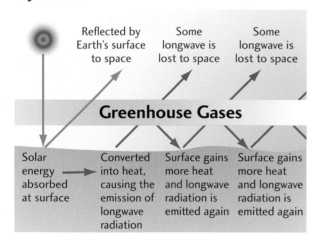

When we think about global warming, we might initially think that we would be better off without cold winters. The negative impact of global warming far outweighs the benefits of warmer winters. **Global warming** refers to the consistent increase in the average ambient temperature on Earth. The increase is believed to be caused by an increase in the amount of greenhouse gases in the atmosphere (see Fig. STSE.8.1 and Table STSE.8.1). These gases, which include carbon dioxide and methane, act like the glass in a greenhouse. As shown in Fig. STSE.8.2, radiant heat energy from the Sun reaches Earth, but much of the reflected heat is kept inside by the atmosphere, which acts like a giant solar blanket. Over the last century, the increase in global population as well as in industrialization has also meant that more energy is used and more waste heat is produced. This increase has resulted in a change in global temperature (see Fig. STSE.8.3), which has far-reaching effects that will upset the delicate balance of Earth's ecosystems.

Parts of Earth covered with ice and snow act as mirrors, reflecting heat away from Earth. As global warming melts these areas, Earth will warm at an even faster rate.

Global warming is responsible for flooding from melted ice and for rapid environmental changes in many ecosystems that negatively affect plant and animal species. Recent efforts to curb the emission of greenhouse gases should be applauded, but it may be a case of too little too late.

**Fig.STSE.8.3**

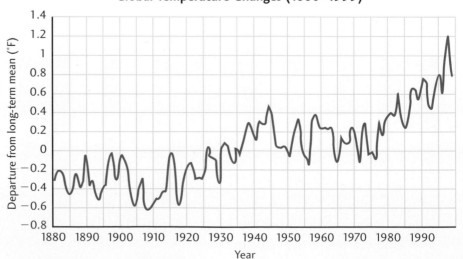

**Global Temperature Changes (1880–1999)**

## Table STSE.8.1
### Gases Involved in the Greenhouse Effect: Past and Present Concentrations and Sources

| Greenhouse gas | Concentration in 1750 | Present concentration | Percent change | Natural and anthropogenic sources |
|---|---|---|---|---|
| Carbon dioxide | 228 ppm | 330 ppm | 29% | Organic decay; Forest fires; Volcanoes; Burning fossil fuels; Deforestation; Land-use change |
| Methane | 0.70 ppm | 1.70 ppm | 143% | Wetlands; Organic decay; Termites; Natural gas & oil extraction; Biomass burning; Rice cultivation; Cattle; Refuse landfills |
| Nitrous oxide | 280 ppb | 310 ppb | 11% | Forests; Grasslands; Oceans; Soils; Soil cultivation; Fertilizers; Biomass burning; Burning of fossil fuels |
| Chlorofluorocarbons (CFCs) | 0 | 900 ppt | Not applicable | Refrigerators; Aerosol spray propellants; Cleaning solvents |
| Ozone | Unknown | Varies with latitude and altitude in the atmosphere | Global levels have generally decreased in the stratosphere and increased near Earth's surface | Created naturally by the action of sunlight on molecular oxygen and artificially through photochemical smog production |

## Design a Study of Societal Impact

Since the late 1980s, several international agreements have been signed by the world's major industrial countries to reduce emissions of greenhouse gases. Have these agreements worked? How does the level of greenhouse gases emitted this year compare to 2, 5, and 10 years ago? How drastic does the decrease in greenhouse gases need to be for the world to avoid the predictions of devastation associated with global warming?

## Design an Activity to Evaluate

Evaluate the performance of several different commercially available travel coffee mugs for their ability to keep coffee hot.

Evaluate whether a thermostat set-back timer saves energy during a simulated 24-hour period. By plotting a cooling curve for a warm liquid left in a freezer, calculate the net heat loss and compare it with the heat energy required to warm the liquid back to its original temperature.

## Build a Structure

Design and construct an insulated box that will maintain the temperature of a heated container of water. Monitor the temperature of the container over time, using a computer interface and a temperature probe. If you hold a competition, the contestant with the smallest drop in temperature after a set amount of time is the winner.

SPECIFIC EXPECTATIONS

**You should be able to**

*Understand Basic Concepts:*
- Define and describe the concepts and units related to thermal energy and kinetic molecular theory as they relate to heat transfer.
- Apply the kinetic molecular theory to explain how thermal energy is transferred in matter by the processes of conduction, convection, and radiation.
- Relate the principle of heat exchange to the law of conservation of energy.
- Use the law of conservation of energy to quantitatively determine the amount of heat transferred between two bodies.
- Define "closed" and "open" systems and relate them to the efficiency of heat transfer.

*Develop Skills of Inquiry and Communication:*
- Design and carry out an experiment to measure the efficiency of transferring electrical energy to thermal energy in an electric heating appliance.
- Demonstrate the safe and appropriate handling of electrical appliances by checking for damaged or hazardous equipment before conducting experiments.
- Analyze and interpret tabulated experimental data to determine the characteristic physical property of specific heat capacity.

*Relate Science to Technology, Society, and the Environment:*
- Analyze the environmental and social impact of global warming.
- Relate the processes of reflection and transmission of radiant solar energy to explain global warming.
- Describe how the knowledge of the processes of conduction, convection, and radiation are used in the design of systems that reduce or enhance heat transfer.
- Relate the natural phenomena of sea and land breezes and seasonal turnover to the process of heat convection in fluids.

**Equations**

$$E_H = mc\Delta t$$

$$mc\Delta t = -(mc\Delta t)$$

$$L_f = \frac{E_H}{m}$$

$$L_v = \frac{E_H}{m}$$

## Conceptual Questions

1. State the principle of heat exchange and discuss how it applies to the law of conservation of energy.

2. Liquids are used to transfer heat in car radiators. Why do we mix water and ethylene glycol in the radiator given that water has a higher heat capacity than ethylene glycol?

3. Explain why it is relatively easy to remove baked potatoes from a hot barbecue without a hot pad if they are wrapped in aluminum foil.

4. Two equal mass samples of copper and iron heated with the same amount of heat energy will achieve different temperatures. Which sample will reach the higher temperature and why?

5. To save energy, many home owners have installed temperature set-back thermostats that set the inside house temperature lower at night during the winter. Some critics have suggested that the furnace has to work harder in the morning to warm the house up again. Write a brief paragraph that will explain to any sceptics that the overall heat flow from the inside to the outside of the house is definitely less.

6. Use the kinetic molecular theory to explain the temperature change that occurs when a cold and a hot liquid are mixed.

7. Why is copper used to cover the bottom of many commercial pots and pans for the stove top?

8. You are spending Labour Day Weekend at the beach and it turns out to be a clear, hot day. Using the concept of heat capacity, describe which warms up faster, the water or the sand. Which of the two will cool down faster at night?

9. As you will read in later chapters, water from lakes such as Lake Ontario and Lake Huron is used to cool steam turbines in many of our nuclear power plants. Lake water is also used by fossil-fuel-burning power plants as well as other types of industrial complexes. After use, this warm water is returned to the lakes. Why would industries use water to cool their machinery? Suggest some of the societal and environmental implications of warming our lakes artificially.

10. Should fireplaces be used as part of support walls in houses? Explain.

11. Why does running hot water over a metal lid on a glass jar make it easier to open?

12. What happens to the size of a hole in the centre of a metal ring when the ring is heated? Explain.

13. Why are railway track sections separated by a small air gap? (Hint: They are called expansion slots.)

14. The background universe temperature is constantly cooling. How does this temperature trend help explain the Big Bang Theory?

15. On a cold day, you grab a shiny, metal fence gate with your bare hand. The post feels very cold. The next gate is made of wood and does not feel cold. Both gates are at the same temperature because they are close together outside. Explain why one gate feels colder than the other.

16. Why does the temperature scale have a lower limit but not an upper limit?

17. Where is the energy going in a process where there is a state change yet no temperature change?

18. Describe the heating/cooling system of a car in terms of heat transfer, temperature differences, state changes, heat capacities, and efficiency.

**19.** Thermograms are pictures which are colour-coded according to the amount of thermal energy radiated from the object. Running from coldest to hottest, the colours are black, blue, pink, red, and white. Describe the colours you would see on a thermogram of a limousine that has been running for a long time. The passenger compartment is separated by a partition and has a curtain on one window. The window on the driver's side is half open.

**20.** In what other areas of study would thermograms be useful diagnostic tools?

**21.** How does the greenhouse effect work in terms of types of radiation?

**22.** Which freezes first, hot water in an ice cube tray or cold water in the same-sized tray?

## Problems

### ▶ 8.2 Thermal Energy and Temperature

**23.** Convert the following:
   **a)** 100°C  = _____ K
   **b)** –25°C  = _____ K
   **c)** –273°C = _____ K
   **d)** 0°C    = _____ K
   **e)** 57 K   = _____ °C
   **f)** 300 K  = _____ °C

### ▶ 8.4 Specific Heat Capacity

Note: Use the specific heat capacities in Table 8.4 when required.

**24.** How much heat energy is gained per kilogram of water when it is heated from 10.0°C to 90.0°C?

**25.** A 400.0 g aluminum cooking pot is heated from 25.0°C to 99.0°C. What amount of heat energy does it absorb?

**26.** What was the initial temperature of a 1.50 kg piece of copper that gains $2.47 \times 10^4$ J of energy when it is heated to a final temperature of 150°C?

**27.** The graph in Fig. 8.25 illustrates the findings of an investigation in which a 1.0 kg mass of three different substances is heated.

**Fig.8.25**

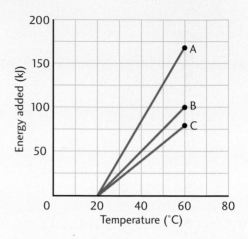

**a)** Find the slope (with units) of each of the three lines.
**b)** Which substance needed the most heat for the same temperature change as the others?
**c)** Which substance has the highest heat capacity?
**d)** How is the slope related to heat capacity?

**28.** What temperature change would occur in each of the following circumstances?
   **a)** 250 g of mercury gains 1.93 kJ of heat energy
   **b)** 5.0 kg of water gains 100 kJ of heat energy

**29.** A 25.0 g piece of nickel, originally at 500°C, has its temperature fall to 100°C when it is placed in a cold water bath. How much energy was lost by the piece of nickel during the cooling process?

### ▶ 8.5 Heat Exchange — The Law of Conservation of Heat Energy

**30.** A 100.0 g aluminum coffee cup at 15.0°C is filled with 250.0 g of piping hot coffee (about the same heat capacity as water) at 95.0°C. After all the heat transfer between the coffee and the cup is completed, what is the final temperature of the coffee (and the cup)?

31. Native Canadians used to boil water from maple tree sap by heating rocks and placing them into vats of sap sitting in hollowed-out tree logs. For this problem, assume that the syrup and the rocks have the heat capacities of water and sand, respectively. What mass of stone, heated to 1000°C, would be needed to increase 20.0 kg of sap from 60.0°C to 85.0°C?

32. A duck wants to take a bath and fills the tub with 50.0 L of water at a temperature of 38.0°C. After taking a phone call from his friend Bob, a lemming, the bath water had cooled by 10.0°C. How much more hot water at 80.0°C must the duck add to return the bath to the desired temperature?

33. A 200 W heater is used to heat 0.10 kg of a liquid from 20.0°C to 80.0°C, which takes one minute.
    a) What is the heat given off by the heater to the liquid?
    b) What is the heat capacity of the liquid?

## 8.6 Changes of State and Latent Heat

34. a) What is the latent heat of fusion of a 1.5 kg substance that requires $3.75 \times 10^4$ J to melt it?
    b) When the substance is cooled to its freezing point, how much heat energy is given off by 1 kg of the substance when it freezes into a solid?

35. What mass of oxygen would freeze by the removal of $7.4 \times 10^4$ J of heat energy?

36. How much heat must be removed by a freezer in order to change twenty 60 g sections of water at 0°C to ice at 0°C?

37. Brandy is made by distilling ethyl alcohol, which is done by boiling the alcohol until it turns into a gas. How much heat is required to completely distil 0.750 kg of ethyl alcohol?

38. A 0.200 kg block of ice at −15°C is placed into a pan on a stove, heated to a liquid, and then to vapour with a final temperature of 115°C. Calculate the total amount of heat required for this process.

## 8.7 Calorimetry — Some Practical Applications

39. The Forensic Sciences Lab in Toronto wants to find out what materials the Romans used in their water pipe systems. A 97.5 g sample of the metal pipe at 20.0°C is placed in a water calorimeter containing 0.10 kg of water at 53.2°C. What is the specific heat capacity of the metal if the calorimeter's final temperature was 52.2°C? Referring to Table 8.4, what are the possibilities for the type of metal used in these Roman pipes? Which do you think was the one that was actually used?

40. What mass of copper at 87.0°C, when added to 300 g of water at 17.0°C in a calorimeter, would yield a final temperature of 26.0°C?

## LAB 8.1 Efficiency of an Electric Appliance

### Purpose

To measure the percent efficiency of an electric appliance such as a tea kettle, a hot plate, or an immersion heater.

### Equipment

An electric water heating appliance (immersion heater with polystyrene cup, electric tea kettle, or hot plate and beaker)

Thermometer

Stopwatch

### Procedure

1. Set up the lab apparatus, as shown in Fig. Lab.8.1.
2. Measure 200 mL of water (0.200 kg) and pour it into a clean, dry heating container (polystyrene cup, electric tea kettle, or hot plate).
3. Place the thermometer into the water and measure the temperature after it as been allowed to sit for about two minutes to reach thermal equilibrium.
4. Turn on the heating apparatus (immersion heater for the polystyrene cup, electric tea kettle, or the hot plate if the container is the beaker) and start the stopwatch at the same time.
5. Keep heating until the water temperature rises a considerable amount (up to about 50°C–60°C)
6. Turn off the heating system. Stop the stopwatch and note the time, but continue to stir the water gently with the thermometer, being careful to record the highest temperature that is reached.

### Fig.Lab.8.1

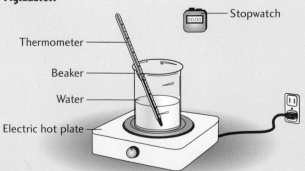

Stopwatch

Thermometer

Beaker

Water

Electric hot plate

### Data

1. This lab requires the mass of an amount of water in the heater, the time that the electricity was on, and the initial and final temperatures of the water.
2. Record the power rating of the heater in watts as it is written on the electrical information label.

### Uncertainty

Instrumental uncertainties of ±0.1 of the smallest division should be assigned to all temperatures and the mass taken. The time should be assigned an appropriate uncertainty based on your reflexes.

### Analysis

1. Calculate the heat gained by the water using the relationship $\Delta E_H = m\Delta tc$
2. Find the maximum heat energy that was produced by the heater by using the relationship $E_H = P\Delta t$, where $P$ is the power rating marked on the heating device and $t$ is the time.
3. Determine the percent efficiency of the energy transfer in the heating apparatus.

### Discussion

1. Look at the percent efficiency values found by other students in the class. Rank the three heating appliances (kettle, hot plate, or immersion heater) from most to least efficient.
2. This experiment could be considered representative of the amount of heat required to make one cup of tea. On average, the school cafeteria heats water for 75 cups of tea in one day for an entire year. How much money would be wasted due to inefficiency if the cost of electrical energy is 1¢ for every $4.5 \times 10^5$ J?

### Conclusion

Summarize your results for your value of the percent efficiency of your heating apparatus.

# LAB 8.2 Specific Heat Capacity

## Purpose
To measure the heat capacity of different metals by using the law of conservation of heat energy.

## Equipment
Safety glasses
250 mL polystyrene coffee cup
Length of thread
Glass rod
Thermometer
100 mL graduated cylinder
Hot plate
Balance
Samples of metals (aluminum, copper, zinc, lead, iron)
400 mL beaker

## Procedure
1. Prepare a data table using the sample table provided.
2. Prepare the lab equipment as shown in Fig. Lab.8.2.
3. Fill the 400 mL beaker half full with water and begin heating it on the hot plate, to be used later in the lab.
4. Measure the mass of one of the metal samples and record it in your data table.
5. Attach a thread to the sample and suspend it in the warming water with the glass rod, as shown in Fig. Lab.8.2. Leave the sample suspended in the water until the water has been boiling for at least five minutes so that you can be sure that the metal reaches the same temperature as the water.
6. Using the balance, find the mass of the polystyrene coffee cup calorimeter. Fill the calorimeter with 100 mL of tap water. Find the combined mass of the cup and water to find the mass of the water added. Measure the temperature of the water.
7. Transfer the metal very quickly to the calorimeter by lifting the glass rod with both hands and sliding the thread and metal off the rod and into the water.
8. Stir the water gently with the thermometer and record the highest temperature that the metal and water reach.
9. Repeat Steps 4–8 for as many other metals as you can in the time that you have.

**Fig.Lab.8.2**

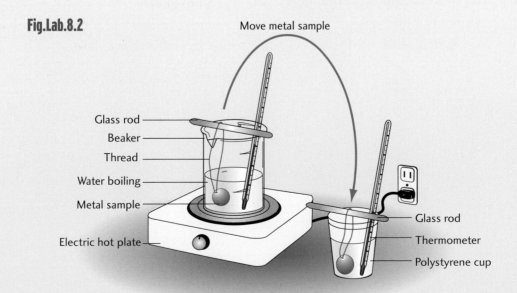

Move metal sample

Glass rod
Beaker
Thread
Water boiling
Metal sample
Electric hot plate

Glass rod
Thermometer
Polystyrene cup

## Data

| | | **Data Table** | | | | |
|---|---|---|---|---|---|---|
| Sample material | Mass of sample (kg) | Initial temperature of sample/ hot water (°C) | Initial temperature of cool water (°C) | Final temperature of sample/ water (°C) | $\Delta t$ of water (°C) | Specific heat capacity of sample (J/kg°C) |
| | | | | | | |
| | | | | | | |
| | | | | | | |
| | | | | | | |
| | | | | | | |
| | | | | | | |

## Uncertainty

Assign both instrumental and procedural uncertainties for each time you take a measurement. The balance and thermometer should be measured to ±0.1 of the smallest division.

## Analysis

Use the principle of heat exchange to calculate the specific heat capacity of each metal ($\Delta E_H = m\Delta tc$). Remember that the heat lost by the metal is the heat gained by the water.

## Discussion

1. Look up the specific heat capacities of all the metals you used in Table 8.4 and list them in your notebook, including their units.

2. Compare the value that you determined in the lab with the accepted values that you found in Question 1 above. Did your value agree with the accepted value to within your experimental uncertainty?

3. If your value did not agree with the accepted value, give possible reasons from your lab technique that could explain the difference. Be careful that your reasons make sense. Spilling water would affect a difference in calculations that could quite easily be dismissed by your final results.

## Conclusion

Summarize your experimental results by referring to your original purpose.

# Special Relativity and Rest Energy

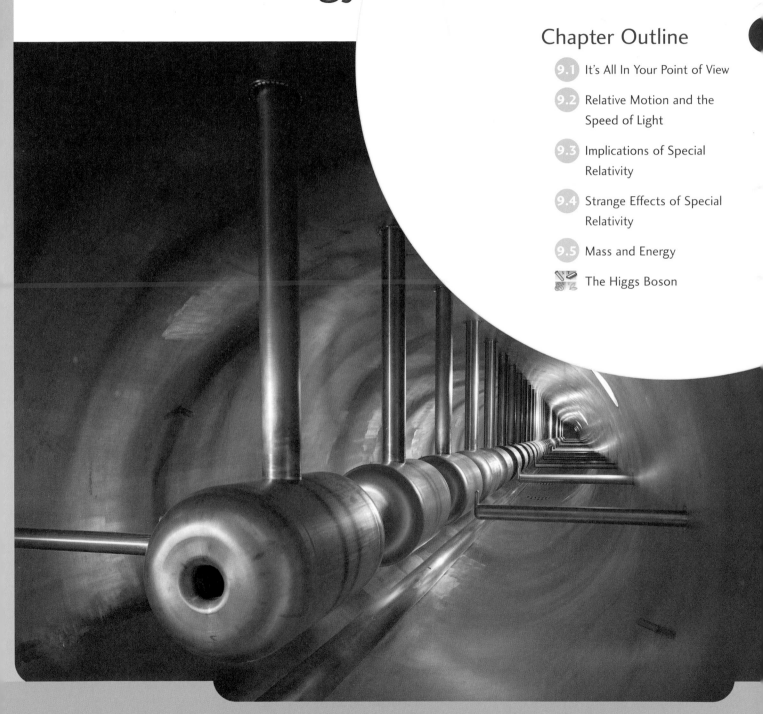

## Chapter Outline

**By the end of this chapter, you will be able to**

- describe various types of motion using different frames of reference
- describe and calculate the variations in time, length, and mass of objects moving at speeds close to the speed of light
- outline the relationship between mass and energy

## 9.1 It's All In Your Point of View

In 1905, Einstein's theory of relativity shocked the world of physics by overturning some long-held beliefs about the universe. Although it involves some complex math, the theory of relativity is based on a very simple set of principles, leading to some interesting situations that challenge our imagination. Einstein understood that our understanding of the universe depended on our point of view, the frame of reference that we use to observe it.

A funny thing happened on my way to school today that could be used to illustrate how important your "point of view" can be. While waiting for the light to turn green at an intersection, the car began to roll backward. At least that is what I thought when I rammed the brake even further into the floor. It turns out that I was not rolling backward at all, in fact I had not even moved a centimetre. The big bus in the lane to my right began to move forward with traffic and for an instant, I thought I was moving backward relative to the bus, even though it was the bus that was moving relative to me (see Fig. 9.1).

The point of view from which we observe motion is called a **frame of reference**. This is the stationary "platform" from which we judge or measure all other motion. Einstein noted that all the laws of mechanics apply the same way, whether you observe them from rest or from a frame of reference that is moving at a constant speed in a straight line. Imagine that you are driving into the city with friends and your buddy passes you a soft drink. This can be done just as safely in the car moving at a constant speed as it could when the car is at rest. If the reference frame has a constant velocity, then it is in a state that can be described by Newton's first law. Since that law is sometimes called the **law of inertia**, Einstein called this point of view an **inertial frame of reference**.

**Fig.9.1** Relative motion

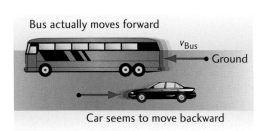

Bus actually moves forward

$v_{Bus}$

Ground

Car seems to move backward

> **Einstein's first principle of relativity** The laws of physics that describe changing circumstances are the same for all inertial frames of reference.

**1. a)** Inertial reference frames are those in which Newton's laws of motion hold true. Consider a person sitting in a car with shiny, slippery seats. To a stationary observer, why would the person sitting in the car remain in the same spot if the car is still or moving forward or backward with a constant speed? What will happen to the person when the car now speeds up, slows down, or turns?

  **b)** To the person in the car, turning a corner causes him or her to accelerate sideways, with no apparent force being applied. Using the concept of frames of reference, explain why this effect is not a violation of Newton's second law of motion.

Note: In the above example, the force of friction between the tires and the road exerts an inward force on the car toward the centre of the curve.

This inward force is called the **centripetal force**. The slippery seat doesn't transfer this force to the person.

## 9.2 Relative Motion and the Speed of Light

We opened this chapter with an example of how things can appear to be different depending on the frame of reference from which we choose to observe them. In the soft drink example on the previous page, our car, its occupants, and their drinks are all moving relative to the ground. But relative to the car, the drinks would not be moving. From the point of view of the drinks, the ground is moving at a constant speed toward them. In the next example, illustrated in Fig. 9.2, using relative velocity, we can show how things appear to move in different frames of reference. If one of your misguided soft drink swilling friends decides to throw his half-empty can out of the car at a velocity of 5 m/s ($_s\vec{v}_c$) forward with respect to the car, which is moving at 25 m/s ($_c\vec{v}_g$), then its velocity is added to the velocity of the car, 30 m/s ($_s\vec{v}_g$) relative to the ground.

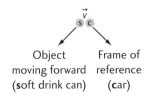

Object moving forward (**soft drink can**)      Frame of reference (**car**)

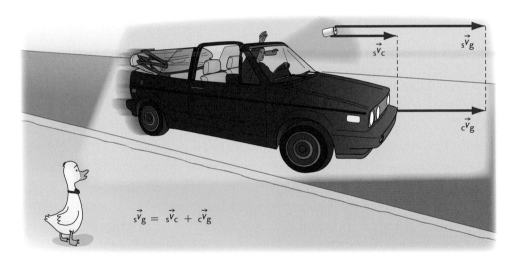

$$_s\vec{v}_g = {}_s\vec{v}_c + {}_c\vec{v}_g$$

**Fig.9.2**   Relative velocities of typical objects

A duck standing beside the road would observe the can moving forward at 30 m/s relative to the ground. We arrive at this answer by simply adding the two velocity vectors, as we learned in Chapter 3. The same method applies to the relative velocities of all ordinary objects.

According to Einstein's second principle of relativity, one exception to this method of calculating relative velocities is the speed of light, $c = 3.0 \times 10^8$ m/s.

Figure 9.3 shows that if your friend in the car shines a flashlight forward ($_L v_c$) as the car moves, the duck still sees the light travelling at velocity $c$, not $c + 25$ m/s, as you might expect. No matter how fast the car moves, an observer on the ground will see light from the car moving at $3.0 \times 10^8$ m/s.

**Einstein's second principle of relativity** The speed of light, $c$, has the same fixed value ($3.0 \times 10^8$ m/s) for all observers.

**Fig.9.3** Relative velocity of light

$$\vec{L}\vec{v}_g \neq \vec{c}\vec{v}_g + \vec{c} \qquad \vec{L}\vec{v}_g = \vec{c}$$

This principle of relativity has some startling implications. In 1853, Jean Foucault discovered that light waves travel at a constant rate of about $3.0 \times 10^8$ m/s, which improved previous estimates from scientists such as James Clerk Maxwell and Galileo. The material or medium that acted as the frame of reference in which light waves were believed to travel was somewhat of a mystery. Today, our cars have their speed measured with respect to the ground, boats with respect to the water, and air planes with respect to the air in which they move. The frame of reference in which the speed of light was to be measured (the light's medium), the **ether**, was thought to be highly elastic so light could travel at such great speeds, but of low density so it wouldn't impede the motion of the planets. The ether was thought to be the universal medium or frame of reference against which all other motions could be measured. In the 1800s, two American physicists, A.A. Michelson and E.W. Morley, designed an experiment to measure the speed of Earth with respect to the ether. This experiment used an extremely sensitive light-measuring apparatus, shown in Figs. 9.4 and 9.5, called an **interferometer**.

Using the interferometer, scientists split a beam of light into two perpendicular paths similar to the two-boat analogy shown in Fig. 9.6(b).

**Fig.9.4** The Michelson interferometer

**Fig.9.5** The optics of an interferometer

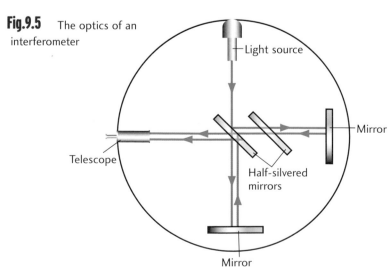

Light source

Mirror

Telescope

Half-silvered mirrors

Mirror

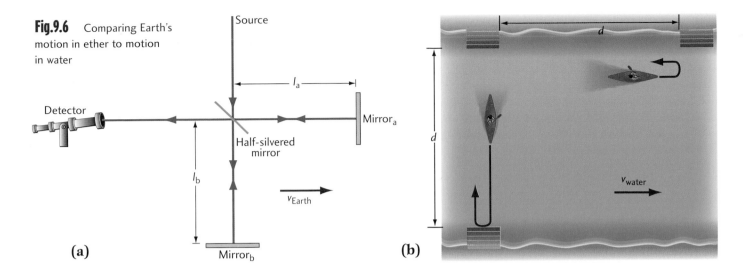

**Fig.9.6** Comparing Earth's motion in ether to motion in water

Source

$l_a$

Detector

Half-silvered mirror

Mirror$_a$

$l_b$

$v_{Earth}$

**(a)**

Mirror$_b$

$d$

$d$

$v_{water}$

**(b)**

If one of the paths was parallel to Earth's motion and the other was perpendicular to Earth's motion, then the two beams would take different times to travel equal distances. Take our beloved couple, Tarzan and Tarzana, from Chapter 3. They take two separate but equidistant trips at the same speed with respect to the water (Fig. 9.6(b)); one directly across and back, and the other downstream and back. We would fully expect them to arrive back at different times. But this is not what happens with light. Michelson and Morley couldn't measure any time difference between the two paths of light, even when using a light interferometer that takes advantage of the interference of two light beams (covered in Chapter 12). This sensitive device would have noticed a time difference as small as $2.0 \times 10^{-17}$ s. But no matter how they did their experiment (direction of device, day or time of year), they always got the same result. This result is often referred to as the **null result**, which explains that an "unsuccessful" experiment in science can be just as informative as a "successful" one. One explanation of the null result was that there was no ether or absolute frame of reference. Another explanation was that Earth was a passive passenger being pushed along with the "ether wind." Today, Einstein's answer is accepted—there is no ether! The speed of light is constant in all directions for all observers. This concept is quite simple, but it has some bizarre implications!

1. Einstein is looking in a mirror while sitting in a rocket that's moving at the speed of light. Explain in your own words what appears in the mirror and the rationale behind your answer.

**Fig.9.7**

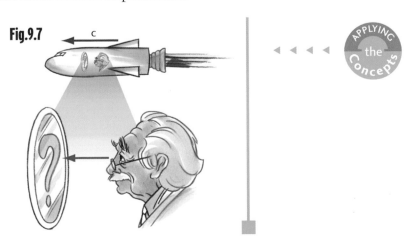

*c*

APPLYING the Concepts

## 9.3 Implications of Special Relativity

### Simultaneity — "Seeing is Believing"

Normally, we judge that an event has occurred by observing the light from the event with our eyes. It sounds obvious. But, if light always moves at the finite speed, *c*, for all observers, this judgement is not as obvious as we thought. At a baseball game, we see the ball being hit, but we do not hear the "crack" of the bat until some time later. Even though light travels incredibly fast, the hit actually occurred before we saw it. The hit and the viewing of it don't occur at the same time because it takes time for the light from the event to reach us. If we had been moving, especially at a high speed, our judgement of the event would be even less accurate.

**Fig.9.8** Exactly when do events occur?

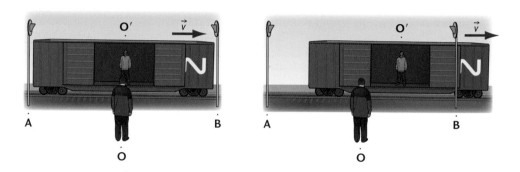

In Fig. 9.8, the warning lights at A and B flash simultaneously. When the flash occurs, observers O and O′ are exactly halfway between A and B. Observer O is on the ground and observer O′ is moving at very high speed to the right. The light from A and B travels the same distance to observer O, and he observes the flashes from both A and B as occurring at the same time. Observer O′, however, is moving at high speed toward B. But light travels at speed *c* for all observers. Since observer O′ is approaching B and receding from A, he sees the flash of light from B *before* the flash from A. Because of these discrepancies, one person's observations and judgements about simultaneous events can't be considered more correct than another's. What you see depends on your frame of reference.

> **Simultaneity** If any two observers are moving with respect to one another, then their judgement of simultaneous events may not necessarily agree.

**Fig.9.9** Simultaneity

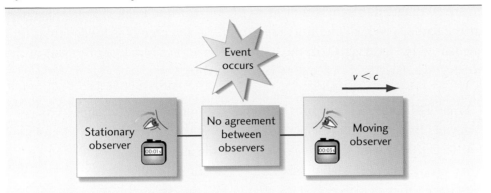

## Time Dilation

The fact that light has the same speed for all observers even affects the results of simple kinematics situations when the behaviour of light is observed by fast-moving observers. Consider what happens to a camera flash when a picture is taken inside a boxcar that is moving at a speed close to the speed of light, as shown in Fig. 9.10.

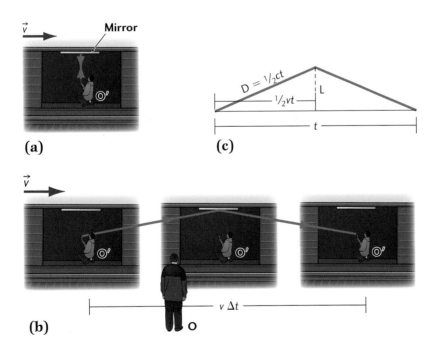

**Fig.9.10** How a stationary observer sees light from a fast-moving train

The fact that two observers may see the same event occur at different times suggests that time is not absolute. Could time pass at a different rate in different reference frames? This possibility is exactly what Einstein's theory predicts.

Consider observer O′ in Fig. 9.10(a) shining a flashlight towards the mirror on the ceiling of the boxcar. He sees light from the flashlight hit the mirror and reflect back, travelling a distance of $2L$ in time $t_0$ $\left(t_0 = \frac{2L}{c}\right)$. Consider observer O on the ground in Fig. 9.10(b). If the boxcar is passing

From 9.10(c),

$$D^2 = L^2 + (\tfrac{1}{2}vt)^2$$

where $v$ is the speed of the boxcar.

$$\left(\frac{ct}{2}\right)^2 = L^2 + \left(\frac{vt}{2}\right)^2$$

$$\frac{c^2t^2}{4} = L^2 + \frac{v^2t^2}{4}$$

$$c^2t^2 = 4L^2 + v^2t^2$$

$$t^2(c^2 - v^2) = 4L^2$$

$$t = \frac{2L}{\sqrt{c^2 - v^2}} = \frac{2L}{c\sqrt{1 - \dfrac{v^2}{c^2}}}$$

Recall that for the observer O'

in the car, $t_o = \dfrac{2L}{c}$

$$\therefore t = \frac{t_0}{\sqrt{1 - \dfrac{v^2}{c^2}}}$$

by him at near the speed of light, then the light from the flashlight appears to travel diagonally across the car to the mirror and back, a larger distance at the same speed, $c$. The time measured by observer O is longer than that measured by observer O' in the boxcar. This effect is a general result of the theory of relativity and is called **time dilation**.

> **Time Dilation** For a stationary observer, moving clocks appear to run slower than they do for someone moving with the clock. For the moving observer, however, it is the clock of the stationary person that appears to be running slower. The moving and the stationary observers each believe that the other's clock is the one that is running slow.

Analyzing Fig. 9.10 for relative distances and solving for $t$, the stationary observer's time, we get the following relativistic equation.

$$t = \frac{t_o}{\sqrt{1 - \dfrac{v^2}{c^2}}}$$

where $t$ is the relativistic time, which is the time measured by the stationary observer.

$t_o$ is the time measured by the moving observer.

$v$ is the speed of the object and $c$ is the speed of light, $3.0 \times 10^8$ m/s.

**EXAMPLE 1**  **Time dilation at speeds close to the speed of light**

A student is late for school and decides to drive to school in her new hi-tech car of rest mass $1.50 \times 10^3$ kg and length 4.2 m at a speed of $2.5 \times 10^8$ m/s. If the entire trip at that speed took 2.0 s according to the student, how long is the trip according to the stationary school principal?

### *Solution and Connection to Theory*

**Given**

$t_o = 2.0$ s      $m_o = 1.50 \times 10^3$ kg      $L_o = 4.2$ m      $v = 2.5 \times 10^8$ m/s
$c = 3.0 \times 10^8$ m/s      $t = ?$

$$t = \frac{t_o}{\sqrt{1 - \dfrac{v^2}{c^2}}} = \frac{2.0 \text{ s}}{\sqrt{1 - \dfrac{(2.5 \times 10^8 \text{ m/s})^2}{(3.0 \times 10^8 \text{ m/s})^2}}} = \frac{2.0 \text{ s}}{}$$

$$t = \frac{2.0 \text{ s}}{0.553} = 3.6 \text{ s}$$

The principal would observe the student's trip to have taken 3.6 s.

Another way to look at time dilation is by using an analogy. Let's say that you are blasting off from Earth towards a distant planet that light will take five minutes to reach. You are travelling at four-fifths the speed of light and you depart at midnight. Five minutes into your trip, you look at your watch and it reads 12:05 a.m. But the image of the time on your watch travels at speed $c$, faster than you. For a stationary observer on the distant planet you are approaching, the time on your watch would read 12:04 a.m. because light from the 12:05 a.m. image on your watch hasn't reached her yet. She would judge your watch to be running slow.

**Fig.9.11**

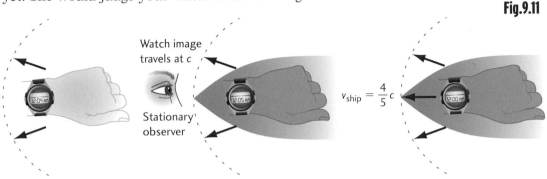

## Length Contraction

When objects are moving at speeds near the speed of light, time becomes relative, not absolute. Similarly with the dimensions of objects. As the object approaches the speed of light, its length in the line of motion decreases, according to the equation

$$L = L_o \sqrt{1 - \frac{v^2}{c^2}}$$

where $L_o$ is the rest length or the normal length of the object at $v = 0$, $L$ is the relativistic length at the speed, $v$, of the object, and $c$ is the speed of light.

### DEDUCTION OF LENGTH CONTRACTION

$t = \dfrac{L_o}{v}$ and $t_0 = t \sqrt{1 - \dfrac{v^2}{c^2}}$ from

the time dilation formula

so $L = vt_0 = vt \sqrt{1 - \dfrac{v^2}{c^2}}$

But $L_o = vt$ so $L = L_o \sqrt{1 - \dfrac{v^2}{c^2}}$

**EXAMPLE 2**   **Length contraction at speeds close to the speed of light**

What is the relativistic length of the car that the student is driving as seen by the principal in Example 1?

### *Solution and Connection to Theory*

**Given**

$t_o = 2.0$ s      $m_o = 1.50 \times 10^3$ kg      $L_o = 4.2$ m      $v = 2.5 \times 10^8$ m/s

$c = 3.0 \times 10^8$ m/s      $L = ?$

$L = L_o \sqrt{1 - \dfrac{v^2}{c^2}} = 4.2 \text{ m} \sqrt{1 - \dfrac{(2.5 \times 10^8)^2}{(3.0 \times 10^8)^2}}$

$L = 4.2 \text{ m}(0.553) = 2.32 \text{ m}$

To the principal, the car would appear to be only 2.3 m long.

## Mass Increase

Just as the "absolutes" of time and length are affected at relativistic speeds, so too is mass. Like time, mass appears dilated or increased to a stationary observer viewing objects travelling at relativistic speeds.

$$m = \frac{m_0}{\sqrt{1 - \frac{v^2}{c^2}}}$$

where $m$ is the relativistic mass, $m_o$ is the "rest" mass, $v$ is the velocity of the object, and $c$ is the speed of light.

---

**EXAMPLE 3**    **Mass increase at speeds close to the speed of light**

In Examples 1 and 2, the student's car would also appear to the principal to gain mass. What would the relativistic mass of the student's car be at the speed of $2.5 \times 10^8$ m/s?

### *Solution and Connection to Theory*

**Given**

$t_o = 2.0$ s      $m_o = 1.50 \times 10^3$ kg      $L_o = 4.2$ m      $v = 2.5 \times 10^8$ m/s
$c = 3.0 \times 10^8$ m/s      $m = ?$

$$m = \frac{m_0}{\sqrt{1 - \frac{v^2}{c^2}}} = \frac{1.5 \times 10^3 \text{ kg}}{\sqrt{1 - \frac{(2.5 \times 10^8)^2}{(3.0 \times 10^8)^2}}}$$

$$m = \frac{1.5 \times 10^3 \text{ kg}}{0.553} = 2.7 \times 10^3 \text{ kg}$$

The principal would observe the student's car to be $2.7 \times 10^3$ kg.

In every relativistic equation, the relativistic factor always appears:

$$\sqrt{1 - \frac{v^2}{c^2}}$$

In the time dilation and mass increase formulas, this component is *divided* into the rest values because relativistic time and mass are larger. With length contraction, this component is *multiplied* by the rest length because relativistic length is shorter than rest length.

**Fig.9.12**   Relativistic Effects

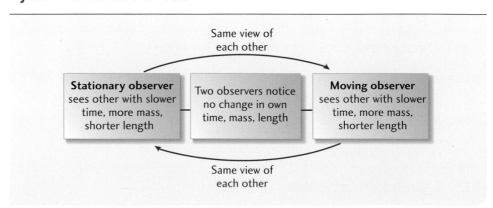

Same view of each other

| Stationary observer sees other with slower time, more mass, shorter length | Two observers notice no change in own time, mass, length | Moving observer sees other with slower time, more mass, shorter length |

Same view of each other

UNIT B: Work, Energy, and Power

1. Explain the concept of time dilation for two people, one stationary and the other moving at close to the speed of light.
2. What would the consequence be if the speed of light was not always the same for all observers?
3. For an object moving in the horizontal direction at near the speed of light, select the aspects of the object that change as it changes reference frames (time, length in the $x$ direction, length in the $y$ direction, mass, and speed).
4. **a)** Two good friends on Earth say good bye to each other as one of them takes off on a trip into space at 85 % the speed of light. If the trip lasts one year, how many years have gone by on Earth?
   **b)** What would the mass of the spaceship appear to be if it had a 1200 kg rest mass?
   **c)** What is the observed length of the ship if it was 5.6 m long while sitting on Earth?

# 9.4 Strange Effects of Special Relativity

## A Fountain of Youth?

A **paradox** is a statement or situation that seems to be contradictory to popular belief but which is true. One of the most interesting aspects of relativity that has made it into the realm of science fiction is that of time travel. One thought experiment that describes the consequences of relativistic speeds is the *twin paradox*. One twin blasts off from Earth at a speed close to $c$, while the other remains on Earth. After an extensive period of time according to the stationary twin, the traveller returns to Earth, appearing much younger than her earthbound sister because the moving clock had slowed.

Are relativistic effects reversible for the two observers? One might expect that from the point of view of the space traveller, it is Earth that moves away at a high speed. Therefore, when Earth "returns," the twin on Earth would appear younger. However, this is not the case. The relativistic effects would only be witnessed by the earthbound twin because she is observing the event from an inertial frame of reference. In contrast, the travelling twin accelerates, decelerates, and stops before returning to Earth, that is, she is in a non-inertial frame of reference.

## Stopping Time

If time slows as speed increases, then it must be possible to stop time. When the speed of a clock reaches $c$, the speed of light, the relativistic term becomes zero.

$$\sqrt{1 - \frac{v^2}{c^2}}$$

Requiring division by zero, this makes the time dilation formula

$$t = \frac{t_o}{\sqrt{1 - \frac{v^2}{c^2}}}$$

mathematically undefined. In physics, this means that time becomes infinitely slow and would represent the clock stopping. Figure 9.13 summarizes what happens to time, length, and mass as well as kinetic energy as speeds approach the speed of light. This figure illustrates that the mass, and therefore the kinetic energy, of objects would become infinitely large at the speed of light. It seems a terrible shame that although many interesting things occur when objects reach the speed of light, they can never be achieved practically. An infinite amount of energy would have to be transferred to an object to push its speed to $c$, since its mass would also have to be increased to an infinite value. This idea implies an absolute *speed limit* — no object with rest mass can ever reach the speed of light. Also, there is no way that time could ever stop.

**Fig.9.13**   Effects on length, time, mass, and energy as an object approaches the speed of light

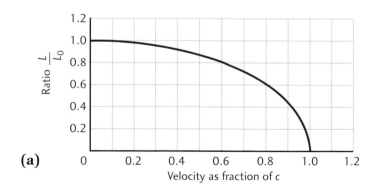

**(a)**

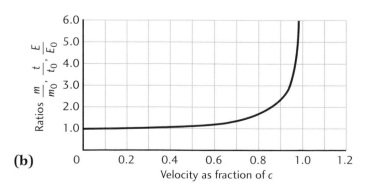

**(b)**

UNIT B: Work, Energy, and Power

## Experimental Confirmations of Special Relativity

Although the effects of relativity seem very strange, they have been confirmed many times. In 1971, J.C. Haffele and R.E. Keating transported a cesium clock (based on the decay rate of the isotope). They flew one clock in a jet plane for 45 hours and compared the time of the clock on the plane to the time of an identical clock on the ground. Although the effect of time dilation was small, there was a measurable difference, one that was predicted by the time dilation formula.

These effects are now commonly seen in high-energy accelerators (Fig. 9.14), where radioactive particles are accelerated to speeds near $c$. The amount of material remaining after travelling in the accelerator is greater than that predicted by the half-life calculation (see Chapter 19) from a stationary reference frame. If one takes into account the effect of time dilation, then the correct value of the remaining material is obtained. To us, the material appears to have a longer half-life.

**Fig.9.14** LEP, the world's most powerful electron-positron collider (Geneva, Switzerland)

1. The average lifetime of a mu-meson (muon) is $2.2 \times 10^{-6}$ s. Mu-mesons are created in the upper atmosphere, thousands of metres above the ground, by cosmic rays. If the speed of a mu-meson is $2.994 \times 10^8$ m/s,
   a) calculate the distance it can travel in its average lifetime $(2.2 \times 10^{-6}$ s$)$.
   b) calculate its relativistic distance using the answer from part a).
   c) calculate the apparent lifetime of the meson from the reference point of an observer on the ground.
   d) calculate the distance the muon travels using the new time from part c).

For parts b) and d), the answers should be the same. The muon is in fact observed on Earth due to relativistic effects.

## 9.5 Mass and Energy

Figure 9.13 implies that as more and more work is done to bring an object closer to the speed of light, the mass of the object also increases. This observation suggests that mass is somehow a storehouse of energy. Einstein (Fig. 9.15) summarized the mass–energy relationship with the equation

$$E = mc^2$$

where the constant, $c$, is the speed of light.

This equation predicts that if any small mass could be converted to energy, the amount of energy released would be incredibly large. The following example illustrates the amount of energy Einstein's equation predicts would be created from the complete transformation of 1 g of matter.

$$E = mc^2$$
$$1 \text{ g} = 1.0 \times 10^{-3} \text{ kg and } c = 3.0 \times 10^8 \text{ m/s}$$
$$E = (1.0 \times 10^{-3} \text{ kg})(3.0 \times 10^8 \text{ m/s})^2$$
$$= 9.0 \times 10^{13} \text{ J}$$

Based on what we learned in Chapter 8, $9.0 \times 10^{13}$ J of energy is enough energy to raise the temperature of about one million large bathtubs (200 L) of water from 0°C to 100°C.

**Fig.9.15**  Einstein at work and at play

**Fig.9.16**  $E = mc^2$

 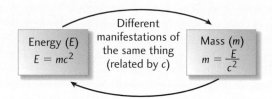

---

**EXAMPLE 4**  **Energy from matter**

How much mass of material must be completely converted to energy in order to provide $5.26 \times 10^6$ J of energy (the amount of energy needed to lift one metric tonne to the top of the CN Tower in Toronto)?

*Solution and Connection to Theory*

**Given**
$E = 5.26 \times 10^6 \text{ J}$     $c = 3.0 \times 10^8 \text{ m/s}$     $m = ?$

UNIT B: Work, Energy, and Power

Rearrange the mass–energy relationship to solve for mass.

$E = mc^2$ so

$$m = \frac{E}{c^2} = \frac{5.26 \times 10^6\,\text{J}}{(3.0 \times 10^8\,\text{m/s})^2} = 5.84 \times 10^{-11}\,\text{kg}$$

One metric tonne can be lifted up the CN Tower by the rest energy stored in only $5.84 \times 10^{-11}$ kg of matter.

The concepts of relativity may seem more difficult to grasp than any other topic in physics we have studied so far. On their own, the equations and concepts are not very difficult, but there is no explanation for them. We haven't discussed *why* the speed of light is the same for all observers, only the *implications* of this assumption.

**Fig.9.17  Summary of Special Relativity**

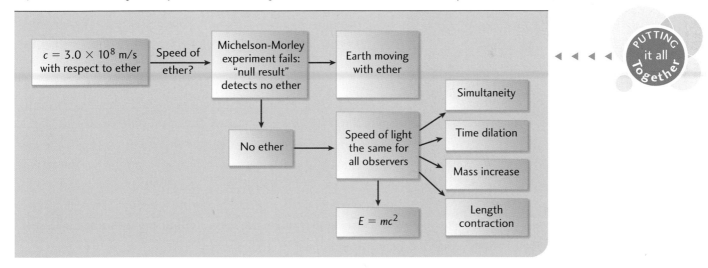

1. If particles in an ion beam are accelerated to 95 % the speed of light, what is the ratio of their relativistic masses compared to their rest masses?
2. What speed must an object have in order for its mass to double?
3. a) Calculate your own mass-equivalent energy.
   b) How many 700 W toasters will run for one hour from your mass-equivalent energy?

# The Higgs Boson

Special relativity is so "special" that special circumstances have to be created in order to verify any of its postulates. For instance, measuring time dilation during aircraft travel required an incredibly precise atomic clock. High-energy facilities, such as those at CERN in Geneva, Switzerland (Fig. STSE.9.1), and Fermilab in Illinois are required to accelerate matter to the point where the effects of relativity can be readily observed.

In November 2000, after 11 years of operation, CERN (Conseil Européen pour la Recherche Nucléaire) shut down its Large Electron-Positron (LEP) Collider (Fig. STSE.9.2).

**Fig.STSE.9.1**   The CERN lab in Geneva, Switzerland

These massive machines use powerful electromagnets to accelerate charged particles to high speed and collide them with matter. In such high-speed collisions, energy of about 115 GeV (giga electron volts) is converted to matter, as described by Einstein's equation $E = mc^2$, producing new and interesting particles. In 1960, British physicist Peter Higgs proposed a model to explain how matter expresses mass. One of the key pieces of evidence needed to verify his theory was the existence of a type of subatomic particle, called a boson, naturally named the Higgs boson. Before it was shut down, the LEP was beginning to show promise. Researchers were seeing some evidence that Higgs particles exist, although only for a fraction of a second (see Fig. STSE.9.3). The LEP will be replaced with a new system called a Large Hadron Collider (LHC). At a cost of about $1.8 billion, the LHC will be ready to begin experimenting in 2005.

**Fig.STSE.9.2**   Inside the LEP tunnel

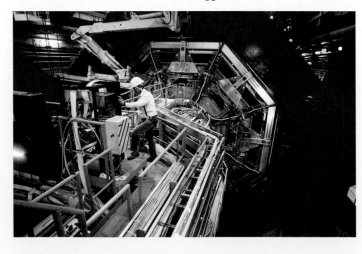

**Fig.STSE.9.3**   View of the L3 detector on LEP that was used to look for evidence of the Higgs boson

## Design a Study of Societal Impact

An enormous amount of energy and money is required to perform research in high-energy physics. Research the estimated costs of various scientific endeavors. List at least five of these research projects in order of decreasing cost. Are these projects also listed in order of decreasing importance? Should public funds be used to fund this type of research? Does the general public benefit from this research?

Do further research on the Higgs boson or the current status of research in the field of special relativity.

## Design an Activity to Evaluate

Research results for special relativity and high-energy physics can be found on the Internet. CERN scientist Tim Berners-Lee invented the World Wide Web in 1990. Choose a topic from special relativity or high-energy physics. Prepare a statistical evaluation of the current research posted on the Internet. Evaluate the content of the material by doing a hit count for various search parameters, or count the number of times a certain phrase or theory (such as string theory or autodynamics) is discussed on each site. Review several Web sites and create a chart to compare opinions about your chosen topic. For example, do some sites believe that matter could travel at or faster than the speed of light? Do other sites express a view to the contrary?

## Build a Structure

Build a physical model to demonstrate an aspect of special relativity that is particularly difficult to grasp, such as the consistency of the speed of light for all observers, or simultaneity. Using sound rather than light, build a model that demonstrates the concept of simultaneity.

SPECIFIC EXPECTATIONS

## You should be able to

*Understand Basic Concepts:*

- Define and describe the concept of frames of reference as it applies to how we view objects moving relative to one another at low or high speeds.
- Describe Einstein's first and second principles of relativity.
- Use qualitative terms to outline how time, length, and mass are affected at speeds approaching the speed of light.
- Use velocity vectors to differentiate between relative velocities of typical objects and the velocity of light.
- Define the concept of simultaneity and use practical analogies to describe how it may be perceived at speeds near that of light.
- Apply simple kinematics formulas and the principle of relativity to derive equations that relate rest time, length, and mass to their relativistic values.
- Use derived relativistic equations to quantitatively evaluate the effects of high-speed travel on time, length, and mass for a moving object.
- Recognize that mass and energy may be considered different manifestations of the same thing.
- Relate mass and energy in quantitative terms by applying the equation $E = mc^2$.

*Develop Skills of Inquiry and Communication:*

- Use physical analogies to communicate the concepts of special relativity that can only be observed at speeds close to the speed of light.
- Outline the Michelson-Morley experiment and relate its apparent failure to the assertion that the speed of light has a fixed value for all observers.
- Illustrate using specific historical references how accepted scientific theories have been confirmed much later by high-technology experimentation.

*Relate Science to Technology, Society, and the Environment:*

- Identify that experimentation in the areas of special relativity and high-energy physics is dependent on the development of extremely expensive and highly technical equipment.
- Recognize that it is difficult to justify the funding of scientific research that may not produce results that are widely applicable or beneficial to society.

## Equations

$$E = mc^2 \qquad t = \frac{t_o}{\sqrt{1 - \dfrac{v^2}{c^2}}} \qquad L = L_o\sqrt{1 - \frac{v^2}{c^2}} \qquad m = \frac{m_0}{\sqrt{1 - \dfrac{v^2}{c^2}}}$$

## EXERCISES

### Conceptual Questions

1. Give some examples of non-inertial frames of reference.

2. Does the room that you are in right now, which is at rest on Earth's surface, constitute an inertial frame of reference? If not, where on Earth's surface is the acceleration greatest? Where is it the least?

3. Explain why the failure of the Michelson-Morley experiment was really a benefit for science.

4. Will two events that occur in the same place and at the same time for one observer be simultaneous to a second observer who is moving with respect to the first?

5. As stationary observers, we would see the relativistic effects of length contraction, mass increase, and time dilation when observing a spacecraft go by at $0.90c$. What would the occupants of the spacecraft say that they observed about us?

6. Suppose that light always carries a wristwatch. What would we observe that watch to be doing as light moved past us? From our point of view, how long does any beam of light last (its effective "lifetime")?

7. At what speed would starlight pass you if you were travelling away from the star at $0.6c$?

8. What would happen to the mass of a 1 kg mass as it approached the speed of light?

9. Density is the mass per unit volume of a substance. From the point of view of an observer at rest, what would happen to the density of the hull of a spacecraft as it approached the speed of light?

10. At a baseball game, the fans judge the "real time" at which a hit occurred as the instant they saw the event. In the baseball park, fans trust their eyes before they trust their ears because the light from the event communicates the event before the sound does. Why will we never be able to communicate in "real time" with robots or people living on Mars?

11. Why would Einstein tell you that you could never go backward in time?

12. Time dilation does not really mean that the mechanism of a moving clock runs slower. What does it really mean?

13. How is it possible to spend 10 years going to Alpha Centauri while 200 years pass on Earth?

14. If mass can be changed to energy, what does this say about the law of conservation of energy or mass?

15. What relativistic effect would we observe on Earth if the speed of light was only 100 km/h?

16. What would it be like on Earth if the speed of light was an infinite value?

17. Apply the principles of relativity to describe any theoretical differences in the mass and length of a CF-18 Hornet jet when it is motionless in the hanger and when it is flying at its top speed. Use this question as an example to explain why it may be difficult to make some scientific theories into scientific laws.

18. How might you respond to one of your friends who states that relativistic effects do not occur at speeds such as 100 km/h?

19. Does the mass of an object change when it is heated? Explain.

**20.** According to the formula for relativistic mass, what would the rest mass of a photon be as it travels at the speed of light?

## Problems

### ▶ 9.3 Implications of Special Relativity

**21.** Two light bulbs, X and Y, are turned on simultaneously, as shown in Fig. 9.18.

Observer I is at rest midway between the light bulbs and they are stationary relative to her. At the time that the light bulbs are turned on, Observer II is at the same position as Observer I, but he is moving at high speed.

**Fig.9.18**

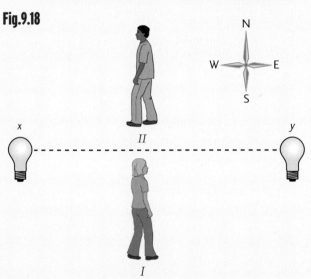

**a)** In which direction is Observer II moving if he sees both the light bulbs turned on simultaneously?

**b)** In which direction is Observer II moving if he sees light bulb X turn on *before* light bulb Y?

**22.** A cruise ship is travelling with a southerly velocity, as shown in Fig. 9.19.

One hundred metres to the west is a coast line with three parallel spotlights that are 30 m apart and are known to always turn on simultaneously. If the ship could move at relativistic speeds and it passed the second spotlight, in what order would the spotlights appear to turn on?

**Fig.9.19**

**23.** The decay of a certain isotope takes $10^{-6}$ s to occur when it is at rest. According to a stationary observer, how much time will this decay take when the isotope is moving at a speed of $5 \times 10^7$ m/s?

**24.** Your teacher takes a round trip to the nearest star, a distance of $9.46 \times 10^{15}$ m, at a speed of $0.9c$. How many days younger would your teacher be upon his return than if he had stayed behind?

**25.** Superman attempts to fly from Earth to Saturn and back in less than 23 s. He flies at $2.91 \times 10^8$ m/s for 46 s. According to a clock on Earth, did he make it on time?

**26.** "When a man sits with a pretty girl for an hour, it feels like a minute, but let him sit on a hot stove for a minute and it is longer than an hour. That's relativity." – Albert Einstein

How fast would a man have to be travelling in order to sit with a pretty girl for an hour, and have it seem like a minute?

**27.** How fast would a spacecraft have to travel in order for one year on the spacecraft to correspond to three years on Earth?

**28.** Twins are 22 years old. One twin volunteers to go on a spaceship and travels through space at $0.90c$ for four years. How old would each twin be when they reunite?

**29.** During high-speed space travel, your wrist watch becomes one second slower every hour compared to a clock on Earth. What must be the speed of your spacecraft?

**30.** The Concorde flies at 400 m/s. How much time must elapse in flight before the pilot's watch and someone's watch on the ground differ by one second?

**31.** The tallest man in Houston, Texas won a free trip on the space shuttle. An observer on Earth finds that the spacecraft speed is $0.7c$ and this man, standing parallel to the ship's motion appears to be 1.6 m tall. What is the man's award-winning height when measured at rest on Earth?

**32.** An alpha particle (nucleus of helium) is $1.3 \times 10^{-6}$ m in diameter and is moving at a speed of $10^8$ m/s. What would the diameter of this particle appear to be in its direction of motion if you were to observe it going by?

**33.** A Formula 1 race car, four metres long, is at the starting line waiting for the race to begin. The dimensions of its engine are 0.5 m $\times$ 0.5 m $\times$ 0.5 m. When the race begins and the car reaches a speed of $0.7c$, the relativistic density of the engine is shown to be 6000 kg/m$^3$. What is the relativistic mass of the engine?

**34.** A person on Earth measures a duck to be 0.40 m long. How long would the duck appear to be to a person in a rocket that is passing by at $0.94c$, as shown in Fig. 9.20?

**Fig.9.20**

**35.** Find the mass of an object whose rest mass is 500 g when it is travelling at $0.10c$, and $0.90c$.

**36.** If an object has doubled its rest mass by moving relative to an observer, at what speed must it be moving?

**37.** When a spacecraft is moving, a stationary observer measures the astronaut's mass to be 99.0 kg. If she knows that on Earth the astronaut has a mass of 70.0 kg, how fast is the spacecraft moving?

**38.** Bob has one kilogram of gold. To make more money, he takes this gold on a spaceship and flies it at $0.8c$. If gold is priced at $2000/kg, what is the price difference between the gold at $0.8c$ and the gold at rest?

## 9.5 Mass and Energy

**39.** How much energy would be released in joules if a 100 kg mass were to be totally converted from mass to energy?

**40.** How much mass is lost in the process known as fission (breaking into smaller pieces) when a uranium nucleus at rest breaks in fragments that have a total kinetic energy of $3.2 \times 10^{-11}$ J?

**41.** How much work must be done to accelerate an electron of rest mass $9.11 \times 10^{-31}$ kg from rest to a speed of $0.95c$?

**42.** How much mass of a material must be converted to energy at a rate of $1.7 \times 10^7$ J/s for 32 days, assuming the process is 100% efficient?

**43.** What amount of energy would be produced from a material which, at a speed of $0.68c$, has the relative density of 58 kg/m$^3$ and a volume of 120 m$^3$? Assume 100% efficiency.

**44.** In PET scanners (positron emission tomography), two gamma rays ($\gamma$-rays) are formed from the total annihilation of one electron of mass $9.11 \times 10^{-31}$ kg and one positron of similar mass. How much energy do these gamma rays possess?

# Light and Geometric Optics

C

10   Reflection and the Wave Theory of Light

11   Refraction

12   Wave Nature of Light

# UNIT C: Light and Geometric Optics

*"Mirror, mirror on the wall..."*
*Through the Looking Glass*
*"Lights, camera, action!"*

The above *common* phases make use of *common* objects. Mirrors, lenses, and cameras are all items we use often. What do they have in common? Light.

This unit will provide you with an understanding of the nature of light. One of the longest-running debates in science has been "What is light?" Some experiments have demonstrated that light is made of individual particles. Other experiments have demonstrated that light is made of waves of energy. Which theory is correct? The answer is both and neither! "Both" is correct because light has a dual nature, able to appear as particles or waves. "Neither" is also correct because light doesn't consist of either particles or waves; it is something much more complex. It can, however, be made to appear as either a particle or a wave. In this chapter, we investigate the wave nature of light.

**Timeline: History of Light and Geometric Optics**

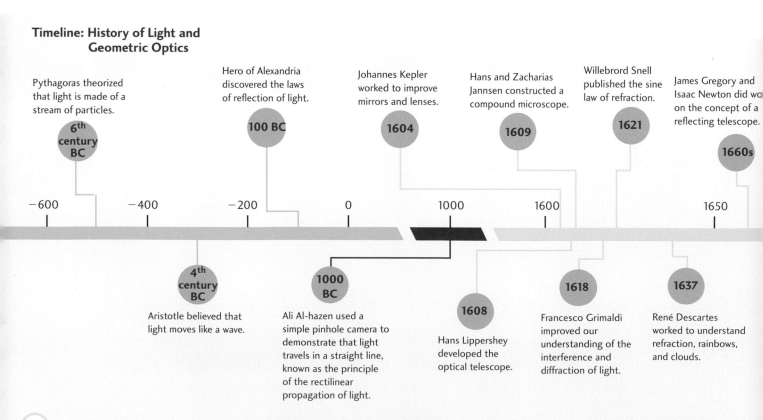

Pythagoras theorized that light is made of a stream of particles.
**6th century BC**

Hero of Alexandria discovered the laws of reflection of light.
**100 BC**

Johannes Kepler worked to improve mirrors and lenses.
**1604**

Hans and Zacharias Jannsen constructed a compound microscope.
**1609**

Willebrord Snell published the sine law of refraction.
**1621**

James Gregory and Isaac Newton did wo on the concept of a reflecting telescope.
**1660s**

−600   −400   −200   0   1000   1600   1650

**4th century BC**
Aristotle believed that light moves like a wave.

**1000 BC**
Ali Al-hazen used a simple pinhole camera to demonstrate that light travels in a straight line, known as the principle of the rectilinear propagation of light.

**1608**
Hans Lippershey developed the optical telescope.

**1618**
Francesco Grimaldi improved our understanding of the interference and diffraction of light.

**1637**
René Descartes worked to understand refraction, rainbows, and clouds.

Do you know how mirrors and lenses create images? Mirrors create an image by reflecting light into your eye. Lenses create an image by bending light into focus.

With some mirrors and lenses, the image is not the same size as the object. What enables mirrors and lenses to make objects look larger or smaller than their original size? Read on and you will "see" for yourself.

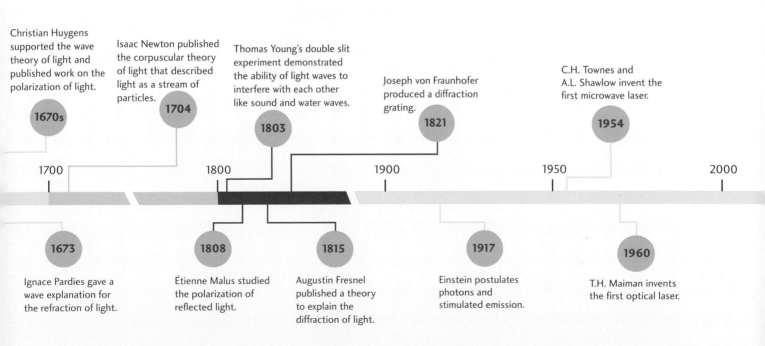

Christian Huygens supported the wave theory of light and published work on the polarization of light.

**1670s**

Isaac Newton published the corpuscular theory of light that described light as a stream of particles.

**1704**

Thomas Young's double slit experiment demonstrated the ability of light waves to interfere with each other like sound and water waves.

**1803**

Joseph von Fraunhofer produced a diffraction grating.

**1821**

C.H. Townes and A.L. Shawlow invent the first microwave laser.

**1954**

1700      1800      1900      1950      2000

**1673**

Ignace Pardies gave a wave explanation for the refraction of light.

**1808**

Étienne Malus studied the polarization of reflected light.

**1815**

Augustin Fresnel published a theory to explain the diffraction of light.

**1917**

Einstein postulates photons and stimulated emission.

**1960**

T.H. Maiman invents the first optical laser.

# 10

# Reflection and the Wave Theory of Light

## Chapter Outline

**By the end of this chapter, you will be able to**

- understand the properties of light as they relate to reflection from plane and curved mirrors
- find the position of images created by mirrors using ray diagrams, calculations, and experimentation
- relate instrumentation and devices we use daily to the principles of reflection

# 10.1 Introduction to Waves

**Fig.10.1** Wavefronts spreading out from a disturbance

Wave phenomena are all around us. If you throw a pebble into still water and watch ripples move away from it, you have just set in motion a host of underlying actions that will form the basis for this chapter. Water waves are visible to our eyes because they have long wavelengths. Light on the other hand, has a very small wavelength. The wave phenomena visible to us will be used to explain the wave actions of light. The photo in Fig. 10.1 illustrates circular wavefronts spreading out from a disturbance.

## Transverse Waves

In Fig. 10.2, a slinky toy, fixed at one end, is swung continuously back and forth from the free end. The action of the sideways motion produces wave formation down the line of the slinky. The direction of the wave is perpendicular to the action creating it. This type of wave is called a **transverse wave**. Light is an example of a transverse wave.

**Fig.10.2** A transverse wave

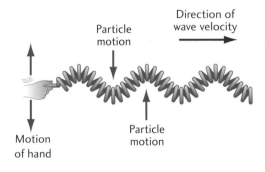

Have you ever been in a stadium where the fans started doing "The Wave"? A column of people in one section of the stadium stands up and sits down while raising their arms, then the people immediately to the right or left of them do the same thing, and so on. The wave they create around the stadium is similar to the slinky example. The particles that create the motion (in this case, the people) move up and down. The direction of the resulting wave is perpendicular to their actions.

Figure 10.3 shows people creating a stadium wave. The wave travels around the stadium because the actions of the people standing up and sitting down are coordinated. When one person sits down and lowers the arms, the person next to him or her must stand up and raise the arms within a very short time interval. In other words, in order for the wave to work, there must be a close relationship between the actions of two consecutive individuals. This relationship of position and time between two consecutive "particles" is called the **phase** of the wave. The motion of the particles is perpendicular to the wave's direction.

**Fig.10.3** Fans doing "The Wave"

Light travels in the same manner. Two consecutive people are replaced by the electric field and the magnetic field. As the electric field vibrates, so does the magnetic field, also in a distinct phase relationship. This action causes the light wave to travel in a direction perpendicular to these motions, just like the stadium wave.

**Fig.10.4** The propagation direction or direction of the wave's velocity is always at right angles to the electric field ($\vec{E}$) and the magnetic field ($\vec{B}$). The electric and magnetic fields are also perpendicular to each other.

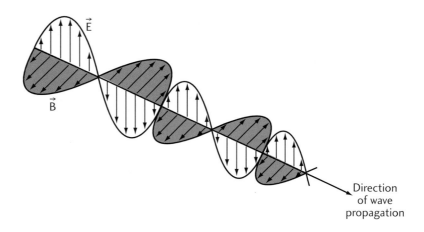

Direction of wave propagation

## Longitudinal Waves

Let's come back to the slinky toy. If you were to push and pull the coils towards and away from you in a regular motion, you create a compressed region that travels down the slinky, followed by a stretched region. This wave is a series of **compressions** and separations (**rarefactions**) travelling in the same direction as the slinky's motion (along its length).

**Fig.10.5** Compression and rarefaction in a longitudinal wave

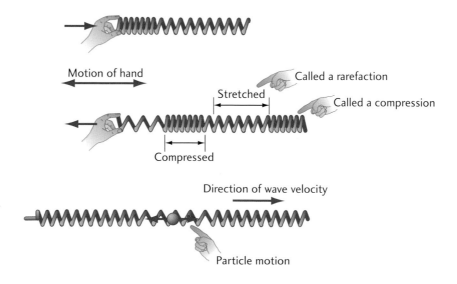

In a slightly different scenerio, a group of students is standing shoulder to shoulder in a circle. One student bumps the person beside him or her, which causes that person to bump the next person. This causes the action

UNIT C: Light and Geometric Optics

to be transmitted around the circle. The transmission of the wave is now in the same direction as the motion of the objects causing the wave. These waves are called **longitudinal waves**. An example of this type of wave is sound, which will be dealt with in a later unit.

## Cyclic Action

In many cases where continuous wave formation occurs, a transverse representation is used for both **longitudinal** and **transverse** waves. Longitudinal sound waves, for example, are often shown on an oscilloscope or computer screen as transverse waves. Figure 10.6 shows the parts of this representative wave.

One complete cycle of any wave action can be described by its period (or frequency) and its length.

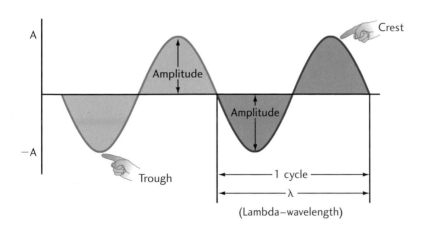

**Fig.10.6** The parts of a representative wave

The **period** of a wave ($T$) is the amount of time ($t$) it takes a wave to complete one cycle. The SI units for the period are seconds (s). Mathematically, $T = \frac{t}{N}$, where $t$ is the total time and $N$ is the total number of cycles.

The **frequency** of a wave ($f$) is the number of these cycles that can occur in a given time period, usually the second. The SI unit for frequency is $\frac{1}{s}$, which can be written as $s^{-1}$, and is called hertz (Hz).

Mathematically, $f = \frac{N}{t}$.

The **wavelength** ($\lambda$) is the length of one complete cycle. The SI unit for wavelength is the metre (m) and its symbol is the Greek letter *lambda*.

The **amplitude** of a wave is the maximum disturbance of the wave from its zero point. Waves have a positive and a negative amplitude.

Looking at the units of period and frequency, we see that they are reciprocals (s and $\frac{1}{s}$). If we translate them into an equation, we obtain the relationship.

$$f = \frac{1}{T} \quad \text{and} \quad T = \frac{1}{f}$$

**EXAMPLE 1**  **Calculations involving *T* and *f***

Calculate the period and frequency of a strobe light flashing 25 times in 5.0 seconds.

### Solution and Connection to Theory

**Given**

$t = 5.0$ s, the total time of the event

$N = 25$, the total number of cycles

$$f = \frac{N}{t}$$

This equation is obtained by checking the units of frequency, which are cycles per second.

$$f = \frac{25 \text{ cycles}}{5.0 \text{ s}} = 5.0 \text{ s}^{-1} = 5.0 \text{ Hz}$$

To calculate the period,

$$T = \frac{1}{f} = \frac{1}{5.0 \text{ s}^{-1}} = 0.20 \text{ s}$$

Notice that $\frac{1}{s^{-1}} = s$.

## Phase

In our description of stadium wave motion, phase was the positional relationship between two consecutive people. Phase can also be defined as the person's position relative to a designated starting position. If we call the sitting position with arms lowered the starting point, then the standing position with arms raised constitutes a phase shift for the person. Similarly, waves also undergo phase shifts. The relative position of the wave compared to a standard representation of it determines the wave's **phase shift**. Figure 10.7 shows a variety of phase shifts. In each case, the wave is completed by a dotted line behind the starting point. The dotted line represents the phase shift of the wave in terms of wavelength.

Fig.10.7   Phase shifts

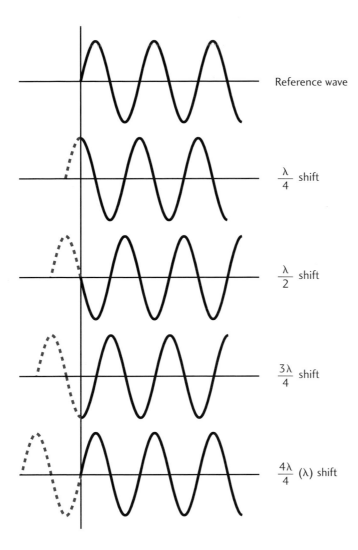

Reference wave

$\dfrac{\lambda}{4}$ shift

$\dfrac{\lambda}{2}$ shift

$\dfrac{3\lambda}{4}$ shift

$\dfrac{4\lambda}{4}$ ($\lambda$) shift

**1.** Calculate the period, in seconds, for the following cyclical events:
   **a)** Five classes every 375 minutes
   **b)** Ten swings of a pendulum in 6.7 s
   **c)** $33\frac{1}{3}$ turns of a turntable in one minute
   **d)** 68 sit-ups in 57 s
**2.** Calculate the frequency, in hertz, for the following cyclical events:
   **a)** 120 oscillations in 2.0 s
   **b)** 45 revolutions of a turntable in one minute
   **c)** 40 pulses in 1.2 hours
   **d)** 65 words typed every 48 seconds
**3.** Convert the period to a frequency for Question 1, and the frequency to a period for Question 2.

◄ ◄ ◄ ◄

## 10.2 The Wave Equation and Electromagnetic Theory

In our kinematics unit, we formulated the equation

$$\vec{v} = \frac{\Delta \vec{d}}{\Delta t}$$

If we substitute wavelength, λ, for Δd and period, T, for Δt, we obtain the equation

$$v = \frac{\lambda}{T}$$

Knowing that

$$\frac{1}{T} = f,$$

we obtain a more common form of the equation,

$$v = \lambda f$$

This is referred to as the **wave equation**.

The speed of light has its own special symbol, $c$, and is equal to $3.0 \times 10^8$ m/s. Thus the wave equation for light and any other wave that travels at this speed is

$$c = \lambda f$$

The speed of light is actually $c = 299\ 792\ 458$ m/s.

### Fig.10.8 Types of Waves

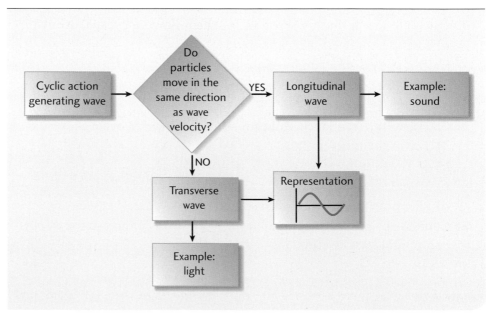

EXAMPLE 2   **Just how fast is *c*?**

Calculate the time it would take light to travel around the world once.

### *Solution and Connection to Theory*

**Given**

Radius of Earth is 6400 km = $6.4 \times 10^6$ m    $c = 3.0 \times 10^8$ m/s

Circumference = $2\pi R$

Therefore, the total distance travelled is

$\Delta d = 2(3.14)(6.4 \times 10^6 \text{ m}) = 4.0 \times 10^7$ m

Rearrange $c = \dfrac{\Delta d}{\Delta t}$ and solve for time.

$\Delta t = \dfrac{4.0 \times 10^7 \text{ m}}{3.0 \times 10^8 \text{ m/s}} = 0.13$ s

To give you an idea of just how fast this is, consider travelling this distance in your car at 100 km/h.

$v = 100$ km/h $= 27.8$ m/s    $\Delta t = \dfrac{4.0 \times 10^7 \text{ m}}{27.8 \text{ m/s}} = 1.44 \times 10^6$ s or 16.7 days.

---

## CONVERTING UNITS

When you convert units, express the pairs of related units as fractions equal to one.

**Case 1** km/h → m/s

$100 \dfrac{\text{km}}{\text{h}} \times \dfrac{1000 \text{ m}}{\text{km}} \times \dfrac{1 \text{ h}}{3600 \text{ s}}$

$= 27.8$ m/s

**Case 2** Seconds → days

$1.44 \times 10^6 \text{ s} \times \dfrac{1 \text{ h}}{3600 \text{ s}} \times \dfrac{1 \text{ d}}{24 \text{ h}}$

$= 16.7$ d

---

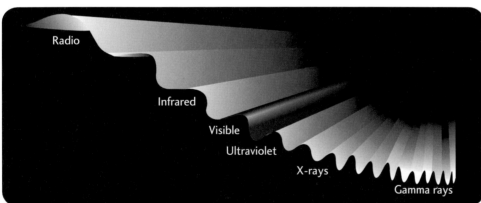

**Fig.10.9**   The electromagnetic spectrum

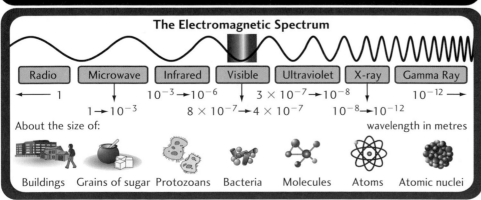

The term "electromagnetic radiation" is used to describe light because light is made up of oscillating electric and magnetic fields. In fact, any wave travelling at speed $c$ is part of the electromagnetic wave family. What distinguishes different members of this family is the size of their wavelengths. The whole range of wavelengths is referred to as the **electromagnetic spectrum**, shown in Fig. 10.9. Though fundamentally the same, different wavelengths break the spectrum up into waves with similar properties. As you can see from the diagram, visible light makes up only a small part of the electromagnetic spectrum.

The wavelengths in the visible range are visible for human beings. Many insects and animals see outside this range. The world viewed by these creatures is very different from ours. For example, certain flowers, when viewed under ultraviolet light, exhibit concentric rings that focus your attention to the pollen area of the plant. The bee, which sees in the ultraviolet range, sees this "bull's-eye" and is guided in by it. Other animals that don't see in the UV range see a plain flower rather than a tasty meal.

### EXAMPLE 3    Frequency of infrared waves

Infrared light is invisible to the human eye except through special sensors. Given the range of wavelengths of infrared light, calculate their corresponding frequencies.

### *Solution and Connection to Theory*

The wavelength range for infrared light is from $1 \times 10^{-3}$ m to about $7 \times 10^{-7}$ m.

Rearrange and solve the equation $c = \lambda f$:

$$f = \frac{c}{\lambda} = \frac{3.0 \times 10^8 \, \text{m/s}}{1 \times 10^{-3} \, \text{m}} = 3 \times 10^{11} \, \text{Hz}.$$

This frequency is for one end of the range. For the other end,

$$\frac{3.0 \times 10^8 \, \text{m/s}}{7 \times 10^{-7} \, \text{m}} = 4.3 \times 10^{14} \, \text{Hz}.$$

The frequency of infrared light is between $3 \times 10^{11}$ Hz and $4.3 \times 10^{14}$ Hz. Radiation in the infrared range is responsible for heat energy. A large portion of the Sun's energy output lies in this range. A variety of electronic applications, such as remote sensors, night vision binoculars, and motion detectors use infrared waves.

## Table 10.1
### Electromagnetic Waves

| Formation method | Wave type | Typical uses |
|---|---|---|
| Electrons oscillate the length of an antenna, driven by electronic circuitry | Radio waves | Carry AM signals in 1000 kHz range, FM in 100 MHz range, TV in 50 MHz and 500 MHz range |
| High-frequency vibrations in small cavities | Microwaves | Microwave ovens and weather radar |
| Electron transitions | | |
| in outer orbits of atoms | Infrared | Heat waves from the Sun |
| in outer orbits of atoms | Visible | Vision and laser communications |
| in inner orbits of atoms | Ultraviolet | Cause sunburn and skin cancer |
| in innermost orbits of atoms | X-rays | Penetrate soft tissue. Used in medical examinations and diagnostics |
| Part of nuclear transformations and energy transitions in nucleus | Gamma rays | High penetrating power. Used to destroy malignant cells in cancer patients |

**EXAMPLE 4** **How long does it take light to reach us from the Sun?**

### Solution and Connection to Theory

#### Given
The distance from the Sun to Earth,

$$\Delta d = 1.49 \times 10^{11} \text{ m} \qquad c = 3.0 \times 10^8 \text{ m/s}$$

Rearrange and solve $c = \dfrac{\Delta d}{\Delta t}$

$$\Delta t = \frac{1.49 \times 10^{11} \text{ m}}{3.0 \times 10^8 \text{ m/s}} = 497 \text{ s or } 8.3 \text{ min.}$$

It is interesting to note that we are actually looking back in time as we gaze into the heavens. Since it took 8.3 minutes for light to travel to Earth, we are looking at the Sun as it was 8.3 minutes ago. If the Sun were to suddenly vanish, it would take us 8.3 minutes to find out! In fact, the farther away an object is in space, the older it is because of the length of time it takes the light from it to reach us. In this respect, the telescope can be considered a time machine.

1. Calculate the frequency of
   a) a red light with wavelength 640 nm.
   b) radio waves with wavelength 1.2 m.
   c) X-rays with wavelength $2 \times 10^{-9}$ m.
2. Calculate the wavelength of
   a) infrared light of frequency $1.5 \times 10^{13}$ Hz.
   b) microwaves of frequency $2.0 \times 10^9$ Hz.
   c) gamma rays of frequency $3.0 \times 10^{22}$ Hz.

### MEASUREMENTS OF CELESTIAL DISTANCES

**Light year**—the distance light travels in one year. This unit is used because of the extraordinarily large distances in intergalactic space. One light year is equal to $9.46 \times 10^{15}$ m. The bright star Sirius is 8.7 light years away.

**Parsec (pc)**—a non-SI unit equal to 3.258 light years ($3.09 \times 10^{16}$ m). The parsec is based on the distance from Earth where stellar parallax is one second of an arc. The great nebula in Andromeda is $6.7 \times 10^5$ pc away.

**Astronomical Unit (AU)**—another non-SI unit equal to $1.50 \times 10^{11}$ m. One AU is the mean radius of Earth's orbit around the Sun. Planet Jupiter is 5.2 AU from the Sun.

◀ ◀ ◀ ◀

# 10.3 Rectilinear Propagation of Light— The Pinhole Camera

**Fig.10.10** Linear propagation of light (light travelling in a straight line) causes the creation of shadows. One of the most spectacular examples is that of a total eclipse of the Sun. In the second diagram, A is the Sun, B the Moon, and C, Earth.

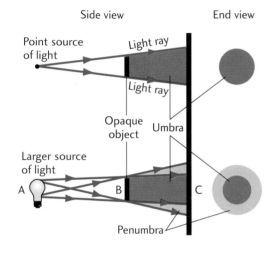

The creation of shadows on a sunny day indicates that light travels in straight lines. **Rectilinear propagation of light** is a fancy way of saying this. In Fig. 10.10, the shadow is sketched out by the object that blocks the light. If light travelled in loops and major curves, no shadows would form. In later sections, we will look at conditions where light bends slightly, but not enough to eliminate shadows.

The creation of upside-down images using a pinhole camera is another illustration of the rectilinear propagation of light. Figure 10.11 shows how an image is formed in a pinhole camera. We select representative light rays from the top and bottom of the object and trace them through the pinhole back to the screen. The rays we draw are straight because light travels in straight lines. These rays carry the information of the image from the selected spot on the object. They are a small sample of the infinite number of possible light rays that can be drawn from the object.

**Fig.10.11A** Another illustration of the principle that light travels in straight lines. Because the light travels in a straight line, the image formed is inverted.

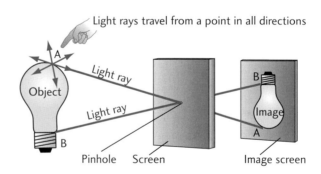

**Fig.10.11B** Magnification derivation

$\theta_1 = \theta_2$
Image and object are equally divided by the midline

$\therefore \overline{AC}$ is equal to $\overline{BC}$
$\overline{DC}$ is equal to $\overline{EC}$

$\triangle ABC$ and $\triangle DEC$ are similar,
$\theta_1 = \theta_2$, and both are isosceles

$\therefore \dfrac{\frac{d_o}{h_o}}{2} = \dfrac{\frac{d_i}{h_i}}{2}$

$\dfrac{h_i}{h_o} = \dfrac{d_i}{d_o}$

This effect is called magnification.

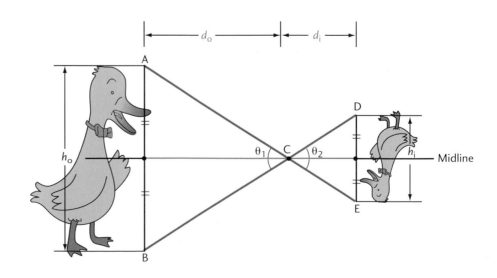

Notice from the diagram that the image formed by the pinhole camera is upside down and smaller than the object. Using geometry, we can obtain the relationship

$$\frac{h(\text{image})}{h(\text{object})} = \frac{d(\text{image})}{d(\text{object})}, \text{ which is written as } \frac{h_i}{h_o} = \frac{d_i}{d_o}$$

These ratios are referred to as the **magnification** ($m$) of the instrument. In other words, $m = \dfrac{h_i}{h_o} = \dfrac{d_i}{d_o}$

---

**EXAMPLE 5** | **Calculating the magnification of a pinhole camera and the size of the object**

A pinhole camera of length 30 cm is used to take a picture of a person standing 5.0 m away. If the photograph produced a 10 cm image, what is the magnification of the camera and how tall is the person?

*Solution and Connection to Theory*

**Given**

$d_i = 30 \text{ cm} = 0.30 \text{ m} \quad d_o = 5.0 \text{ m} \quad h_i = 10 \text{ cm} = 0.10 \text{ m} \quad h_o = ?$

$$m = \frac{d_i}{d_o} \qquad m = \frac{0.30 \text{ m}}{5.0 \text{ m}} = 0.06$$

This figure is used to find the height of the object.

$$m = \frac{h_i}{h_o} = 0.06 \qquad h_o = \frac{h_i}{m} = \frac{0.10 \text{ m}}{0.06} = 1.7 \text{ m}$$

The person is 1.7 m tall.

**ALTERNATIVE SOLUTION**

Since $m = \dfrac{h_i}{h_o} = \dfrac{d_i}{d_o}$,

$$\frac{h_i}{h_o} = \frac{d_i}{d_o}$$

$$\frac{0.1 \text{ m}}{h_o} = \frac{0.3 \text{ m}}{5.0 \text{ m}}$$

$$h_o = \frac{5.0 \text{ m}(0.1 \text{ m})}{0.3 \text{ m}} = 1.7 \text{ m}$$

You could put a photographic film in place of the screen of a pinhole camera, expose it to the image, and develop the picture. Early versions of cameras worked like this. However, there are certain kinds of images that cannot be captured on film.

The image produced on the screen of a pinhole camera is called a **real** image because it is projected on the screen. There are, however, images that cannot be projected onto a screen. One example is your image in a plane (flat) mirror. These images are **virtual** images and will be studied in later sections.

We now have a method of describing all images created by whatever instrument we are using. The image produced by the pinhole camera can be described as upside down (inverted), smaller than the object, and real. The pinhole camera results also verify that light travels in straight lines.

**Fig.10.12**  Image Type Summary

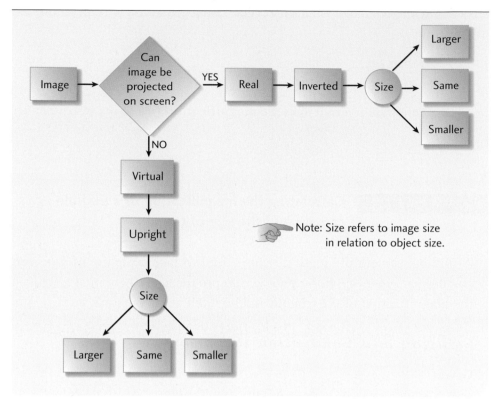

Note: Size refers to image size in relation to object size.

1. Calculate the magnification of a pinhole camera if
   a) the height of the object is 12 m and the height of the image is 2.5 cm.
   b) the length of the pinhole camera is 30 cm and the distance of the object from the camera is 5.5 m.
2. Calculate the size of the image if
   a) the magnification is 0.05 and the object is 3.0 m tall.
   b) the object is 4.4 m tall and is 6.0 m away from a camera, length 25 cm.

## ▶ 10.4  Introduction to Reflection

In principle, light could be called a perpetual motion machine. As long as it is moving through a vacuum, it will continue to do so until it hits or passes through a material or field. The effect of light bouncing off materials is called **reflection**. Light passing through materials is called **transmission**. **Refraction** is the bending of transmitted light and is examined in Chapter 11.

In order to understand these and other phenomena, we need to create a method of visualizing the motion of light and the information it carries with it. Consider the example in Fig. 10.13 of ripples emanating from the place where your pebble was dropped. The waves move out in all directions from the source and eventually disappear because of the water's resistance to motion.

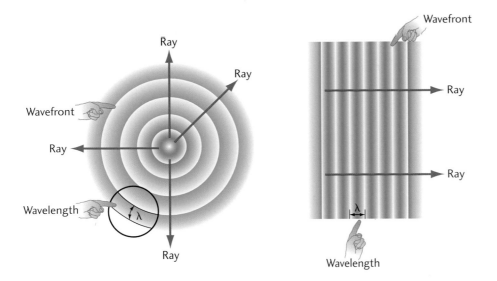

Now consider a source of light such as a light bulb. The waves of light emanate in all directions, disappearing very gradually as air particles absorb them. We can indicate the direction of propagation of the wave with an arrow drawn perpendicular to the **wavefronts** moving out. This arrow is called a **ray**. The ray will become a useful tool in explaining how to locate and describe images formed by light through the processes of reflection and refraction.

In **optics**, the **normal** is a line drawn perpendicular to a surface. It is used as the reference from which angles are measured. This is different than the standard system where angles are measured from the $x$ axis.

Figure 10.14 shows the difference between the two systems. The standard angle of 60°, measured from the $x$ axis, becomes 30° in the optics system, measured from the normal.

A wavefront is a surface on which all the points are at the same phase of motion. A wavelength is the distance between two adjacent wavefronts.

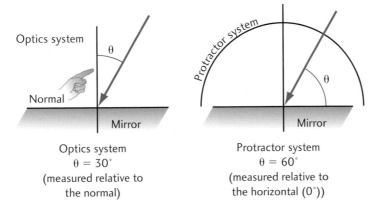

**Fig.10.14** Measuring angles in the standard and optics systems

We will now use the optics system of measuring angles to study reflection. In Fig. 10.15, a ray of light strikes the mirror and reflects off it. The place where the ray makes contact with the surface of the mirror is called the **point of incidence**. We draw a normal at this point.

**Fig.10.15** Incident and reflected rays

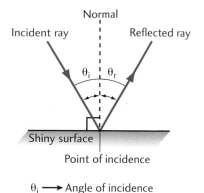

Normal

Incident ray          Reflected ray

$\theta_i$    $\theta_r$

Shiny surface

Point of incidence

$\theta_i$ ⟶ Angle of incidence
$\theta_r$ ⟶ Angle of reflection

The incoming or **incident** ray's angle is designated with a subscript 1 or i. The angle symbol is the Greek letter *theta*, $\theta$. We write "the incident angle of 60°" as $\theta_i = 60°$.

When a series of incident rays is drawn, it is called a **beam**. Figure 10.16 illustrates parallel, diverging, and converging beams. Notice that the flashlight produces a slightly divergent beam which looks parallel close to the source. The laser beam also diverges slightly, but this effect is observed over much greater distances.

When incident rays enter in parallel and are reflected in parallel, we use the term **regular** or **specular** reflection. When incident rays are reflected from a rough surface, the term **diffuse** reflection is used.

**Fig.10.16** Types of rays

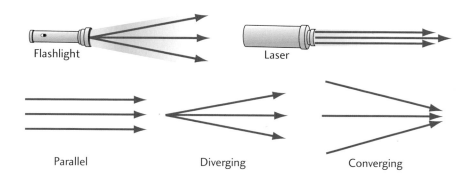

Flashlight          Laser

Parallel        Diverging        Converging

Figure 10.17 shows these effects. It is interesting to note that all surfaces possess irregularities. If the surface irregularities are smaller than the wavelength of incident light, then you get regular reflection. If the irregularities are close to the same size or greater than the wavelength of light, diffuse reflection occurs. You can also draw normals to these surfaces. Each tiny surface acts like a regular reflecting surface. However, because each of these tiny surfaces is at a different angle, we get diffuse reflection.

**Fig.10.17** Specular and diffuse rays

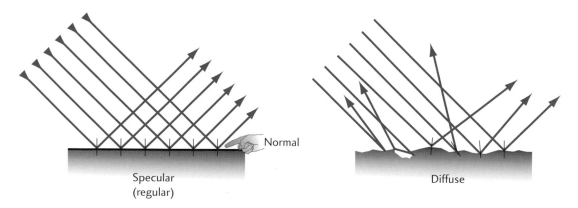

Normal

Specular (regular)           Diffuse

**Fig.10.18** Wave Action Summary

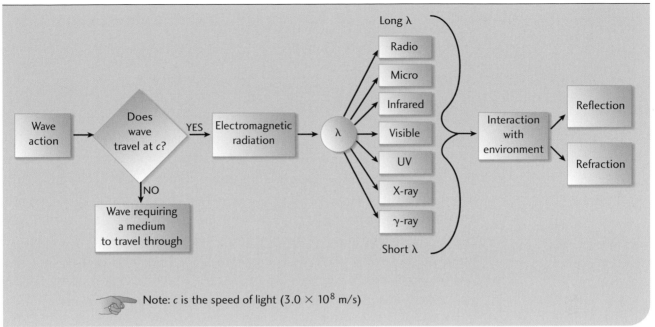

Note: c is the speed of light ($3.0 \times 10^8$ m/s)

# 10.5 Images in Plane Mirrors— A Case for Reflection

When a ray of light is incident on a flat, shiny surface, it is reflected in the manner shown in Fig. 10.19. The angle of incidence, $\theta_i$, is equal to the angle of reflection, $\theta_r$. If you were to move the incident ray around to another plane, the reflected ray would follow, as is illustrated in Fig. 10.19B.

Reflection also applies to other phenomena. For example, today's stealth aircraft (Fig. 10.20) use angled surfaces to reflect incident radar upward or in a direction away from the radar station.

**Fig.10.19A** 1. Angle of incidence equals angle of reflection
2. Both rays (incident and reflected) lie in the same plane

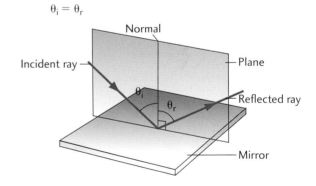

$\theta_i = \theta_r$

**Fig.10.20** The F-117A stealth plane

**Fig.10.19B**

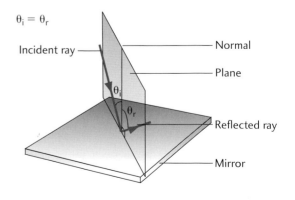

$\theta_i = \theta_r$

CHAPTER 10: Reflection and the Wave Theory of Light

The following laws summarize the reflection of light from a flat surface.

> The Laws of Reflection for Flat Surfaces
> 1. The angle of incidence equals the angle of reflection ($\theta_i = \theta_r$).
> 2. Both the incident and reflected rays are in the same plane.

## Images in Plane Mirrors

Reflection is responsible for producing **virtual images**, which are images that cannot be captured on a screen. Consider the sight you see when you look in the mirror each morning. Your beaming, radiant face, ready for the day's challenges, is located somewhere inside the mirror. In optics, this image is described as rightside up (erect), of the same size as the object, virtual, and located the same distance behind the mirror as you are in front of the mirror. However, everything is reversed. If you wink with your right eye, the image's left eye winks back. If you wave your left arm, the right arm of your image does the waving. This is called **lateral inversion** and is illustrated in Fig. 10.21.

**Fig.10.21** The virtual image in a mirror is exactly the same as the object except it has a left-right inversion

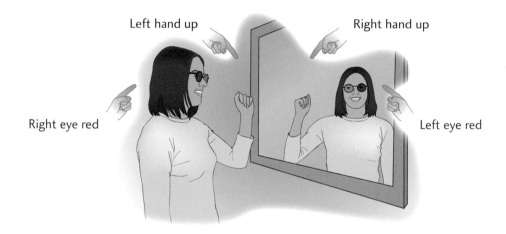

Left hand up      Right hand up

Right eye red      Left eye red

## Formation of Virtual Images

**Fig.10.22** Notice how the image of the spider is located an equal distance behind the mirror as the object is in front.

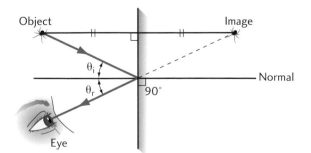

Object    Image

$\theta_i$

$\theta_r$   90°

Normal

Eye

Figure 10.22 shows the formation of a mirror image. Notice that in the ray diagram, the reflected ray is extended behind the mirror, indicating its *apparent* origin. Because our brain and eye interpret patterns based on the premise that light travels in straight lines, we believe that the rays are emanating from a position behind the mirror. This type of image is called a **virtual** image and cannot be captured on a screen. The figure also shows the normal drawn at the point of incidence perpendicular to the surface. This point is chosen halfway between the object and the person's eye. By doing this, you insure the law of reflection, $\theta_i = \theta_r$.

Animals have a hard time realizing that the mirror produces an image. If you put a cat or dog in front of a mirror, many of them will react by looking behind the mirror or attacking it, believing the image to be a real animal. See the dogs in Fig. 10.23.

**Fig.10.23** Dogs looking in a mirror

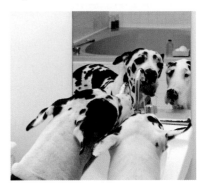

EXAMPLE 6 **How tall is a full-length mirror?**

### Solution and Connection to Theory

A duck standing in front of a mirror (Fig. 10.24) sees the rays coming from its feet at the point $C$ halfway down the mirror. Thus, the bottom half of the mirror can be missing and you'd still see your feet. To complete the image diagram of the duck, you select various body parts and draw rays going from them to the mirror and reflecting back. A normal is drawn at the point where the incident ray hits the mirror. This method allows you to use $\theta_i = \theta_r$ in order to obtain the correct reflecting angle.

**Fig.10.24**

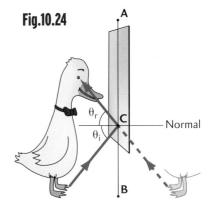

## Multiple Image Formation

The phenomenon of multiple images occurs when more than one mirror is used. For two mirrors placed at right angles to each other, you obtain the two images you'd expect, as well as a third one. This is due to an extra reflection occurring before it enters your eyes.

In Fig. 10.25, the object sits in a corner formed by two mirrors. If you move the mirrors closer together, you produce more than three images. The formula for finding the number of images is

$$N = \left(\frac{360°}{\theta}\right) - 1$$

where $\theta$ is the angle between the mirrors, measured in degrees. For Fig. 10.26, $\theta$ is 90°. From the formula, $N = 3$, meaning that three images are produced.

Note that if the angle, $\theta$, equals zero degrees (meaning the mirrors are parallel to each other), $N$ is undefined. The implication is that as the angle gets closer and closer to zero, the number of images, $N$, approaches infinity. If you look at Fig. 10.26, the images created by two parallel mirrors ($\theta = 0°$) appear to be layered one upon another, extending back as far as the eye can see. Losses of energy upon each reflection cause the more distant images to fade until they eventually disappear.

**Fig.10.25**

$$N = \left(\frac{360°}{\theta}\right) - 1$$

For two mirrors at right angles ($\theta = 90°$),

$$N = \left(\frac{360°}{90°}\right) - 1 = 3$$

As you can see from the diagram, three images are seen.

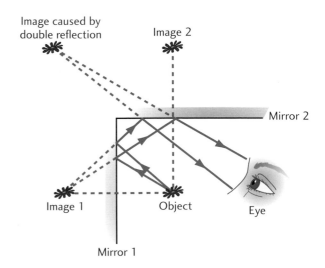

Image caused by double reflection

Image 2

Mirror 2

Image 1

Object

Eye

Mirror 1

## HOW THE EYE SEES AN IMAGE
## IN A PLANE MIRROR (FIG. 10.27)

1. Draw a perpendicular line from the object to the mirror.

2. Extend your line an equal distance behind the mirror.

3. Draw a normal halfway between the object and the eyeball.

4. Use the fact that the angle of incidence equals the angle of reflection to draw the rays from object to mirror to eye.

5. Extend the reflected ray back behind the mirror until it crosses the extended line.

**Fig.10.26**  Images in two parallel mirrors

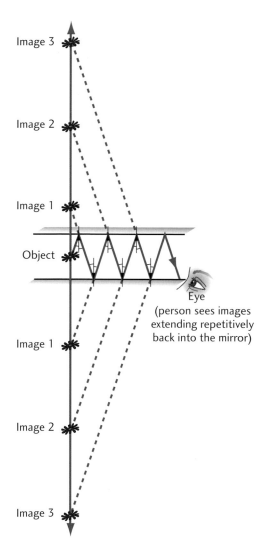

**Fig.10.27**

**(1)**

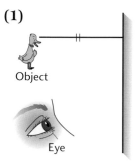

**(2)**

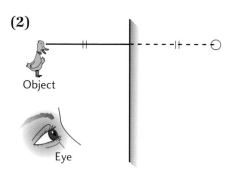

**(3)**

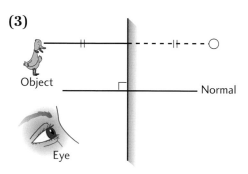

**(4)**

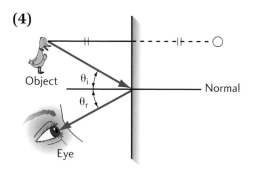

**(5)**

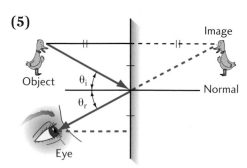

Try this at home by holding a mirror in front of yourself while standing in front of another mirror. The reflecting surfaces should be facing each other.

1. State the two laws of reflection.
2. Describe the image produced in a mirror (five aspects).
3. What happens to the apparent size of a room that has at least one wall tiled with mirrored tiles? Why?

# 10.6 Applications of Plane Mirrors

## Stage Ghosts—Optical Illusions

During the Victorian era, stage ghosts were used in various theatre productions. Imagine the sensation for an audience ignorant of physics laws produced in an era before electricity when a ghost appears on stage! Figure 10.28 reveals the secret of how the illusion is created.

The key is the pane of transparent glass in front of the stage. The light illuminating the actor, hidden from the audience, is reflected off the pane of glass before it reaches the audience's eyes. The area behind the actor has a dark, rough surface so as not to reflect the light. The audience, sitting in a dimly lit room, then sees a vivid image of the actor that appears to be able to move through solid objects on stage. The pane of glass is slid away during a scene change.

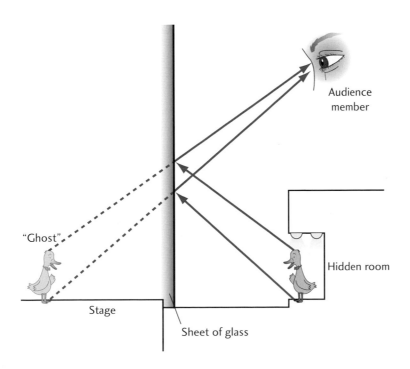

**Fig.10.28** An actor is hidden away from direct view of the audience. The small cubicle he is standing in is illuminated. A high-transparency piece of glass is moved in front of the stage during a scene change. The actor's image is reflected off the surface of the glass, which acts like a mirror. The audience sees the image of the actor on stage. Because the scene is dimly lit, the image of the actor is relatively clear. The real actors on stage know where the image is supposed to be and thus can walk right through it.

## Silvered Two-way Mirrors

If you look at a hand mirror, you will notice that the reflective material is deposited on the back of a piece of glass. There is an opaque layer that then covers the metal layer, protecting the thin metal coating. If the coating is made of a transparent material, it will allow some light to pass through the reflective coating. What is obtained is a mirrored surface that you can see through but those on the outside cannot. This is a common feature of many types of sunglasses. It is also used in the construction of modern skyscraper windows.

A benefit of silvered two-way mirrors for building owners is that the sunlight reflects off the building in the summer months, thereby reducing the costs of air conditioning. They also have an aesthetic quality, reflecting images of the sky and clouds.

**Fig.10.29** Buildings in the daytime reflect the light of the day. But at night, when the lit interior of the building is brighter than the night-time light, the inside of the building is seen.

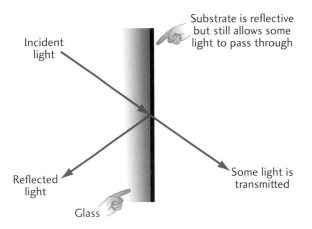

Incident light

Substrate is reflective but still allows some light to pass through

Reflected light

Glass

Some light is transmitted

**Fig.10.30** Inside a kaleidoscope

$$\left( \text{using } N = \left( \frac{360°}{\theta} \right) - 1 \right)$$

End of tube view

Mirror
60°
Mirror

Side view

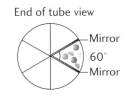

Translucent screen at back

Bits of coloured glass

Mirrors placed at 60° to each other

Person looks through here

$$N = \left( \frac{360°}{\theta} \right) - 1$$
$$= 5$$

Therefore, 5 images are seen.

## Kaleidoscope

This child's toy is a visual delight of changing colours as the toy is rotated. The effects are produced by multi-coloured glass pieces that tumble around when the toy is turned. The multiple images are produced by two mirrors positioned at an angle other than 90° to each other. The angle determines the number of images produced. Recall the formula $N = \frac{360}{\theta} - 1$. Using this formula, we can see in Fig. 10.30 that five reflections are produced for the two mirrors positioned 60° to each other.

UNIT C: Light and Geometric Optics

# Day–Night Rearview Mirrors

When driving at night, the headlights of cars reflected in the rearview mirror can be a distraction for the driver. By flipping a lever on the mirror, the lights are dimmed and the distraction is minimized. Refer to Fig. 10.31. To make this type of mirror, a piece of glass is cut into a thin wedge shape that is thicker at the top. The back surface is silvered so that when the glass is positioned for direct reflection, it acts as a typical mirror. This is its daytime position.

For nighttime driving, the mirror is angled up. This means that the mirror produces an image on your car ceiling, which is usually not noticeable because of its neutral colour and texture. It is the glass surface of the mirror that now acts like a weak reflector itself. About 4% of the light hitting the glass actually gets reflected from this glass surface. The other 96% passes through the glass. This *reflection* produces a dimmer image that doesn't blind or distract the driver.

**Fig.10.31**   The physics of a rearview mirror

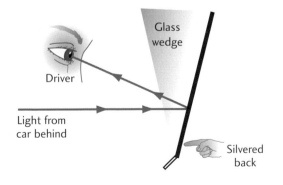

**Day position** Image is formed from reflection off **silvered** surface

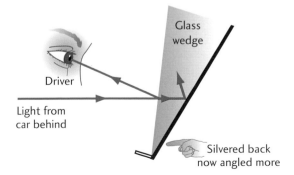

**Night position** Image is formed from reflection off **glass** front. This image is much dimmer

# 10.7 Curved Mirrors

Figure 10.32A represents a slice from a fully silvered sphere (reflecting surfaces both inside and outside). The outside part of the sphere forms a bulging piece called a **convex** or **diverging** mirror. The inside of the sphere is called a **concave** or **converging** mirror. Both types of mirrors are called **spherical mirrors** because they originate from a sphere. Figure 10.32B illustrates another type of curved mirror, the parabolic mirror, which originates from a parabola.

Figure 10.33 introduces the terminology for the study of the optics of curved mirrors.

**Fig.10.32A**  Spherical mirrors

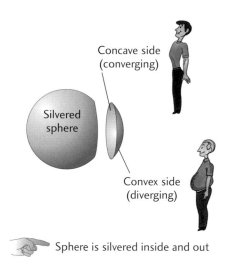

Concave side (converging)

Silvered sphere

Convex side (diverging)

Sphere is silvered inside and out

**Fig.10.32B**  Parabolic mirrors correct for edge rays not coming to a focus. Parabolic radio antennae are used for celestial studies and even searching for extraterrestrials.

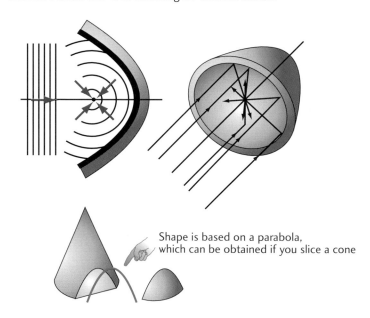

Shape is based on a parabola, which can be obtained if you slice a cone

**Fig.10.33**  Parts of a curved mirror

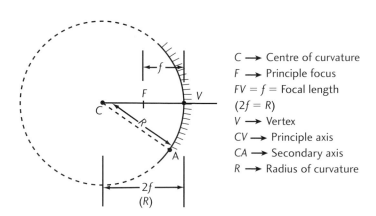

$C \longrightarrow$ Centre of curvature
$F \longrightarrow$ Principle focus
$FV = f$ = Focal length
($2f = R$)
$V \longrightarrow$ Vertex
$CV \longrightarrow$ Principle axis
$CA \longrightarrow$ Secondary axis
$R \longrightarrow$ Radius of curvature

**Fig.10.34**  A solar heat collector is an application of curved mirrors

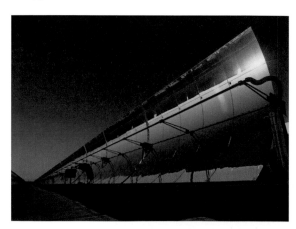

UNIT C: Light and Geometric Optics

# Ray Diagrams for Converging Mirrors

**Fig.10.35**

| Incident ray | Reflected ray | Diagram |
|---|---|---|
| Parallel to principle axis | Through focus | 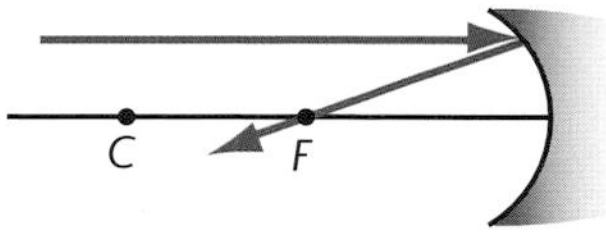 |
| Through focus | Parallel to principle axis | 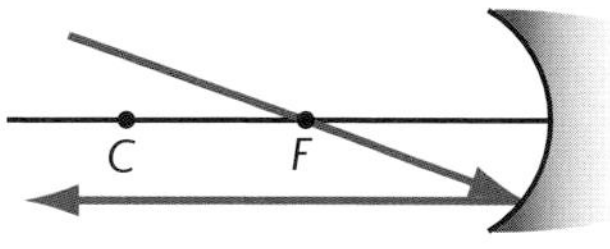 |
| Through centre of curvature | Back through centre of curvature | 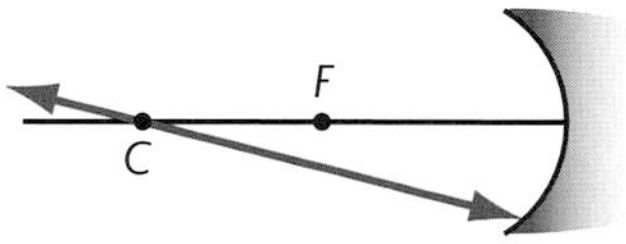 |
| To vertex | Point acts like plane mirror ($\theta_i = \theta_r$) | 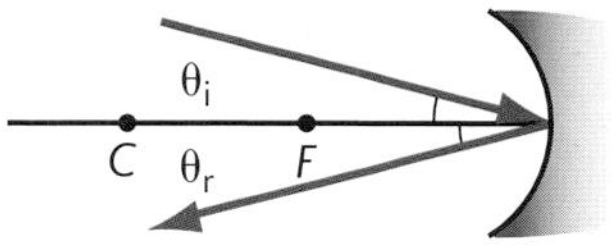 |

Just as we did for the plane mirror, we use a ray method to locate images created by curved mirrors. The method of finding the image involves locating the place where two reflected rays cross or appear to cross. There are four possible rays you can use, as shown in Fig. 10.35. Two rays is the minimum number you need to find the image. A third ray can be used to check your diagram. Also, be aware that given certain object positions, not all four rays can be used.

The ray diagram in Fig. 10.36 illustrates one possible object position. To locate the image, we will use a ray of light starting from the duck's head. The reflected rays cross at the location of the image of the duck's head. The feet are located on the principle axis, so the image of the feet will also be along this line. Knowing the top and bottom positions of a duck allows us to draw the complete image. Figure 10.36 walks us through the method of producing the image in steps.

In Fig. 10.37, other possible object positions are chosen that are at or farther than the focus. The ray diagrams are now done in one step without all the steps being shown. Notice that all the possible rays were used. However, unless specified, you only need to use two out of the possible four rays when constructing the ray diagram.

**Fig.10.36**  Drawing ray diagrams for converging mirrors

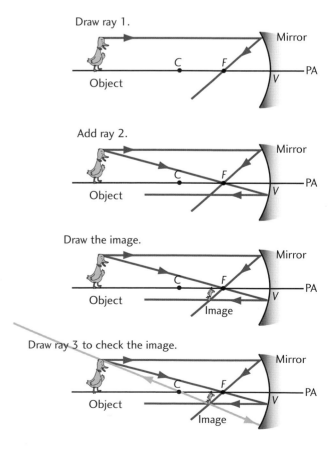

Draw ray 1.

Add ray 2.

Draw the image.

Draw ray 3 to check the image.

**Fig.10.37**  Real images in converging mirrors

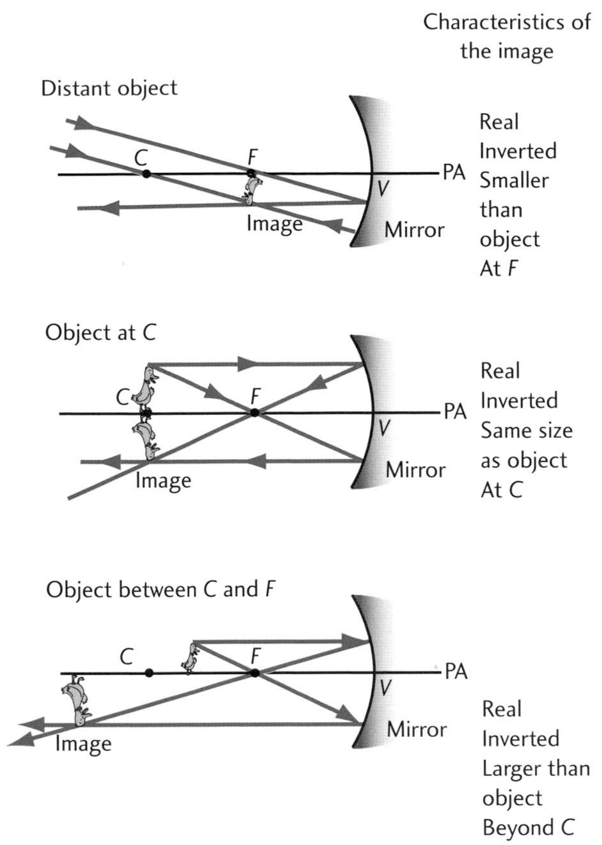

Distant object

Characteristics of the image

Real
Inverted
Smaller than object
At *F*

Object at *C*

Image    Mirror

Real
Inverted
Same size as object
At *C*

Object between *C* and *F*

Image    Mirror

Real
Inverted
Larger than object
Beyond *C*

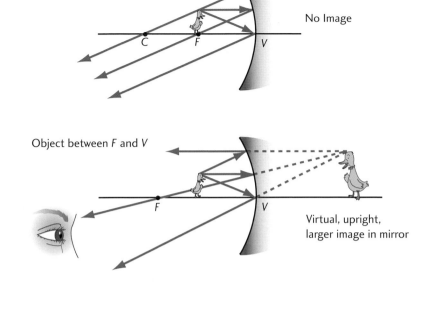

**Fig.10.38**  No image or a virtual image in a converging mirror

Object at *F*

No Image

Object between *F* and *V*

Virtual, upright, larger image in mirror

In Figs. 10.36 and 10.37, the images produced have all been real. The next, two diagrams shown in Fig. 10.38 produce no image and a virtual image, respectively. Just as with the plane mirror, reflected rays are extended back to a point where they apparently cross. This is where the image is located.

An eyeball is provided in the diagram to remind you that to see the image, you must look into the mirror. Dotted lines indicate the apparent paths taken by the reflected light rays used in determining the location of the image.

## Ray Diagrams for Diverging Mirrors

The rules for drawing ray diagrams for diverging mirrors are similar to those for converging mirrors, except you must remember that the rays cannot physically enter the mirror. This creates the effect of rays bouncing off the surface, apparently originating from a focus inside the mirror. The special incident rays are shown in Fig. 10.39 along with a ray diagram.

The bonus in learning how to locate an image in this type of mirror is that there is only one possible ray diagram. Diverging mirrors always form virtual images that are smaller than the object.

| Incident ray | Reflected ray | Diagram |
|---|---|---|
| Parallel to principle axis | Reflects out, as though coming from $F$ | 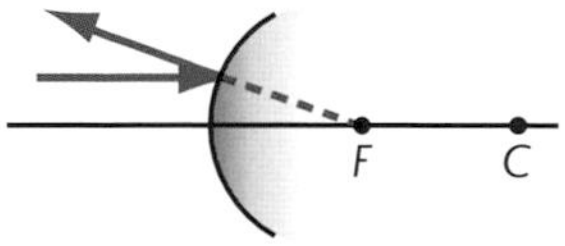 |
| Directed at focus ($F$) | Reflects back parallel to principle axis | 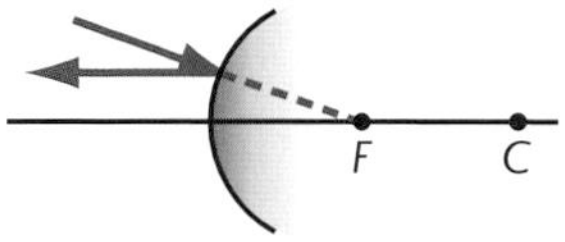 |
| Directed at centre of curvature ($C$) | Reflects straight back on itself | 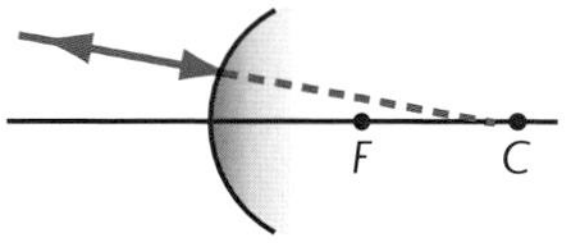 |
| To vertex ($V$) | Plane mirror $\theta_i = \theta_r$ | 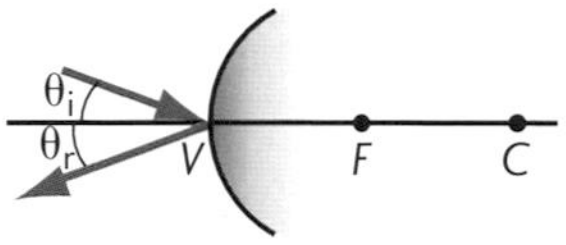 |

**Fig.10.39** Ray diagrams for diverging mirrors

**Fig.10.40** Drawing a ray diagram for a diverging mirror

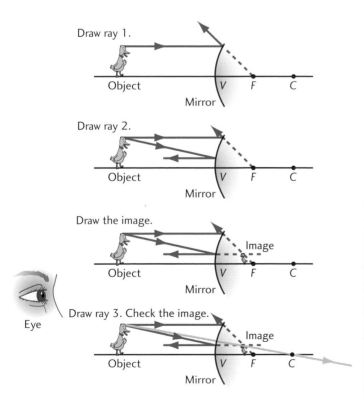

Draw ray 1.

Draw ray 2.

Draw the image.

Draw ray 3. Check the image.

Eye

## CONSTRUCTING SCALED RAY DIAGRAMS FOR SPHERICAL MIRRORS

In most situations, an accurate numeric answer is required. Therefore, you need to construct the ray diagrams to scale. Here are the steps to creating the diagrams:

1. Read the problem over and take note of the distances used.
2. Choose a scale so as *not* to use up the whole width or length of your page. Leave about a quarter page to each side. This will ensure that if images are formed behind the mirror or a large distance beyond the centre of curvature of the mirror, you will still have room.
3. Draw in the appropriate mirror. Lightly shade the non-reflective side of the mirror to ensure that you remember which rules to apply.
4. Draw the principle axis, a horizontal line through the centre of the mirror. The intersection of these two lines is the vertex. Measure the focus from the vertex, and mark the focus with an $F$.
5. Measure out twice the focal length (i.e., the radius) from the vertex and mark this point with a $C$. This point is the centre of curvature. It is important that these measurements are as accurate as possible.
6. Draw the object to scale and use the appropriate rays to construct the image.
7 Measure the asked-for quantities.
8. Convert the values back, using your scaling factor.

**Fig.10.41** Images in Different Mirrors

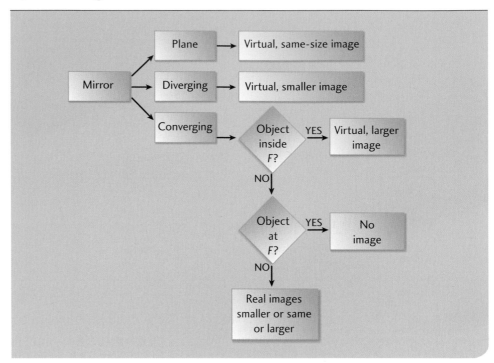

1. Summarize what happens to an image produced in a converging mirror as the object is moved in from infinity (far away).
2. Can a diverging mirror be made to produce a real image? Explain.
3. **a)** For an object 3 cm tall and a mirror of focal length 12 cm, construct ray diagrams with the object at the following positions: 2.5$f$, 2.0$f$, 1.5$f$, $f$, and 0.5$f$. Use three rays for each diagram.
   **b)** For the same object and a mirror of focal length 12 cm, construct ray diagrams for the object positions 2$f$, $f$, and 0.5$f$.

# 10.8 Calculations for Curved Mirrors

The relationship between diagrams and equations is a symbiotic one. Although the calculation method is quicker, it is still useful to be able to draw the ray diagram. It allows you to visualize the values you obtained using the formula method and, in some cases, catch errors made in the calculations.

The **curved mirror equation** is

$$\frac{1}{f} = \frac{1}{d_o} + \frac{1}{d_i}$$

where $d_o$ is the object distance, $d_i$ is the image distance, and $f$ is the focal length. This equation is derived in Fig. 10.42A.

UNIT C: Light and Geometric Optics

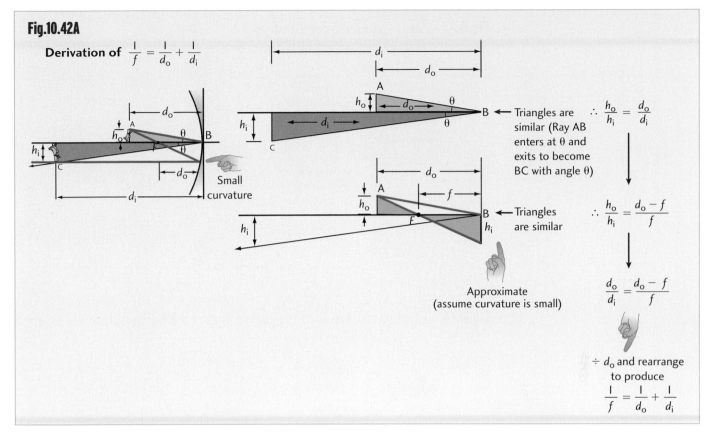

**Fig.10.42A**

**Derivation of** $\dfrac{1}{f} = \dfrac{1}{d_o} + \dfrac{1}{d_i}$

Triangles are similar (Ray AB enters at $\theta$ and exits to become BC with angle $\theta$)

$\therefore \dfrac{h_o}{h_i} = \dfrac{d_o}{d_i}$

Triangles are similar

$\therefore \dfrac{h_o}{h_i} = \dfrac{d_o - f}{f}$

$\dfrac{d_o}{d_i} = \dfrac{d_o - f}{f}$

Approximate (assume curvature is small)

$\div\, d_o$ and rearrange to produce

$\dfrac{1}{f} = \dfrac{1}{d_o} + \dfrac{1}{d_i}$

Small curvature

Figure 10.42B shows how the variables of the curved mirror equation are measured.

The magnification formula for curved mirrors is almost the same as the one for the plane mirror.

$$m = -\frac{d_i}{d_o} \quad \text{or} \quad m = \frac{h_i}{h_o}$$

where $h_i$ is the height of the image and $h_o$ is the height of the object. The negative sign is explained in the next section.

## The Meaning of Negatives in Optics

In the study of optics, the negative sign is used with virtual distances and for images that are inverted. The sign will naturally occur during a calculation using the curved mirror equation. However, in a magnification calculation or statement, if you are only given the heights of the object and image, you must insert the negative sign yourself if you know the image is inverted.

**Fig.10.42B**   Curved mirror equation

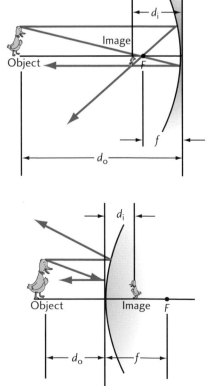

**EXAMPLE 7    Negative magnification**

A real image, 4.0 cm high and inverted, is formed in a converging mirror. If the object is 20 cm in size, the magnification is $m = \dfrac{h_i}{h_o} = \dfrac{4.0\ \text{cm}}{20\ \text{cm}} = 0.2$. Since the image is inverted, you write the magnification as $-0.2$.

Fig.10.43   Sign Convention Summary

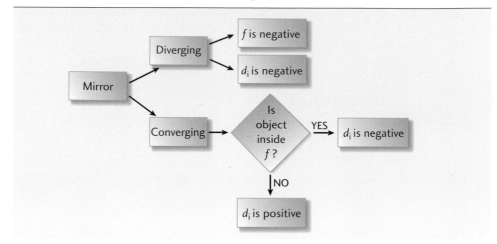

Fig.10.44   Using Positive and Negative Signs with Equations

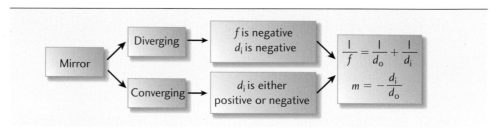

---

**EXAMPLE 8**   **Calculating a real image position and magnification for a converging mirror**

A concave mirror with a 20 cm focal length has a candle placed in front of it 30 cm from the vertex. Find the image position and magnification for this situation.

**Fig.10.45**   Converging mirror with larger inverted image

*Solution and Connection to Theory*

**Given**

$d_o = 30$ cm     $f = 20$ cm     $d_i = ?$

$$\frac{1}{f} = \frac{1}{d_o} + \frac{1}{d_i} \qquad \frac{1}{d_i} = \frac{1}{f} - \frac{1}{d_o} \qquad \frac{1}{d_i} = \frac{1}{20\ \text{cm}} - \frac{1}{30\ \text{cm}}$$

$$\frac{1}{d_i} = 0.017\ \text{cm}^{-1} \quad d_i = 60\ \text{cm}$$

$$m = -\frac{d_i}{d_o} = -\frac{60\ \text{cm}}{30\ \text{cm}} = -2.0$$

Notice that the magnification has a negative value. This indicates that the image is inverted. The positive sign of the image distance ($d_i$) indicates that the image is real. The image is larger than the object by a factor of two. The situation is illustrated in the photo of the converging mirror containing a larger inverted image (Fig. 10.45).

EXAMPLE 9 **Calculating a virtual image position and magnification for a converging mirror**

For the mirror in Example 8, the object is moved to 5.0 cm from the vertex. Find the image position and magnification.

*Solution and Connection to Theory*

**Given**

$f = 20$ cm  $\quad d_o = 5.0$ cm  $\quad d_i = ?$

$$\frac{1}{f} = \frac{1}{d_o} + \frac{1}{d_i} \qquad \frac{1}{d_i} = \frac{1}{f} - \frac{1}{d_o}$$

$$\frac{1}{d_i} = \frac{1}{20 \text{ cm}} - \frac{1}{5.0 \text{ cm}} \qquad \frac{1}{d_i} = -0.15 \text{ cm}^{-1} \qquad d_i = -6.7 \text{ cm}$$

$$m = -\frac{d_i}{d_o} = -\left(\frac{-6.7 \text{ cm}}{5.0 \text{ cm}}\right) = 1.3$$

Notice that, in this case, the magnification is positive, indicating that the image is upright. The image is larger than the object by a factor of 1.3. The negative image distance indicates that the image is virtual. The situation is illustrated in the photo of the converging mirror with a larger virtual image (Fig. 10.46).

**Fig.10.46**  Mirror with larger upright image

EXAMPLE 10 **Calculating image position and magnification for a diverging mirror**

Given a convex mirror with focal length 20 cm, a candle is placed 5.0 cm away from the vertex. Find the image position and magnification.

*Solution and Connection to Theory*

**Given**

$f = -20$ cm  $\quad d_o = 5.0$ cm  $\quad d_i = ?$

$$\frac{1}{f} = \frac{1}{d_o} + \frac{1}{d_i} \qquad \frac{1}{d_i} = \frac{1}{f} - \frac{1}{d_o}$$

$$\frac{1}{d_i} = \frac{1}{-20 \text{ cm}} - \frac{1}{5.0 \text{ cm}} \qquad \frac{1}{d_i} = -0.25 \text{ cm}^{-1} \qquad d_i = -4.0 \text{ cm}$$

$$m = -\frac{d_i}{d_o} \qquad m = -\left(\frac{-4.0 \text{ cm}}{5.0 \text{ cm}}\right) \qquad m = 0.80$$

In this case, the magnification is positive, indicating an upright image, and the image distance is negative, meaning that the image is virtual. The image is smaller than the object by a factor of 0.80. In fact, all images in these types of mirrors are smaller and virtual (see Fig. 10.47).

**Fig.10.47**  Mirror with smaller upright image

The following example is trickier. It involves two equations and two unknowns. Here, you are given the magnification and one of $d_o$, $d_i$, or $f$. You must isolate one of the unknowns in the magnification equation, substitute it into the mirror equation, then solve.

---

**EXAMPLE 11** **Find the image and object distances for a converging mirror (two equations and two unknowns)**

A trucker looks in her convex side mirror and sees the image of her face. If the focal length of the mirror is 50 cm and the magnification of the mirror is 0.10, find the image and object distances.

### *Solution and Connection to Theory*

**Given**

$$d_o = ? \qquad m = +0.10 \qquad d_i = ? \qquad f = -50 \text{ cm}$$

Set up the two equations.

$$\frac{1}{-50 \text{ cm}} = \frac{1}{d_o} + \frac{1}{d_i} \text{ and } 0.10 = -\frac{d_i}{d_o}$$

Rearrange the magnification equation and solve for $d_i$.

$$d_i = (-0.10)d_o$$

Replace the $d_i$ in the first expression with $(-0.10)d_o$.

$$\frac{1}{-50 \text{ cm}} = \frac{1}{d_o} + \frac{1}{(-0.10)d_o}$$

$$-0.02 = \frac{1-10}{d_o}$$

$$d_o = 450 \text{ cm}$$

Now solve for the image distance using either equation.

$$m = -\frac{d_i}{d_o} \qquad d_i = (-0.10) \, 450 \text{ cm} = -45 \text{ cm.}$$

Remember to make the focal length negative for a convex mirror. The image distance turns out to be negative, which is correct, because the convex mirror always creates virtual images. This result proves that our solution is correct.

**Fig.10.48** Method of Solving Mirror Problems

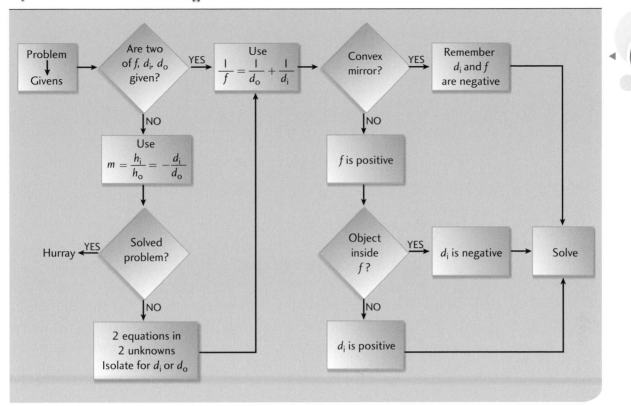

1. Calculate the image positions and magnifications for an object 3 cm tall and a mirror of focal length +12 cm with the object at the following positions: 2.5$f$, 2.0$f$, 1.5$f$, $f$, 0.5$f$.
2. Calculate the image positions and magnifications for an object 3 cm tall and a mirror of focal length −12 cm with the object at the following positions: 2.5$f$, 2.0$f$, 1.5$f$, $f$, 0.5$f$.

# 10.9 Applications and Aspects of Curved Mirrors

## Spherical Aberration

In principle, spherical reflectors form relatively sharp images, especially if a small part of the reflector is used around the principle axis. However, the rays far away from this area, especially on a large mirror, cross the principle axis at different distances, causing the image to blur. This effect is called **spherical aberration**. To correct the blurring, a parabolic mirror is used, as illustrated in Fig. 10.49. Because the parabolic mirror has smaller angles of reflection at the top and bottom than the spherical mirror, the reflected rays all cross at the same point, the focus.

**Fig.10.49** Diagrams showing the focussing obtained with a spherical mirror and the point focus with a parabolic mirror.

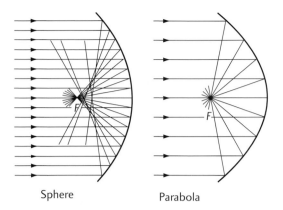

Sphere          Parabola

## Flashlight and Headlight Reflectors

By positioning the lightbulb of a flashlight or headlight at the focus of a parabolic reflector, the rays will emerge in a nearly parallel beam. If you compare the focussing of parallel incident rays (Fig. 10.49) to the flashlight diagram (Fig. 10.50), you'll notice they are the same except for the direction of the rays. In ray diagrams, you can use the **principle of reversibility**, i.e., you can change the directions of the rays and still have a viable ray diagram.

**Fig.10.50** A flashlight reflector

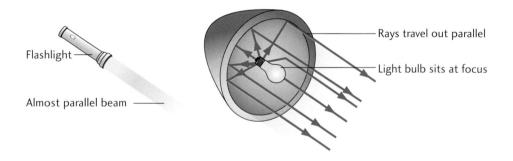

Flashlight

Almost parallel beam

Rays travel out parallel

Light bulb sits at focus

## Solar Furnaces

**Fig.10.51** The world's largest solar furnace in the French Pyrenees

A solar furnace focusses the Sun's rays so intensely that it is able to burn a hole in a thick sheet of steel. The world's largest solar furnace is located in Odeillo, in the French Pyrenees (Fig. 10.51). It consists of nearly 20 000 mirrors. The Sun's rays hit the parabolic reflector and meet at the focal point, which can reach a temperature of 3800°C. The solar furnace is used as a solar power plant. The Sun's rays heat the boiler, located at the focal point of the reflector, and create high-pressure steam, which rotates a turbine. The furnace is also used for water desalination, hazardous waste detoxification, heat production, and research on the thermophysical properties of materials in concentrated sunlight.

# Reflecting Telescope

In Fig. 10.52, the telescopes shown use a parabolic mirror to collect light from the night sky. The light is then projected onto a mirror that directs the light to the eyepiece.

## Why mirrors and not lenses?

- An advantage in using mirrors instead of lenses is that only one surface must be ground faultlessly. It is easier to evaporate metal onto a substrate (the process used to make mirrors) than it is to grind a lens from glass.

**Fig.10.52**

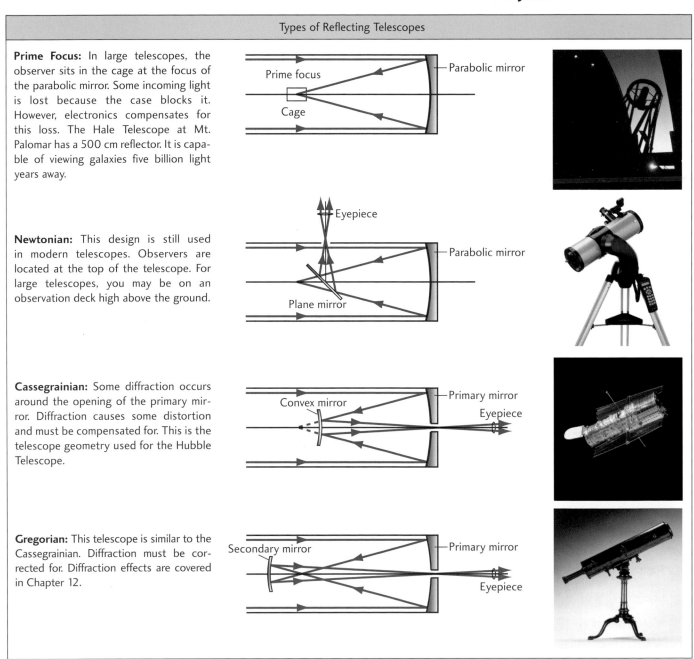

### Types of Reflecting Telescopes

**Prime Focus:** In large telescopes, the observer sits in the cage at the focus of the parabolic mirror. Some incoming light is lost because the case blocks it. However, electronics compensates for this loss. The Hale Telescope at Mt. Palomar has a 500 cm reflector. It is capable of viewing galaxies five billion light years away.

**Newtonian:** This design is still used in modern telescopes. Observers are located at the top of the telescope. For large telescopes, you may be on an observation deck high above the ground.

**Cassegrainian:** Some diffraction occurs around the opening of the primary mirror. Diffraction causes some distortion and must be compensated for. This is the telescope geometry used for the Hubble Telescope.

**Gregorian:** This telescope is similar to the Cassegrainian. Diffraction must be corrected for. Diffraction effects are covered in Chapter 12.

**Fig.10.53A** "Objects in mirror are closer than they appear." Because the mirror is convex, it produces a smaller virtual image. This produces the illusion that the object (vehicle) is farther from you than it really is.

**Fig.10.53B** Because of the wide-angle-viewing capabilities and upright image, this type of mirror is used in security-type applications.

- The support of larger mirrors is also easier because they can be supported by the non-silvered side. To see the size advantage gained by mirror telescopes, one of the largest refracting telescopes has a 1.0 m diameter lens (Yerkes Telescope in Williams Bay, Wisc.). The reflector telescope on Palomar Mt. in the USA is 5.1 m in diameter.
- The process of reflection is not wavelength dependent. Thus, mirror telescopes do not suffer from chromatic aberration as refracting telescopes do. Since the mirror is much larger than the lens, it can collect more light and therefore increase the range of the telescope.

## A Side Rearview and a Security Mirror

In Fig. 10.47, a diverging mirror was described by calculation. Figures 10.53A and B illustrate it once again. These two types of mirrors are diverging mirrors that give us a wide-angle view of an area. This property makes the diverging mirror ideal for security reasons. As well, the image is always upright (rather than upside down), which makes viewing much easier.

Notice the wording on the side rearview mirror. Why are the objects closer than they appear?

## Shaving and Makeup Mirror

Both these types of mirrors are concave mirrors, which have a relatively large focal length. When your face is near the mirror, your image is larger than your face and upright, as seen in Fig. 10.54. This occurs because you (the object) are inside the focus. The image produced is virtual and larger, allowing you to trim that last little whisker, or pluck one more eyebrow.

**Fig.10.54** In the case of a close-up mirror, a concave mirror with a relatively large focal length is used. The person has his/her face inside *f* and sees a larger virtual image of him or herself in the mirror.

UNIT C: Light and Geometric Optics

## Monster Mirrors in Astronomy

CELT (California Extremely Large Telescope), the world's largest optical telescope, is still in the design stage. A $500 million project, it will bring objects into even better focus than our current space-based telescopes. With a 30.5 m wide primary mirror and state-of-the-art distortion cancellation optics (that cancel out the effects of the bending of light as it passes through the atmosphere), this telescope will allow astronomers to look at the extreme edge of the universe.

**Fig.10.55** The world's largest radio telescope at Arecibo Observatory (305 m reflecting surface)

In Europe, astronomers are designing the OWL (Overwhelmingly Large Telescope), which will have a primary mirror 100 m in diameter! This project is also up against a monster production cost.

**1.** Research the workings of the Hubble telescope (Fig. 10.56). Compare its resolving power to telescopes based on Earth.

**Fig.10.56**

**2.** Compare the CELT to the Hubble Telescope in terms of cost and maintenance problems.
**3.** Debate the issue of cost of producing mega physics projects. Would monies be better spent on smaller, more varied projects? (You may wish to investigate the benefit of the new Large Hadron Collider that has a projected cost of $1.8 billion.)

# Infrared Light in NightShot™ Video Cameras

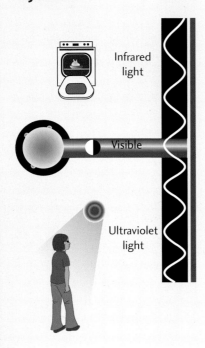

Infrared light

Visible

Ultraviolet light

When you look at light, what you see is only a small part of what you get. Electromagnetic radiation with wavelength on either side of the visible spectrum (shown in Fig. STSE.10.1) is also important to society. Ultraviolet radiation has a shorter wavelength than visible light but transmits much more energy. Ultraviolet radiation is used to make black lights as well as causing skin to tan and burn. Infrared radiation has a longer wavelength than visible light. Infrared radiation, given off by warm objects, has a wavelength of 1–100 m. Infrared radiation is able to pass through glass and clothing. It can also be reflected from some surfaces. A heat-sensitive camera can be used to detect this "light" that we cannot normally see. The heat-sensitive camera is better known as "night vision." Many new video cameras come with a feature that allows you to record images emitting or reflecting infrared radiation. The sample photos in Figs. STSE.10.2–10.5 were taken using a Sony camera's NightShot™ feature. The camera can not only "see" the heat from hot objects (Fig. STSE.10.3), but also the infrared signal from a TV remote control that's invisible to us (Figs. STSE.10.4 and 10.5). Some cameras also come with an infrared "light" that can illuminate subjects in low or no light situations in what is called "0 lux." The resulting image that we see on the video tape is played back in black and white. These cameras are used extensively in night-time video surveillance because they can see through tinted car windows, behind dark sunglasses, and in other places invisible to the naked eye. The first versions of NightShot™ were so sensitive that the camera could even see through light summer clothing.

## Design a Study of Societal Impact

Police are now using laser technology in some of their speed detection devices rather than standard radar. What wavelength of light is used? What are the limitations and improvements of this new technology over the radar systems?

Recently, it has become known that police have used concealed video cameras and face feature recognition software in casinos to allow them to keep track of suspected card sharps and cheaters. Write an essay that discusses invasion of privacy issues, especially if NightShot™ cameras can see through clothing.

Many glow-in-the-dark applications are augmented by the use of a black light. What is meant by this term? Does the use of this light pose any safety hazards? How is UV light used in water treatment?

Tanning salons tan the skin using artificial light. Some tanning salons are connected to health clubs. Research tanning salons and answer the question, "Are tanning beds safe?" Has the amount of UV radiation we are exposed to from the Sun increased in recent decades, or are we more aware of the hazards?

## Design an Activity to Evaluate

Design a mobile experiment that tests the sensitivity to light of cameras on the market. Take your experiment to a store that sells video cameras. Cameras are usually on display using tripods or a similar mounting device. Give each of the cameras the same "eye test" by holding up a page of text in front of each camera at different distances under different room light conditions (measured with a light meter).

If the video camera is digital, it may be used to take digital still images. If you save them in the proper graphic format, you can run these photos of text through text recognition software. Use the software as a "judge" of the quality of the various brands of video cameras.

Evaluate the effectiveness of various brands of UV filter sunglasses or sunscreens. Place a lens from a pair of sunglasses between a UV lamp and a piece of fluorescent material that has been shielded from stray light. Use a simple light meter to indirectly measure the amount of visible light emitted from the fluorescent material. Test sunscreens by applying some to a transparent material or the fluorescent material itself.

Go into a dark room that has an incandescent light bulb controlled by a dimmer switch. Use a diffraction grating or a NightShot™ video camera to observe the spectrum produced when the light is fully turned on. (See resources for diffraction gratings.) Slowly turn the dimmer switch down while looking through the grating. What happens to the spectrum? What connection does this effect have to infrared radiation?

**Fig.STSE.10.2** "Seeing" heat from a fire

**Fig.STSE.10.3** "Seeing" heat from a stove

**Fig.STSE.10.4** "Seeing" infrared radiation

**Fig.STSE.10.5**

SPECIFIC EXPECTATIONS

**You should be able to**

*Understand Basic Concepts:*
- Describe light in terms of the wave theory.
- Define and use terms associated with the wave theory.
- Use the wave equation to calculate the speed of a wave.
- Describe the normal as used in optics.
- Draw ray diagrams to locate an image in a pinhole camera and plane mirror.
- Describe the types of images produced by pinhole cameras and plane mirrors.
- Describe various applications of plane mirrors.
- Describe the general characteristics of converging and diverging mirrors.
- Label the parts of the converging mirror.
- Use ray diagrams to locate and describe images produced by curved mirrors.
- Use the curved mirror equations to calculate the image position and size.

*Develop Skills of Inquiry and Communication:*
- Demonstrate and illustrate reflection and image creation in plane and curved mirrors using ray diagrams.
- Predict the image position and characteristics of a converging and diverging mirror using ray diagrams and algebraic equations.
- Verify through experimentation the predictions made using ray diagrams and calculations.
- Explain the wave theory of light in terms of the properties of light studied in this chapter.

*Relate Science to Technology, Society, and the Environment:*
- Describe how images are produced in optical illusions such as stage ghosts.
- Describe and evaluate the effectiveness of partially silvered surfaces in applications such as rearview mirrors, buildings, and sunglasses.
- Describe the use of mirrors in optical instruments such as telescopes. Evaluate their effectiveness over lens instruments.
- Describe how concave mirror geometries are used in the communications industry.
- Evaluate the need for new, very expensive optical instruments in astronomy.

**Equations**

$$T = \frac{1}{f}$$

$$c = \lambda f, \quad c = 3.0 \times 10^8 \text{ m/s}$$

$$\frac{1}{f} = \frac{1}{d_o} + \frac{1}{d_i}$$

$$m = -\frac{d_i}{d_o} = \frac{h_i}{h_o}$$

$$N = \left(\frac{360}{\theta}\right) - 1$$

## Conceptual Questions

**1.** Relate the motion of a spring vibrating back and forth to that of a light wave.

**2.** Why is the sine wave pattern appropriate for both transverse and longitudinal wave representations?

**3.** Why would it be advantageous to transmit information by light rather than by electricity in wires? How does this technology improve computer designs? (Hint: Electricity doesn't travel at the speed of light.)

**4.** Whether you are close to or far away from a plane mirror, you always see the same amount of your body. Explain this phenomenon.

**5.** If you were to shine a laser beam into a container made from the best silvered mirrors money can buy (the container's interior sides are silvered), would the beam of light be trapped in there forever, after you turned the laser beam off?

**6.** Stealth aircraft, such as the F-117A (see Fig. 10.20), is invisible to radar. The outside of the plane is covered with flat surfaces that are tilted at different angles. Why?

**7.** A submarine periscope, using two silvered plane mirrors, views a duck standing on a floating log. Describe the image of the duck in terms of type, size, and orientation.

**8.** At what speed does an image appear to move towards you as you move closer to a plane mirror with speed $v$?

**9.** In ray diagrams, the paths of light are reversible. Satellite dishes are another example of this reversibility. Use the reversibility of light rays to explain how a satellite dish collects and sends out signals.

**10.** Why does all the sunlight hitting a concave mirror always focus at the focal point of the mirror?

**11.** The spoon is an example of two kinds of mirrors. What images would you expect to see when looking at each side of the spoon?

**12.** What happens to the focal length of a converging mirror as the centre of curvature is increased (the mirror is less bent)? At its maximum, what does the focal length become, and what type of mirror do you have?

**13.** Why would you use a converging mirror rather than a diverging mirror
**a)** to cook a hotdog using sunlight?
**b)** to view your face in order to perfect the makeup job or look for hair missed in shaving?
**c)** as a flashlight reflector?

**14.** Why would you use a diverging mirror rather than a converging mirror for
**a)** a rearview side mirror?
**b)** a store security mirror?

**15.** What are the advantages of using a parabolic mirror over a spherical one?

## Problems

### ▶ 10.1 Introduction to Waves

**16.** Copy the diagram of a wave in your book (Fig. 10.57). From measurements and information taken directly from the diagram, find the
**a)** wavelength.
**b)** amplitude.
**c)** period.
**d)** frequency.
**e)** speed of the wave.

**Fig.10.57** For this problem, note that there are two different scales used (d(m) and t(s)).

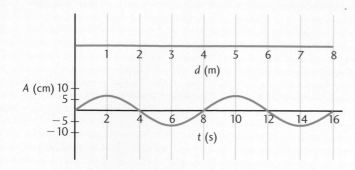

17. For the wave in Problem 16, redraw it so the wavelength is
    a) doubled.
    b) halved.
    For each case, find the wavelength, amplitude, period, frequency, and speed.

18. A plastic duck at the end of a spring is pulled down and released. If the duck moves up and down 10 times in 3.2 s, find the period and frequency of oscillation.

19. What is the period and frequency of a person's heart if it beats 72 times in one minute?

20. An electric shaver blade vibrates at 60 Hz. What is the period of vibration?

21. A piston in a car moves up and down 150 times per minute (150 rpm). Find
    a) the frequency in Hz (rps).
    b) the period of vibration.

22. In the "olden days," there were three rotational speeds used in playing vinyl records. They were 78 rpm, 45 rpm, and $33\frac{1}{3}$ rpm. Convert each of these values to Hz and then find the period of rotation.

23. For Problem 22, how many turns would occur for each speed in 1 hour, 2 minutes, and 12 seconds?

▶ **10.2 The Wave Equation and Electromagnetic Theory**

24. For the following wavelengths of light, calculate the corresponding frequency ($c = 3.0 \times 10^8$ m/s):
    a) Red, 650 nm
    b) Orange, 600 nm
    c) Yellow, 580 nm
    d) Green, 520 nm
    e) Blue, 475 nm
    f) Violet, 400 nm
    It should be noted that these are representative values—each colour has a range of frequencies associated with it.

25. Calculate the time it would take light leaving Earth to reach
    a) the Sun ($1.49 \times 10^{11}$ m away).
    b) the Moon ($3.8 \times 10^8$ m away).
    c) Pluto ($5.8 \times 10^{12}$ m away).
    d) Mercury ($9.1 \times 10^{10}$ m away).
    Convert the times to minutes and hours as well.

26. Recalculate the times in Problem 25 using the velocity of
    a) a fast car, 300 km/h.
    b) a satellite, 30 000 km/h.

27. Find the distance light travels in one year. This distance is referred to as a light year.

28. If we see the light coming from a galaxy 100 light years away, how long ago was the light emitted?

29. When a light bulb is turned on at one end of a football stadium, how much time elapses before its light reaches you? Assume a distance of 160 m.

30. British Columbia is about a 50 h drive from Southern Ontario. Assume a distance of 4000 km. How many times faster is it travelling there at the speed of light?

## 10.3 Rectilinear Propagation of Light— The Pinhole Camera

**31.** Draw an object 2.0 cm high. Draw a pinhole camera 10 cm away and 4.0 cm deep. Using two rays, one from the top and one from the bottom of the object, locate the image in the camera. Measure the height of the image and calculate the magnification.

**32.** For Problem 31, use the formula method to find the magnification and the height of the image.

**33.** Calculate the distance from a pinhole camera to a person who is 2.1 m tall and whose image is 8.5 cm high, given that the camera is 25 cm long.

**34.** Find the height of a building given that a 20 cm long pinhole camera produces a 5.0 cm high image and is 300 m away.

**35.** If the magnification is 0.10 for an image of a person 6.5 m away, what is the length of the camera?

**36.** For Problem 35, if the student is 205 cm tall, how big is the image?

## 10.4 Introduction to Reflection

**37.** Copy the given pictures of various shapes of wavefronts and draw rays representing their direction of travel.

**Fig.10.58**

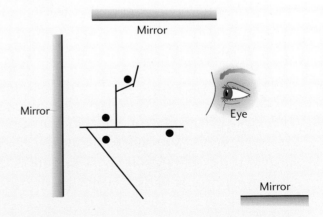

**38.** Copy the wavefront representation of reflection, and draw in the normal, the incident, and the reflected rays. Label the angles.

**Fig.10.59**

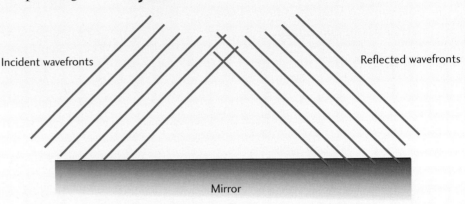

Incident wavefronts    Reflected wavefronts

Mirror

**39.** For the case of diffuse reflection, draw a bumpy surface in your notebook. Draw a series of normals on the various parts of the surface. Draw incident and reflected rays at these points.

## 10.5 Images In Plane Mirrors—A Case for Reflection

**40.** Copy the following diagram into your notebook. Use normals and the law of reflection to determine if you can see the objects.

**Fig.10.60**

Mirror

Mirror

Eye

Mirror

**41.** If the angle between the incident and reflected rays is 46°, what is the angle of incidence?

**42.** The incident angle is 40° relative to the surface of the mirror. What is the angle of reflection relative to the normal?

**43.** For Fig. 10.61, draw a ray diagram in your notebook to find the image. Describe the characteristics of the image.

**Fig.10.61**

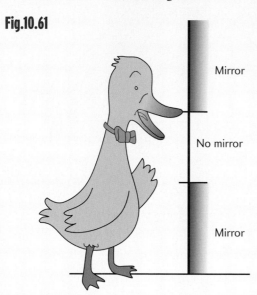

Mirror

No mirror

Mirror

**44.** You are sitting in front of a mirror 2.0 m away and you see the image of a friend standing 0.5 m behind you. How far does your friend's image appear to be from you? Show your calculations or reasoning.

**45.** Use scaled diagrams to find out if a person 1.7 m tall from feet to eyes standing in front of a mirror 1.8 m away will see her feet given that the mirror is 1.5 m tall (standing on the ground).

### 10.7 Curved Mirrors

**46.** Use a scaled diagram to find the location of the image of a 7.0 cm whiteout bottle if it is situated at the following locations in front of a concave mirror with focal length 10 cm:
**a)** Object is 20 cm from vertex.
**b)** Object is 15 cm from vertex.
**c)** Object is 25 cm from vertex.
For each situation, describe the image in terms of type, size, and orientation.

**47.** A person looks at his face in a converging mirror of focal length 50 cm. If the person's face is 40 cm from the vertex of the mirror, locate the image of the face, given that it is 28 cm long. Use a scaled diagram.

**48.** Where would the objects have to be placed in Problems 46 and 47 in order for no image to appear?

**49.** What are the radii of curvature for the mirrors used in Problems 46 and 47?

**50.** Repeat Problem 47 for a convex mirror.

**51.** Complete the following ray diagrams in your notebook to show all objects, images, and rays.

**Fig.10.62**

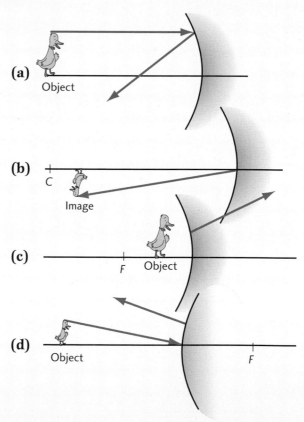

**(a)** Object

**(b)** C    Image

**(c)** F    Object

**(d)** Object    F

**52.** You are standing a great distance from a large, concave mirror. As you walk towards it, describe what is happening to your image in terms of type, orientation, and size.

**53.** Repeat Problem 52 for a diverging mirror.

## 10.8 Calculations for Curved Mirrors

**54.** A thumb of height 8.0 cm is held in front of a concave mirror of focal length 10 cm. The image formed is 12.0 cm from the vertex of the mirror. Find
  **a)** the position of the object.
  **b)** the magnification.
  **c)** the size of the image.
  **d)** the type and orientation of the image.

**55.** In classical physics experiments, a candle is placed in front of a converging mirror with focal length 15 cm. If the candle sits at the centre of curvature and has a flame 1.5 cm tall,
  **a)** find the object distance.
  **b)** find the image position.
  **c)** calculate the magnification.
  **d)** find the image size.
  **e)** describe the image.
  **f)** If you use a sheet of paper to locate the image, what problem may occur?

**56.** A converging shaving/makeup mirror has a focal length of 17 cm. If the person's face is positioned 12 cm from the vertex of the mirror and is 22 cm long, find
  **a)** the image position.
  **b)** the magnification.
  **c)** the size of the image.
  **d)** the orientation and type of the image.

**57. a)** For a concave mirror of focal length 20 cm, where must you place an object such that no image is produced?
  **b)** Use the mirror formula to calculate the image position for this case.

**58.** The Palomar Telescope has a focal length of 18 m. If the Sun's diameter is about $1.39 \times 10^9$ m and its distance from Earth is $1.49 \times 10^{11}$ m, how large is the telescope's image of the Sun?

**59.** Looking at the back of a spoon, you see an image of your radiant 22 cm long face. If the focal length of the spoon is 5.5 cm and your face is 10.0 cm away from the spoon,
  **a)** what type of mirror is the spoon?
  **b)** what sign should the focal length have?
  **c)** what is the image position?
  **d)** what is the magnification and size of the image?
  **e)** Describe the image.

**60.** Complete the following chart in your notebook:

| Mirror | $f$ (cm) | C (cm) | $d_o$ (cm) | $d_i$ (cm) | m | Real/virtual | Orientation |
|---|---|---|---|---|---|---|---|
| concave | +10 | 20 | 30 | ? | ? | real | inverted |
| ? | +15 | ? | 30 | ? | ? | ? | inverted |
| ? | −15 | −30 | ? | −10 | ? | virtual | ? |
| convex | ? | −26 | 16 | ? | ? | ? | ? |
| ? | +30 | ? | 30 | ? | ? | ? | ? |
| converging | 20 | ? | 10 | ? | ? | ? | ? |
| ? | ? | ? | 20 | ? | $-\frac{1}{2}$ | real | ? |
| plane | ? | ? | 50 | ? | ? | ? | ? |

**61.** A side-view diverging mirror has a focal length of 50 cm. The driver sees an image of a car that is 10 m behind her and 1.8 m high. Find
  **a)** the image position.
  **b)** the image size.
  **c)** Describe the image.

**62.** Where would the object be relative to a diverging mirror with focal length 20.0 cm if the mirror produces an image that's $\frac{1}{2}$ the size of the object?

**63.** A converging mirror produces an image twice the size of the object. If the focal length is 20 cm, find
  **a)** the object distance.
  **b)** the image distance.
  **c)** the type of image.

## LAB 10.1 Pinhole Camera

### Purpose
To create and study the pinhole camera.

### Equipment
Cardboard box (supplied by student)
Thin oiled or waxed paper (translucent)
Scissors and compass point
Glue stick
Candle or other light source
Opaque sheet (about $8\frac{1}{2}'' \times 11''$) or use a school camera

### Procedure
1. Cut a square hole at one end of the box, leaving a border of about 1.5 cm.
2. Glue the wax paper onto the box from the inside to cover the square hole.
3. Put the lid on the box and punch a small, circular hole in the centre of the other end of the box.
4. Measure the length of the box.
5. Punch two holes in the opaque sheet, about 5 cm apart.
6. With the opaque sheet in front of the light source and the holes vertical, move the camera back and forth until you see two sharp dots (the small hole is pointed at the light source).
7. Cover one hole on the opaque sheet and observe which one disappears. Repeat with the other hole.
8. Now turn the opaque sheet so the holes are horizontal. Repeat Step 7.
9. Remove the opaque sheet and focus the image of light on the translucent paper through the small hole.
10. Measure the size of the image and note its orientation.
11. Measure the distance from the camera to the light.
12. Measure the size of your light source.
13. Point the small hole of the camera out a window or go outside and focus a high object on the translucent sheet.
14. Measure the distance from the small hole of the camera to the object. You may have to pace it off and measure your step size.
15. Punch a larger hole in the camera. Study the effects on the image by noting its sharpness, brightness, and size.

### Data
Design a chart for the following information:
1. Name of the object
2. Image characteristics (size, type, orientation)
3. Distance to the object and image distance, (length of the box)
4. Size of the object

### Uncertainty
Estimate the uncertainty of finding the image position by having different group members find the focus, $f$. Use the range of scatter of the distances as an indicator of the uncertainty.

### Analysis
1. Summarize the findings of the experiment with the opaque sheet.
2. Calculate (image distance)/(object distance). This ratio is the magnification, expressed as $\frac{d_i}{d_o}$.
3. Find the size of the objects using the relationship $\frac{d_i}{d_o} = \frac{h_i}{h_o}$, where $h_i$ is the image height and $h_o$ is the object height.

### Discussion
1. Use the opaque sheet part of the lab results to explain how the pinhole camera forms images. Use the expression "linear propagation of light" in your explanation.
2. Compare the calculated object size to the measured size. Do they agree within the uncertainty you decided on? If not, try the experiment again or remeasure the object size.
3. Was your calculation of the distant object's size reasonable? Try to obtain reliable height information about the object you chose.
4. What effect did the larger hole have on the experiment?

### Conclusion
Summarize the aspects of the pinhole camera.

## Purpose

To study the characteristics of a concave mirror.

## Equipment

Light source (either a small light bulb or candle)
Concave mirror of known focal length
Optics bench
Blank thin white paper

## Procedure: Checking the Focal Length of the Mirror

1. Darken the room and light the light source (light bulb or candle).
2. Have one member of the group hold the mirror with one hand and move a small sheet of paper in front of the mirror back and forth until an image of a **distant** light source comes into focus. (Stand on one side of the room and focus on the light source on the other side of the room.)
3. Have another group member measure the distance from the paper to the mirror. This distance is the focal length of the mirror.

## Procedure: Investigating the Characteristics of the Mirror

1. Complete the chart in the data section based on the focal length you measured.
2. Position the mirror and the object (the light) at the calculated object distance. Move the paper screen around until a **sharp** image is formed.

**Fig.Lab.10.1**

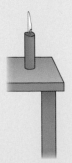

3. Measure the image distance and note the orientation and relative size of the image.
4. Do this for all the object positions in the chart except $0.5 \times f$. For $0.5 \times f$, the image is virtual and located "inside" the mirror. For this case, the parallax method is used to determine $d_i$.

## Parallax Method

1. Place an unlit candle or other short object at $0.5 \times f$. Look into the mirror. You should see a larger image of the object.
2. Move a pencil that is taller than the mirror behind the mirror until you feel it is at the place where the image appears to be (Fig. Lab.10.2).
3. Try to line up the image and the part of the pencil above the mirror. Move your head from side to side. If the image and the pencil split apart, then you haven't found the correct image position(Fig. Lab.10.3). When you find the correct position, the image and the object stay aligned with each other as you shift your head from side to side.
4. Measure the image position (pencil to mirror). Remember that the image position is negative. Record the characteristics of the image.

**Fig.Lab.10.2**

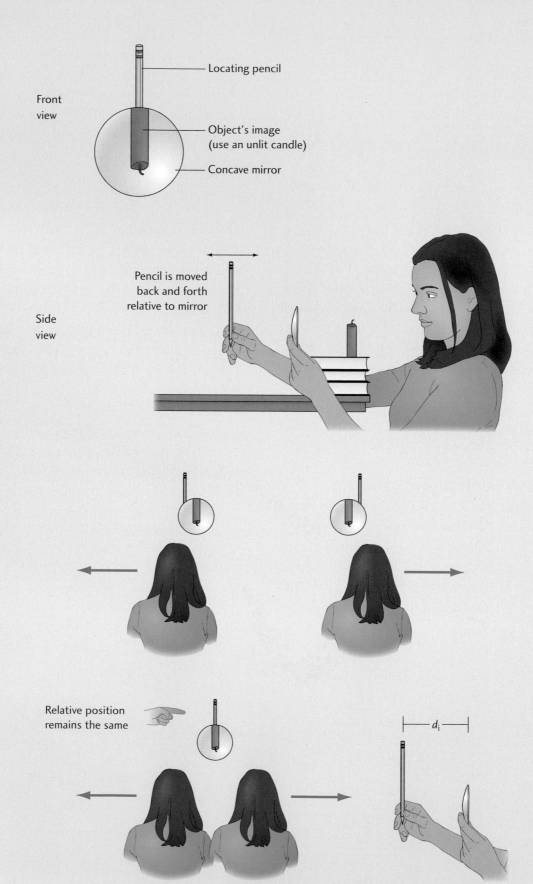

Front view

Locating pencil

Object's image (use an unlit candle)

Concave mirror

Side view

Pencil is moved back and forth relative to mirror

**Fig.Lab.10.3**

Relative position remains the same

$d_i$

UNIT C: Light and Geometric Optics

## Data

| $f =$ _____ | | | | |
|---|---|---|---|---|
| $d_o$ (cm) | $d_i$ (cm) | Type | Size | Orientation |
| 2.5 f | | | | |
| 2.0 f | | | | |
| 1.5 f | | | | |
| 1.0 f | | | | |
| 0.5 f | | | | |

First calculate the object positions. Then fill in the chart as you proceed through the experiment.

## Uncertainty

Determine the range through which the image stays in focus. You can use this range as part of the procedural uncertainty. The alignment of the screen and the optics bench may also contribute.

## Analysis

1. In a separate chart, calculate $f$ using the data from your table and the equation $\frac{1}{f} = \frac{1}{d_o} + \frac{1}{d_i}$.
2. Include a column in this chart for the percent deviation. Use the actual (given) value of $f$ for comparison.
3. Include in this chart a column for the magnification, which is calculated using $m = -\frac{d_i}{d_o}$.

## Discussion

1. Prove that the image was at the focus, $f$, when the object was far away.
2. How well did your values of $f$ agree with the actual value? Were you consistently off by the same amount? Account for possible reasons for the discrepancies.

3. Check the magnification value and the size. Are they in general agreement?
4. You may have found an image when the object was at $f$. However, it probably looked very different from the other images. If you found the image, describe it and give a possible explanation for its appearance (no image is expected). If you found no image, what did you see on the screen?
5. Why couldn't you use the screen method for the object at $0.5 \times f$?
6. Why is the value of the image position negative $0.5 \times f$?

## Conclusion

Summarize the characteristics of the converging mirror. Draw a ray diagram to verify each line of your data chart.

## Extension

1. Determine the focal length of a mirror by using a series of $d_o$ and corresponding $d_i$ values.
2. Check this value by using an alternate method.

**LABORATORY EXERCISES**

### Purpose

To study the characteristics of the convex mirror. This lab is difficult because all the images are virtual. The method is the same as that used to locate the virtual image for the converging mirror.

### Procedure

1. Repeat the converging mirror lab, only select 3–5 different object positions. Start with a large object distance and then decrease it in regular increments.
2. Try and locate the image position using the parallax method. Remember that the sign of the image position is negative.
3. Observe and record the relative size of the image. Try to compare the image size as the object distance is decreased.

### Analysis

Same as for the previous lab.

### Discussion

1. Why are the focal length and the image distance negative for this mirror?
2. Can you come up with a method of showing how the parallax method works using your hands?
3. Were your $f$ values consistently off by the same amount or were they random?

### Conclusion

Summarize the characteristics of a diverging mirror.

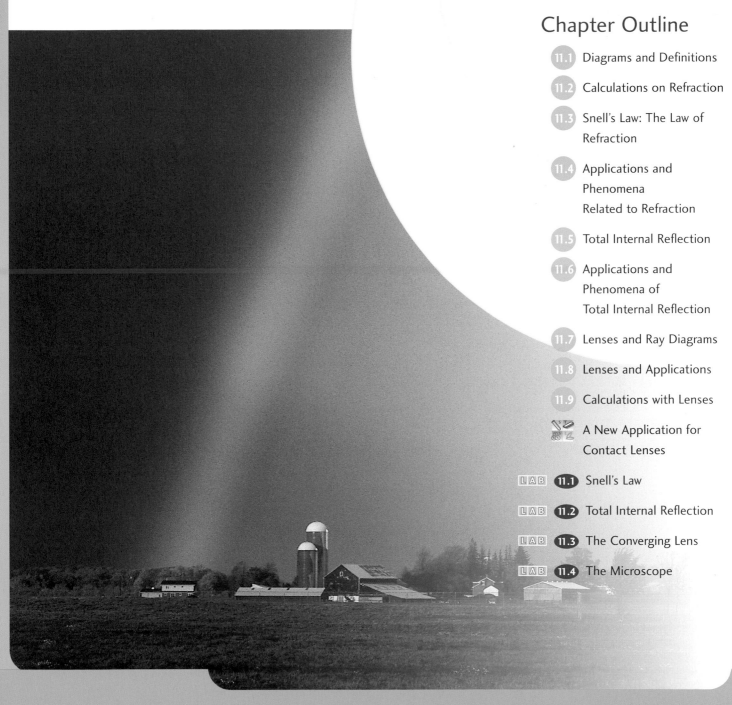

# Refraction

## By the end of this chapter, you will be able to

- understand the properties of light and its transmission from one medium to another
- illustrate the behaviour of light through experimentation, ray diagrams, and equations
- relate refraction to entertainment, communications, and optical instruments

# 11.1  Diagrams and Definitions

**Fig.11.1**  Refraction effects

**Refraction** is the bending of light as it enters a different optical medium. The visible clues indicating that light bends are illustrated in Fig. 11.1. Notice how the straw appears broken when entering the water. The effect shown in Fig. 11.1 is created because light travels in a straight line and light changes its speed when it enters a different medium.

Figure 11.2 shows a ray of light travelling from air into water. The angle of incidence and the angle of refraction are indicated. Notice that the **normal** is perpendicular to the medium boundaries. As with mirrors, all angles are measured with respect to the normal.

**Fig.11.2**  Measuring refraction

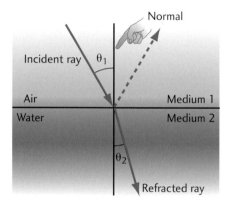

$\theta_1$ angle of incidence
$\theta_2$ angle of refraction

In Fig. 11.2, subscript 1 refers to incidence variables and subscript 2 refers to variables associated with the refracted ray. In this case, optical medium 1 is air, and optical medium 2 is water. If the ray were coming out of the water, then the subscripts would be reversed (air would become medium 2 and water would become medium 1). To illustrate this effect, you can reverse the directions of the arrows on the diagram and relabel the two mediums.

In Fig. 11.3, imagine that the fish has swallowed a laser pointer. As the fish moves, the laser beam hits the water's surface at different angles. The laser light beam follows the ray direction predicted by refraction laws. From the refraction diagrams, we can make the following observational statements:

1. The refracted ray bends *toward* the normal when travelling from air to water *(less optically dense to more optically dense)*.
2. The refracted ray bends *away from* the normal when travelling from water to air *(more optically dense to less optically dense)*.

UNIT C: Light and Geometric Optics

**Fig.11.3** Whether light starts at the fisherman or at the fish, the path of light is the same. Notice the pointed-out ray does not exit the water. This is a special case of total internal reflection and will be explained in Section 11.5.

To decide if the ray is bending toward or away from the normal, lightly extend the incident ray into the second medium. In Fig. 11.4, the two possible refractions are both shown along with the extended incident ray. The area between the extended ray and the refracted rays is shaded. The region shaded red illustrates the refracted ray bending toward the normal. The region shaded blue illustrates the refracted ray bending away from the normal.

**Fig.11.4** Refraction direction depends on the optical density of the two mediums

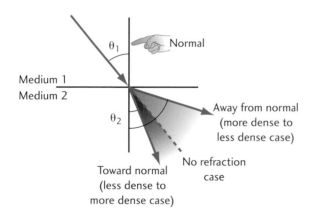

When light bends, it also undergoes a speed change. In the 1800s, James Clerk Maxwell postulated that the speed of light was $3.0 \times 10^8$ m/s in a vacuum. In the 1900s, Albert Einstein further postulated that nothing can exceed this speed. This means that all other speeds are less than the speed of light in a vacuum. We therefore use the speed of light in a vacuum as a standard to determine the "braking ability" of any optical medium that light enters (i.e., the ability of a medium to slow down the speed of light). *The bending of light is caused by a change in the speed of light when light enters the medium at an angle other than 90°.* Therefore, if we can measure the angle of refraction, we can determine the braking ability of the medium. The more optically dense the medium, the more energy it absorbs, and the more it is able to slow the speed of light.

Armand Fizeau (1819 – 1896) and Albert Michelson (1852 – 1931) obtained a value for the speed of light ranging from $3.13 \times 10^8$ m/s to $2.99796 \times 10^8$ m/s. The current value of $c$ is $2.997\ 924\ 58 \times 10^8$ m/s.

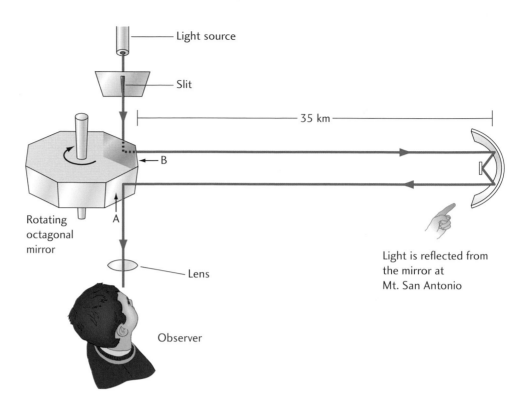

**Fig.11.5** Michelson measured the speed of light using an accurate distance measurement between Mt. Wilson and Mt. San Antonio, California. Without the rotating eight-sided mirror spinning, the position of the reflected light is measured at the observer position. The mirror is then set rotating and timed accurately. The rotational speed was adjusted in such a way as to have side B now reflecting the light to the observer rather than side A. Thus, the light now travelled to Mt. San Antonio and back in $\frac{1}{8}$th of the period of rotation of the octagonal mirror. Knowing the distance and the time, a value of $2.997928 \times 10^8$ m/s was obtained for the speed of light.

▷ ▷ ▷ ▷

1. Find common, everyday examples of refraction. Think about every time light passes through a transparent medium.
2. Find examples of partial reflection and refraction. Look at situations where you view a medium at an angle.
3. What can you tell from the direction of the bend of the refracted ray relative to a normal?

# ▶ 11.2 Calculations on Refraction

## Index of Refraction

In the last section, we saw that the bending of light is caused by light changing its speed as it crosses a medium boundary. The more optically dense the medium, the more the speed of light is slowed. The measure of the slowing of the speed of light is called the **index of refraction**. The **absolute index of refraction** is the ratio of the speed of light in a vacuum to the speed of light in the other medium. Expressed mathematically,

$$n = \frac{c}{v}$$

where $c$ is the speed of light in a vacuum, $v$ is the speed of light in the other medium, and $n$ is the absolute refractive index of the medium.

UNIT C: Light and Geometric Optics

EXAMPLE 1   **Refractive index of diamond**

Calculate the index of refraction of a diamond if the speed of light in a diamond is $1.24 \times 10^8$ m/s.

### *Solution and Connection to Theory*

**Given**

$c = 3.00 \times 10^8$ m/s   $v = 1.24 \times 10^8$ m/s   $n = ?$

The formula is $n = \dfrac{c}{v}$.

Remember to include units.

$$n = \frac{3.00 \times 10^8 \text{ m/s}}{1.24 \times 10^8 \text{ m/s}} = 2.42$$

The refractive index of a diamond is 2.42. Notice that the units have cancelled out. Because $n$ is a ratio, it is a unitless value.

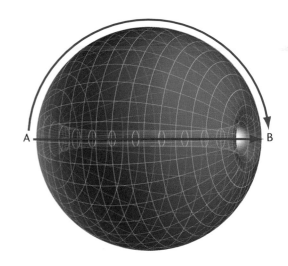

**Fig.11.6**   Quantum warp tunnelling

EXAMPLE 2   **Warp drive?**

Calculate the speed of light in a hypothetical material you have discovered and named in honour of yourself. Its refractive index is 0.90.

### *Solution and Connection to Theory*

**Given**

$c = 3.00 \times 10^8$ m/s   $n = 0.90$   $v = ?$

$n = \dfrac{c}{v}$

Rearrange for $v$.

$$v = \frac{c}{n} = \frac{3.00 \times 10^8 \text{ m/s}}{0.90} = 3.3 \times 10^8 \text{ m/s}$$

The speed of light in our hypothetical medium is greater than the speed of light in a vacuum!

The answer in Example 2 clearly violates Einstein's law, which means that no substance like it is known at the present time. But who knows; people have been proven wrong before.

**"WARP 7, SCOTTY"**

Many of the current proposals for travelling faster than the speed of light involve hyperspace or an effect where the configuration of space changes as you reach the forbidden speed. These methods involve bending space so that your destination point lies closer to you than before. Now the distance you cover is less than that light would have travelled, which decreases your flight time. So, it appears as though you are travelling at a speed greater than $c$.

## Relative Index of Refraction

If you know the indices of refraction for two materials (e.g., air and water), you can find the **relative index of refraction** between them, expressed as $\frac{n_2}{n_1}$.

---

**EXAMPLE 3** **Calculating relative indices of refraction**

A ray of light travels through a water–glass boundary and back again. Calculate the relative indices of refraction.

### Solution and Connection to Theory

*For travelling from water to glass:*

**Given**
$$n_1 = 1.33 \qquad n_2 = 1.52$$

$$\frac{n_2}{n_1} = \frac{1.52}{1.33} = 1.14$$

The ray is going from a less optically dense material to a more dense material, so $n > 1$ and the ray bends towards the normal.

*For travelling back from glass to water, change the subscripts of* n.

**Given**
$$n_1 = 1.52 \qquad n_2 = 1.33$$

$$\frac{n_2}{n_1} = \frac{1.33}{1.52} = 0.88$$

In this case, the ray is going from a more optically dense material to a less dense material and speeding up, so $n < 1$ and the ray bends away from the normal.

---

You must remember that the relative values just calculated are not the type of value you look up. Refraction tables always provide absolute indices of refraction for individual substances.

1. Calculate the speed of light for the following mediums:
   a) water ($n = 1.33$)
   b) diamond ($n = 2.42$)
   c) plexiglass ($n = 1.51$)
2. Calculate the refractive index for a substance if the speed of light in that medium is
   a) $2.1 \times 10^8$ m/s.
   b) $1.5 \times 10^8$ m/s.
   c) $0.79c$.

# 11.3 Snell's Law: The Law of Refraction

We mentioned earlier that light travels at different speeds in different optical mediums. The different mediums cause light to bend as it changes speed. But the medium is not the only factor affecting refraction. If the incident ray is along the normal, its incident angle is 0° and the ray does not refract. As the angle of incidence increases, the degree of refraction of the ray also increases. In other words, the amount of refraction depends on two factors: the index of refraction as well as the angle of incidence. This relationship is called **Snell's law** and is usually written in the following form:

$$n_1 \sin\theta_1 = n_2 \sin\theta_2$$

where $\theta_1$ is the angle of incidence, $\theta_2$ is the angle of refraction, $n_1$ is the index of refraction for the incident medium, and $n_2$ is the index of refraction for the refracting medium.

Before solving for any of the possible variables ($n_1$, $n_2$, $\theta_1$, $\theta_2$), you should become familiar with using the sine and inverse sine functions on your calculator.

### Table 11.1
#### Index of Refraction

| Substance | $n$ |
| --- | --- |
| Vacuum | 1.000 |
| Air | 1.000 29 |
| Water | 1.33 |
| Ethyl alcohol | 1.36 |
| Glycerin | 1.47 |
| Crown glass | 1.50 |
| Flint glass | 1.91 |
| Diamond | 2.42 |

**Fig.11.7** Trigonometric ratios

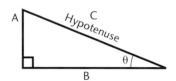

Pythagoras' formula: $A^2 + B^2 = C^2$

Ratios of sides:
$$\cos\theta = \frac{B}{C} \left( \frac{\text{Adjacent side to angle}}{\text{Hypotenuse}} \right)$$

$$\sin\theta = \frac{A}{C} \left( \frac{\text{Opposite side to angle}}{\text{Hypotenuse}} \right)$$

$$\tan\theta = \frac{A}{B} \left( \frac{\text{Opposite side to angle}}{\text{Adjacent side to angle}} \right)$$

---

## EXAMPLE 4 Using Snell's law

Find the angle of refraction for light travelling from air to diamond if the angle of incidence in air is 20°.

### Solution and Connection to Theory

**Given**

$n_1 = 1.00$    $n_2 = 2.42$    These values can be found in Table 11.1.

$\theta_1 = 20°$    $\theta_2 = ?$

The equation is $n_1 \sin\theta_1 = n_2 \sin\theta_2$.

Since we are solving for $\theta_2$, we rearrange for $\sin\theta_2$.

$$\sin\theta_2 = \sin\theta_1 \frac{n_1}{n_2}$$

Substitute the values.

$$\sin\theta_2 = \sin 20° \frac{1.00}{2.42} = 0.34 \times 0.41 = 0.14$$

To find the angle, we need to use the $\sin^{-1}$ function.

$$\theta_2 = \sin^{-1} 0.14 \qquad \theta_2 = 8.0°$$

The angle of refraction is 8.0°. The ray of light went from a less dense to a more dense medium. Therefore, the angle of refraction is less than the angle of incidence and the light is bent towards the normal.

**CALCULATOR TRIG KEYS**

**Fig.11.8**

EXAMPLE 5    Index of refraction calculated using Snell's law

Calculate the index of refraction for a substance where the angle of incidence is 30.0°, the angle of refraction is 50.0°, and the index of refraction of the second substance is 1.50.

### Solution and Connection to Theory

**Given**

$n_2 = 1.50$      $\theta_1 = 30.0°$      $\theta_2 = 50.0°$      $n_1 = ?$

$$n_1 \sin\theta_1 = n_2 \sin\theta_2$$

Now rearrange for $n_1$

$$n_1 = \frac{n_2 \sin\theta_2}{\sin\theta_1}$$

and substitute values.

$$n_1 = 1.50 \times \frac{\sin 50.0°}{\sin 30.0°} \qquad n_1 = 1.50 \times 1.53 = 2.30$$

The index of refraction of the first substance is 2.30.

Notice that the angle of incidence in Example 5 is less than the angle of refraction, which means that the light bends away from the normal. For this case, $n_1$ should be greater than $n_2$. As you can see, the answer agrees with the theory.

## Fig.11.9   Effects of Refraction

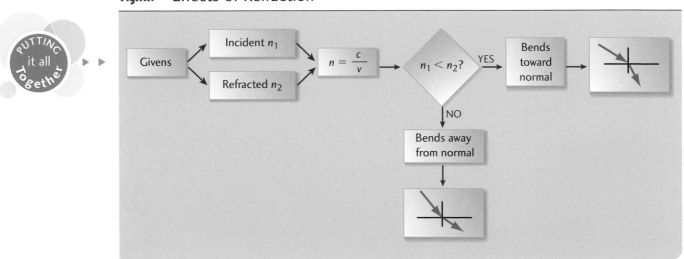

PUTTING it all Together

1. Calculate the angle of refraction for light as it passes from air to each of the mediums in Section 11.2, Applying the Concepts, Question 1, at an angle of 25°.
2. An angle of incidence of 20° in water results in an angle of refraction of 15°.
   a) Is the second medium more or less optically dense than the first medium?
   b) Find the refractive index of the second medium.
   c) Find the speed of light in each medium.
   d) Repeat this question for an angle of refraction of 25°.

# 11.4 Applications and Phenomena Related to Refraction

## Apparent Depth

In Fig. 11.10, a fisherman has spotted a fish. As you can see in the photograph, the fish appears to be in a different location, much closer to the surface than it really is. The ray diagram illustrates the reason for this optical illusion. Notice how the principle of linear propagation of light once again comes into play. If we project the rays representing the tip of the fish in the opposite direction, i.e., as they cross the boundary from water to air, the rays bend away from the normal and enter our eyes. The brain then constructs an image by projecting the rays back into the water in a straight line, the same distance from the surface as the fish. The fish, too, has an odd view of the fisherman.

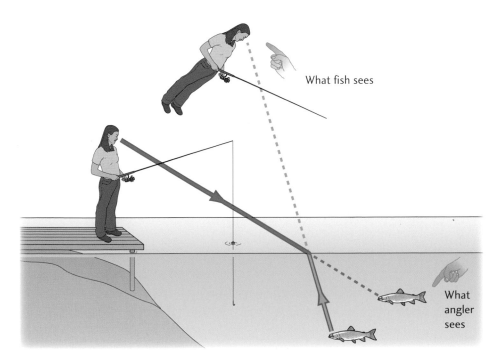

**Fig.11.10** Image positions produced by refraction

What fish sees

What angler sees

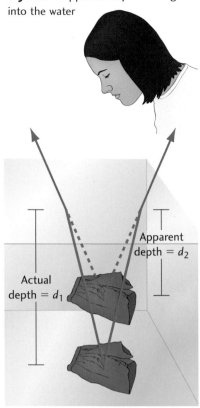

**Fig.11.11** Apparent depth looking into the water

**Fig.11.12** Apparent height looking out of the water

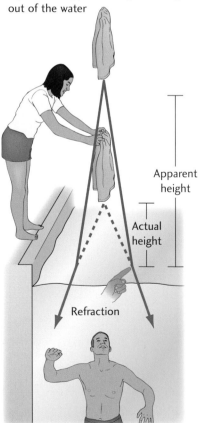

Refraction

If you look straight down into the water, the relationship between apparent depth and actual depth is expressed by the equation

$$d_2 = d_1 \frac{n_2}{n_1}$$

where $d_2$ is the apparent depth and $d_1$ is the actual depth of the object in the water.

Imagine yourself at the side of a swimming pool looking down into the water. You see a bathing suit at the bottom of the pool (Fig. 11.11). You decide to retrieve the garment. Your first instinct is to dive in. However, having taken physics, the following diagram pops into your head.

As you can see, the suit appears at a shallower depth than it really is. To see just how much shallower, the formula for apparent depth also pops into your head.

---

**EXAMPLE 6**   **Calculating apparent depth of the lost shorts**

If the swimming pool is 2.50 m deep and contains regular water, at what depth do the shorts appear to be?

***Solution and Connection to Theory***

**Given**
Because the light travels from the water to your eyes in air,

$n_1(\text{water}) = 1.33$

$n_2(\text{air}) = 1.00 \qquad d_1 = 2.50 \text{ m}$

$d_2 = d_1 \dfrac{n_2}{n_1} = 2.50 \text{ m} \dfrac{1.00}{1.33} = 1.88 \text{ m}$

which is a difference of 25 %. Your decision on the type of entry into the water will have to take this difference into account.

---

If you were at the bottom of the pool looking up at a person holding your towel in the air (Fig. 11.12), the effect you would experience would be opposite to that in Example 6. The apparent height of your towel is greater than its actual height. This effect is the same as that in Fig. 11.10, where the fish sees a ghostly angler floating in the air. Watch for this effect the next time you're in a pool.

## Dispersion

When white light travels through a triangular cross-section piece of glass called a **prism**, a "rainbow" appears on the other side. This effect, shown in

UNIT C: Light and Geometric Optics

**Fig.11.13** Dispersion by a prism separates white light into its component colours

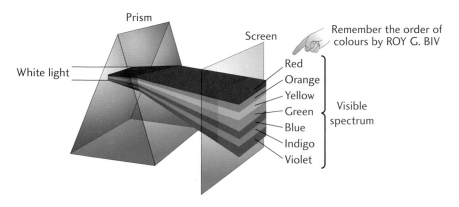

Prism

Screen

Remember the order of colours by ROY G. BIV

White light

Red
Orange
Yellow
Green
Blue
Indigo
Violet

Visible spectrum

**Fig.11.14** The index of refraction changes slightly with wavelength

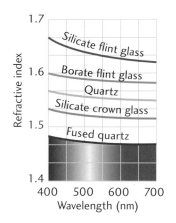

Silicate flint glass
Borate flint glass
Quartz
Silicate crown glass
Fused quartz

Refractive index

1.7
1.6
1.5
1.4
400   500   600   700
Wavelength (nm)

Fig. 11.13, is called **dispersion**. Dispersion is a method of demonstrating that white light is composed of many different wavelengths (colours) of light.

Dispersion occurs because refractive indices are wavelength dependent. (See Fig. 11.14.) Notice that the difference in the refractive index varies across the spectrum. In fact, the refractive index for crown glass ranges from 1.698 for violet light to 1.662 for red light. This 2 % difference occurs each time the light refracts across the glass boundary. As you can see in Fig. 11.15, there are two refractions occurring when light travels through a prism because light travels across two sets of boundary changes. The surfaces of the prism are cut in such a way as to cause the light to bend in the same direction twice. This effect enhances the 2 % difference in the indices of refraction and allows the different wavelengths to separate enough to be seen by the naked eye.

**Fig.11.15** Because of the triangular shape of a prism, the refraction at 1 and 2 are both in the same direction. This enhances the separation of the different wavelengths of light.

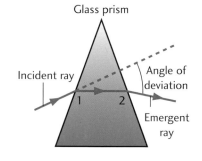

Glass prism

Incident ray

Angle of deviation

1       2

Emergent ray

## Optical Illusion of Water Patches on Dry Pavement

A common mirage seen by many people is illustrated in Fig. 11.16. When driving along a highway on a sunny day, you often see "water patches" ahead of you on the road. As you approach them, they vanish, while more form just ahead of you. The illustration in Fig. 11.16 explains how refraction causes these "water patches" to appear on the road.

**Fig.11.16** Formation of a mirage

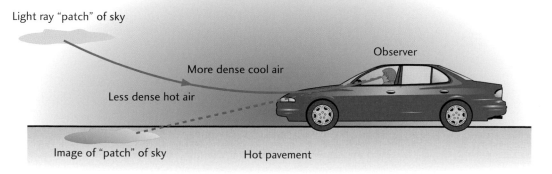

Light ray "patch" of sky

Observer

More dense cool air

Less dense hot air

Image of "patch" of sky        Hot pavement

Different layers of air in the atmosphere have different temperatures. Temperature affects the density of air, and density affects the index of refraction of light. On a sunny day, the hot pavement on the road further accentuates the temperature gradient in the air. When we see "water patches" on the road, we assume that the light rays entering our eyes are coming from the road ahead. In fact, we are seeing images of "patches" of sky that are formed by the Sun's rays refracting through air of varying density. The "patches" appear as puddles on the pavement ahead.

## Apparent Sunsets

The actual sunset is not an optical illusion. It really does drop below the horizon. However, the event occurs earlier than we see it. Figure 11.17 illustrates that the Sun has already moved below the horizon while you are still observing the sunset. The rays of light bend due to the different temperature layers of air, causing an effect similar to that of the mirage of wet pavement. The image of the Sun we see is created by extending the rays entering our eyes back to the point where the converging rays appear to cross.

**Fig.11.17** Light from the Sun is still visible after it descends below the horizon

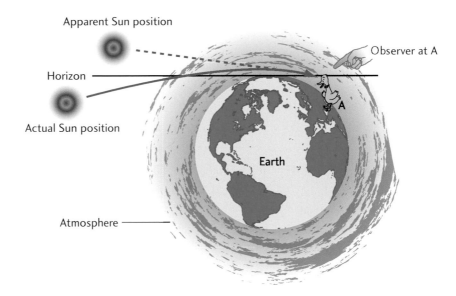

Refraction downward of light rays from the Sun as they enter the atmosphere makes the Sun still visible after sunset

## Heat Waves and Similar Effects

When you look at a hot object, such as a running car, the air above the hot engine appears to be shimmering. This effect is caused by the constantly changing air densities due to the convection of air, which in turn cause the layers of air to develop different refractive properties. The light rays are bent at different angles that change as the air moves around, causing the distortion we observe. The same type of shimmering occurs when you look at light above an open container of gas or other volatile liquid. In this case, the evaporating material above the can has a different refractive index that creates the effect.

Similarly for twinkling stars. The twinkling is like the shimmering effect. The light from the star travels through ever-changing air temperature layers in the atmosphere. The small changes in the refractive indices of these layers cause a slight bending of the light in different directions. According to Fig. 11.18, the light rays are slightly displaced to either side of their true position. We perceive this effect as a twinkle.

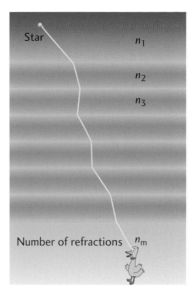

**Fig.11.18** Twinkling star effect caused by different temperature layers of atmosphere

Planets don't twinkle because they are disks rather than point sources (stars). The change in position due to refraction is unnoticeable against the disk shape.

# 11.5 Total Internal Reflection

**Total internal reflection of light** is a method of transmitting information that is widely used in the communications industry. Information is transmitted at the speed of light through a **light pipe** or **fibre optic cable**. Light enters a medium, gets trapped inside it, and must travel the whole length of the material before it can escape. In Fig. 11.19, the image of the object is transmitted down the bent cable until it is clearly seen at the other end.

This method for transmitting information is very successful because only a very small percentage of light is lost along the way. The following example will clarify what happens.

**Fig.11.19** Light passing through a fibre optic cable

EXAMPLE 7   **A first look at total internal reflection**

What happens when light tries to travel from plastic ($n = 1.60$) to air if the angle of incidence is 60°?

### Solution and Connection to Theory

**Given**

$n_1 = 1.60$ $\qquad$ $n_2 = 1.00$ $\qquad$ $\theta_1 = 60°$ $\qquad$ $\theta_2 = ?$

Use Snell's Law and rearrange the equation.

$$\sin\theta_2 = \sin\theta_1\left(\frac{n_1}{n_2}\right)$$

Solve for $\theta_2$.

$$\sin\theta_2 = \sin 60°(1.60)$$

$$\theta_2 = \sin^{-1}0.87(1.60) = \sin^{-1}1.39$$

When you try to solve for the angle of refraction, your calculator comes up with the *error* message. This is not a mistake. The calculator is trying to tell you that no angle of refraction exists, which means that no light is exiting the material. In fact, almost all of the light is reflected back into the material.

**Fig.11.20** Total internal reflection

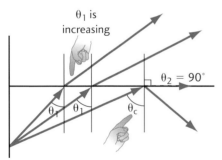

Ray when $\theta_2 = 90°$ is reflected back into the more dense material

To observe total internal reflection, place a transparent microscope slide on a printed page. View the slide from directly overhead where the print is seen clearly. Move your head back slowly, away from the printed page. At the critical angle, the glass becomes a mirror and the print vanishes. The rays travelling from the glass cannot escape and are reflected back.

Figure 11.20 illustrates what happens in this case. The diagram shows a series of rays exiting the water with ever-increasing angles of incidence. The angles of refraction are also increasing until they get to a point where they travel along the medium boundary betwen air and water. From this point on, the refracted rays cannot exit the material. They are reflected internally back into the water. The water acts as a mirror.

The angle of incidence, $\theta_1$, is now labelled $\theta_c$ and is called the **critical angle**. At the critical angle, the refracted angle is 90°. You can see that at this point, the refracted ray does not exit the material. If you combine these conditions with Snell's Law, you obtain the method of calculating the critical angle for any pair of mediums:

$$n_1\sin\theta_1 = n_2\sin\theta_2$$

$$n_1\sin\theta_c = n_2\sin 90°$$

$$\sin\theta_c = \frac{n_2}{n_1}$$

$$\theta_c = \sin^{-1}\frac{n_2}{n_1}$$

Note that *total internal reflection occurs only for light travelling from a more optically dense medium to a less optically dense medium*. In Fig. 11.21, we have reversed the mediums so that the incident ray is in the

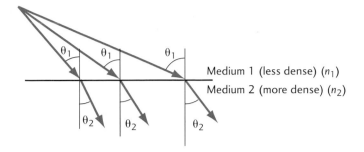

Medium 1 (less dense) $(n_1)$
Medium 2 (more dense) $(n_2)$

less dense medium. Now, as we increase the angle of incidence, the angle of refraction increases, but it always remains smaller than the incident angle. This means that the angle of incidence reaches 90° before the angle of refraction does. Thus, the light will always refract, not reflect.

---

**EXAMPLE 8** **Critical angle calculation**

Calculate the critical angle for a water–air boundary.

### Solution and Connection to Theory

**Given**

$n_1(\text{water}) = 1.33 \qquad n_2(\text{air}) = 1.00 \qquad \theta_c = ?$

$\theta_c = \sin^{-1}\dfrac{n_2}{n_1} = \sin^{-1}\dfrac{1.00}{1.33} = 48.8\,°$

Thus, the critical angle for a water-air boundary is 48.8°.

---

In other words, in Example 8, for angles of incidence of 48.8° and greater, total internal reflection occurs. Almost all of the light is reflected back into the medium. Also note that *we chose the medium with the largest refractive index (water) to be* $n_1$. This is because total internal reflection occurs only for light passing from more optically dense to less optically dense mediums.

## Evanescent Waves

From Fig. 11.22, you can see that a small amount of light travels along the boundary between the two mediums at or beyond the critical angle. This light amplitude dissipates (evanesces) rapidly as it enters the less dense medium. In fact, it becomes negligible after only a few wavelengths of distance into the refracting medium. That's only about $10^{-7}$ m! Although the percentage of energy absorbed through evanescence is small, it is still one of the ways in which energy is absorbed in the fibre optics system.

**Fig.11.22** Energy absorbed during total internal reflection

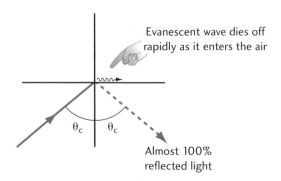

Evanescent wave dies off rapidly as it enters the air

$\theta_c \qquad \theta_c$

Almost 100% reflected light

## Job Opportunities

**Fig.11.23**   Fibre optic routing centre

Fibre optics can transmit more information more quickly over longer distances. The rapidly growing field of fibre optic technology offers unlimited potential to new university and college graduates: research positions involved in developing new fibre and better optical switching devices, engineering positions in industry, and positions for optical cable installers and technicians, especially for high-speed computer networking. Fibre optics are used in cable links between telephone substations; interoffice computer links; cable TV; closed circuit television security systems; optical sensors used to detect gas and chemical concentrations, pressure, temperature, and most other measuring devices; and medical instruments used to probe inside the body. Jobs involving the sales and manufacture of components for all these applications are also in high demand.

1. State the conditions required to produce total internal reflection.
2. **a)** Find all the possible critical angle cases for the following refractive indices: 1.2, 2.3, 1.52, 1.65.
   **b)** Calculate the critical angles for these refractive indices.

## 11.6  Applications and Phenomena of Total Internal Reflection

### Rainbow

A rainbow is a common effect with an uncommon number of principles involved. To explain the appearance of the rainbow and its secondaries (lighter rainbows above the main one), the effects of dispersion, refraction, and total internal reflection must be considered. In order to see a rainbow, you need rain in front of you and the Sun shining behind you. You must face the rain drops, and your eyes, the centre of the arc of the rainbow, and the Sun must be roughly aligned. If the Sun is too high above the horizon, only a small part of the arc is visible. The angle between the observer and the top of the rainbow's arc makes an angle of 42° with the horizon (see Fig. 11.24). In the case of the primary rainbow, this is the angle of inclination for seeing the colour red, with violet occurring at an angle of inclination of about 40°. The arc shape occurs because the observer is at the apex of a cone from which the refracted rays emerge (see Fig. 11.24).

Figure 11.25 illustrates how the colours of the rainbow are formed. There are two main visible rainbows that appear, but the secondary rainbow is not always intense enough to be seen. Both rainbows are formed as a result of each ray of sunlight separating into its component colours, with the rain droplets acting as miniature prisms. For simplicity's sake, Fig. 11.25 illustrates

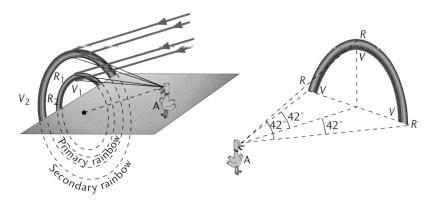

**Fig.11.24** How an observer sees a rainbow

The primary and secondary rainbows
as seen by an observer at A

Formation of primary rainbow

**Fig.11.25** How a rainbow's colours are produced

the path of light in one droplet. The white light enters the drop at the top. Since the refractive index depends on wavelength and white light is made up of many different wavelengths, the different colours in white light are refracted differently. Red, the longest wavelength, is refracted the least and violet, the shortest wavelength, is refracted the most. As well, the water–air boundary causes total internal reflection in the back of the droplet. For the primary rainbow, the light reflects once inside each drop and comes back out. Since all the droplets are acting in the same way, the overall effect is a uniform spectrum of colour.

Figure 11.25(b) also illustrates a second type of refraction. In this case, the light enters the bottom of the droplet and undergoes two consecutive total internal reflections. More light is absorbed because of the extra reflection, so the secondary rainbow is much fainter than the primary rainbow. The extra reflection also causes the colours in the rainbow to be reversed, so violet is now at the top. The angle of inclination at which we see this rainbow varies from 51° for red to 54° for violet. If the ray of light undergoes three consecutive total internal reflections in the water droplet, a tertiary rainbow is created, but it is so faint that it is barely visible.

## Fibre Optics and Phones

In recent years, fibre optic technology has replaced the electrical transmission of information. Huge trunk lines used in transmitting phone signals have been replaced by small, easy to repair, lightweight pipes. A single fibre can carry tens of thousands of phone calls that normally would require as many wires! A thin, transparent cladding surrounds the fibre. The cladding has a low index of refraction to ensure that there is no cross-talk between fibres and to prevent losses through leakage of light. (See Fig. 11.26B.)

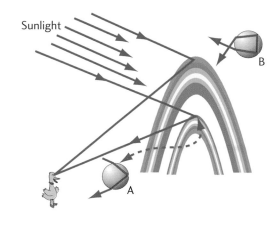

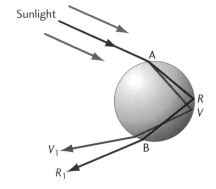

**(a)** Dispersion of sunlight by
a single raindrop (primary rainbow)

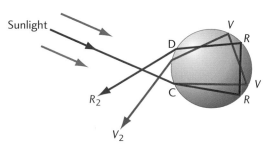

**(b)** Dispersion of sunlight by
a single raindrop (secondary rainbow)

**Fig.11.26A** Transparent fibres transmit light

**Fig.11.26B** Fibre optic digital telecommunication cables

## Medical Applications

Besides replacing wires in signal transmission applications, fibre optics are extensively used as viewing instruments in medicine. A device called an **endoscope**, shown in Fig. 11.27A, is used to look inside the body. The scope is connected to a monitor through an amplifier and is used to make the diagnostic observations.

**Fig.11.27A** An endoscope contains fibre optic cables

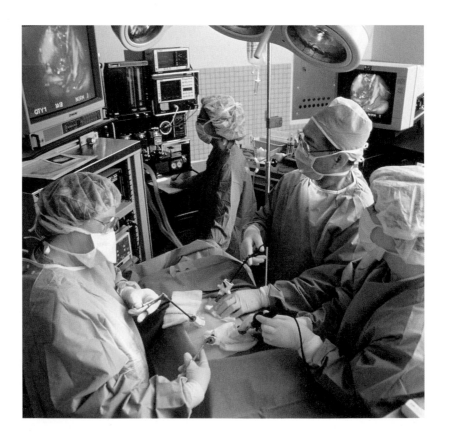

In Fig. 11.27B, a kidney is harvested (removed) using long-handled surgical tools while viewing the procedure through an instrument called a **laparoscope**.

Fig.11.27B

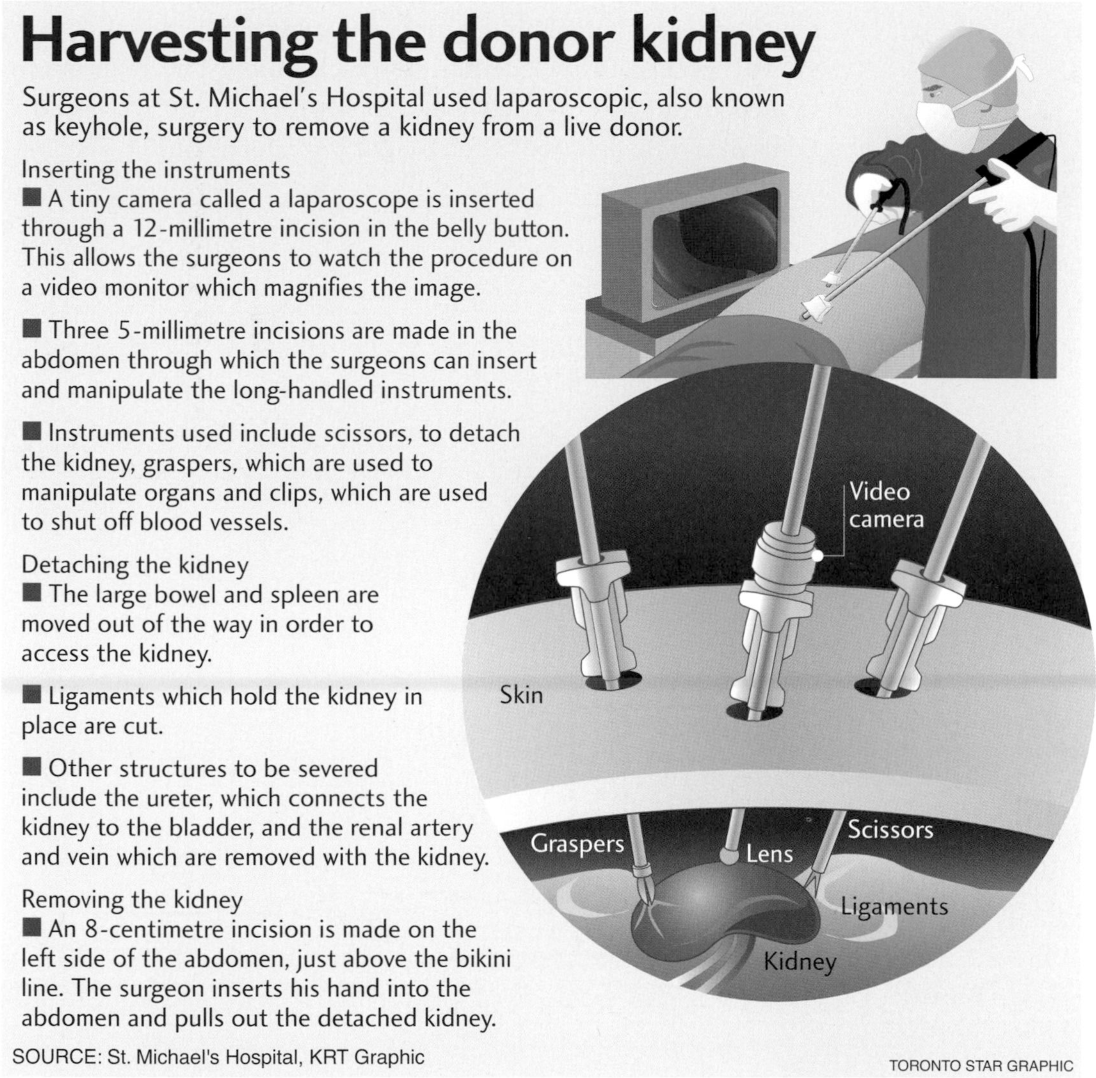

# Harvesting the donor kidney

Surgeons at St. Michael's Hospital used laparoscopic, also known as keyhole, surgery to remove a kidney from a live donor.

Inserting the instruments
■ A tiny camera called a laparoscope is inserted through a 12-millimetre incision in the belly button. This allows the surgeons to watch the procedure on a video monitor which magnifies the image.

■ Three 5-millimetre incisions are made in the abdomen through which the surgeons can insert and manipulate the long-handled instruments.

■ Instruments used include scissors, to detach the kidney, graspers, which are used to manipulate organs and clips, which are used to shut off blood vessels.

Detaching the kidney
■ The large bowel and spleen are moved out of the way in order to access the kidney.

■ Ligaments which hold the kidney in place are cut.

■ Other structures to be severed include the ureter, which connects the kidney to the bladder, and the renal artery and vein which are removed with the kidney.

Removing the kidney
■ An 8-centimetre incision is made on the left side of the abdomen, just above the bikini line. The surgeon inserts his hand into the abdomen and pulls out the detached kidney.

SOURCE: St. Michael's Hospital, KRT Graphic

Video camera

Skin

Graspers    Lens    Scissors

Ligaments

Kidney

TORONTO STAR GRAPHIC

This technique is also used in surgeries on joints. Before fibre optics, a knee had to be completely opened up to perform cartilage surgery. Now, tiny incisions replace the huge "war wounds." Figure 11.28 shows a surgeon using a laproscope to view the inside of the knee, as well as small surgical instruments to accomplish the cutting and scraping task with minimal damage to the joint. The name given to this technique is **arthroscopic surgery**.

## Sign and Display Illumination

Fibre optics also save on light bulb costs for signs and displays. A single light bulb can be used with a series of fibre

**Fig.11.28**    Arthroscopic knee surgery

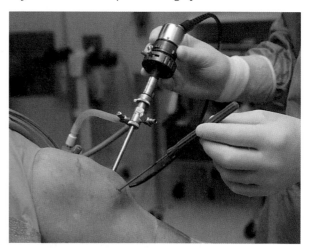

**Fig.11.29** The efficiency of using fibre optics in signs

optic cables, the ends of which form whatever message you wish to show. In Fig. 11.29, the fibre optic cables run from a central light bulb to the face of the sign, where they are arranged in the appropriate pattern. This solution also saves time and money previously needed to replace hard-to-reach bulbs. The bulb is now located in an easy-to-reach spot. No scaffold is required and traffic need not be diverted when a light bulb burns out.

## Optical Instruments

Optical instruments, such as binoculars, or the periscope, use glass prisms instead of a mirror to reflect light. The instruments illustrated in Fig. 11.30 produce sharper, brighter images because almost 100 % of the light is used to form the image by way of total internal reflection. Mirrors lose a lot of light at each reflection plane.

**Fig.11.30A** Prisms in binoculars make the final image upright and the binoculars more compact

**Fig.11.30B** Prisms are used to reflect light in a periscope

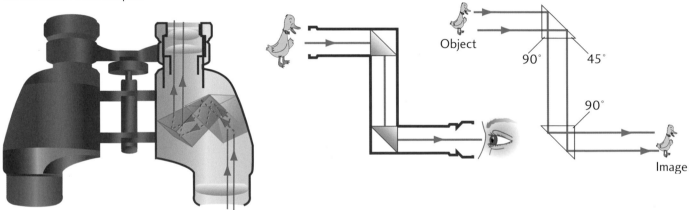

## Reflectors

**Fig.11.31** Plastic reflectors use total internal reflection to make objects visible at night

Bicycle and trailer reflectors (Fig. 11.31) use total internal reflection to bounce light back toward its source. Light rays enter the reflector and hit one of the back surfaces angled at 45°, which is more than the critical angle. The ray reflects internally and hits the opposite surface angled at 45°, reflects internally again, then exits the reflector. Glass beads on the surface of a stop sign work in a similar way to reflect light back to drivers.

## Why Diamonds Sparkle

The same principle gives a diamond its characteristic sparkle. With values of $n_2 = 2.42$ (diamond) and $n_1 = 1.00$ (air), $\theta_c = 24°$, the critical angle for the diamond–air boundary. Notice in Fig. 11.32 that before cutting, the diamond is drab and unappealing. The diamond cutter cuts the faces of the diamond to an angle that gives the maximum amount of total internal reflection. The more faces a diamond has, the more times it reflects light internally. If you were to repeat the calculation for glass, the critical angle would be 42°. Thus, fewer faces could be cut on the same-size object, so there would be less reflection of light inside the piece of jewellery. Consequently, the glass does not sparkle as much as the diamond.

**Fig.11.32** The diamond is cut with angles that maximize the number of internal reflections, thus increasing the sparkle effect.

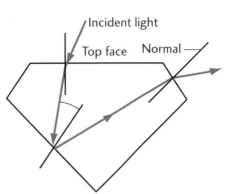

1. In Section 2.4, Question 4, we introduced the 407 Express Toll Route (ETR). On the 407, the transponder in your car sends a radio signal to a receiver on an overhead bridge at your entry and exit points. The signal is then relayed through fibre optic cables to a main computer.

   **a)** Research the efficiency of the transponder and cabling network in transmitting information. State what kind of equipment is used and what errors may occur in data processing from the time when the transponder emits its initial signal.

   **b)** Create a flow chart showing how the ETR system works, starting from the car's entry point.

**Fig.11.33** 407 ETR signal receiver

## 11.7 Lenses and Ray Diagrams

Figure 11.34 illustrates two different types of lenses: converging and diverging. The **converging lens** has a convex shape. The parallel incident rays are refracted through the lens and converge (i.e., meet) at one point, the **focus**. The **diverging lens** has a concave shape. When the parallel incident rays are refracted by it, the refracted rays diverge (move away from each other).

As with mirrors, you can predict and describe where lens images are formed. The rules for converging lenses are similar to the rules used for mirrors. Figure 11.35 shows all the possible rays used in lens-ray diagrams. To simplify ray diagram construction, the refractions at the two surfaces are not shown. The total effect is shown occurring at the centre line of the lens.

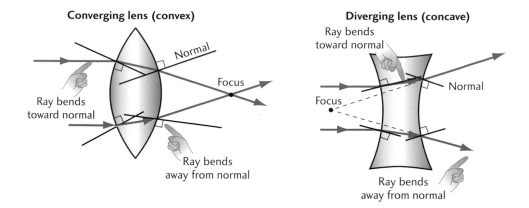

**Fig.11.34** Rays parallel to the principle axis refract to produce a focal point

**Converging lens (convex)**

Normal

Ray bends toward normal

Focus

Ray bends away from normal

**Diverging lens (concave)**

Ray bends toward normal

Normal

Focus

Ray bends away from normal

**Fig.11.35**

| | Thin Lens Ray Diagram Rules (Converging Lens) | | |
|---|---|---|---|
| | Incident ray | Refracted ray | Diagram |
| 1. | Parallel to principle axis | Through focus | 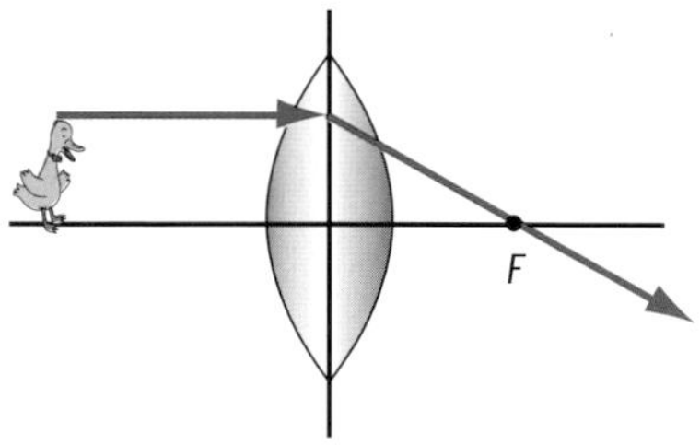 |
| 2. | Through optic centre | Sides of the glass are parallel. Ray moves along same path. | 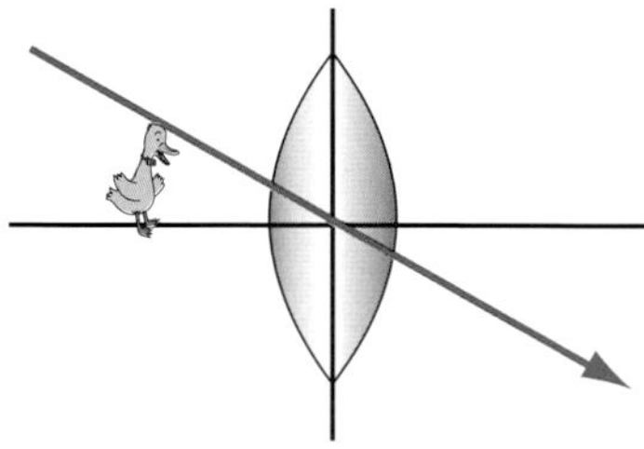 |
| 3. | Through focus | Parallel to principle axis | 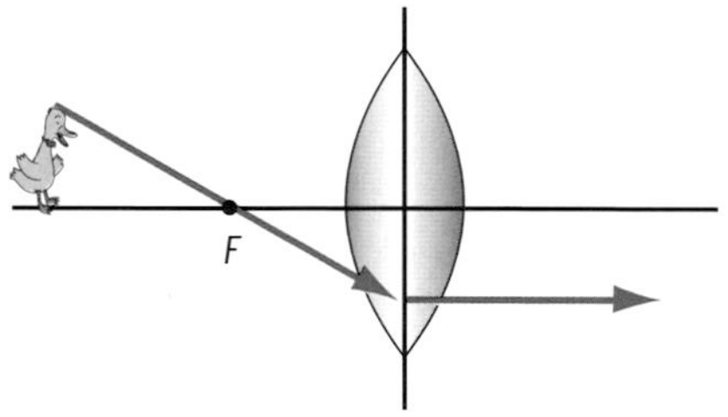 |

The converging lens forms both types of images, real and virtual. As with mirrors, a **real** image is located at the point where the refracted rays cross. A **virtual** image is formed where refracted rays *apparently* cross. Again, only two rays are required to locate the image, while a third one is used to check your diagram. Figure 11.36 is a summary of ray diagrams for the converging lens.

As with mirrors, diverging lenses produce only a smaller virtual image and have one ray diagram. Figure 11.37 shows the rays for finding an image.

**Fig.11.36** Formation of images by a converging lens

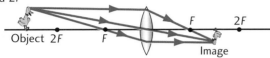

Object between *F* and 2*F*
Image real, larger, inverted, beyond 2*F*

Object at 2*F*
Image real, same size, inverted, at 2*F*

Object beyond 2*F*
Image real, smaller, inverted, between *F* and 2*F*

Object within *F*
Image virtual, larger, upright, behind object

**Fig.11.37** Ray diagrams for diverging lenses

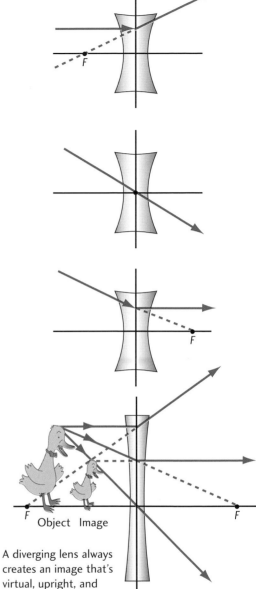

A diverging lens always creates an image that's virtual, upright, and smaller than the object

## CONSTRUCTING SCALED RAY DIAGRAMS FOR LENSES (FIG.11.37)

1. Read the problem over and take note of the sizes of the distances used.
2. Choose a scale so as not to use up the whole width or length of your page. Leave about a quarter of the page to each side blank. This will ensure that images formed farther from the lens will remain on the page.
3. Draw the appropriate lens, with a centre line.
4. Draw the principle axis and locate the focus.
5. Locate the object position and draw it to scale at that point.
6. Complete the ray diagram using two rays.
7. Measure the asked-for quantities.
8. Convert back to the original values using your scaling factor.

**Fig.11.38** Image Types in Lenses

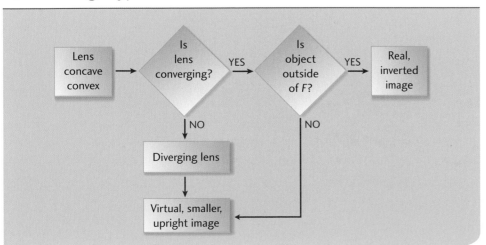

# 11.8 Lenses and Applications

## Eye

The eye is a variable focussing lens and image detector. By contracting or relaxing the muscles connected to the lens, the shape, and hence the focal length of the lens, is changed. This process is called **accommodation**. Figure 11.39 shows the two extreme positions the eye can adopt. In one case, the eye is relaxed and is viewing a distant object. In the other case, the eye works hard to focus on a nearby object by contracting the lens, making it more convex.

**Fig.11.39** Our eyes accommodate to focus on objects at different distances

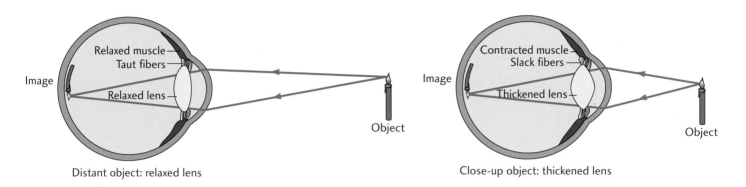

Distant object: relaxed lens

Close-up object: thickened lens

The lens is not the sole focussing agent in the eye. The cornea, aqueous humor, and vitreous humor all refract the light as well. In fact, these elements contribute to about 75 % of the total focussing strength of the eye. However, these elements are passive, i.e., they have fixed focal lengths. Our ability to focus on objects at different distances relies on the lens's ability to change its focal length. It's comparable to the fine-tuning adjustments on microscopes. The relationship of all these parts of the eye is shown in Fig. 11.40.

**Fig.11.40** Parts of the eye

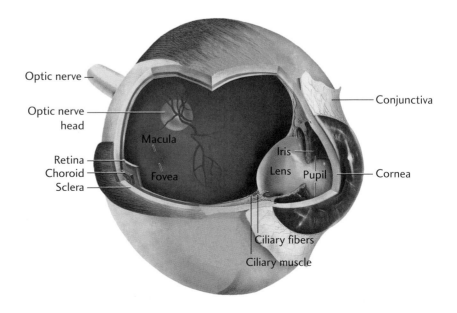

UNIT C: Light and Geometric Optics

# Eye Defects and Corrections

For many of us, the ability to see objects clearly is a problem. The shape and size of the eye may not be compatible with the focal length range of the lens. This incompatibility creates the need for corrective glasses, contact lenses, or surgery.

The chart in Fig. 11.41 summarizes the three main eye problems people have and the method of correcting each problem. It is important to note that eye shape and lens strength need only vary by small amounts before vision problems are encountered.

**Fig.11.41**

### Some Common Eye Defects

| Problem | Cause | Ray diagram | Corrective lens |
|---|---|---|---|
| Far-sightedness (Hyperopia) (Or presbyopia if the aging process is referred to) | Eyeball too short. As one ages, the eye is less able to accommodate near point increases | 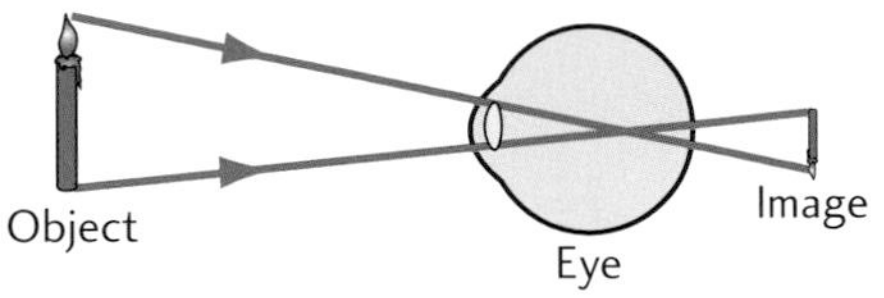 The image comes to a focus behind the retina | 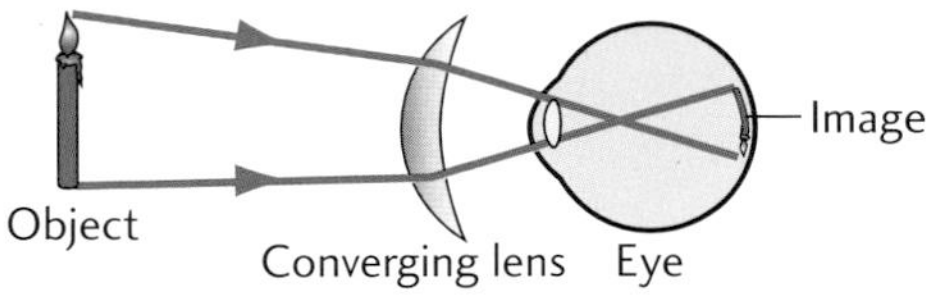 A converging lens corrects the defect |
| Near-sightedness (Myopia) | Eyeball too long | 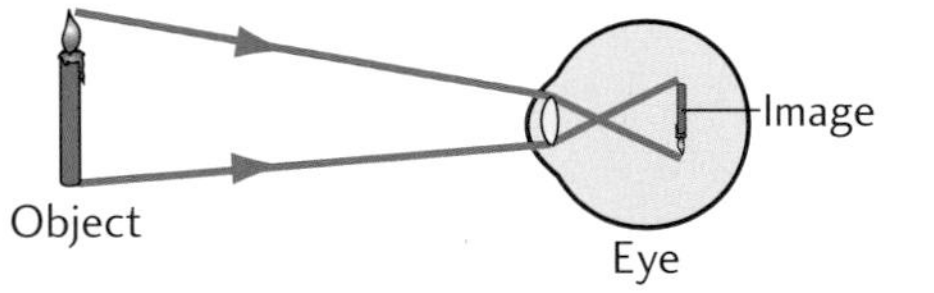 The image comes to a focus in front of the retina | 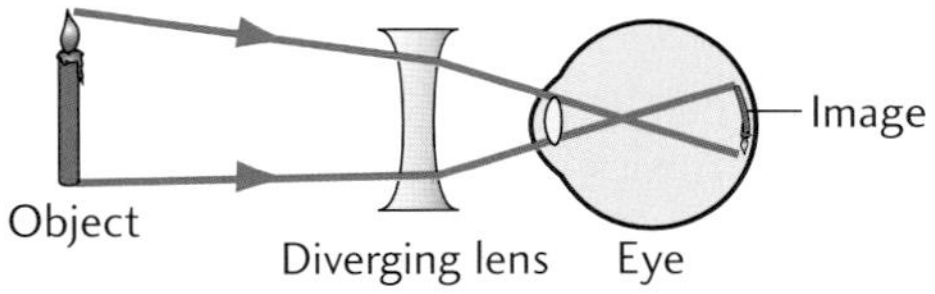 A diverging lens corrects the defect |
| Astigmatism | Out-of-round cornea or lens | 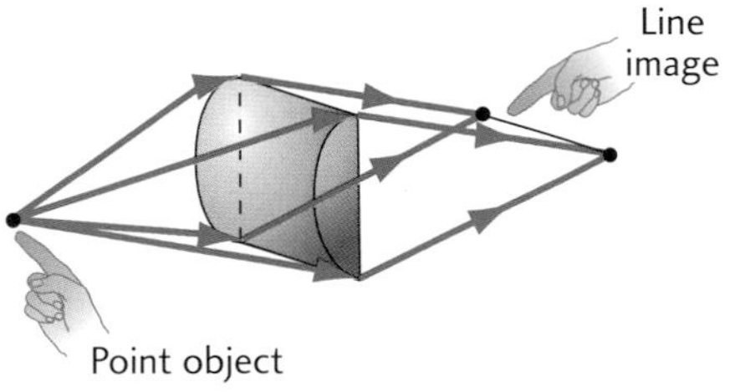 Point objects are focussed as short lines | A cylinder lens corrects the defect |

# Refractive Eye Surgery

Instead of committing yourself to wearing glasses or contact lenses, there is now a surgical method of correcting eye problems, illustrated in Fig. 11.42. Using a diamond blade, precision cuts are made in the cornea. The centre or optical zone of the cornea is not touched because this is where the

**Fig.11.42** Laser eye surgery

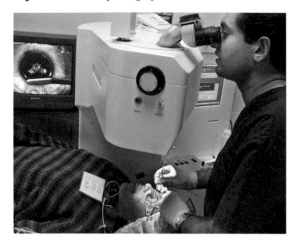

focussing is done. When the eye heals, its final shape has changed slightly due to the formation of scar tissue. This slight change is enough to change the focussing characteristics of the eye and thereby correct vision.

A process called **radial keratotomy** using an **excimer laser** is similar to refractive eye surgery. Figure 11.43, shows the eye already cut by a laser. This technique uses a laser to cut around the cornea, allowing the surgeon to lift a flap of cornea up and remove some of the material underneath. The flap is then replaced and allowed to heal. Once again, the cornea shape has been changed slightly, thereby correcting the original problem.

**Fig.11.43** Altering the cornea shape with laser surgery

"Excimer" stands for "excited dimer," an inert gas atom bound to a halide atom under excited states only, so they are extremely short lived. When they de-excite, they release UV light. The benefit of the excimer laser is that it doesn't generate a lot of heat. Because of the energy required to cut through tissue, conventional lasers generate so much heat that they damage surrounding tissue. The excimer laser causes tissue to turn directly into gas by breaking the bonds of the molecules of the tissue, so there is no heat damage.

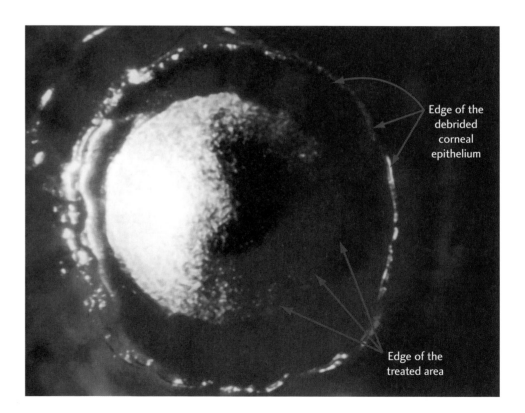

Edge of the debrided corneal epithelium

Edge of the treated area

## Multiple Lenses — Microscope

In cases where two or more lenses are used, ray diagrams are built in stages. We use the image of the first lens as the object for the second lens. In Fig. 11.44, the ray diagram for the microscope is shown. The first lens, called the **objective,** creates a real inverted image. This image falls inside the focal length of the second lens, called the eyepiece or **ocular.** The second image is a virtual image and larger than the real image.

**Fig.11.44** Formation of an image by a microscope

**Light path through microscope**

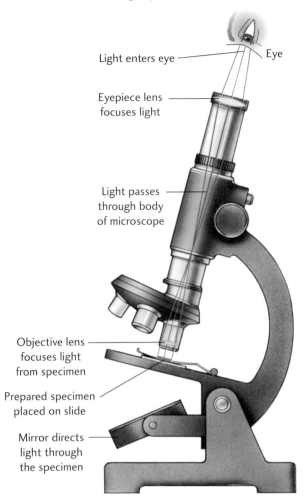

Light enters eye
Eye

Eyepiece lens focuses light

Light passes through body of microscope

Objective lens focuses light from specimen

Prepared specimen placed on slide

Mirror directs light through the specimen

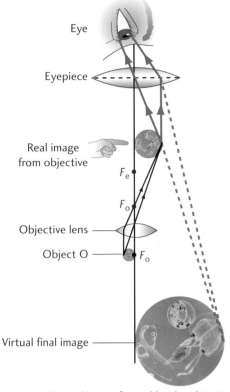

Eye

Eyepiece

Real image from objective

$F_e$

$F_o$

Objective lens

Object O $F_o$

Virtual final image

The real image formed by the objective acts like the object for the eyepiece lens

## Multiple Lenses — Astronomical Telescope

The refracting telescope, also known as the astronomical telescope, is used to view distant objects. Once again, there are two converging lenses used and, like the microscope, they are also called the objective and the eyepiece (see Fig. 11.45). The method of analyzing this instrument is the same as that for the microscope. The big difference is that the object is extremely far away. Because of this distance, the real image formed by the objective is smaller than the image created by the microscope. (Recall for the microscope, the object was close to the objective and hence the real image was larger.) Both instruments then form a virtual image. Because you focus the eyepiece in order to relax the eye, the final image position is far away. The real image formed by the objective must therefore be near the focal length of the eyepiece. The distance between the two lenses is therefore $f_{objective} + f_{eyepiece}$, which is the length of the telescope. The final image is inverted.

### TWO-LENS MAGNIFICATIONS

The total magnification for two lenses is the product of their individual magnifications, $m_{total} = m_1 \times m_2$. For example, typical biology microscopes used in high school have an eyepiece with a magnification of 10× and an objective lens of magnification 40×. This combination produces a total magnification of 400×. Compare this magnification to an electron microscope, which has a magnification of 300 000×.

**Fig.11.45** Image formation by an astronomical telescope

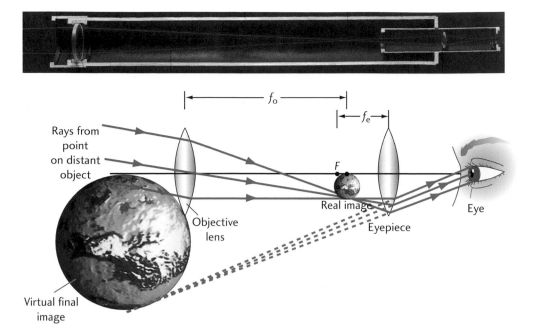

To convert the astronomical telescope to a terrestrial telescope, an extra lens is added to flip the image over one more time to make it upright. This way when sailors yell "land ho," they won't be pointing to the stars.

**APPLYING the Concepts**

▷ ▷ ▷ ▷ ▷

1. Summarize what happens to the image produced in a converging lens as the object is brought from far away to inside the focus.
2. Create ray diagrams with three rays in each showing the image location for an object outside of the focus, at the focus, and inside the focus.
3. Summarize how a diverging lens works. Use two different object positions and construct ray diagrams illustrating your summary.

## 11.9 Calculations with Lenses

As with mirrors, we can calculate image positions and magnifications for various lenses. The formulas used are the same as those for curved mirrors, which we learned in Chapter 10.

**Fig.11.46** The thin lens formula

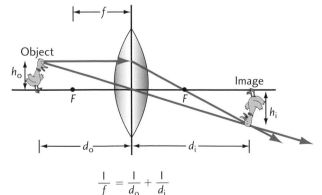

$$\frac{1}{f} = \frac{1}{d_o} + \frac{1}{d_i}$$

$$\text{and} \quad m = \frac{h_i}{h_o} = -\frac{d_i}{d_o}$$

Figure 11.46 shows the location of the variables used in relation to the lens.

$$\frac{1}{f} = \frac{1}{d_o} + \frac{1}{d_i}$$

The formula $\frac{1}{f} = \frac{1}{d_o} + \frac{1}{d_i}$ is referred to as the **thin lens formula** or the **Gaussian lens formula**. It relies on the assumption that air is one of the mediums and that the thickness of the lens is small compared with its focal length.

The lens-maker formula is closely related to the thin lens formula and takes into account the refractive index of the material. This consideration is especially important since eyeware ranges from glass to protective plastics. The formula is $\frac{1}{f} = (n - 1)\left(\frac{1}{r_1} - \frac{1}{r_2}\right)$, where $r_1$ and $r_2$ refer to the radii of curvature of the two surfaces.

The focal length of a converging (convex) lens is designated as positive. Therefore, its radius of curvature is also positive. The focal length of the diverging (concave) lens is considered to be negative. Therefore, its radius of curvature is negative.

The sign convention rules for the lens formula variables are summarized in Table 11.2. The conventions for positive and negative values are the same as for mirrors. Note that for two-lens combinations, such as the microscope, the object for the eyepiece is the image from the objective lens and carries a negative sign.

**Table 11.2**
**Lens Sign Conventions**

| Lens | $d_o$ | $d_i$ | $f$ | Image type | Notes |
|------|-------|-------|-----|------------|-------|
| Converging | + | + | + | real | $d_o > f$ |
| Converging | + | − | + | virtual | $d_o < f$ |
| Diverging | + | − | − | virtual | $h_i < h_o$ |
| **Microscope** | | | | | |
| objective | + | + | + | real | $h_i > h_o$ |
| eyepiece | + | − | + | virtual | image of first lens is object of second lens |
| **Telescope** | | | | | |
| objective | + | + | + | real | $h_i < h_o$ |
| eyepiece | + | − | + | virtual | image of first lens is object of second lens |

**EXAMPLE 9**   **Real image formed by a converging lens**

If a converging lens has a 30 cm focal length and is focussed on a person 1.00 m away, find the image position and the lens's magnification.

*Solution and Connection to Theory*

**Given**
$f = 30 \text{ cm} = 0.30 \text{ m} \quad d_o = 1.00 \text{ m} \quad d_i = ? \quad m = ?$

$\frac{1}{f} = \frac{1}{d_o} + \frac{1}{d_i}$

Rearrange and solve for $d_i$ and $m$.

$$\frac{1}{d_i} = \frac{1}{0.30 \text{ m}} - \frac{1}{1.00 \text{ m}}$$

$$\frac{1}{d_i} = 2.33 \text{ m}^{-1} \qquad d_i = 0.43 \text{ m}$$

$$m = -\frac{d_i}{d_o} = -\frac{0.43 \text{ m}}{1.00 \text{ m}} = -0.43$$

The image is located 0.43 m away from the lens. A positive value for $d_i$ indicates that the image is real. The magnification of the image must therefore be negative, indicating that its orientation is inverted.

---

**EXAMPLE 10** **Virtual image using a converging lens**

A converging lens is being used as a magnifying glass. If the focal length of the lens is 15 cm and an ant that is 10 cm away is being viewed, find the location of the image and its magnification.

### Solution and Connection to Theory

Note that you do not need to convert cm to m when all the givens are in cm.

**Given**

$f = 15 \text{ cm} \qquad d_o = 10 \text{ cm} \qquad d_i = ?$

$$\frac{1}{f} = \frac{1}{d_o} + \frac{1}{d_i}$$

Rearrange the equation to solve for $d_i$.

$$\frac{1}{d_i} = \frac{1}{f} - \frac{1}{d_o}$$

Substitute the values,

$$\frac{1}{d_i} = \frac{1}{15 \text{ cm}} - \frac{1}{10 \text{ cm}}$$

$$d_i = -30 \text{ cm}$$

The negative sign indicates that the image is on the same side of the lens as the object.

To find the magnification,

$$m = -\frac{d_i}{d_o} = -\left(\frac{-30 \text{ cm}}{10 \text{ cm}}\right)$$

$$m = 3$$

As expected, the image is larger than the object. Because the magnification is positive, the object is right side up, as illustrated in Fig. 11.47.

**Remember:** When dealing with diverging lenses, you must be careful not to omit the negative sign associated with the focal length and the image position.

**Fig.11.47**

UNIT C: Light and Geometric Optics

**Fig.11.48** View through a diverging lens

**EXAMPLE 11**

A diverging lens of focal length 200 cm is used to correct a person's near-sightedness. Find the image position for an object 3.00 m away.

### Solution and Connection to Theory

**Given**

$f = -200 \text{ cm} = -2.00 \text{ m}$     $d_o = 3.00 \text{ m}$     $d_i = ?$

Notice the negative sign of the focal length because the lens is diverging. The units are converted in order to be consistent.

$$\frac{1}{f} = \frac{1}{d_o} + \frac{1}{d_i}$$

Rearrange to solve for $d_i$.

$$\frac{1}{d_i} = \frac{1}{f} - \frac{1}{d_o} \qquad \frac{1}{d_i} = \frac{1}{(-2.00 \text{ m})} - \frac{1}{3.00 \text{ m}} \qquad d_i = -1.20 \text{ m}$$

The image position is negative, indicating that it is located in front of the lens. The answer is correct because diverging lenses always produce virtual images, as illustrated in Fig. 11.48.

## Refractive Power

In the field of optometry, the refractive power, $P$, of a lens is used to describe the ability of a lens to focus. It is defined as

$$P = \frac{1}{f}$$

where $f$ is measured in metres. The units for $P$ are **diopters**.

$$\text{Since } \frac{1}{f} = \frac{1}{d_o} + \frac{1}{d_i},$$

$$\text{then } P = \frac{1}{d_o} + \frac{1}{d_i}.$$

**EXAMPLE 12** **Power of a diverging lens**

If a diverging lens has a focal length of 50 cm, what is its power in diopters?

### Solution and Connection to Theory

**Given**

$f = -50 \text{ cm} = -0.50 \text{ m}$

$$P = \frac{1}{f} = \frac{1}{-0.50 \text{ m}} = -2.0 \text{ diopters}$$

Notice that you had to convert the units to metres in order to solve for $P$. You also had to add the negative sign to the focal length because the lens is diverging.

## Power of Accommodation

As we learned in Section 11.8, accomodation is the ability of a lens to adjust the focus depending on the object's location. The power of accommodation is the maximum range of the focus, usually in diopters. The range of the focus is the difference between the lens in a relaxed state (looking at a far object) and the lens in a maximum working state (looking at close objects). Figure 11.39 illustrates the two conditions of the eye.

**EXAMPLE 13**  **Calculating the power of accommodation of an average teenager**

A teenager with an image distance of 1.9 cm (distance from cornea to retina) can clearly see objects that are far away. He can also focus sharply on objects 0.25 m away. Find his power of accommodation in diopters.

### Solution and Connection to Theory

1.9 cm is the average focussing distance for an eye. It is slightly less than the diameter of the eye (2.0 cm−2.5 cm). When someone looks out at a distant object, $\frac{1}{d_o}$ becomes extremely small and is approximated to be zero. This is like saying that the object is at infinity. Therefore, for the relaxed lens (looking at a far object),

**Given**

$d_o = $ infinity    $d_i = 1.9 \text{ cm} = 0.019 \text{ m}$

$P = \frac{1}{d_o} + \frac{1}{d_i}$   (because $\frac{1}{f} = P$)    $P = 0 + \frac{1}{0.019 \text{ m}} = 52.6 \text{ diopters}$

$P = 53$ diopters

For the lens working hard (looking at a near object),

**Given**

$d_o = 0.25 \text{ m}$    $d_i = 0.019 \text{ m}$

$P = \frac{1}{0.25 \text{ m}} + \frac{1}{0.019 \text{ m}} = 56.6 \text{ diopters}$

$P = 57$ diopters

Thus, the power of accommodation for the teen is

57 diopters − 53 diopters = 4.0 diopters.

We normally express our ability to see in terms of a number such as 20/20. This ratio is a measure of **acuity**, the sharpness or clarity of an image. The numbers mean that you can see an object 20 feet away as well as a person who does not need glasses sees the object 20 feet away. If you have 20/100 vision, then you must be 20 feet away from the object in order to see what a person with 20/20 vision sees at 100 feet. The fact that you have 20/20 vision does not necessarily mean that your eyes are perfect. Factors such as depth perception, focussing ability, colour vision, and peripheral awareness are all part of the testing procedure. Incidentally, the 20/20 metric version is 6/6 (metres instead of feet). The eye chart used to check these values is shown in Fig. 11.49.

**Fig.11.49** The common chart used by most ophthalmologists was produced by Herman Snellen in 1862. To measure a person's acuity, the patient stands 20 feet from the chart and reads as many letters as he or she can. If he or she manages to read the first eight lines, his or her acuity is termed normal, or 20/20.

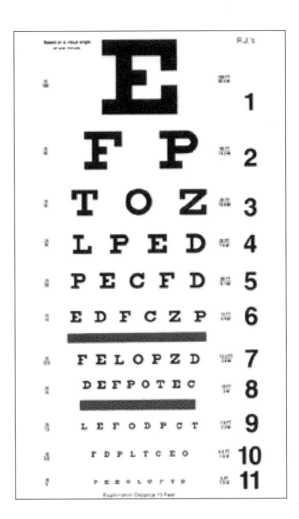

In general, young children have a greater power of accommodation because they can clearly see objects that are very close to them. As we age, the lens in our eye becomes less flexible and its ability to accommodate decreases until we are forced to get corrective eyewear.

## Near and Far Points

These two points are related to the accommodation process of the eye. The **far point** is the distance to the farthest object a fully relaxed eye can focus on. Nearsighted people have a smaller (closer) far point. The **near point** is the closest distance to an object that the eye can focus on clearly. Far-sighted people have a larger value for the near point.

## Fig.11.50 Using the Thin Lens Equation

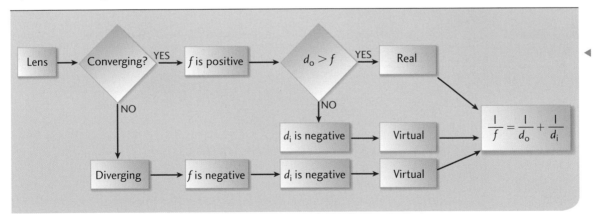

1. For the following variables, create three different problems involving each variable as the unknown and solve for it.
   **a)** $f = +10$ cm, $d_o = 15$ cm, $d_i = 30$ cm
   **b)** $f = +10$ cm, $d_o = 5$ cm, $d_i = -10$ cm
   **c)** $f = -10$ cm, $d_o = 15$ cm, $d_i = -6$ cm

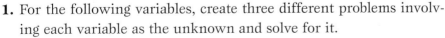

# A New Application for Contact Lenses

**Fig.STSE.11.1**

On March 11, 2000, during a hockey game, an accidental high stick left Toronto Maple Leaf defenseman Bryan Berard with severe damage to his right eye (Fig. STSE.11.1). Losing both his iris and pupil, Berard was unable to focus and could make out shapes only.

In an undamaged eye, the iris provides a small opening, called an aperture, for light to pass through, like in a camera. The smaller the opening, the less the visual distortion. With the hope of correcting his vision, Berard was fitted with an EpiCon™ contact lens, like the one depicted in Fig. STSE.11.2, made in Montreal by the Canadian company UltraVision Corporation.

The EpiCon™ contact lens is made with a transparent polymer called carbosilfocon. It is painted with an artificial iris and pupil. Although this lens is designed for those suffering from keratoconus, or cone-shaped, cornea, in Berard's case, it was supposed to control the amount of light entering his eye. Acting as a finer aperture, it was to reduce the distortion of images. Although it improved his vision, it was not enough to allow him to return to professional hockey.

**Fig.STSE.11.2**  An EpiCon™ lens can act as an artificial iris

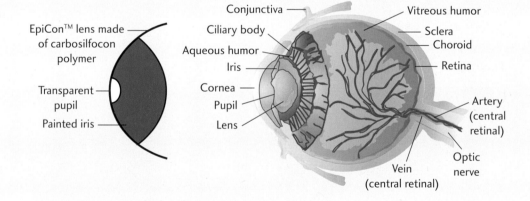

## Design a Study of Societal Impact

Currently, the cost of EpiCon™ contact lenses isn't covered by the Canadian public health care system. What other costs will the health care system need to cover if this product is not used? Research other medical procedures, such as laser eye surgery, that are not covered by any health insurance package.

How will the high-profile news coverage of Bryan Berard's condition affect sales of the EpiCon™ contact lens? If there had been no media coverage, would this new technology have received as much funding?

Medical research is very expensive. Who decides which diseases and medical problems will be researched? How are the decisions made? Is profit the driving force behind medical research? Which diseases and medical conditions get the majority of research dollars? What percentage of research dollars is dedicated to diseases that are primarily found in the Third World, such as malaria?

## Design an Activity to Evaluate

Build a model of the eye using a round-bottom flask and rubber stopper, water and cornstarch, a converging lens, black paper, and a retort stand, as shown in Fig. STSE.11.3. Use the model eye described in the accompanying section to evaluate the effect of different lens combinations on the focal point. The original lens corresponds to the permanent lens of the human eye. The water and cornstarch produce a mixture called a colloid, which allows you to see where the light focusses. Add other lenses, such as diverging lenses, between the light source and the model to see how they change the focal point of the lens-eye combination, as illustrated in Fig. STSE.11.4.

**Fig.STSE.11.3**  An apparatus that can show the focal point of a lens system

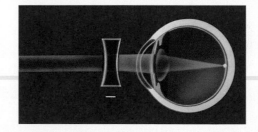

Black paper to act as aperture

Converging (convex) lens

Round bottomed flask

Water and cornstarch

Projector

Held together with a retort stand

**Fig.STSE.11.4**  Adding a lens changes the path of incoming light

## Build a Structure

Build an optical device, such as a telescope or microscope, using lenses of different focal lengths and other materials found around the home or school lab. First research the placement of the lenses and object with a ray bench or similar device in order to simulate what you are making before you begin.

Hold a pinhole camera competition in which you are required to form an image of a specific size and attitude (upright or inverted) on a screen, given the size only of the original object. Make calculations that help predict the position in the room and the "camera settings" required to reach your objective.

## You should be able to

*Understand Basic Concepts:*

- Define and describe concepts and units related to refraction, partial reflection, index of refraction, total internal reflection, critical angle, focal point, and image types.
- Describe the process of refraction in terms of light bending relative to the normal.
- Describe the process of refraction in terms of a speed change and the refractive index of a material.
- Describe the wave model of light and how it is used to explain refraction effects such as mirages, rainbows, and apparent depth.
- Use Snell's law to find any of the following: the angle of incidence, angle of refraction, and indices of refraction.
- Calculate the apparent depth of an image.
- Describe the conditions necessary to produce total internal reflection.
- Calculate the critical angle between two given mediums.
- Describe how converging and diverging lenses create images by using ray diagrams.
- Describe the images created in lenses in terms of type, size, orientation, and position relative to the lens.
- Use the thin lens equation to calculate the image position of lenses.
- Describe the effect of converging and diverging lenses and explain why each type of lens is used in specific optical devices.
- Describe and calculate the power of accommodation of an eye.

*Develop Skills of Inquiry and Communication:*

- Demonstrate refraction, partial reflection, and total internal reflection of light at the interface of a variety of media and illustrate using ray diagrams.
- Carry out experiments to verify Snell's law.
- Predict the image positions and characteristics of converging and diverging lenses using ray diagrams and calculations.
- Verify these predictions through experimentation.
- Carry out experiments involving the transmission of light in order to compare experimental (empirical) results to those predicted by Snell's law and the thin lens formula.
- Construct, test, and refine a prototype telescope and microscope.

*Relate Science to Technology, Society, and the Environment:*

- Describe jobs and job aspects related to optics.
- Describe various applications involving lenses, including eye defects and corrections.
- Describe and evaluate how lasers have influenced eye surgery.
- Describe and evaluate how fibre optics have influenced the fields of medicine and industry.
- Analyze, describe, and explain optical effects that are produced by equipment such as telescopes, microscopes, periscopes, and binoculars.

## Equations

$$\frac{1}{f} = \frac{1}{d_o} + \frac{1}{d_i}$$

$$m = -\frac{d_i}{d_o} = \frac{h_i}{h_o}$$

$$n_1 \sin\theta_1 = n_2 \sin\theta_2$$

$$n = \frac{c}{v}$$

$$d_2 = d_1\left(\frac{n_2}{n_1}\right)$$

$$P = \frac{1}{f} \quad \text{(diopters)}$$

## Conceptual Questions

**1.** How do stars look to the human eye on the Moon as opposed to Earth?

**2. a)** Where would you aim a spear in order to hit a fish if you are viewing it from the air?
**b)** Would you change the aiming direction if you used a laser gun?

**3.** If you had to straighten out a refracted ray that went through a lens with focal length +15 cm, what could you do?

**4.** Can a mirage be captured on film? What type of image is it?

**5.** If you are under water looking up at a person sitting with his legs in the swimming pool, and you are at the critical angle, what do you see?

**6.** Whose glasses could be used to start a fire with sunlight, a near-sighted person's or a far-sighted person's?

**7.** Relate dispersion to refraction.

**8. a)** Chromatic aberration is the blurring of images produced by lenses. It arises because the index of refraction is wavelength dependent. Describe how an image would look under chromatic aberration.
**b)** Why doesn't chromatic aberration occur with mirrors?
**c)** Research what a triplet lens arrangement does?

**9.** For each of the following optical instruments, describe what lens or lens combination you would use:
**a)** Magnifying glass
**b)** Spotlight
**c)** Fish-eye lens (large view, but smaller in size)
**d)** Normal camera lens
**e)** Telescope to view the stars
**f)** Telescope to view ships and other far-off terrestrial objects

**10.** Why is total internal reflection a better way to reflect light than metallic surfaces (conventional mirrors)?

**11.** Which optical instruments produce virtual images and which ones produce real images?

**12.** Why do images appear sharper under water when wearing a diving mask than when not wearing a diving mask? (Maybe a fish needs a mask filled with water to see on land.)

**13.** Does a diamond sparkle as much under water? Explain.

**14.** When you sit at the computer for a long time, your eyes get tired. To rest them, you must look out at a distant object. Why does this action work?

**15.** You discover a new substance that can be cut into a shape that causes it to glitter more than diamond. Describe this substance in optical terms.

**16.** When you look at a person who is wearing glasses, you can tell whether he/she is near-sighted or far-sighted by looking at the size of his/her eyes. Explain.

**17.** How does refraction affect the length of the day?

**18.** Massive celestial objects bend light by means of gravity. How would the image of a star be affected by this phenomenon? Use your knowledge of lenses to answer this question.

**19.** Describe the optical effects of partial reflection, refraction, and total internal reflection when looking into a fish tank.

**20.** Would a lens made from diamond be weaker, stronger, or of the same strength as a glass lens if the two lenses had the same shape?

**21.** You see a rainbow in front of you through a fine mist with the sun behind you (during a sunshower). This effect is caused by total internal reflection and dispersion. Draw a sketch of the situation and try to explain how these effects combine to create a rainbow. Don't worry about the colour sequence.

22. There are optical tricks where an object in a glass disappears after a transparent liquid is poured into the glass. Similarly, a coin at the bottom of the glass becomes visible at a given angle when water is poured in. Explain what happens each time.

23. Describe what happens to the wavelength, frequency, and speed of light as it enters substances from a vacuum.

## Problems

### ▶ 11.1 Diagrams and Definitions

24. Copy the blobs of glass in Fig. 11.51, into your notebook. Take note of the refractive indices and sketch a ray through the object, starting at the points indicated. Include a normal for each boundary crossing.

**Fig.11.51**

**(a)**

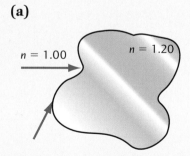

**(b)**

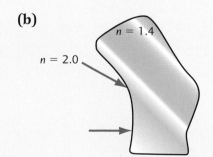

**(c)**

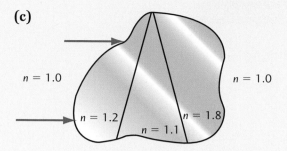

25. Repeat Problem 24 (a) and (b) for a refractive index of 1.9 for the glass blobs.

26. In your notebook, sketch a ray through the rectangular piece of glass in Fig. 11.52.

**Fig.11.52**

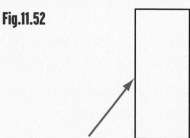

27. What happens to the diagram in Problem 26 if the refractive index of the material increases? Sketch this case.

### ▶ 11.2 Calculations on Refraction

For the following problems, use $3.00 \times 10^8$ m/s as the speed of light.

28. Calculate the speed of light in
    a) diamond ($n = 2.42$).
    b) crown glass ($n = 1.52$).
    c) water ($n = 1.33$).
    d) ice ($n = 1.30$).

29. Calculate the relative index of refraction for light travelling from the materials in Problem 28 to air.

30. Calculate the index of refraction of the material if the speed of light in the material is
    a) $1.58 \times 10^8$ m/s (zircon).
    b) $2.05 \times 10^8$ m/s (fused quartz).
    c) $2.0 \times 10^8$ m/s (benzene).
    d) $3.8 \times 10^8$ m/s (unknown science fiction material).

**31.** Given that the refractive index of water is 1.33, how long does it take light to travel from one end of a lake to the other end if the lake is 12 km long?

**32.** It takes $4.0 \times 10^{-11}$ s for light to travel through this substance. If the distance the light travelled is 0.50 cm, find
**a)** the speed of light in the substance.
**b)** the index of refraction of the substance.
**c)** the name of the substance.

▶ **11.3 Snell's Law: The Law of Refraction**

**33.** For the following angles, find the sine of the angle:
**a)** 30°  **b)** 60°  **c)** 45°  **d)** 12.6°
**e)** 74.4°  **f)** 0°  **g)** 90°

**34.** For the following inverse sine values ($\sin^{-1}$), find the corresponding angle:
**a)** 0.342  **b)** 0.643  **c)** 0.700
**d)** 0.333  **e)** 1.00

**35.** What is the angle of refraction for the following substances if the incident angle in air is 30°?
**a)** Water (1.33)
**b)** Diamond (2.42)
**c)** Ethyl alcohol (1.36)
**d)** Zircon (1.90)

**36.** Repeat Problem 35 using ice as the incident medium (1.30).

**37.** Calculate the angle of incidence for an angle of refraction of 10° for
**a)** diamond (2.42) to air.
**b)** air to diamond.
**c)** air to water (1.33).
**d)** water to diamond.

**38.** Calculate the index of refraction of medium 2 if medium 1 is air and the angles of incidence and of refraction are given:
**a)** 40° and 30°
**b)** 30° and 12°
**c)** 77° and 50°

**39.** Recalculate the index of refraction in Problem 38 if the incident medium is water (1.33).

**40.** A ray of light enters from air, travels into an aquarium filled with water, then exits back into air. Find the angles of refraction for each boundary ($n_{water} = 1.33$, $n_{glass} = 1.52$). Assume that the first angle of incidence is 20°.

**41.** Deriving Snell's Law
**a)** For the situation in Fig. 11.53, calculate the index of refraction of the water.
**b)** Use Fig. 11.54 and $v = f\lambda$ to prove that $\frac{\sin\theta_1}{\sin\theta_2} = \frac{\lambda_1}{\lambda_2} = \frac{v_1}{v_2}$. (Hint: Use side AB.)
**c)** Use $n = \frac{c}{v}$ to prove that $n_1\sin\theta_1 = n_2\sin\theta_2$.
**d)** In your notebook, draw a ray diagram representation of Fig. 11.54.

**Fig.11.54**

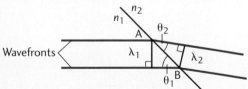

**Fig.11.53**

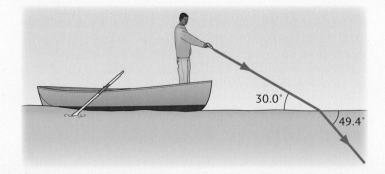

### ▶ 11.4 Applications and Phenomena Related to Refraction

**42.** Calculate the apparent depth of a pair of swim trunks lying at the bottom of a 3.0 m deep swimming pool ($n_{water}$ = 1.33).

**43.** What is the depth of the pool if the shorts appear to be 1.50 m below the water's surface?

**44.** Someone found your towel and is standing by the pool, holding it in the air. The person is 170 cm tall and has an arm length of 70 cm. If you're looking up from under the water, how high does the towel appear to be above the water?

**45. a)** Given that $n_{red}$ = 1.52, $n_{violet}$ = 1.54, and the angle of incidence is 30°, calculate the angle of refraction for each colour (air to glass).
   **b)** Use the angle obtained in part a) as the new angle of incidence and calculate the angle of refraction for the two wavelengths as they travel from glass to air.

**46.** Draw a diagram of a prism in your notebook. Trace rays representing red and violet light through the prism based on the angles obtained in Problem 45.

**47.** How does the mirage of a floating ship amongst the clouds occur? (Refer to the mirage created in the desert and apparent sunsets.)

### ▶ 11.5 Total Internal Reflection

**48.** Derive the equation $\sin\theta_c = \frac{n_2}{n_1}$, starting from Snell's law.

**49.** Why can't total internal reflection occur when a ray travels from a less dense to a more dense material? A diagram may help in the explanation.

**50.** Assume the second medium is air, unless otherwise stated. Calculate the critical angle for

**a)** diamond (2.42).
**b)** water (1.33).
**c)** glass (1.50).
**d)** diamond to water.

**51.** If the critical angle is 30°, calculate the index of refraction of a substance
   **a)** surrounded by air.
   **b)** surrounded by water (1.33).

**52.** Given the refractive indices of air (1.00), water (1.33), and glass (1.50), calculate the possible critical angles for an aquarium.

**53.** For the following refractive indices, calculate all the possible critical angles: $n_{diamond}$ = 2.42, $n_{zircon}$ = 1.90, $n_{ice}$ = 1.30.

### ▶ 11.7 Lenses and Ray Diagrams

**54.** Use a scaled diagram to find the image of a candle 5.0 cm tall situated at the following positions in front of a converging lens of focal length 15 cm:
   **a)** 30 cm   **b)** 25 cm   **c)** 15 cm   **d)** 10 cm
   For each case, describe the image in terms of type, size, and orientation.

**55.** Repeat Problem 54 for a diverging lens.

**56.** A person has a collection of convex lenses with the following focal lengths: 5 cm, 20 cm, 50 cm. If she places an object 5 cm tall, 25 cm from each lens, use a scaled diagram to find the image size and magnification for each lens.

**57.** A magnifying glass of focal length 20 cm is used to magnify print 3.0 mm high. How big is the image and what is the magnification if the print letter distance from the lens is
   **a)** 19 cm?   **b)** 15 cm?   **c)** 10 cm?   **d)** 4 cm?

**58.** Repeat Problem 57 for a diverging lens.

**59.** In your notebook, complete the ray diagrams in Fig. 11.55.

**Fig.11.55**

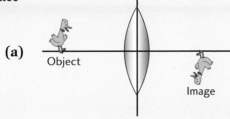

(a) Object / Image

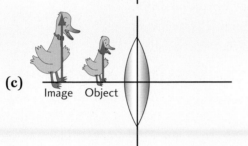

(b) F

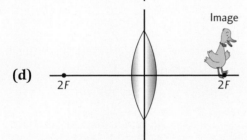

(c) Image Object

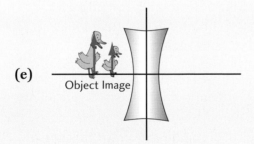

Image

(d) 2F / 2F

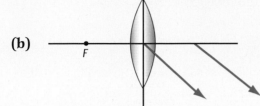

(e) Object Image

## 11.8 Lenses and Applications

**60.** Complete the ray diagram of a telescope in your notebook (Fig. 11.56). Measure the object and first image as well as the first image and second image, and calculate the magnifications. Compare these magnifications to the magnification of the object to the final image.

**Fig.11.56**

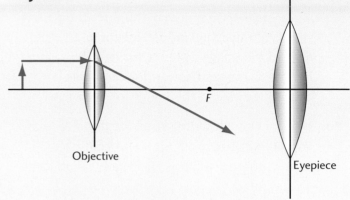

Objective / Eyepiece

**61.** A converging lens with a focal length of 15 cm has an object 5 cm tall placed 40 cm to the left of it. To the right, 30 cm away, is a converging lens of focal length 10 cm. Use a scaled ray diagram to locate the final image. Find its magnification.

**62.** Repeat Problem 61 for a −10 cm diverging lens.

**63. a)** Sketch the conditions of near-sightedness and far-sightedness using an object and an eye with a lens.
**b)** Draw another set of diagrams with the appropriate corrective lens and a ray sketch of how the lens corrects the problem.

## 11.9 Calculations with Lenses

**64.** Use the thin lens and magnification formulae to check your results from Problem 54.

**65.** Use the thin lens and magnification formulae to check your results from Problem 55.

**66.** Use the thin lens and magnification formulae to check your results from Problem 56.

**67.** Use the thin lens and magnification formulae to check your results from Problem 57.

**68.** Use the thin lens and magnification formulae to check your results from Problem 58.

**69.** Two lenses for a camera have the following focal lengths: 35 mm and 100 mm. If a person stands 5.0 m away and is 150 cm tall,
   **a)** find the image distance for each lens.
   **b)** find the magnification for each lens.
   **c)** find the size of the image for each lens.

**70.** Using a camera with a focal length of 35 mm, you take a picture of the Moon (radius = $1.74 \times 10^6$ m). What is the Moon's diameter on the film?

**71.** A converging lens of focal length 10 cm is used to view an ant 5.0 cm away. If the ant is 6.0 mm long, how large is the image of the ant?

**72.** A lens has a magnification of +2.0. If the focal length is +10 cm, find
   **a)** the image position.
   **b)** the object position.
   **c)** What type of lens is it?

**73.** A lens has a magnification of −0.5. If the focal length of the lens is −20 cm, find
   **a)** the object position.
   **b)** the image position.
   **c)** What type of lens is it?

**74.** Complete the following chart in your notebook:

| Lens | $f$ (cm) | $d_o$ (cm) | $d_i$ (cm) | $m$ | Image real/ virtual | Orientation |
|---|---|---|---|---|---|---|
| convex | 20 | 25 | ? | ? | real | ? |
| concave | −20 | 25 | ? | ? | virtual | ? |
| ? | ? | 20 | 20 | −1 | ? | ? |
| ? | ? | 15 | −10 | ? | ? | ? |
| ? | ? | ? | 10 | −0.5 | real | inverted |

**75.** For the following focal lengths, calculate the power of the lens in diopters:
   **a)** 10 cm
   **b)** 30 cm
   **c)** −40 cm

**76.** For a lens with a power of 5 diopters, if an object 5 mm in size is placed 10 cm away, find
   **a)** the image position.
   **b)** the magnification.
   **c)** What type of lens is it?

**77.** The magnification of a lens is 0.5 with a power of −5 diopters. Find
   **a)** the object position.
   **b)** the image position.
   **c)** What type of lens is it?

**78.** For a compound microscope, the objective (first lens) has a focal length of 1.5 cm and an eyepiece (second lens) of 2.0 cm. The distance between the lenses is 14 cm. If viewing tiny print 1.0 mm in height and 1.7 cm from the objective, find
   **a)** the position of the first image produced.
   **b)** What type of image is it?
   **c)** the position of the second image.
   **d)** What type of image is it?
   **e)** the size of the final image.
   **f)** the magnification of the microscope.
   **g)** the orientation of the final image in relation to the object.

**79.** A person with an image distance of 2.0 cm can see distant objects clearly. He can also focus on objects 0.40 m away. Calculate the power of accommodation for this person.

## Purpose

To use Snell's law to find the refractive index of various materials.

## Equipment

Semicircular plastic piece
Semicircular water container (sometimes referred to as a cheese box)
Sugar water, Salt water
Other non-toxic liquids
Ray box with single slit aperture or laser
Protractor, Blank paper

## Procedure

1. On the blank sheet, trace the semicircular shape of the plastic piece.
2. On the straight side of the semicircle, mark the centre and draw a normal at this point.
3. Draw in a series of incident rays at 10°, 20°, 30°, 40°, 50°, 60°, and 70° from the normal.
4. Darken the room. Place the semicircular cheese box containing water on the page, matching the outline of the semicircle. Shine a ray along the normal to check the position of the box.
5. Shine the light along the rays drawn on the sheet. Mark the point at which they exit the cheese box. Make sure you keep track of which incident ray goes with each refracted ray.
6. After completing the experiment, remove the cheese box and draw in the refracted rays.
7. Measure the angles of refraction.
8. Repeat the experiment using a different liquid or the plastic semicircular piece. This experiment can be extended to more than just two substances.

**Fig.Lab.11.1**

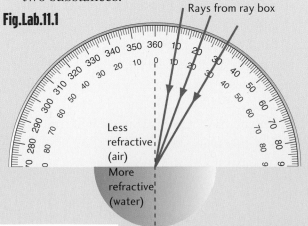

Rays from ray box

Less refractive (air)

More refractive (water)

## Data and Analysis Chart

Construct the following chart for each substance used. In this experiment, the analysis part is the sine calculations.

| Angle of incidence | Angle of refraction | $\sin\theta_1$ | $\sin\theta_2$ | $\dfrac{\sin\theta_1}{\sin\theta_2}$ |
|---|---|---|---|---|
| $(\theta_1)$ | $(\theta_2)$ | | | |
| 0 | (nothing required for this angle) | | | |
| 10 | | | | |
| 20 | | | | |
| 30 | | | | |
| 40 | | | | |
| 50 | | | | |
| 60 | | | | |
| 70 | | | | |

## Discussion

1. The ratio of $\frac{n_2}{n_1}$ turns out to be the refractive index of the material used in the experiment. Why is this so?
2. Did the refracted rays bend towards or away from the normal? Use the angles obtained in the experiment to answer this question.
3. What is special about the incident angle of 0°?
4. If you used more than one substance, how does the refractive index of the other substance(s) affect the size of the angle of refraction?
5. What other rays are present besides the incident and refracted rays?
6. Look up the refractive index of the material you used and compare it to the experimental value. Account for any differences.
7. Why do we use a semicircular shape for this experiment?

## Conclusion

Summarize result(s).

## LAB 11.2 Total Internal Reflection

### Purpose
To study the effect of total internal reflection and calculate the critical angle.

### Equipment
Semicircular plastic piece
Semicircular water container (sometimes referred to as a cheese box)
Sugar water, Salt water
Other non-toxic liquids
Ray box with single slit aperture or laser
Protractor, Blank paper

### Procedure
1. On the blank sheet, trace the semicircular shape of the plastic piece.
2. On the straight side of the semicircle, mark the centre and draw a normal at this point.
3. Draw a series of incident rays at 10°, 20°, and 30° from the normal.
4. Darken the room and shine the light along 0°. Note where the ray emerges.
5. Move the light source so that it follows the incident paths. Mark the angles at which the refracted rays emerge.
6. Continue to move the light source at ever-increasing angles of incidence until no more refracted rays emerge. Measure and record this angle.

### Fig.Lab.11.2

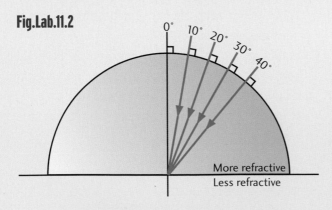

7. Note where the light exits. Measure this angle relative to the normal.
8. Increase the angle of incidence again. Note where the ray emerges. Measure this angle.

### Data
Create a chart to summarize the results. No calculation column is required.

### Analysis
1. Look up the refractive index of the material used and calculate the critical angle using the formula $\sin\theta_c = n_{substance}$, where $n_1 = 1.00$ (air).
2. If you cannot look up the index of refraction for your material, then calculate the index of refraction using your experimental critical angle.

### Discussion
1. What is special about the incident angle of 0°?
2. Did the refracted rays bend away or towards the normal? Use the angles obtained in the experiment to help explain this question.
3. How does the index of refraction affect the critical angle?
4. Where does the light go when and after the critical angle is reached?
5. Did the reflected light obey the law of reflection?

### Conclusions
Summarize the results.

### Extension: Finding the Refraction Index and Critical Angle of an Unknown Material
1. Design and implement a lab to find the refraction index of an unknown optical medium. Consider air to be the incident medium.
2. After finding the refraction index, use it to calculate the critical angle for total internal reflection between air and the unknown medium.
3. Find the critical angle experimentally.
4. Compare the angle measured to the angle calculated using percent deviation.
5. Account for any discrepancies.

## Purpose

To study the characteristics of a convex (converging) lens.

## Equipment

Light source (either a small light bulb or candle)
Convex lens of known focal length
Optics bench
Blank thin white paper

## Procedure

Checking the focal length of the lens:

1. Darken the room and turn on the light sources for the experiment.
2. Have one member of the group hold the lens with one hand and move a small sheet of paper back and forth in front of the lens until an image of a **distant** light source comes into focus. (Stand on one side of the room and focus on a light source on the opposite side of the room.)
3. Have another group member measure the distance from the paper to the lens. This distance is the focal length of the lens. The procedure is similar to the one used in the converging mirror lab.

## Procedure

Investigating the characteristics of the lens:

1. Complete the chart in the data section using the focal length of the lens.
2. Position the lens and the object (light) at the calculated object distance. Move the paper screen around until a **sharp** image is formed.
3. Measure the image distance and note the orientation and relative size of the image.
4. Do this for all object positions except 0.5f. At 0.5f, look through the lens to see the image.

## Data

| $f =$ _____ | | | | |
|---|---|---|---|---|
| $d_o$ (cm) | $d_i$ (cm) | Type | Size | Orientation |
| $2.5 \times f$ | | | | |
| $2.0 \times f$ | | | | |
| $1.5 \times f$ | | | | |
| $1.0 \times f$ | | | | |
| $0.5 \times f$ | | | | |

First calculate the object positions. Then fill in the chart as you proceed through the experiment. Uncertainty: Determine the range through which the image stays in focus. You can use this range as part of the procedural uncertainty. The alignment of the screen and the ruler may also contribute to the uncertainty.

## Analysis

1. In a separate chart, calculate $f$ using the data from your table and the equation $\frac{1}{f} = \frac{1}{d_o} + \frac{1}{d_i}$.
2. Include a column in this chart for the percent deviation. Use the actual (given) value of $f$ for comparison.
3. In this chart, include a column for the magnification, which is calculated using $m = -\frac{d_i}{d_o}$.

## Discussion

1. Prove that the image was at the focal length when the object was far away.
2. How well did your values of $f$ agree with the actual value? Were you consistently off by the same amount? Account for possible reasons for the discrepancies.

3. Check the magnification value and the size you recorded in the lab. Are they in general agreement?

4. You may have found an image when the object was at $f$, but it probably looked very different from the other images. If you found an image, describe it and give a possible reason for its appearance (no image is expected). If you found no image, what did you see on the screen?

5. Describe the virtual image when the object was placed inside $f$. Where would this orientation be useful?

## Conclusion

Draw a ray diagram to verify each line in your data chart.

## Extension: The Diverging Lens

Design and carry out an experiment to

1. find the focal length of a diverging lens.
2. locate the image produced by the lens and determine its characteristics.

# LAB 11.4 The Microscope

## Purpose

To construct and study an experimental setup simulating a microscope.

## Equipment

Various converging lenses (relatively low focal lengths)
Optical bench setup

## Procedure

1. Select various lenses and find their focal lengths using the procedure from the converging lens lab.
2. Decide on the combination of lenses you wish to try. Place the lenses on the test bench so that the distance between them is equal to the sum of their focal lengths.
3. At a distance just beyond the focus of the objective, place a piece of paper with a small letter on it. In you have an optics bench with an illuminated object, it may be used instead of the piece of paper.
4. Look through the eyepiece (ocular) lens and move the lenses slightly until a sharp image is produced. Remember that the image must be inverted and larger.
5. Try other combinations of lenses.

## Data

1. Record the focal lengths of the lenses used.
2. Record the distance between the lenses.
3. Record the distance from the objective lens to the object (paper with letter on it).
4. Record the size of the letter.

## Analysis

1. Calculate the real image position using the objective lens only.
2. Find the magnification and hence the image size produced by the objective lens.
3. Let the image of the objective now become the object for the eyepiece. Calculate its object position using the distance between the lenses and the position of the new object (objective's image) relative to the objective.
4. Calculate the image position for the eyepiece.
5. Calculate the magnification for the eyepiece and the size of the image.
6. Knowing the size of the final image and the original size of the letter, find the total magnification.

## Discussion

1. What type of image is created by
   a) the objective?
   b) the eyepiece?
2. Find another method of finding the final magnification for your microscope.
3. What changes would you make to this experiment if you wished to build an astronomical telescope?
4. Draw a scaled ray diagram illustrating your setup.

## Conclusion

Summarize the criteria for building a microscope.

# Wave Nature of Light

## Chapter Outline

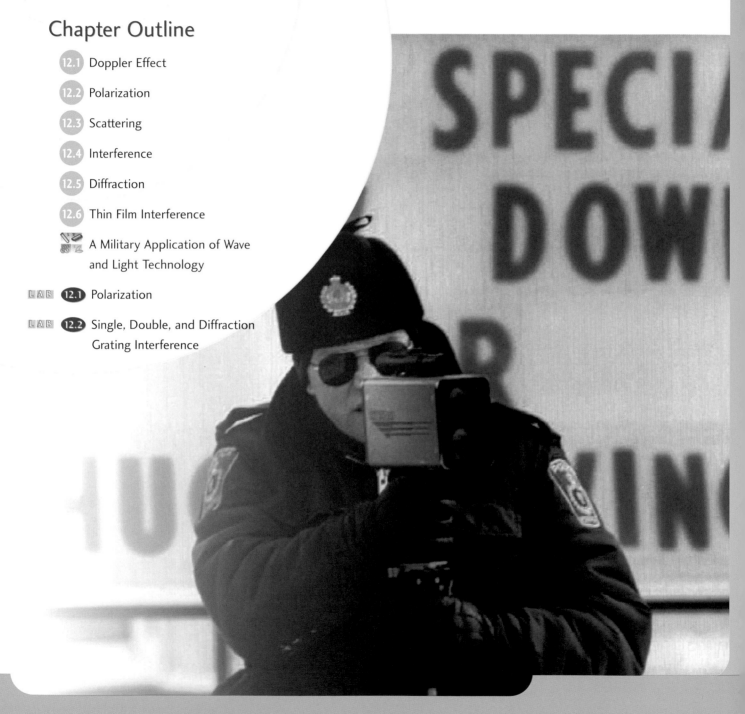

### By the end of this chapter, you will be able to

- explain various aspects of light in terms of the wave theory of light
- determine velocities of objects and their directions relative to an observer using the Doppler effect
- use equations related to interference and diffraction of light

# 12.1 Doppler Effect

We've all experienced the effect of a car racing past us with the characteristic sound of the motor changing its pitch as it goes by. It almost seems like the motor itself slows down as it passes you. This phenomenon is called the **Doppler effect**. It occurs because in one instance, the car is approaching you, and in the other instance, the car is moving away from you. Figure 12.1 shows a car approaching person 1. The car is moving in the same direction as the sound waves being emitted. This motion causes a bunching up of the sound waves as they move toward the person's ear. The person detects more waves per second and hears a higher-pitched sound. For person 2, the car is moving away and the sound waves spread out. Person 2 detects fewer sound waves per second and hears a lower-pitched sound. The Doppler effect is dependent on the speed of the vehicle and the speed of sound, as you will learn in Chapter 13.

Light, like sound, has wave properties, so it too exhibits the Doppler effect. However, the speed of light remains constant to all observers in all reference frames, as postulated by Einstein (see Chapter 9). Therefore, the Doppler effect for light is calculated slightly differently from that for sound.

The equation for calculating the Doppler effect for light is

$$f_2 = f_1\left(1 \pm \frac{v_r}{c}\right)$$

where $f_1$ is the emitted frequency from the source, $f_2$ is the observed frequency, $v_r$ is the relative speed of the object between the source and the observer, and $c$ is the speed of light.

Notice the "$\pm$" sign. The "+" sign is used when the objects are approaching each other, and the "$-$" sign is used when the objects are moving away from each other.

## Radar Guns

If we consider the case where the objects are approaching each other, we use the "+" sign in the equation. In order to find the relative speed, $v_r$, between the objects, we can set $f_2 - f_1$ to be $\Delta f$ to obtain

$$\Delta f = \frac{f_1 v_r}{c}$$

$$v_r = \left(\frac{\Delta f}{f_1}\right)c$$

When using this equation in a situation where light rays from a source are reflected from a moving object, we must multiply $f_1$ by two. This is because

**Fig.12.1** The Doppler effect causes changes in the pitch of sound from a moving source

### DERIVATION OF THE DOPPLER EQUATION

Let $f_1$ be the emitted frequency.

Let $f_2$ be the frequency observed by the speeding car.

Then $f_3$ is the frequency re-emitted by the car (after reflection) and observed by the police.

Use the original equation with a + sign for objects approaching each other:

$$f_2 = f_1\left(1 + \frac{v_r}{c}\right)$$

Rearrange this equation to obtain

Eq. 1 $\quad f_2 - f_1 = f_1\left(\dfrac{v_r}{c}\right)$ (police car to speeder)

Eq. 2 $\quad f_3 - f_2 = f_2\left(\dfrac{v_r}{c}\right)$ (speeder back to police car)

Now add Equations 1 and 2 to get

$$f_3 - f_1 = f_1\left(\frac{v_r}{c}\right) + f_2\left(\frac{v_r}{c}\right)$$

which is approximately equal to

$$f_3 - f_1 = 2f_1\left(\frac{v_r}{c}\right) \text{ ($f_1$ and $f_2$ are close}$$
in frequency and $v_r \ll c$)

If we let $\Delta f$ represent the difference in frequency between the emitted ray and the received ray, then

$$\Delta f = 2f_1\left(\frac{v_r}{c}\right) \quad \text{or} \quad v_r = \left(\frac{\Delta f}{2f_1}\right)c$$

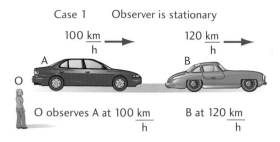

Case 1    Observer is stationary

$100 \frac{km}{h}$    $120 \frac{km}{h}$

A    B

O

O observes A at $100 \frac{km}{h}$    B at $120 \frac{km}{h}$

Case 2    Observer is inside car A

$0 \frac{km}{h}$    $20 \frac{km}{h}$

A    O    B

Observer O sees B pull away at $20 \frac{km}{h}$

Case 3    Observer is inside car B

$20 \frac{km}{h}$    $0 \frac{km}{h}$

A    B    O

Observer O watches A fade back, away from B at $20 \frac{km}{h}$

the original radar gun emits waves that are reflected from a moving object. The object then re-emits them, thus becoming a new source. We now have two separate instances of relative velocity (Fig. 12.2). The first instance occurs when the light waves leave the source and the other instance occurs when the waves reflect off the moving object. Thus the equation becomes

$$v_r = \frac{\Delta f}{2f_1} c$$

One of the uses of this principle is in radar detection techniques used to catch speeders. Figure 12.3 illustrates how the radar gun is pointed at the approaching car and fires focussed electromagnetic radiation at it. These waves hit the car and reflect back to the police officer, where they are measured by a sensitive detector.

**Fig.12.3**   Rader guns measure the speed of cars

> ### EXAMPLE 1    Calculating speed using a radar gun
>
> A stationary police officer on the side of the highway points a radar gun at a speeding car coming toward him. If the gun emits electromagnetic waves at $9.0 \times 10^9$ Hz and detects waves differing by 2000 Hz from the original wave, what was the speed of the car?
>
> ### Solution and Connection to Theory
>
> **Given**
> $f_1 = 9.0 \times 10^9$ Hz    $\Delta f = 2000$ Hz    $v_r = ?$
>
> The appropriate form of the equation is
>
> $$v_r = \left( \frac{\Delta f}{2f_1} \right) c \quad v_r = \left( \frac{2000 \text{ s}^{-1}}{18.0 \times 10^9 \text{ s}^{-1}} \right) 3.0 \times 10^8 \text{ m/s} \quad v_r = 33 \text{ m/s}.$$
>
> Converted to km/h, the value is 120 km/h. Since the speed limit is 100 km/h on most highways, this speed may result in a hefty fine!

The same equation can be used for stationary radar traps as well as for those in a moving vehicle. This is possible because the equation involves the relative velocity between two vehicles. Since the police know their own speed, they can find your speed knowing the relative velocity obtained from the equation.

Radar guns have also become common tools used in various sports. They are used to find speeds of pucks, baseballs, footballs, and other projectiles. The data collected from these measurements can be used to improve the athlete's techniques.

In astronomy, the wavelength of radiation is commonly measured instead of the frequency. By combining the wave equation, $v = \lambda f$, and the Doppler equation for light, $f_2 = f_1(1 \pm \frac{v_r}{c})$, we can produce a blended formula useful to astronomers.

From our knowledge of the visible light spectrum, we know that blue light has a shorter wavelength than red light. Thus, if the wavelength received by the telescope is decreasing because of the apparent motion of two celestial objects, the light is said to be **blue shifted**, meaning that $\Delta\lambda$ is negative. Notice in Fig. 12.6 that the observed spectrum does not line up with the reference spectrum. The observed wavelength is shorter, so the shift is towards the blue end of the spectrum.

**Fig.12.4**   Fans using radar guns at a baseball game

## DOPPLER EQUATION IN ASTRONOMY

$$v_r = \left(\frac{\Delta\lambda}{\lambda}\right)c$$

$v_r$ is the relative speed between observer and source.

$\Delta\lambda = \lambda_2 - \lambda_1$ where $\lambda_1$ is the accepted wavelength as measured in a laboratory experiment and $\lambda_2$ is the wavelength measured as it comes from space.

If $\Delta\lambda$ is positive, the objects are moving away from each other.

If $\Delta\lambda$ is negative, the objects are moving toward each other. These two cases are illustrated in Fig. 12.5.

**Fig.12.5**

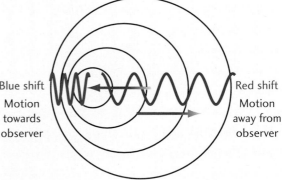

Observer

Blue shift
Motion towards observer

Red shift
Motion away from observer

**Fig.12.6**   Blue shift

• Consider a reference wave

• If it is blue shifted, it gets compressed.

The effect of a blue shift is shown below.

Notice how the lines have shifted towards the blue end.

Reference (lab) spectrum

Absorption lines from star

EXAMPLE 2    Blue shift

If the wavelength of emitted light from a celestial object is 475 nm, and it is known that the wavelength of this colour is 525 nm, is the object approaching or receding?

### Solution and Connection to Theory

**Given**

$\Delta\lambda = \lambda_2 - \lambda_1$, where $\lambda_1$ is the known wavelength and $\lambda_2$ is the observed wavelength.

Therefore, $\lambda_1 = 525$ nm    $\lambda_2 = 475$ nm

475 nm − 525 nm = −50 nm

Because this value is negative, we know that the two objects are approaching each other. We can also explain the motion by observing that the emitted wavelength is shorter than the known wavelength. This means that the value of the emitted wavelength is closer to the blue end of the spectrum. Blue shifts indicate that the objects are approaching each other.

A **red shift** means that the objects are moving apart. As in Fig. 12.6, Fig. 12.7 shows two spectra on top of each other. This time, the observed wavelength is shifted towards the red end of the reference wavelength. It turns out that all major celestial objects we have observed, such as galaxies, nebulae, and quasars, are red shifted and therefore moving away from us. This observation lead to the expansion or **Big Bang Theory** of the universe.

**Fig.12.7**    Red shift

• Consider a reference wave

• If it is red shifted, it gets stretched out.

The effect of a red shift is shown below.

Notice how the lines have shifted towards the red end.

Reference (lab) spectrum

Absorption lines from star

## EXAMPLE 3   Finding the speed of a galaxy

A known wavelength of 520 nm is observed to be 530 nm from a distant galaxy. What is the speed of this galaxy relative to Earth? Is it receding or approaching?

### *Solution and Connection to Theory*

**Given**

$\lambda_1 = 520$ nm $= 5.20 \times 10^{-7}$ m
$\lambda_2 = 530$ nm $= 5.30 \times 10^{-7}$ m
$c = 3.0 \times 10^8$ m/s

$$v_r = \left(\frac{\Delta\lambda}{\lambda_1}\right)c$$

$$v_r = \left(\frac{(5.30 \times 10^{-7}\ \text{m} - 5.20 \times 10^{-7}\ \text{m})}{5.20 \times 10^{-7}\ \text{m}}\right)3.0 \times 10^8\ \text{m/s}$$

$$= 5.8 \times 10^6\ \text{m/s}$$

This galaxy is moving at a speed of 20 million km/h!

Because $\Delta\lambda$ is positive, we know that the galaxy is moving away from us. This is also evident because the observed wavelength has moved toward the red end of the spectrum and is said to be red shifted.

**Fig.12.8**   The light from galaxies and other celestial objects is red shifted (as illustrated by the red end of the spectrum coming towards us in the picture). The farther away they are, the greater their red shift. Therefore, everything is apparently moving away from us, meaning that the universe is expanding. If you project this effect backwards in time, then everything must have originated at a point. The basic premise behind the Big Bang Theory is that this point exploded and expanded 10 to 15 billion years ago.

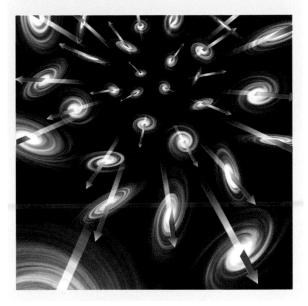

1. Calculate the speed of an approaching car if it is detected using a stationary radar gun emitting waves of $9.2 \times 10^9$ Hz and the rebounding wave is different by 2000 Hz.
2. Explain the red and blue shift in terms of movements of celestial objects. Use the fact that the speed of light must remain constant.
3. a) Calculate the speed of a galaxy that has a known wavelength of 450 nm and an observed wavelength of 480 nm.
   b) Is this a red shift or a blue shift?
   c) Is this galaxy moving toward us or away from us?
   d) Reverse the two given wavelengths and repeat the exercise.

**Fig.12.9** Summary of Doppler Effect

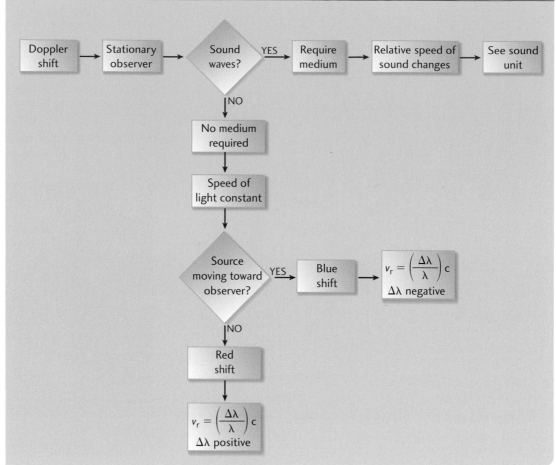

## 12.2 Polarization

Light is composed of randomly oriented, oscillating perpendicular *electric* and *magnetic* fields. When discussing polarization, we are concerned with the electric field only. **Polarization** of light is the removal of one component of its electric field such that it is no longer randomly oriented. In **unpolarized light**, the electric field can oscillate in any direction, as long as it is perpendicular to the direction in which the wave travels. In Fig. 12.10, the electric fields are shown oscillating in all possible directions. The oscillations are perpendicular to the direction of propagation of the light wave.

If you look at any given electric field direction, it can be broken up into two parts called **components**. The two components are the horizontal and vertical directions of the electric field. Figure 12.11 shows a variety of electric field directions, with their corresponding components in a different colour. If the electric field points along a component direction, then the other component is zero (recall Chapter 3 on vector components).

UNIT C: Light and Geometric Optics

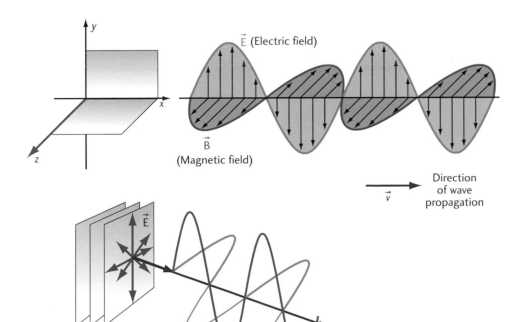

**Fig.12.10** For unpolarized light, the electric field is randomly oriented (can oscillate in any direction).

If one of these components gets absorbed by the medium, then only one component will remain. This means that the electric field lines will oscillate in that direction only, no matter what original orientation they had. This type of light is said to be **plane polarized** or **linearly polarized**. The effect is shown in Fig. 12.12. It is analogous to a skipping rope vibrating up and down, side to side, and in all other possible directions. However, if the skipping rope is fed through a narrow slot in a wall (can be in any direction), the skipping rope can vibrate in the direction of the slot only. All the other directions hit the sides of the slot's walls and are dampened.

**Fig.12.11** Any vector can be broken down to two components $(x, y)$. The two components are perpendicular to each other. Two component vectors added together always produce the original vector.

**Fig.12.12**

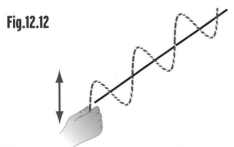

**(a)** Transverse waves on a rope polarized in a vertical plane

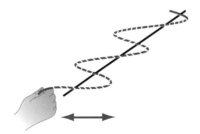

**(b)** Transverse waves on a rope polarized in a horizontal plane

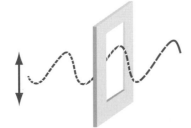

**(a)** Vertically polarized wave passes through a vertical slit

**(b)** Horizontally polarized wave does not fit through the vertical slit

The process of linearly polarizing light does not have much visual effect because the electric field carries no visual information. Thus the intensity of the light will decrease, but not the image clarity or detail. The method shown in Fig. 12.12 can be used to explain how a polarizing filter or **Polaroid** works.

## Polarization of Light using Polaroids

A Polaroid is a trade-marked name created by Edwin Land in the early 1930s. In a sheet of clear plastic, he embedded tiny crystals of an iodine compound aligned in regular rows, much like a picket fence. As light passes through this polarizing material, one of its electric field components is absorbed. The other component moves through unhindered. Thus, the Polaroid has a **preferential direction of transmission**. It is like the slot in a wall that allows a skipping rope to vibrate in one direction only (Fig. 12.12). If you place two Polaroids with their transmission directions perpendicular to each other, virtually no light will pass through them as shown in Fig. 12.13. Two Polaroids with their transmission directions oriented parallel to each other allow the light to pass through both of them.

**Fig.12.13A**   A pair of "crossed" Polaroids with their transmission directions 90° to each other. No light gets through where the two overlap.

**Fig.12.13B**   Two Polaroids with their transmission direction parallel. Each Polaroid appears grey because it absorbs roughly half of the incident light where they overlap. Light passes through both.

One of the more common uses for Polaroids is in the manufacture of sunglasses. **Glare**, is caused by light reflecting off shiny surfaces, such as glass, water, and bald heads. It is partially polarized in most instances. Glare causes eye fatigue and screens out useful image information. If the Polaroids are positioned in the lenses at 90° to the offending glare's polarization direction, then the glare gets blocked out and you see a sharper image. Compare the images of the person standing in the water taken using a camera with a polarizing filter and a camera without a polarizing filter (Fig. 12.14). The information arriving to the film in the case of the polarizing filter is cleaner and clearer

**Fig.12.14**   Polaroid filters remove reflected light

because the "optical noise" is removed. Fishing glasses are typically made with Polaroids because of the glare arising from light reflecting off the water. This way, even if you don't catch the fish, at least you can see it clearly.

## Malus' Law

As light passes through one Polaroid, its intensity decreases by half:

$$I_1 = \tfrac{1}{2} I_0$$

where $I_0$ is the intensity of the incident ray of light and $I_1$ is the intensity of the ray exiting the polarizer.

Malus' law determines the change in intensity of the light that passes through two polarizers. According to Malus' law, the intensity of the ray of light exiting the second polarizer (also known as the analyzer) in relation to the incident ray is

$$I_2 = \tfrac{1}{2} I_0 \cos^2\theta$$

If we are only interested in the change in intensity of the light ray through the second polarizer, then the $\tfrac{1}{2}$ is omitted and the equation becomes

$$I_2 = I_1 \cos^2\theta$$

The angle $\theta$ is the angle between the polarizing directions of the two polarizers. The value for the intensity is a maximum when the polarizers are parallel. The angle is then $0°$ and the $\cos 0°$ is 1. Therefore, $I_2 = I_1$. Minimum intensity occurs when the two polarizing directions are $90°$ to each other ($\cos 90° = 0$; therefore, $I_2 = 0$).

**EXAMPLE 4**   **Using Malus' Law**

If two Polaroids are crossed with an angle of $60°$ between their polarizing directions, what percentage of light gets through both Polaroids?

## Solution and Connection To Theory

**Given**

$\theta = 60°$ $\qquad \dfrac{I_2}{I_1} = ?$

$I_2 = \frac{1}{2} I_o \cos^2 \theta$

$I_2 = \frac{1}{2} I_o \cos^2 60°$

$\qquad = \frac{1}{2}(0.25) I_o$

Therefore, $\dfrac{I_2}{I_o} = 0.125$

As a percent, this value is 12.5% $(0.125 \times 100\%)$. Thus, 12.5% of the light travels through both Polaroids.

## Polarization by Reflection

As mentioned in the last section, polarization occurs when light reflects off a shiny surface. After reflection, the component of the electric field parallel to the surface is unchanged. The other component is partially absorbed, causing the light to become partially polarized. Figure 12.15(a) shows a ray diagram representation of this situation.

**Fig.12.15** An unpolarized wave reflects off the surface of the water. The reflected ray is partially polarized, predominately in one direction. The refracted ray is unpolarized.

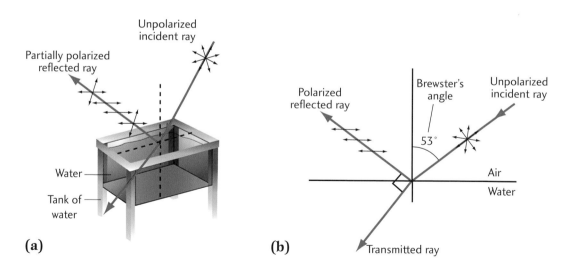

**(a)**

**(b)**

Most reflections create partially polarized light. However, 100% polarization can occur at a special angle of incidence. This angle is called **Brewster's angle**. At this angle, the reflected and refracted rays are 90° apart and the reflected ray is completely polarized. The conditions necessary for complete polarization by reflection are shown in Fig. 12.15(b). The main change from Fig. 12.15(a) is that the refracted and reflected rays are separated by 90° and the reflected ray then has only one polarization component.

We can calculate Brewster's angle using the formula

$$\tan\theta_B = \frac{n_2}{n_1}$$

where $n_1$ is the refractive index of the incident medium, $n_2$ is the refractive index of the refraction medium, and $\theta_B$ is Brewster's angle.

BREWSTER'S ANGLE

At Brewster's angle,
$\theta_1 = \theta_B$ and $\theta_2 = 90° - \theta_1$

Substitute into Snell's law
$n_1\sin\theta_1 = n_2\sin\theta_2$
$n_1\sin\theta_B = n_2\sin(90° - \theta_B)$
$n_1\sin\theta_B = n_2\cos\theta_B$

$$\frac{\sin\theta_B}{\cos\theta_B} = \frac{n_2}{n_1}$$

$$\tan\theta_B = \frac{n_2}{n_1}$$

**EXAMPLE 5**    **Brewster's angle for air–water boundary**

Calculate the angle at which all of the reflected light is 100 % polarized if light reflects from water.

### Solution and Connection to Theory

**Given**
$n_1$ (air) = 1.00     $n_2$ (water) = 1.33

$$\tan\theta_B = \frac{n_1}{n_2} \qquad \theta_B = \tan^{-1}\frac{1.33}{1.00} = 53°$$

At an incident angle of 53°, the reflected light is totally polarized.

Light scattered from the sky is also polarized. If you look at the sky while wearing Polaroid sunglasses, tilting your head from side to side will make the sky appear to change its tint (darker or brighter). The particles in the air preferentially scatter blue wavelengths over the other colours, so the sky appears blue. The scattering is like a reflection and thus produces some polarization.

## Polarization by Anisotropic Crystals

In 1669, Swedish physician Erasmus Bartholinus noticed that a piece of crystal, known as Icelandic spar (calcite), produced two images when light refracted through it. The reason for this phenomenon is that the crystal separates the two components of the electric field. Each image is therefore 100 % polarized. The photograph in Fig. 12.16 shows the two images of the text the crystal sits on. By rotating the crystal, one of the images rotates around the other. You can check the polarization of the images by placing a Polaroid filter on top of the crystal. One of the images will vanish. If the Polaroid is rotated, the other image will appear and the original one will vanish.

The two rays are named rather appropriately. The **o ray** is the **ordinary ray**, which means that it does nothing special. It obeys Snell's Law and its speed is not changed as it travels through the crystal. The **e ray**, or **extraordinary ray**, on the other hand, obeys Snell's law in a more complicated way. Its speed varies depending on the angle at which it enters the crystal.

**Fig.12.16** The calcite crystal produces two images. Each is 100% polarized. When a Polaroid is placed on top of the crystal, one image disappears. A Polaroid rotated 90° to the first Polaroid causes the other image to disappear.

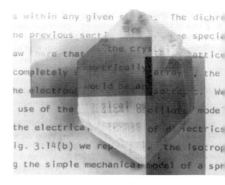

**Fig.12.17**

$e$ ray → Extraordinary ray: Refractive index is angle dependent

$o$ ray → Ordinary ray: Refractive index is constant

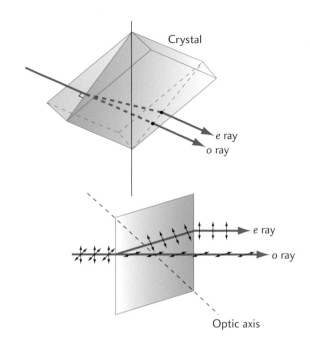

Crystal

$e$ ray
$o$ ray

$e$ ray
$o$ ray

Optic axis

"Birefringence" means "refracting twice." The word "refringence" used to be used instead of "refraction." The actual word stems from the Latin word *frangere*, meaning "to break." Many crystals are birefringent. Other examples of crystals are mica, sugar, and quartz. These crystals are important because they are used in various special optics instruments.

This angle is measured relative to an **optic axis**, which is an imaginary line through the crystal. The $e$ ray has a refractive index that is dependent on an angle. Materials exhibiting different refractive indices are said to be **birefringent**. What makes the optic axis special is that when unpolarized light enters along it, only one ray emerges. The representation of the different rays is given in Fig. 12.17. Note that the optic axis is not a visible line in the crystal, but rather a measured direction.

**Fig.12.18** Each eye sees a different image. The brain combines the two perspectives to produce the final three-dimensional image.

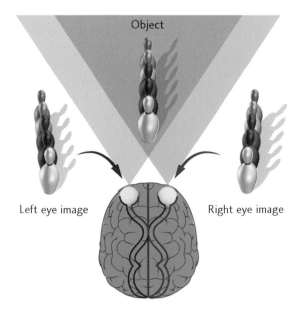

Object

Left eye image          Right eye image

## Stereoscopic Images

In the animal world, there are many different kinds of eyes. Their structure and location create different types of images and different ways of viewing the world. As illustrated in Fig. 12.18, humans have eyes that are close together, side by side, which gives us binocular type vision. Each eye picks up slightly different information from its surroundings. Our eyes produce the 3D effect by blending two slightly different images together in the brain. To see this effect, try closing one eye, then the other eye while looking at a pencil held at arm's length. The image of the pencil should shift each time you look at it with the other eye. The brain, specifically the visual cortex, produces the 3D image by combining the similarities between the images of the two eyes, then adding in the differences.

## Three-dimensional Movies

In order to produce 3D movies, two specially positioned cameras are used to film the scenes. The space between them duplicates the separation of our eyes. Two projectors are used to project the images on the screen, each using a polarizing filter. By placing the two polarizing filters in orthogonal orientations (90°) to each other, the images on the screen are also polarized in opposite directions. The scene on the screen appears doubled and blurry. When you put the special Polaroid sunglasses on, provided to you by the theatre, you see in 3D. The lenses of the 3D glasses have their polarizing directions oriented at 90° to each other. The left eye receives images from the left projector only, and the right eye receives images from the right projector only. We thereby fool the brain into thinking that it's receiving two images of *the same object*, one from each eye. The brain puts the "two images" together to produce stereoscopic images. A cheaper version of this technique uses red and blue filters instead of fancy Polaroid glasses (Fig. 12.19).

**Fig.12.19** Viewing a 3D movie

1. **a)** Describe polarized light.
   **b)** Describe how polarized light is produced by reflection, polarizing materials, and anisotropic crystals.
2. Describe what happens when a polarizing material is used to look at light coming from
   **a)** a doubly refracting crystal.
   **b)** a reflection from a glass window.
   **c)** a blue sky.
   **d)** a friend standing in a swimming pool.

◄ ◄ ◄ ◄   APPLYING the Concepts

## 12.3 Scattering

In the polarization section, we mentioned that light scattered off air particles is polarized. This section explains the scattering process of light. As the sunlight passes through the atmosphere, it gets randomly redirected by air. This redirection of light gives the sky its colour.

The scattering process is similar to a buoy in the water. Notice in Fig. 12.20 that as waves go by the duck buoy, they cause it to start moving up and down with the same frequency as that of the original wave. This motion causes more waves to go out from the buoy. Now imagine thousands of duck buoys all doing the same thing. The ordered wave that first came in is now a mass of ripplets moving in all different directions.

**Fig.12.20** A single wave comes in and bends around each duck buoy, creating secondary sources of waves.

Shorter wavelengths of light are scattered more by the atmosphere, making the sky look blue and sunsets red.

Scattering of light by the sky

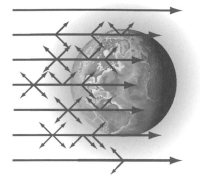

Like the buoy, air molecules absorb and then re-emit the light waves. The shortest wavelengths are scattered more easily than the longer ones because the electrons in molecules are able to take up energies of the shorter wavelengths more easily. As you will learn in the sound unit, objects tend to absorb energy readily if it causes them to vibrate at their **natural resonant frequency**. For electrons in air molecules, the natural resonance is closest to the ultraviolet end of the spectrum. Therefore, the longer the wavelength of light, the less energy is absorbed by the electrons and the less scattering of light occurs.

If you look at the picture of the light reaching Earth in Fig. 12.21, you notice that when the Sun is at solar noon (directly overhead), the distance the light travels through the atmosphere is a minimum. At sunset, this distance is a maximum.

**Fig.12.21** Light travels a greater distance through the atmosphere at sunset than at noon

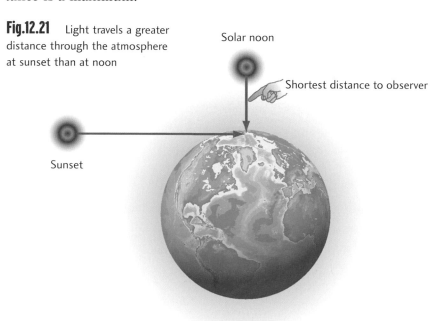

Solar noon

Shortest distance to observer

Sunset

## SCATTERING

The extent of scattering of light by air molecules is proportional to $\frac{1}{\lambda^4}$. The wavelengths of visible light range from about 0.70 $\mu$m (red) to 0.40 $\mu$m (violet). The table here shows the relative amounts of various colours that are scattered.

| Colour | red | orange | yellow | green | blue | violet |
|---|---|---|---|---|---|---|
| Wavelength ($\mu$m) | 0.70 | 0.60 | 0.58 | 0.52 | 0.48 | 0.40 |
| Relative number of scattered waves | 1 | 2 | 3 | 4 | 5 | 10 |

Therefore, at solar noon, the sky is blue because it is a mixture of the colours of light that scatter best: an unequal mixture of violet, blue, green, and yellow light. At sunset, the light has to travel the extra distance through the atmosphere. By the time it nears the surface of Earth, most of the short wavelengths have been scattered. The remaining longer wavelengths, which are in the red end of the spectrum, reach our eyes and we see a red Sun at sunset. The atmosphere near Earth's surface has more dust particles and, near cities, more pollutants, which are of the right size to scatter red wavelengths better. Thus, on nights when pollution is high, we see red sunsets

(Fig. 12.22). However, in some areas of Earth, the pollution level is so high, that no Sun is seen at all. In theory, you could then create whatever colour of sky you wish by putting particles in the atmosphere that are most suited to scatter that particular wavelength of light.

**Fig.12.22**   The colours of the sky are caused by the scattering of light

1. Describe the scattering effect in terms of wavelength of light and colours as seen by a person looking at the sky.
2. How could you use the scattering effect of light to measure the pollution count in the air?

# 12.4  Interference

The combining of two or more waves to produce a single wave is called the **principle of superposition**. As the waves meet, they occupy the same space at the same time. At this point, the *amplitudes* of the waves combine in one of two ways, as illustrated in Fig. 12.23. When the amplitudes are both in the same direction, they are added together. This is called **constructive interference**. When the amplitudes are in opposite directions, they cancel out, or subtract. This is called **destructive interference**.

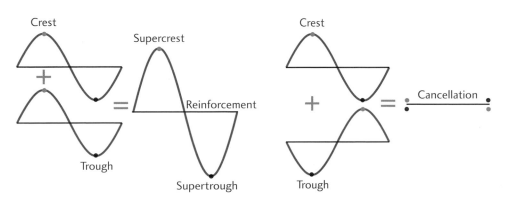

**Fig.12.23**   Constructive and destructive interference

## Phase Shift

Light can be represented by a sine wave. In Chapter 10, we learned about the parts of the wave and its motion. Now we will consider the wave's appearance based on its starting point.

The travelling wave is a continuous string of sine waves. In Fig. 12.24, two such travelling waves are side by side. They look exactly alike. However, if we shift one of the waves over by part of a wavelength, they become very different.

**Fig.12.24** Stare at the two waves. It is very difficult to tell them apart.

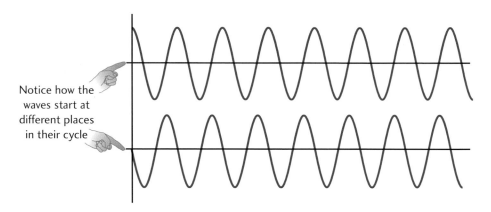

Notice how the waves start at different places in their cycle

**Fig.12.25** Possible phase shifts

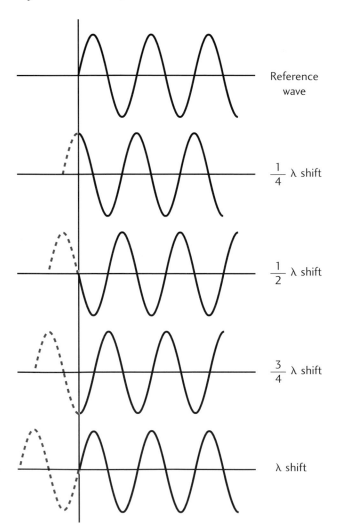

Reference wave

$\frac{1}{4} \lambda$ shift

$\frac{1}{2} \lambda$ shift

$\frac{3}{4} \lambda$ shift

$\lambda$ shift

If you want to add the two waves together, it matters a great deal where each wave starts its cycle. In the case of the non-shifted waves, the crests and troughs all line up and add constructively. But in the case where one of the waves is shifted, the addition is more complicated. At some points along the wave, interference is constructive and at other points it is destructive. By starting one wave at a different point in its cycle, the manner in which the two waves interfere changes. The wave that is moved is said to be **phase shifted**. Figure 12.25 illustrates the common phase shifts.

The two extremes of interference are pure constructive, where all points between the two waves add, and pure destructive, where all points on the two waves subtract. The two waves in Fig. 12.26 are added in phase and out of phase. The effect is to produce super crests and super troughs in one case, and complete cancellation in the other.

The net effect of constructive interference using light waves is to create bright areas called **maxima**. The net effect of destructive interference is to create total cancellation areas, called **nodal lines** or **minima**. This is best visualized using two sources of waves in a tank of water (Fig. 12.27). The interference pattern created shows the nodal areas where the waves have cancelled and the bright areas where super crests and super troughs are formed.

**Fig.12.26**  2D interference pattern

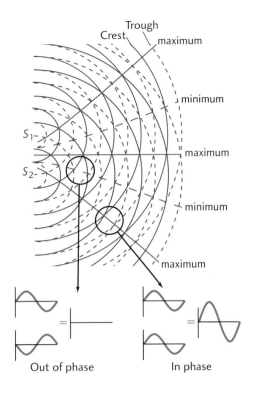

Crest
Trough
maximum
minimum
maximum
minimum
maximum
S₁
S₂

Out of phase     In phase

**Fig.12.27**  Wave interference pattern for two identical wave sources in water

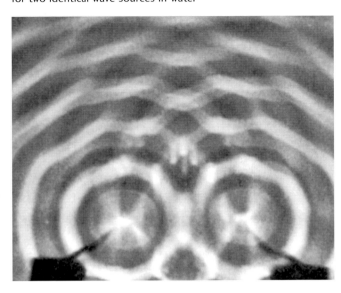

**Fig.12.28**  Summary of Wave Aspects of Light

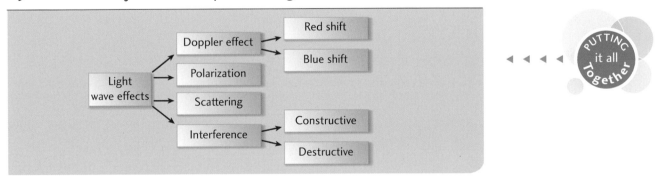

Light wave effects — Doppler effect → Red shift, Blue shift; Polarization; Scattering; Interference → Constructive, Destructive

PUTTING it all Together

# Effects of Interference

To see the interference effects on light, we must create conditions that allow us to view something too small for the human eye to see. In order to do so, we use openings through which light passes that are comparable in size to the wavelength of light. If light passes through a large hole, it produces a bright spot on a screen, as you would expect. If the hole was made smaller, say the size of a tiny pin prick, the same bright spot appears. However, where you expect to see darkness, a series of bright, equally spaced circles appears. The light has moved into a region it was not expected to be in. The same holds true if two holes or slits are used. Figure 12.29 illustrates the expected patterns and the patterns produced.

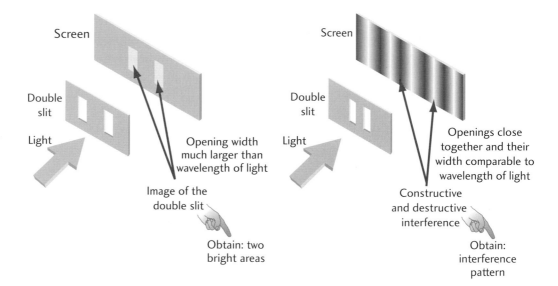

**Fig.12.29** For visible light interference to occur, the two slits must be narrow and close together

Screen

Double slit

Light

Opening width much larger than wavelength of light

Image of the double slit

Obtain: two bright areas

Screen

Double slit

Light

Openings close together and their width comparable to wavelength of light

Constructive and destructive interference

Obtain: interference pattern

## COHERENCE

In order to see the effects of interference, the light sources must be **coherent**. The waves of both sources must maintain a constant phase relationship at all times. In the double slit experiment, if two incandescent or fluorescent light bulbs were used, there would be no interference pattern because each light bulb emits light in random orientations. There is no stable relationship between the two waves arriving at any given point. Therefore, they cannot establish either a maximum or a minimum. Coherence can be achieved by placing one light bulb behind a barrier with two small openings. You could also use two lasers as long as one laser is tunable.

This phenomenon is called diffraction. It will be further discussed in the next section.

In the early 1800s, an experimenter named Thomas Young derived an equation for which he became famous: Young's **double slit formula**. It predicted where maxima or minima would occur given the slit separation distance, the wavelength of light used, and the **order number** (the number from the centre of the pattern) of the maximum or minimum you wish to find. The angle of deviation in the equation (see Fig. 12.30) is measured from the centre line, drawn from the midpoint between the sources to the screen. The equation is:

$$n\lambda = d\sin\theta_n$$

where $n$ is the order number and $d$ is the separation between slits, or

$$n\lambda = \frac{dx_n}{L}$$

as illustrated in Fig. 12.30, where $x_n$ is the distance from the centre line to the bright line of constructive interference in the pattern and $L$ is the distance from the pattern to the slit.

**Fig.12.30** Constructive interference will occur at $P$ when the path difference $= n\lambda$ ($n = 0, 1, 2,...$). But the $\frac{\text{path difference}}{d} = \sin\theta$ or the path difference $= d\sin\theta$. ∴ a bright spot will appear at $P$ when $d\sin\theta = n\lambda$ ($n = 0, 1, 2,...$)

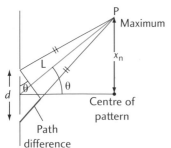

P
Maximum

L

$x_n$

d

θ  θ

Centre of pattern

Path difference

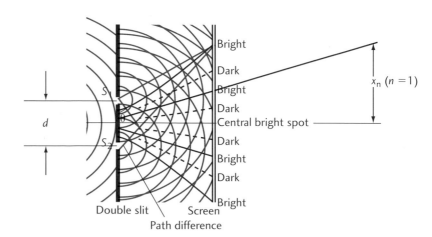

Bright
Dark
Bright
Dark
Central bright spot
Dark
Bright
Dark
Bright

$x_n$ ($n = 1$)

d

S₁

S₂

Double slit

Screen

Path difference

UNIT C: Light and Geometric Optics

EXAMPLE 6 **Young's double slit experiment calculation**

A monochromatic source of 450 nm illuminates two slits that are $3.0 \times 10^{-6}$ m apart. Find the angle at which the first-order maximum occurs. For a screen that is 1.0 m away from the slit, how far will the first-order maximum be from the centre line?

### Solution and Connection to Theory

**Given**

$n = 1 \quad d = 3.0 \times 10^{-6}$ m $\quad \lambda = 450 \times 10^{-9}$ m $= 4.50 \times 10^{-7}$ m $\quad \theta_1 = ?$

$n\lambda = d\sin\theta_n$

$\theta_1 = \sin^{-1}\dfrac{n\lambda}{d} \quad \theta_1 = \sin^{-1}\dfrac{1(4.50 \times 10^{-7}\text{ m})}{3.0 \times 10^{-6}\text{ m}} = 8.6$

$\theta = 8.6°$

For the screen at 1.0 m, the distance from the centre line for the first-order maximum is given by $\sin 8.6° = \frac{x_1}{1.0\text{ m}}$. Therefore, the maximum is 0.15 m or 15 cm from the centre line.

In Young's double slit formula, the angle of deviation depends on the wavelength. As a result, if white light illuminates the double slit, the first-order maximum will appear coloured. The angle between red and violet for the slits in Example 6 would be about 5°. In order to spread the colours farther apart and make them brighter, physicists have developed **diffraction gratings** made of a series of many slits. A typical diffraction grating has about $10^6$ slits per metre, which gives an angle of about 25° between red and violet light. The diffraction grating has the same effect as the double slit except that the interference pattern is sharper, brighter, and spread over a much wider angle. In Young's double slit equation, $d$ now refers to the spacing between consecutive slits.

Compact discs contain closely spaced grooves. If you look at a compact disc illuminated by a relatively small bright white light, you will see a multicoloured surface, the effect of a reflection diffraction grating.

In the field of spectroscopy, the **spectrometer** is used to measure wavelengths of light accurately using a diffraction grating (Fig. 12.31). The instrument allows you to accurately measure the angles of bright maxima. By using the double slit formula, you can calculate the wavelength. The narrower the opening between the slits of the diffraction grating, the sharper the interference lines and the more precise the instrument.

Instruments such as the spectrometer can be used to identify elements and compounds found in a variety of applications. Astronomers use the diffraction grating principle to analyze the light from stars in order to determine the composition of the star. This information can then lead to theories on the actual processes that keep a star burning.

**Fig.12.31** A spectrometer is used
to measure wavelengths of light

Biologists also use this principle in studying different types of molecular structures. DNA, for example, will absorb only specific colours of light. If you are looking for a particular molecular structure in a sample, you can bathe the sample in light and then observe the absorption spectrum using a spectrometer. This method gives you an idea of the relative concentration of the molecular structure in the material based on the intensity of the lines present in the interference pattern.

The effect of the diffraction grating is used in photography and movies to produce multiple images or the effect of visible rays coming out of lights. It adds a fairy-tale quality to a photo of a Christmas tree with lights, for example. The effect is occasionally seen when looking at the rear lights of the car ahead through a scratched windshield. The lights will have fringes around them, caused by the grating effect.

 ▶ ▶ ▶ ▶

**1. a)** Compare the interference patterns produced by a double slit and a diffraction grating.
   **b)** What happens to the pattern as the opening(s) in the slits grow(s) larger?
**2.** Calculate the angle of the second maximum for monochromatic light of wavelength 550 nm if it illuminates
   **a)** a double slit with a slit separation of $2.5 \times 10^{-6}$ m.
   **b)** a diffraction grating with 10 000 slits in 1.0 m.
**3.** For Question 2, given that the screen is 1.0 m away from the slits, find the distance from the centre at which the second-order maximum occurs.

## ▶ 12.5 Diffraction

Waves, like solid objects, carry energy. However, waves deliver the energy differently to us. If you're standing beside a tree and someone throws a ball at you, the ball delivers the energy of motion it has when it hits you. If you stand behind a tree, the ball can't hit you and no energy is delivered. If someone shouts at you and you are standing behind a tree, you still hear the person. The sound wave has the ability to bend around the tree. Light, however, doesn't seem to bend around the tree. In the section on the effects of interference, we learned that interference becomes noticeable when the openings through which light passes are comparable in size to the wavelength of light used.

Therefore, we don't see the effect of light bending. There is a somewhat arbitrary distinction between interference and diffraction. We usually define **interference** as *a superposition effect originating from two or more discrete sources of waves.* Examples are the double slit and diffraction grating effects. *If a single source causes an interference effect such that the combining*

*waves originate from a single wavefront*, the effect is called **diffraction**. Examples of this effect are single slit setups and the bending of waves around sharp edges (see Fig. 12.32).

In actuality, both these processes are usually present in all of the mentioned examples. The photograph of the razor blade (Fig. 12.32) shows the diffraction effect. Near the edge of the blade, a pattern of light and dark bands appears. In places where a shadow is expected, these fringes also appear. The light has bent around a corner.

Diffraction also occurs when light travels through a single narrow slit. The interference patterns for a single slit and a double slit are compared in Fig. 12.33.

**Fig.12.32** Cases 1–3: amount of diffraction varies with the size of the object in relation to the size of the wavelength (λ) of the water. Below: Photograph of razor blade shows the fuzzy edges and ripples created by the diffraction of light.

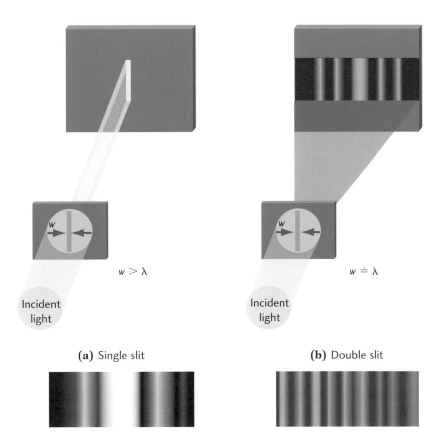

**Fig.12.33** The single slit interference pattern, like its related effect, the double slit pattern, occurs when the opening (w) is about the same size as the wavelength of light used. The two patterns are comprised of alternating light and dark bands corresponding to areas of constructive and destructive interference. The main differences in the patterns are:
1. The single slit has a distinctive double width central maximum.
2. The single slit pattern rapidly decreases in intensity.

**Fig.12.34** Where minima occur in a single slit interference pattern

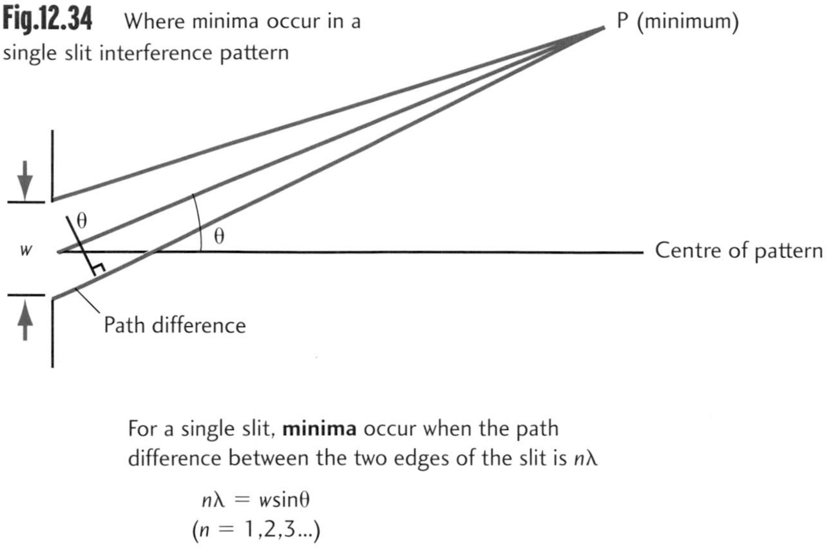

P (minimum)

θ

w

θ

Centre of pattern

Path difference

For a single slit, **minima** occur when the path difference between the two edges of the slit is $n\lambda$

$$n\lambda = w\sin\theta$$
$$(n = 1,2,3...)$$

To calculate **minima** occurring in a pattern, use the formula

$$n\lambda = w\sin\theta_n$$

where $n$ designates the nodal line (minimum) you wish to locate, $w$ is the width opening, and $\theta_n$ is the angle measured from the centre line for the given minimum. This formula is illustrated in Fig. 12.34.

**EXAMPLE 7** **Calculating the angle of the second nodal line for a single slit**

A slit with a width of $2.0 \times 10^{-5}$ m is illuminated by a red light of wavelength 620 nm. At what angle does the third-order minimum occur?

### Solution and Connection to Theory

**Given**
$$w = 2.0 \times 10^{-5} \text{ m} \quad n = 3 \quad \lambda = 620 \text{ nm} = 6.20 \times 10^{-7} \text{ m} \quad \theta_3 = ?$$

$$n\lambda = w\sin\theta_n \quad \sin\theta_n = \frac{n\lambda}{w}$$

$$\theta_3 = \sin^{-1}\frac{3(6.20 \times 10^{-7} \text{ m})}{2.0 \times 10^{-5} \text{ m}} \quad \theta_3 = 5.3°$$

If we wish to solve for a maximum instead of a minimum, we need only change $n\lambda$ to $(n+\frac{1}{2})\lambda$, where $n \geq 1$ and $\frac{1}{2}$ represents the phase shift. Remember that this equation does not include the wider, central maximum.

The effects of light diffraction are not commonly seen by us because they are only present in situations where the obstacle or aperture is comparable to that of the wavelength of light (too small for us to notice).

APPLYING the Concepts ▶ ▶ ▶ ▶

1. a) Compare the interference patterns produced by a single slit, a double slit, and a diffraction grating.
   b) What happens to the pattern as the opening(s) in the slits grow(s) larger?
2. a) Calculate the angle of the second-order maximum for monochromatic light of wavelength 550 nm if it illuminates a single slit of width $2.2 \times 10^{-5}$ m.

**b)** Calculate the angle of the second-order minimum for monochromatic light of wavelength 550 nm if it illuminates a single slit of width $2.2 \times 10^{-5}$ m.

**3.** For Question 2, given that the screen is 1.0 m away from the slit, find the distances from the central maximum at which the second-order minimum and maximum occur.

## 12.6 Thin Film Interference

The colours we see on soap bubbles and films, as well as on gas and oil slicks on water, are caused by the interference of light (Fig. 12.35). The film's thickness and the refractive index of the medium play important roles in causing this effect.

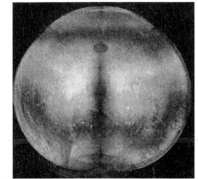

**Fig.12.35** Colours produced by light interference in thin films (soap bubbles)

### Path Difference Effect

Light hits the surface of the film and partially reflects. It also partially enters the film, reflects off the lower surface, comes out again, and combines with the light reflected from the surface to produce interference. The path difference in the film in terms of number of wavelengths determines the relative phase difference between the two waves. For example, consider the situation in Fig. 12.36. If the thickness of the film is $2\lambda$, then the total path the light travels is $4\lambda$. The light wave looks the same as the original wave and should interfere constructively.

Similarly, if the total path difference is a multiple of $\frac{\lambda}{2}$, destructive interference is produced. Since each wavelength obeys these rules, the thickness of the film will cause constructive interference for some colours and destructive interference for others.

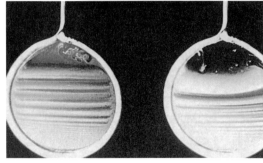

**Fig.12.36** Reflection and interference in a thin film

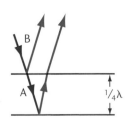

A travels $= 2\lambda + 2\lambda = 4\lambda$ more than B      A travels $= \frac{\lambda}{4} + \frac{\lambda}{4} = \frac{\lambda}{2}$ more than B

## Refractive Index Effect

The other effect that plays a role in thin film interference has to do with the incident medium's refractive index compared to the refractive index of the soap or oil slicks.

> When light travels from a less dense to a more optically dense medium, the *reflected* ray undergoes a phase change equivalent to $\frac{\lambda}{2}$ shift. When light travels from a more dense to a less optically dense medium, no phase shift occurs in the reflected wave.

## Combining the Effects

From the wave equation, $c = f\lambda$, the frequency of the light is constant and
$$v_1 = c = f\lambda_1$$
$$v_2 = f\lambda_2$$

Divide Equation 1 by Equation 2:
$$\frac{c}{v_2} = \frac{f\lambda_1}{f\lambda_2}$$
$$\frac{c}{v_2} = \frac{\lambda_1}{\lambda_2}$$

where $v_2$ is the speed of light in the new medium, and $\lambda_1$ and $\lambda_2$ are the wavelengths of light in air and the second medium, respectively.

When you add these two effects together, you produce the *net interference* between the two rays studied. If the net effect is constructive, a bright colour is seen. If the net effect is destructive, no colour is seen. We also need to remember that the wavelength of light changes when it enters a new medium.

---

**EXAMPLE 8** **Explaining interference effects for gasoline on water**

A gasoline slick of thickness 340 nm forms on the surface of water. If the wavelength of light considered is 476 nm and the refractive indices of gas and water are 1.40 and 1.33, respectively, will constructive or destructive interference occur for light falling perpendicular to this surface?

### *Solution and Connection to Theory*

**Given**

$n_1 = 1.00 \qquad n_2 = 1.40 \qquad n_3 = 1.33 \qquad \lambda_{air} = 476 \text{ nm} \qquad \lambda_{gas} = \dfrac{\lambda_{air}}{n_2}$

$\lambda_{gas} = \dfrac{476 \text{ nm}}{1.40} = 340 \text{ nm} = 3.40 \times 10^{-7} \text{ m}$

$t(\text{thickness}) = 340 \text{ nm} = 3.40 \times 10^{-7} \text{ m}$

A sketch of the situation is shown in Fig. 12.37.

The thickness of the gas film is $\dfrac{3.40 \times 10^{-7} \text{m}}{3.40 \times 10^{-7} \text{m}} = \lambda (1 \text{ wavelength})$.

Therefore, the total path difference is $2 \times \lambda = 2\lambda$.

The top wave reflects from a surface that has a larger refractive index than the incident index. Therefore, there is a $\frac{\lambda}{2}$ shift upon reflection. The wave travelling through the gas film reflects from a more dense (1.40) to a less dense (1.33) surface, and therefore undergoes no phase change. The net effect is $2\lambda$ and $\frac{\lambda}{2}$, which produces destructive interference.

Fig.12.37

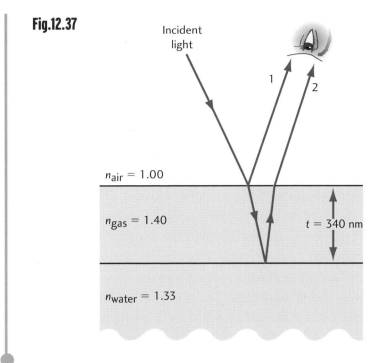

To produce constructive interference in a situation like Example 8, you would need a thickness that, when doubled (because the light travels down and back up through the material), is an odd number of half-wavelengths of the light in question. Thus the minimum thickness is $\frac{\lambda}{4}$ because when doubled, it becomes $\frac{\lambda}{2}$. For our question, this is thickness $\frac{1}{4} \times 3.40 \times 10^{-7}$ m $=$ $8.50 \times 10^{-8}$ m. The two waves are now *both shifted by* $\frac{\lambda}{2}$ and will interfere constructively.

**Fig.12.38** Summary of Diffraction and Interference Effects

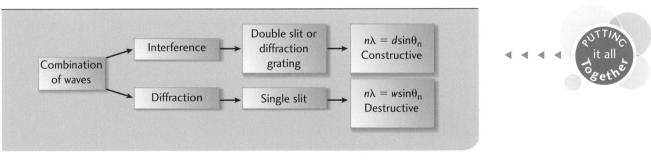

1. Explain the appearance of the multicoloured bands seen in soap bubbles. Why do the colours move and shift?
2. A thin gasoline film on water of thickness 510 nm is illuminated by light with wavelength that is also 510 nm. If the refractive index of gas is 1.40 and the refractive index of water is 1.33, will constructive or destructive interference occur for light falling perpendicular to this surface?

# A Military Application of Wave and Light Technology

In the 1980s, U.S. president Ronald Reagan funded work on a missile defense system. The Strategic Defense Initiative, or SDI (also referred to as **Star Wars**), planned to use space-based lasers to shoot down intercontinental ballistic missiles (ICBMs). The National Missile Defense program (NMD), revived by the Bush administration in 2001, has been under development for the last 10 years. Essentially, NMD remains an anti-missile shield. It uses different wavelengths of electromagnetic radiation and satellite technology to augment a ground-based missile defense system. Early warning systems will detect and track incoming ballistic missiles with infrared light. Ground-based radar will track missiles and send information to orbiting satellites. The satellites will relay data between radar and interceptor missiles. Plans have also been proposed to develop lasers that would be able to shoot down missiles from either airborne aircraft or from remote-controlled satellites.

The physics of these systems may be simple, but difficult and expensive to implement. Early test results have revealed that the system is unreliable.

**Fig.STSE.12.1**   The components of the NMD system

3. Satellites carry data between radars and interceptor missiles

Enemy missile

1. Early warning system detects and tracks ballistic missiles with infrared light

2. Ground-based radar tracks missiles and distinguishes real ones from decoys

4. Interceptor missile launched to intercept and destroy incoming missile

## Design a Study of Societal Impact

Research the cost of maintaining a program such as NMD. Are there economic benefits to the system? Are there any environmental problems associated with this program? Is there a need for this "Son of Star Wars" defense system?

Does Canada's commitment to the 1958 NORAD (North American Aerospace Defense Command) pact make us automatically committed to this project? How have other countries reacted to the development of the NMD program?

Critics of NMD claim that it is doomed to fail because the cost of developing a new missile that can evade NMD is low compared to the cost of developing an NMD program that can intercept the missile. What are some non-military alternatives that could be developed to ensure protection against missile attack?

## Design an Activity to Evaluate

Use the light sensor described in the "Build a Structure" section to perform different correlation studies. Calibrate the voltmeter you use with a standard light meter, if it is available. Once calibrated, use the meter to verify the inverse square law for light by registering light intensity at various distances. Check the device for linear response to light by assuming an inverse square relationship for the voltage output and then reading the output at different prescribed distances.

Research the various wavelengths of light that the photocell is most sensitive to by applying coloured filters to the incident light you are using.

## Build a Structure

Build a light/laser light receiver using photosensitive resistors (photocells), available at any electronics supply store. Wired in series with a simple battery and a common resistor, the voltage drop across either resistor is dependent on the light hitting the photocell. In pairs or groups, work on communicating over large distances using a simple flashlight (in dark conditions) or a laser using codes of your own design. Hold a competition to code and send an intact message over the longest possible distance. Some helium–neon photocells have a special input port that can modulate the laser beam, given the correct type of input. Use the correct kind of sensor to decode the original modulation.

SPECIFIC EXPECTATIONS

## You should be able to

*Understand Basic Concepts:*

- Explain the Doppler effect.
- Calculate the velocity of a moving vehicle using the Doppler effect equation.
- Explain red shift and blue shift and calculate the speeds of galaxies.
- Explain polarization of light by reflection, and by using anisotropic crystals and polarizing materials.
- Use Malus's law to calculate the amount of light transmitted through crossed Polaroids.
- Calculate Brewster's angle given the refractive index of the material light refracts into.
- Describe scattering effects like the blue colour of the sky.
- Define phase shift between two waves and superposition of waves.
- Describe how phase shift and superposition of waves produce the effects seen with double slits and diffraction gratings.
- Calculate the position of maxima and minima using the interference equations.
- Describe diffraction effects and relate them to interference effects.
- Describe the pattern obtained by single slit interference.
- Calculate the position of maxima and minima using the single slit equations.
- Describe how coloured fringes are produced in soap bubbles (and similar effects).
- Determine the type of interference given the thickness of a thin film, the refractive indices of the mediums, and the wavelength of light.

*Develop Skills of Inquiry and Communication:*

- Analyze spectral data and determine a celestial object's relative velocity directions.
- Evaluate the role of the Doppler shift in formulating the Big Bang Theory.
- Identify the interference patterns produced by the interaction of light through a single slit, a double slit, and a diffraction grating.
- Analyze the patterns produced by interference qualitatively and quantitatively.
- Determine why soap bubbles create coloured fringes.

*Relate Science to Technology, Society, and the Environment:*

- Describe and explain the design and technologies related to electromagnetic radiation, such as portable cell phones.
- Evaluate the role of cell phone technology in society.
- Analyze and use the concepts of refraction, diffraction, and wave interference to explain the basis of 3D movies, the spectrometer, and radar guns.

## Equations

$$f_2 = f_1 \left( 1 \pm \frac{v_r}{c} \right)$$

$$v_r = \left( \frac{\Delta f}{2f} \right) c$$

$$\tan\theta_B = \frac{n_2}{n_1}$$

$$I_2 = \tfrac{1}{2} I_0 \cos^2\theta$$

$$n\lambda = d\sin\theta_n \qquad n\lambda = \frac{dx_n}{L} \text{ (double slit)}$$

$$n\lambda = w\sin\theta_n \qquad n\lambda = \frac{dx_n}{L} \text{ (single slit)}$$

## Conceptual Questions

1. Explain the terms "red shift" and "blue shift." Use the wavelength range for visible light (400 nm to 750 nm) to help with the explanation.

2. Differentiate between relative speed and absolute speed (speed relative to the ground) using the situations of two cars approaching one another and two cars moving in the same direction. (Change the perspective from which you observe the speeds.)

3. When astronomers find a red-shifted celestial object, they say that the object is moving away from us (Earth). Can the red shift be interpreted as the Earth moving away from the celestial object?

4. Someone presents a pair of sunglasses to you and declares that they have polarized lenses. How can you check that this is true?
   a) by breaking them?
   b) by not breaking them and having no other sunglasses available to you?

5. What is the effect on transmitted light of
   a) two crossed Polaroids with their transmission axes parallel to each other?
   b) two crossed Polaroids with their transmission axes at right angles to each other?
   c) two crossed Polaroids with their transmission axes at an angle (other than 0° or 90°) to each other?

6. Why does rotating a Polaroid on top of a doubly refracting crystal cause one image to appear and the other one to disappear?

7. How do you know that the light scattered by particles in the sky is polarized?

8. Explain why we see a blue sky during part of the day and a red sky during another part.

9. The midnight sun, which is seen in the northern part of Canada, has a sky that is red all day. Explain this phenomenon in terms of scattering.

10. Industrial cities and cities with heavy traffic experience a certain amount of light decrease. Explain how you can get a measure of how much pollution there is on a given day by means of scattering of light.

11. Why can't we see around corners yet we can hear around corners (sound and light both have wave properties)?

12. Why doesn't the light from the headlights of your car cause an interference pattern?

13. Radio waves are part of the electromagnetic spectrum. Why do radio and television stations use two or more antennae to transmit their signals?

14. Gas has a refractive index of 1.40 and produces a dark band near the thin end of the slick. Another material with an index of refraction of 1.28 produces a bright band at the thin end of the slick. If both materials are the same in thickness throughout and are both on top of water (refractive index of 1.33), explain the difference.

15. What does shifting the phase between the sources in a double slit experiment do to the interference pattern?

16. As you are fishing using a hook and bobber, waves travel by the bobber. What would be the bobber's motion if it was bobbing on waves bigger than itself? smaller than itself?

## Problems

### 12.1 Doppler Effect

17. A galaxy is moving away from us at $1.5 \times 10^7$ m/s. What is the frequency of light observed by us if the emitted wave is $7.0 \times 10^{14}$ Hz?

18. A galaxy is moving away from us at $2.5 \times 10^7$ m/s. What is the frequency of light observed by us if the wavelength of the emitted light is 500 nm?

19. What would the frequencies become in Problems 17 and 18 if the galaxy was moving towards us?

20. A galaxy emits light of wavelength 600 nm. On Earth, we measure the wavelength to be 604 nm.
    a) Is the galaxy moving toward or away from us?
    b) Calculate its speed.
    c) Assume that the galaxy is moving at this speed but in the opposite direction. Find the measured wavelength.

21. What is the speed of a car detected by a radar gun with frequency $7.8 \times 10^9$ Hz if the difference in frequencies between emitted and received wavelength is 2000 Hz? Assume that the rader gun is stationary and the car is approaching it approximately head on.

22. a) If the radar gun is moving at a speed of 50 km/h in the same direction as the car in Problem 21, what is the speed of the car now?
    b) What is the speed of the car if the radar gun is moving at 50 km/h in the opposite direction to the car?

23. A police car is travelling at 80 km/h behind a speeder travelling at 160 km/h. If the difference in frequencies between emitted and received wavelength is 3000 Hz, what is the frequency of the radar gun?

## 12.2 Polarization

24. Calculate Brewster's angle for the following combination of mediums:
    a) air–water (1.33)
    b) air–glass (1.50)

c) glass–water
d) ice(1.30)–water

25. Brewster's angle was found to be 60° from air. What is the refractive index of the medium?

26. Two Polaroids are crossed in such a way as to not allow any light through. Now a third Polaroid is placed in between the two at an angle to both original Polaroids. Why is light once again transmitted?

27. Calculate the percentage of light travelling through two crossed polarizers if the angle between the polarizing directions is
    a) 10°.
    b) 30°.
    c) 70°.
    d) 85°.

28. What angle should be between the polarizers to reduce the intensity of light by 60%?

29. Three polarizers are placed on top of one another. If the angle between the first two is 60° and the angle between the first and third is 70°, find the percentage of the total light exiting the third Polaroid.

## 12.3 Scattering

30. According to theory, scattering is inversely proportional to the wavelength of light: Scattering $\alpha \frac{1}{\lambda^4}$.
    a) Does violet light (400 nm) scatter more or less than red light (700 nm)?
    b) Set the scatter to be 1 for the less scattered wave. By what factor is the other wave scattered more?

31. If green light is scattered five times more than red light, what is the wavelength of green light if red light is 700 nm?

32. How much more or less is infrared light $(1.0 \times 10^{-6}$ m) scattered than violet light (400 nm)?

## 12.4 Interference

33. For the following pairs of waves, determine if the interference is constructive, destructive, or partial.

**Fig.12.39**

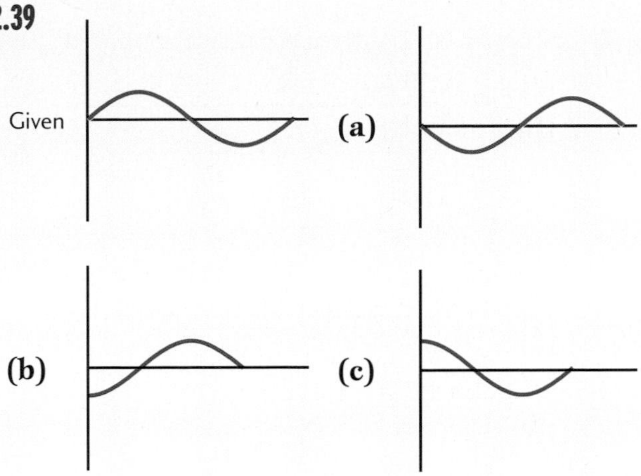

Given (a)

(b) (c)

34. Copy the following wave interference diagram (Fig. 12.40) and label the nodal lines and maxima with the appropriate order number. Use measurements from the diagram to calculate the wavelength. The circles are crests. Troughs are not shown.

**Fig.12.40**

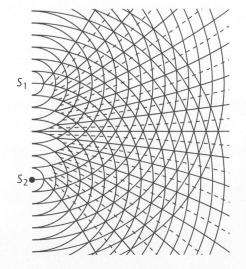

$S_1$

$S_2$

35. In Young's double slit experiment, a monochromatic source of wavelength 550 nm illuminates slits that are $4.0 \times 10^{-6}$ m apart. Find
   a) the angle at which the first-order maximum occurs.
   b) the angle at which the first-order minimum occurs.

c) the angle at which the third-order maximum occurs.
   d) the angle at which the third-order minimum occurs.

36. Given that the second-order maximum occurs at 22° and light of wavelength 600 nm is used, what is the double slit separation?

37. Two slits are 0.015 mm apart and the second-order maximum is 7.8 mm away from the centre line. If the screen is 1.1 m away, what is the wavelength of light used?

38. In an interference experiment, yellow light of wavelength 580 nm illuminates a double slit. If the screen is 1.3 m away and the distance between the centre line and the ninth dark spot is 3.0 cm, find the slit separation.

39. A diffraction grating has $10^6$ slits per metre. If green light of wavelength 540 nm is used, find the angle at which the first-order maximum occurs.

40. A diffraction grating with 2000 slits per centimetre is used with red light of wavelength 650 nm. Find the order number of the nodal line occurring at 11.25°.

41. What is the distance to the second-order maximum for a diffraction grating with $2 \times 10^4$ slits per millimetre if the screen is 0.9 m away and orange light with wavelength 600 nm is used?

42. a) For what minimum double slit separation does no interference (no nodal lines) occur? Assume a wavelength of 650 nm.
   b) How many wavelengths is the slit separation?

## 12.5 Diffraction

43. For a single slit of width $1.0 \times 10^{-5}$ m illuminated by red light of wavelength 640 nm, find the angle at which
   a) the second-order minimum occurs.
   b) the second-order maximum occurs.

**44.** Monochromatic light illuminates a single slit of $1.2 \times 10^{-2}$ mm width. If the first-order minimum occurs at 4°, what is the wavelength of light used?

**45.** For a single-slit pattern, the width of the central maximum is 6.8°. Given that violet light of wavelength 400 nm was used, find the width of the slit.

**46.** Light of wavelength 595 nm passes through a slit $1.23 \times 10^{-3}$ cm wide. Given that the screen is 1.2 m away, calculate the position relative to the centre line of
**a)** the third-order minimum.
**b)** the second-order maximum.

**47.** What is the angular width of the central maximum produced by a single slit of width $1.00 \times 10^{-3}$ cm if it is illuminated by blue light of wavelength 470 nm?

**48.** Light of wavelength 496 nm shines on a single opening $5.6 \times 10^{-4}$ m wide. If the screen is 3.5 m away and the first nodal line is 3.1 mm from the centre of the pattern, find the size of the central maximum
**a)** in millimetres
**b)** in degrees.

**49. a)** What is the minimum width of a single slit where no interference pattern occurs? Assume light of wavelength 500 nm (no first nodal line occurs).
**b)** How many wavelengths wide is the opening?

▶ **12.6 Thin Film Interference**

**50.** For the following diagrams of reflection off thin films, state whether there is constructive or destructive interference. The wavelengths given are the wavelengths of light within the film.

**Fig.12.41**

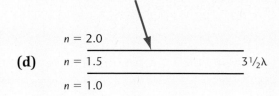

**51.** Light reflects off a thin film of gasoline ($n = 1.40$) on water ($n = 1.33$). If the wavelength of the light is 560 nm and the thickness of the film is $2.60 \times 10^{-6}$ m, will a bright or dark area result?

**52.** For light of wavelength 600 nm, what is the minimum thickness of a film that will produce maximum interference if the refractive index of the film is
**a)** 1.44?
**b)** 1.23?
Assume the film is on top of water ($n = 1.33$).

**53.** Light of wavelength 550 nm strikes a soap film ($n = 1.33$) that is surrounded by air. What is the minimum thickness needed to produce
**a)** a dark spot?
**b)** a bright spot?

## Purpose
To study various aspects of polarization.

## Equipment
Three Polaroids per group
Calcite crystal
Crumpled cellophane
Thin piece of mica
Calculator
Lucite ruler with holes of various shapes (or a broken piece of lucite ruler)

## Procedure
Record your observations for the following:
1. Take two Polaroids and cross them. Hold them up to a light and rotate one of the Polaroids around.
2. Position two Polaroids in a manner such that no light gets through. Put a third Polaroid in between them at an angle to the first two.
3. Place a calcite crystal on a page of written text. Rotate the crystal around.
4. Place one Polaroid on top of the crystal.
5. Rotate the Polaroid over top of the crystal.
6. Sandwich the mica between the Polaroids, hold them up to a light, and rotate the Polaroids.
7. Repeat Step 6 for the ruler piece.
8. Place a Polaroid on top of a calculator LCD readout and rotate the Polaroid.
9. If it is a sunny day, look out the window through a Polaroid filter. Either tilt your head or rotate the Polaroid.
10. Stand to one side of a reflection in a window such as that of the class door. Observe the reflection of the class in the window. Put a Polaroid filter in front of your eyes. Rotate the filter and adjust your position slightly until the image disappears.
11. Have a group member measure the angle relative to a normal to the glass. Use a protractor and metre stick.

## Analysis
1. Why does the intensity of the transmitted light change as you rotate the Polaroids around?
2. What law calculates the amount of light transmitted?
3. Why does light pass through three Polaroids positioned in the manner described in the procedure but no light passes through with two Polaroids.
4. Why does the calcite crystal produce two images such that one image rotates around the other? Which image is produced by the $o$ ray?
5. Why does a Polaroid cut out only one image at a time from the calcite crystal?
6. Why are colours produced in the mica and the LCD readout when a polarizing filter is put on top of them?
7. How do you know where the stressed areas or points are when viewing the broken lucite ruler between polarizing filters?
8. Why does the blue sky change its tint with polarizing filters and not with ordinary sunglasses?
9. Find the refractive index of glass and calculate Brewster's angle. Compare it to the measured angle from the experiment.

## Conclusion
Summarize what polarized light is and what phenomena prove its existence.

**LABORATORY EXERCISES**

## Purpose
To compare the interference patterns produced by single-slit, double-slit, and diffraction gratings.

## Equipment
Red and blue filters
Single slits with different openings
Double slits with different spacings
Diffraction gratings with different spacings
Showcase lamp
Retort stand
White screen

## Procedure
1. Stick a sheet of white paper to the wall. Position the showcase lamp in front of the screen using a retort stand.
2. Darken the room and look at the lit lamp through the diffraction grating with the greatest number of slits per metre. Note what you see. Take special care to write the order of appearance of the colours and the number of times you see each colour.
3. Repeat Step 2 for the single- and double-slit gratings. Again, choose the grating with the smallest opening and the smallest spacing.
4. Repeat Steps 1 to 3 using first a red filter with slits, then a blue filter.
5. Tape a ruler if it is visible enough or draw centimetre markings on the white screen. Try to determine the spacing of the maxima by counting the number of bright bands seen in a known range. (Divide the distance by the number of maxima.)
6. Compare the number of bands seen and the clarity of the pattern for a diffraction grating with the fewest slits per metre and one with the most slits per metre. Try using a red filter, then a blue filter, then plain white light (no filters).
7. Repeat Step 6 for the double-slit grating with the largest spacing and the one with the smallest spacing.
8. Repeat Step 6 for the single-slit grating with the largest opening and the smallest opening.

## Analysis and Discussion
1. Compare the general appearance of the interference patterns in terms of spacing between bands, sharpness of pattern, size of central band, and intensity of the pattern as you move farther from the centre of the pattern. Record your answers in chart form.
2. Which colour has the longest wavelength and which colour has the shortest wavelength, red or blue? Which colour had the greatest number of bands for each type of interference instrument? Which colour had the largest spacing (distance between consecutive orders)? Record your answers in chart form.
3. For each type of interference instrument, what does decreasing the slit separation (increasing the number of slits in the case of a diffraction grating) do to the pattern?

## Conclusion
Which instrument produces the best interference pattern in terms of sharpness? What effect does the size of the opening have on the sharpness of the pattern?

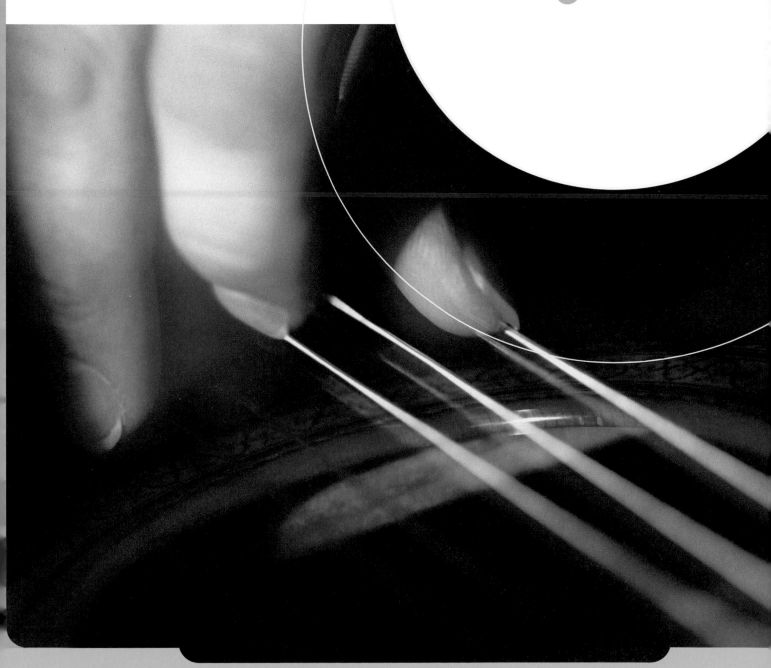

# Waves and Sound

# UNIT D:  Waves and Sound

We have all watched movies in which the properties of sound and the sound track are an important part of the story.

For example, many old western movies contain scenes where someone puts his or her ear onto a railway track to listen for the approach of a distant train. How well would this technique work? Would you really hear the train sooner by listening with your ear on the steel railway track? Before you answer, consider that sound is a form of energy. This energy is able to travel, or be transferred, through the vibration of molecules. Table 13.1 shows that sound travels more than 15 times faster through steel (iron) than through air. Perhaps those cowboys in the movies were really physics teachers on summer vacation at the Dude Ranch!

Another example of the use of sound in movies occurs in the *Star Wars* series. Spaceship battle scenes are accompanied by sound effects of missiles firing and targets exploding. These sound effects may help promote a dramatic storyline, but in reality, they are impossible because sound cannot travel in a vacuum. An explosion in space doesn't produce any sound. The science fiction thriller *Alien* used the inability of sound to travel in a vacuum as a promotional idea. Advertising posters for the movie, designed to capture the horror of being attacked by an alien monster, read "In space, nobody can hear you scream."

**Timeline: History of Waves and Sound**

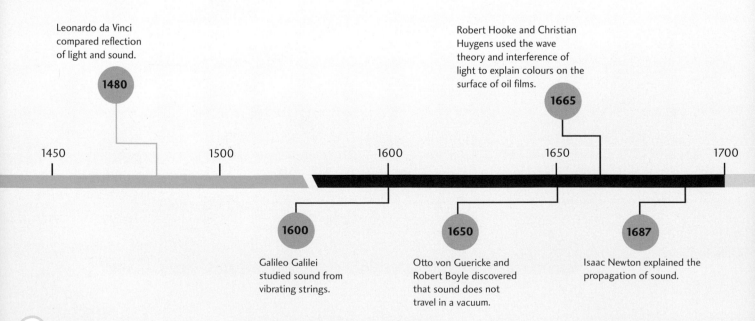

Leonardo da Vinci compared reflection of light and sound.

**1480**

Robert Hooke and Christian Huygens used the wave theory and interference of light to explain colours on the surface of oil films.

**1665**

1450  1500  1600  1650  1700

**1600**

Galileo Galilei studied sound from vibrating strings.

**1650**

Otto von Guericke and Robert Boyle discovered that sound does not travel in a vacuum.

**1687**

Isaac Newton explained the propagation of sound.

This unit may not provide you with a career in the movies, but it will give you a better understanding of what you hear during a movie. Other topics in this unit will allow you to answer many other sound-related questions such as: How fast does sound travel? Why does a car that is moving towards you sound different than a car moving away from you? Why are dogs and bats able to hear sounds you cannot?

This unit will also introduce you to many interesting and important applications of sound. There are medical applications such as ultrasound, navigational tools such as sonar, design applications of music halls, and musical instruments. Now that's an earful!

Remember: you heard it here first.

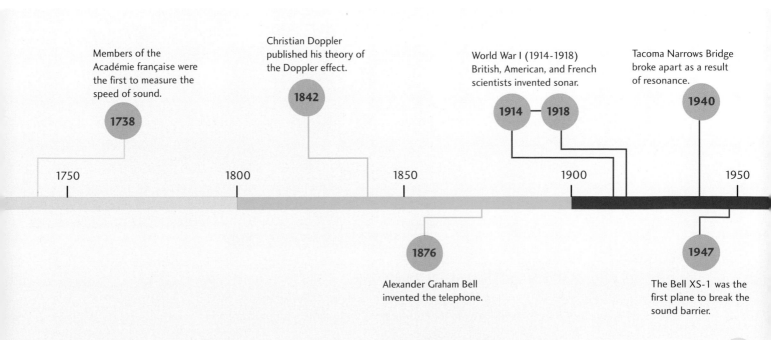

Members of the Académie française were the first to measure the speed of sound.

**1738**

Christian Doppler published his theory of the Doppler effect.

**1842**

World War I (1914-1918) British, American, and French scientists invented sonar.

**1914** — **1918**

Tacoma Narrows Bridge broke apart as a result of resonance.

**1940**

1750    1800    1850    1900    1950

**1876**

Alexander Graham Bell invented the telephone.

**1947**

The Bell XS-1 was the first plane to break the sound barrier.

# Basics of Sound

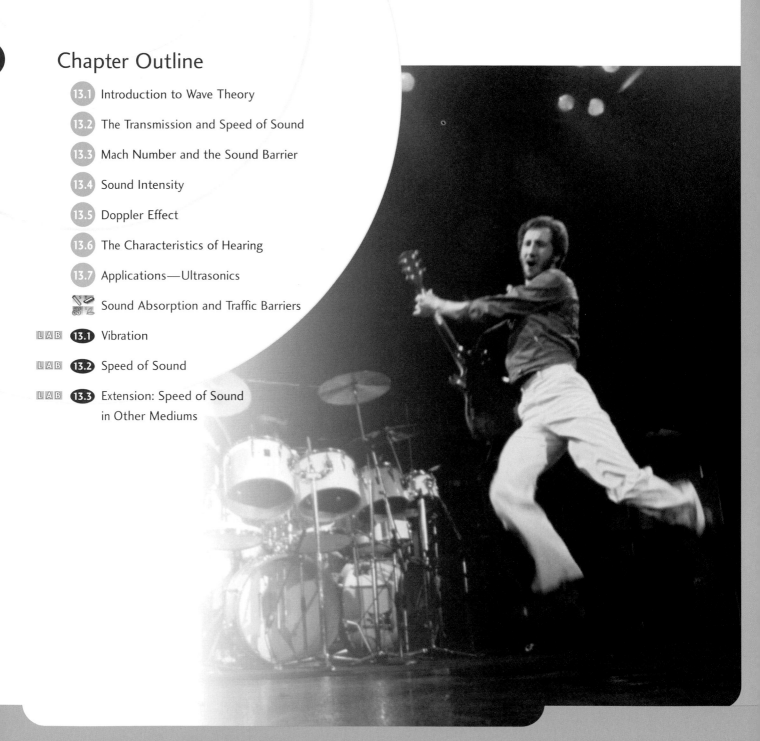

## Chapter Outline

**By the end of this chapter, you will be able to**

- demonstrate an understanding of the properties of mechanical waves and sound
- understand the principles underlying the production, transmission, interaction, and reception of sound
- describe and explain aspects of sound in the areas of entertainment, health, and technology

# 13.1 Introduction to Wave Theory

Sound, like light, is a wave. It shows many of the properties discussed in the Light and Geometric Optics chapters. In this unit, we will review the underlying principles of wave theory. These principles will lead us into topics such as the sound barrier, sonic booms, and music. The photo in Fig. 13.1 is of the Thrust SSC, which broke the land speed record, going at 1.007 and 1.003 times the speed of sound. In this chapter, you will learn about the speed of sound and about the consequences of breaking the sound barrier.

**Fig.13.1** Batmobile, move over! Oct. 13, 1997: The Thrust SSC broke the sound barrier with runs of 1.007 and 1.003 times the speed of sound.

## Types of Waves

The two general types of waves are **transverse** and **longitudinal**. Both types of waves require the action of an oscillating or vibrating source, the motion of which is called **simple harmonic motion**. This motion creates a wave that moves away from the source with its own velocity.

The relationship between the direction of motion of the generating source and the velocity of the wave determines the type of wave. In Fig. 13.2, we see a picture of a person generating a wave by continuously shaking the spring from side to side. The motion of the person's hand is at right angles to the resultant wave direction.

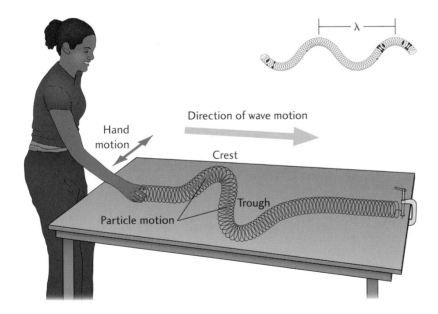

**Fig.13.2** The person moves her hand across the table, from side to side. This motion causes waves to move down the table. The motion of the source is perpendicular to the velocity direction of the wave. This type of wave is called transverse.

**When the direction of travel of the wave is perpendicular to the motion of the source, the wave is transverse.** Waves in the stretched strings of musical instruments are an example of this type of wave.

The spring can also be compressed and released periodically (move back and forth), causing compressions and extensions to travel along the length of the spring. This motion is illustrated in Fig. 13.3. The person uses a sawing

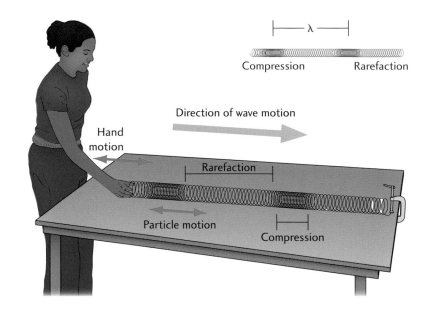

Water waves are a combination of the action of both kinds of waves, transverse and longitudinal. The particles of water move in circular paths, so sometimes they are parallel to the direction of wave motion, and at other times they are perpendicular to the direction of wave motion. People sitting in a boat find themselves moving in a circular clockwise path, in the direction of wave motion (see Fig. 13.4).

**Fig.13.4**

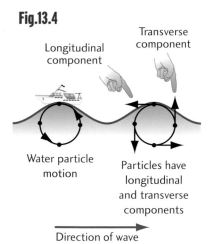

motion on the spring, which causes these periodic patterns of compression and release to travel in the direction of the push–pull action.

**When the travel of the wave is parallel to the motion of the source, the wave is longitudinal.** Sound is an example of this type of wave.

## Aspects of Periodic Waves

Both the transverse and longitudinal waves are recurring cycles of the same motion. The motion is represented mathematically by the sine wave. The different parts of the wave are reviewed in Fig. 13.5.

The terms used to describe sound waves are the same as those used to describe light waves (see Chapter 10).

**Fig.13.5** The particles transmitting the wave action are all moving perpendicular to the direction of motion. The wave particles are indicated by the small arrows. At the maximum amplitude points, the particles are momentarily at rest as they change direction.

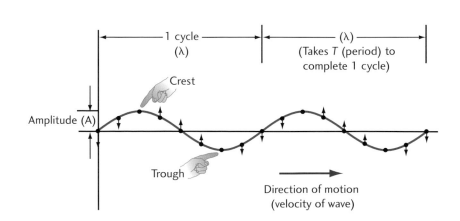

A **cycle** is a complete sequence of motion that repeats itself. The **wavelength** ($\lambda$) is the length in metres (m) of one cycle, given the symbol *lambda*. The **period** ($T$) is the time to complete one cycle and is measured in seconds (s). The **frequency** is the number of cycles in a given time period. It is measured in cycles per second. The term "cycles" is usually left off and the unit becomes $s^{-1}$ or $\frac{1}{s}$. This unit is named **hertz** (Hz) in SI. It honours Heinrich Rudolf Hertz (1857-1894), a physicist specializing in electricity and magnetism. The **amplitude** of a wave is the maximum disturbance of a wave from its zero point (negative or positive), measured in metres (m).

Another common unit for frequency is **rps** or revolutions per second, which is another way of expressing hertz. A common term from the vinyl era of records is **rpm**, or revolutions per minute. Early record players played at a high rotational speed in order to minimize the background noise of the crude needle in the record grooves. These records were called 78s because the turntable rotated 78 times a minute. The next generation of records, the singles hits, played at 45 rpm and the long-playing records at—$33\frac{1}{3}$ rpm.

## Wave Equation

Waves are travelling disturbances and hence have a velocity associated with them. The simple form of the velocity equation,

$$\vec{v} = \frac{\Delta \vec{d}}{\Delta t}$$

can be adjusted to reflect the variables used with periodic motion. The distance travelled in one cycle is the *wavelength* and the time it takes is the *period*. Thus, we can rewrite the equation as

$$v = \frac{\lambda}{T}.$$

But $T = \frac{1}{f}$ since $T$ is measured in seconds and $f$ is measured in 1/second. Replacing $T$ with $\frac{1}{f}$, we obtain the standard form of the **wave equation,**

$$v = \lambda f$$

**EXAMPLE 1**   **Calculate period and frequency**

Calculate the period and frequency of a tuning fork whose tines vibrate back and forth 375 times in 3.00 seconds.

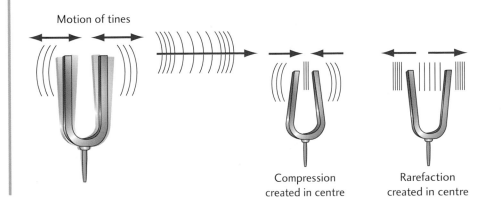

Motion of tines

Compression created in centre

Rarefaction created in centre

**Fig.13.6**   A tuning fork produces longitudinal sound waves

### Solution and Connection to Theory

**Given**

$\Delta t = 3.00$ s     number of cycles $N = 375$     $T = ?$     $f = ?$

$T = \dfrac{\Delta t}{N}$, which gives you the *time per cycle.*

$T = \dfrac{3.00 \text{ s}}{375} = 0.00800 \text{ s} = 8.00 \times 10^{-3}$ s

$f = \dfrac{1}{T} = \dfrac{1}{8.00 \times 10^{-3} \text{ s}} = 125 \text{ s}^{-1} = 125$ Hz

The period of the tuning fork is $8.00 \times 10^{-3}$ s and its frequency is 125 Hz.

---

**EXAMPLE 2**     **Calculating the speed of the wave**

Calculate the speed of the sound wave leaving the tuning fork in Example 1 if the wavelength of one cycle is 275 cm.

### Solution and Connection to Theory

**Given**

$f = 125$ Hz     $\lambda = 275 \text{ cm} = 2.75$ m     $v = ?$

$v = \lambda f = 2.75 \text{ m} \times 125 \text{ s}^{-1} = 344$ m/s

The speed of sound is close to this value at an average temperature and density of air.

**Fig.13.7**  Summary of Wave Types

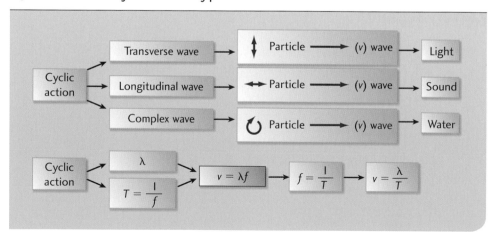

UNIT D: Waves and Sound

## Animals with Sonar, Part I: Bats and Dolphins

1. Dolphins (Fig. 13.8B) have a large repertoire of sounds that can be classified under two general types: those sounds used to locate objects, termed **echolocation** (sonar), and those emitted to express emotional states. Dolphins emit pulses and clicks in groupings at a rate of over 690 clicks per 2.3 s. The sounds have a frequency of typically 130 kHz (Fig. 13.8A).

   **a)** Find the period and frequency of emission of pulses.

   **b)** Given that the speed of sound is 344 m/s, find the wavelength of the emitted pulse.

**Fig.13.8A**

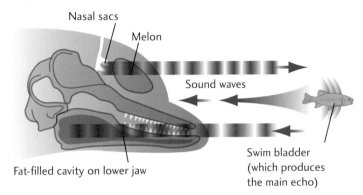

2. Bats' sonar abilities allow them to detect the difference in objects as close as 0.3 mm. This distance is the width of a pencil line drawn on paper. The bat's sonar, prorated to its power usage, is about a million times more sensitive than any radar device engineers have devised. The bat sends out an equivalent of 60 pulses in 0.3 s. The typical frequency range of the sounds lies around 30 kHz.

   **a)** Calculate the period and frequency of the rate of emission of the pulses.

   **b)** Calculate the wavelength of the sound given that the speed of sound is 340 m/s.

The frequency emitted by a bat reflects off its prey. If the wavelength is too small, the sound diffracts around the object and no information is returned. A brown bat emitting 3 mm waves can detect objects as small as 0.2 mm, like insects.

**Fig.13.8B**

3. Birds also use **echolocation** for navigation. Their clicks and pulses are low frequency compared to the high-frequency pulses of dolphins and bats, which makes them less effective. The oilbird migrates from Trinidad to Bolivia. Its sounds are in the human hearing range and are emitted at a rate of 7.5 clicks in 0.3 s. Calculate the period and frequency of the clicks.

## 13.2 The Transmission and Speed of Sound

**Fig.13.9** If the belljar is evacuated, no sound is heard from the bell

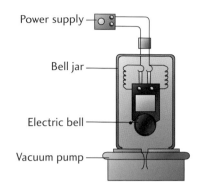

Power supply

Bell jar

Electric bell

Vacuum pump

"I can't hear you!!!"

### Medium Dependence

Sound is a longitudinal wave that requires a medium to travel in. Some schools have a demonstration where a bell rings inside a jar. The experimental setup is shown in Fig. 13.9. As the air is pumped out of the jar, the sound gradually disappears. When the air is returned to the jar, the sound returns. Thus, in order for sound to be transmitted, a medium must be present.

In air, the only type of vibration possible is longitudinal. Air cannot sustain a transverse motion because air particles drift off. To understand how your voice is transmitted to another person, refer to Fig. 13.10. The vibrations from a source, such as your voice box, set up a pressure fluctuation that causes the neighboring air pressure to change. This pattern through the air is then continued. No net movement of air takes place, but the pressure changes are transmitted out of your mouth at a speed determined by the number and type of molecules ready to pass on the pressure fluctuation. Thus, your voice sounds different in helium (high pitched). The dense areas of air transmitting a sound wave are called **compressions** and the less dense areas are called **rarefactions**.

The motion of sound is similar to people dancing the *bump* in a dense crowd. They bump the people ahead of them, creating a greater pressure. This motion gets transmitted as long as people continue to compress, leaving a rarefaction behind them. It is the disturbance that is transmitted, not the individual particles.

Table 13.1 shows the speeds of sound in different materials.

**Fig.13.10** The lungs force the air out and through the vocal cord. These folds of skin vibrate as the air rushes by them, producing sound in the form of compressions and rarefactions of air (pressure waves). These waves are amplified and modified by the group of parts collectively called the **resonators**. They are the pharynx, mouth, and nasal cavity.

| Table 13.1 Speed of Sound | | |
| --- | --- | --- |
| Material | Density (kg/m³) | Speed of sound (m/s) |
| Air | 1.29 | 331 |
| Hydrogen | 0.09 | 1284 |
| Mercury | 13 546 | 1452 |
| Water | 1 000 | 1498 |
| Copper | 8 930 | 3800 |
| Oak | 650 | 3850 |
| Glass (crown) | 2 600 | 5000 |
| Iron | 7 800 | 5000 |
| Aluminum | 2 710 | 5100 |

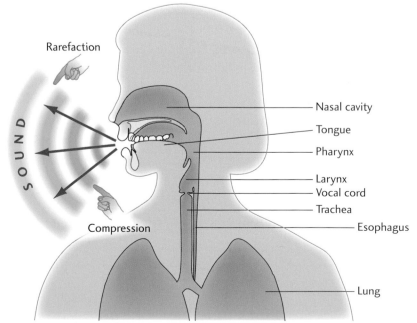

Rarefaction

Nasal cavity

Tongue

Pharynx

Larynx

Vocal cord

Trachea

Esophagus

S O U N D

Compression

Lung

**Fig.13.11**   Factors Affecting the Speed of Sound

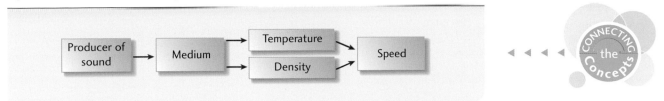

Generally speaking, **the stiffer the material, the faster the speed of sound**. It follows that the speed of sound is greatest in solids and least in gases. This idea is an application of particle theory from your chemistry class. Figure 13.12 shows that the particles are closer together in a solid. They are therefore more immediately responsive to one another's motions. As the spacing between particles increases, the responsiveness of the particles to one another's motion decreases, which affects the speed of the sound wave.

**Fig.13.12**   The stronger the bonds between molecules, the faster they tend to transmit sound

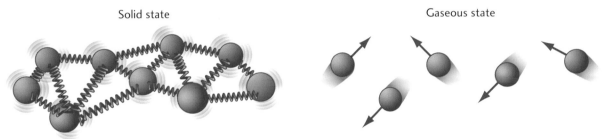

Solid state

Gaseous state

Molecules of a solid behave as if they were held together by springs. Their proximity allows the vibrations caused by sound energy to be easily transmitted.

Gas molecules are separated by great distances. Hence, transmission of energy is less efficient.

In western movies, you may have seen a cowboy kneel down and put his ear to the ground in order to listen for hoof beats a long distance away. This technique is effective because sound travels faster through the ground than in the air. However, some of the benefits of the shorter travel time are negated by the greater rate of decrease in *amplitude* of the wave in the denser medium. This decrease means that the wave dies out faster when travelling through a solid than a gas.

**EXAMPLE 3**   **Comparing speed in various mediums**

Suppose you're on a field trip to the beach, standing on an old-fashioned boardwalk made of hardwood. You have accidentally gotten into trouble and need every microsecond you can to get away. You need to know when the vice-principal is approaching (his army boots make a loud thumping sound). If the boardwalk is 800 m long, how much extra time will you have if you can hear the footsteps through the wood?

The speed of sound in wood is 4000 m/s if the sound is moving with the grain. If it moves across the grain, then the speed drops to 1000-2500 m/s.

**Fig.13.13** Sound travels faster with the grain

*Solution and Connection to Theory*

**Given**

$v_{air} = 340$ m/s $\qquad v_{hardwood} = 4000$ m/s $\qquad \Delta d = 800$ m $\qquad \Delta t = ?$

$$v = \frac{\Delta d}{\Delta t} \qquad \Delta t = \frac{\Delta d}{v}$$

$$\Delta t_{air} = \frac{800 \text{ m}}{340 \text{ m/s}} = 2.35 \text{ s}$$

$$\Delta t_{hardwood} = \frac{800 \text{ m}}{4000 \text{ m/s}} = 0.20 \text{ s}$$

The extra time you have to get away is 2.35 s − 0.20 s = 2.15 s. You have 92% more time to react. Good luck!

## Dependence of Speed on Temperature

For sound travelling through air, there is a small effect due to the temperature of the air. Air particles move faster as the temperature increases. As the temperature rises, so does the speed of sound based on the following formula:

$$v = 332 \text{ m/s} + \left(0.6 \, \frac{\text{m/s}}{\text{°C}}\right) (T \text{ °C})$$

The speed is measured in m/s and the temperature ($T$) is measured in degrees Celsius.

> **EXAMPLE 4** **Calculating the speed of sound in air**
>
> Given a summer temperature of 20°C, find the speed of sound.
>
> $$v = 332 \text{ m/s} + \left(0.6 \, \frac{\text{m/s}}{\text{°C}}\right) (T \text{ °C})$$
>
> $$= 332 \, \frac{\text{m}}{\text{s}} + \left(0.6 \, \frac{\text{m}}{\text{s °C}}\right) (20\text{°C})$$
>
> $$= 332 \, \frac{\text{m}}{\text{s}} + 12 \, \frac{\text{m}}{\text{s}} = 344 \, \frac{\text{m}}{\text{s}}$$

## Estimating the Distance from a Lightning Strike

In 3.0 s, sound travels roughly one kilometre. In the imperial system of measurement, in 5.0 s the sound wave travels roughly one mile.

The speed of light is immensely faster than the speed of sound. You see lightning instantaneously, followed by the sound of thunder. For every three-second count, the sound has travelled about one kilometre. Thus, if you see lightning strike and have counted to 12 before you hear the thunder, the storm is

UNIT D: Waves and Sound

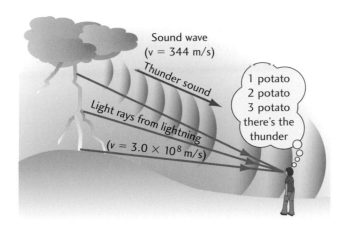

$$12 \text{ s} \times \frac{1 \text{ km}}{3 \text{ s}} = 4 \text{ km away.}$$

The time it took the light to reach you is $\Delta t = \dfrac{\Delta d}{v}$

$$\text{time} = \frac{\text{distance}}{\text{speed}} = \frac{4 \times 10^3 \text{ m}}{3.0 \times 10^8 \text{ m/s}} = 1.3 \times 10^{-5} \text{ s.}$$

Not a time our eyes can react in!

1. Use the particle theory to explain why sound travels fastest in solids and slowest in gases.
2. Calculate the speed of sound in air and in wood given that it travels 8000 m and takes 2.35 s in air and 0.20 s in wood. How many times faster is it in wood?
3. The sound of thunder occurs 12.3 s after lightning is seen. How far away is the storm if the temperature is
   **a)** 0°C?   **b)** 10°C?   **c)** 30°C?   **d)** −10°C?

# 13.3 Mach Number and the Sound Barrier

When aircraft (and now cars) get close to or go faster than the speed of sound, a different unit is often used to describe their speed. It's called the **Mach number**, named after Ernst Mach, a prominent physicist from the late 1800s. Mach 1 is defined as the speed of sound at a given air temperature. If you are travelling at greater than Mach 1, your speed is said to be **supersonic**. If you are below Mach 1, your speed is **subsonic**. Speeds greater than or equal to Mach 5 are **hypersonic**. In the following examples, you will learn how to calculate Mach numbers.

**EXAMPLE 5**   **Finding the Mach number**

What is the Mach number for a plane flying at 839 m/s in air of temperature 6°C?

## Solution and Connection to Theory

**Given**

$$v_{plane} = 839 \text{ m/s} \qquad T = 6°C \qquad v_{sound} = ?$$

$$v_{sound} = 332 + 0.6T = (332 + 0.6(6°C))\text{m/s} = 335.6 \text{ m/s}$$

This speed is Mach 1.

$$\frac{839 \text{ m/s}}{335.6 \text{ m/s}} = 2.5$$

Therefore, the plane is flying at Mach 2.5, and its speed is supersonic.

---

### SUPERSONIC FLIGHT

Fighter planes (Fig. 13.15) fly in the range of Mach 2-3. Concordes fly at about Mach 1.2, and normal passenger planes — at Mach 0.8–0.9. The X-15A-2, which is a manned jet that must be flown to a release altitude by a jumbo jet, reaches Mach 6. The reason for the "piggyback ride" is to keep the weight of the craft to a minimum by minimizing the amount of fuel in the fuel tanks. For major speeds, the space shuttle, on re-entry, hits Mach 25. The Apollo 10 spacecraft was moving at an incredible Mach 37 on its re-entry.

---

| EXAMPLE 6 | **Converting Mach numbers to speed** |

A fighter jet is flying at Mach 3.2 in air of temperature 2.0°C. What is the plane's speed?

## Solution and Connection to Theory

**Given**

$$v_{plane} = \text{Mach } 3.2 \qquad T = 2.0°C \qquad v_{sound} = ?$$

$$v_{sound} = 332 + 0.6T = (332 + 0.6(2.0))\text{m/s} = 333 \text{ m/s}$$

The speed of the plane is 333 m/s $\times$ 3.2 = 1066 m/s

**Fig.13.15** Compare these speeds to that of a bullet: $v = 2635 \frac{km}{h}$

Concorde 1 500 $\frac{km}{h}$

X-15A-2 7 297 $\frac{km}{h}$

Shuttle (re-entry) 29 880 $\frac{km}{h}$

Appollo 10 space craft (re-entry) 39 897 $\frac{km}{h}$

## Sound Barrier

The term "sound barrier" is used in aviation to describe the buildup of sound waves in front of a plane as it nears the speed of sound. This effect happens because the plane is catching up with its own jet noises. Consider the situation in Fig. 13.16 where a student runs around a track, yelling as loudly as possible. Normally, the sound travels away from the student because its speed is so much greater than the student's. Assume that a genetically engineered student can now run close to the speed of sound. As the student yells, the sound waves try to move away from our noisy friend. However, they are followed by more sound waves from the continual hollering because the student is right behind the sound. This pressure buildup in the air molecules creates a barrier to further speed increase by the student. Breaking this barrier requires a great deal of energy. Fortunately for the school's windows, the student does not have the extra energy and never breaks the sound barrier.

When people were first trying to reach the speed of sound, the problem was not in the extra energy needed to reach this speed, but in the plane's inability to steer and maintain lift when approaching this speed. Near Mach 1, the steering mechanisms on the plane became locked so the pilot could not

**Fig.13.16** As a sound-emitting object approaches the speed of sound, sound energy builds up ahead of it

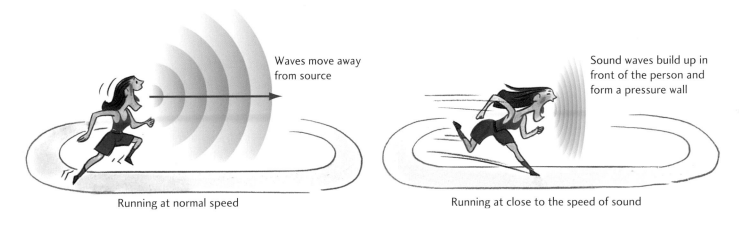

Waves move away from source

Running at normal speed

Sound waves build up in front of the person and form a pressure wall

Running at close to the speed of sound

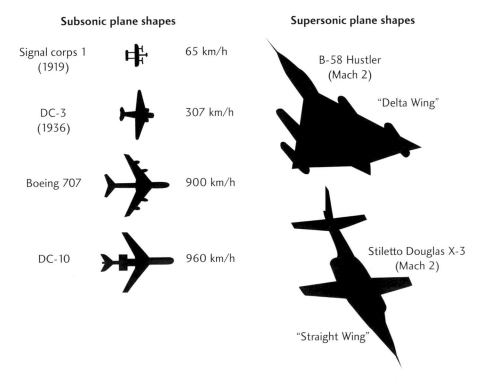

**Subsonic plane shapes**

Signal corps 1 (1919)        65 km/h

DC-3 (1936)                  307 km/h

Boeing 707                   900 km/h

DC-10                        960 km/h

**Supersonic plane shapes**

B-58 Hustler (Mach 2)

"Delta Wing"

Stiletto Douglas X-3 (Mach 2)

"Straight Wing"

**Fig.13.17** Various airplane designs and their top speeds. Notice the differences in shape between the subsonic and the supersonic planes.

steer the plane. The manual controls became too stiff to move due to the great air pressure surrounding the plane. Many test pilots lost their lives because the plane could not be pulled out of a nose dive.

This problem was corrected by new steering designs, the advent of the jet engine, as well as changes to the shape of the wing (pulled back and smaller). The first plane to break the sound barrier was the Bell XS-1 experimental rocket on October 14, 1947.

## Sonic Boom

Like a boat leaving a wake of water waves behind it, a plane breaking the sound barrier leaves a pressure wake behind it. As is seen in Fig. 13.18, the pressure waves spread out and move down towards the ground in an ever-expanding cone. There are two of them, one from the nose and one from the wing tips of the plane.

If this **sonic shock** wave hasn't died out sufficiently during its travel through the air, then people on the ground hear two thunderous booms or loud cracks when the sound reaches the ground. The general effect is to

**Fig.13.18** A plane travelling near the speed of sound produces a sound "wake" similar to that produced by a speed boat

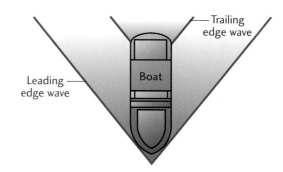

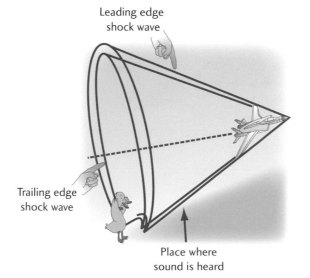

Two shock waves form when a plane flies at supersonic speeds. A sonic boom is the arrival of the shock wave on the ground.

Model of X-15 rocket in a wind tunnel shows the shock waves that form around the plane's edges as it moves at supersonic speeds.

startle animals and people. In some cases, the **acoustic pressure** is sufficiently large to shatter glass, not something owners of skyscrapers wish to deal with. For this reason, supersonic travel is prohibited over North America unless the plane is sufficiently high, allowing pressure waves to die off well before they reach the ground.

This shock wave is really the buildup of numerous waves constructively interfering to produce a superwave. The interference aspect of sound waves is treated in detail in Chapter 14. However, the effect is shown in Fig. 13.19. The plane catches up to the waves of sound ahead of it and causes them to squeeze together. A pressure barrier is built up, which requires extra energy to get through. When the plane breaks through the sound barrier, it leaves the sonic wave behind, which then travels down to the ground.

The sonic boom is not a one-time phenomenon. Many people believe that the loud cracks are heard only when the plane breaks the sound barrier the first time. In fact, the pressure wave is being generated continually from the front and back of the plane as long as the plane is flying near the speed of sound. As a plane flies over a region, the pressure cones follow, creating sonic booms for that area.

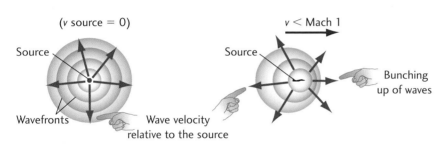

Stationary source wavefronts are spreading out uniformly

Plane is travelling at less than the speed of sound. Doppler effect occurs.

**Fig.13.19** The effects of a source's motion on the sound waves it generates

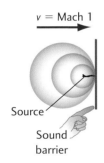

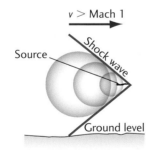

At Mach 1, a barrier of pressure builds up. As the plane breaks through it, the shock wave is left behind, which travels down to the surface of Earth. We hear it as a loud "boom."

**Fig.13.20** Summary — Sound from a Moving Source

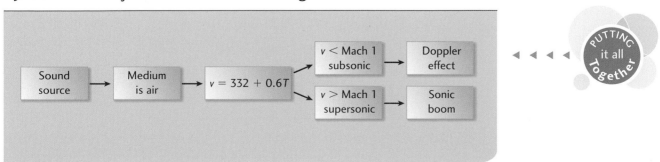

  ▶ ▶ ▶ ▶

1. What is the speed of a plane flying at Mach
   a) 2.1 and 3°C?          b) 0.4 and 35°C?
   c) 1.9 and 0°C?          d) 5.1 and −2°C?
2. Convert the speeds in Question 1 to km/h.
3. Describe the process of a sound barrier forming. What happens when the object finally breaks through the sound barrier? Is a sonic boom necessarily going to occur?

## 13.4 Sound Intensity

As sound emanates from a source, it forms an ever-growing sphere of sound waves around the source (refer to Fig. 13.21). This phenomenom is similar to a rock thrown into a lake and creating ripples that move away. Just like the water waves dissipate as they move away, the sound intensity also decreases with distance.

**Fig.13.21**  The sound waves emitted from a source travel out in spherical wavefronts. Since area grows as $r^2$ ($area_{sphere} = 4\pi r^2$) and intensity $= \frac{power}{area}$, we can see that the intensity is decreasing by factors of $\frac{1}{r^2}$, where $r = 1, 2, ...$ ($\frac{1}{4}, \frac{1}{9}, \frac{1}{16}$ ...) as you move away from the source.

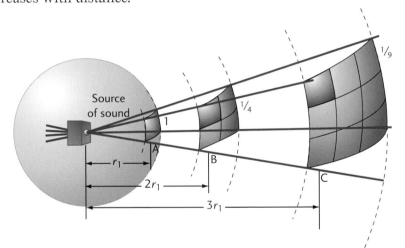

The **intensity (I)** of the wave is defined as the rate of power (P) that passes through a surface with an area (A) perpendicular to the wave's direction. Recall from Chapter 7 that power is the rate at which work is done. It is the rate at which energy is transformed divided by time. If the time used is one second, then the power is measured in joules per second (J/s) or watts (W). The units for area are m², thus the intensity of sound is measured in watts/area (W/m²). From this information, we can write

$$I = \frac{P}{A}$$

In Fig. 13.21, we saw that the source of sound created a sphere of sound moving away from it. The area of a sphere is $A = 4\pi r^2$, where r is the radius of the sphere as well as the distance the sound wave has travelled at the time you calculate the area. We can now substitute for area in the equation $I = \frac{P}{A}$, to obtain

$$I = \frac{P}{4\pi r^2}$$

From this equation, we can infer that as the distance increases, the sound intensity changes by a factor of $\frac{1}{r^2}$. This equation is similar to the force of gravity calculations in Chapter 5 and is another example of the **inverse square law**. The ratio of intensities emitted from a single sound source at different distances can be calculated by the following equation:

$$\frac{I_1}{I_2} = \frac{(r_2)^2}{(r_1)^2}$$

### EXAMPLE 7 — Decrease in intensity of sound due to distance

A helicopter hovers overhead during an airshow, causing sound waves to emanate uniformly. If the first listener is 700 m away and the second listener is 1000 m away, by how much has the intensity level of the sound decreased when it reaches listener 2?

*Solution and Connection to Theory*

**Given**

$r_1 = 700$ m    $r_2 = 1000$ m    $\dfrac{I_1}{I_2} = ?$

$\dfrac{I_1}{I_2} = \dfrac{(r_2)^2}{(r_1)^2}$    $\dfrac{I_1}{I_2} = \dfrac{(700 \text{ m})^2}{(1000 \text{ m})^2} = 0.49$

Thus, the intensity level is almost one half by the time it reaches listener 2.

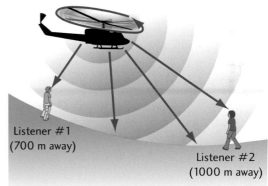

**Fig.13.22** Sound intensity depends on distance from the source

Listener #1
(700 m away)

Listener #2
(1000 m away)

## The Decibel System

Human beings have an enormous range of hearing. We can hear noise with intensities from as low as $10^{-12}$ W/m² to greater than 1.0 W/m². With such a wide range of values (12 orders of magnitude or a million million), it is easier to use a **logarithmic system** to measure units of sound intensity. These numbers are based on the exponents of numbers.

The decibel unit of sound intensity is defined as

$$\beta = 10 \log\left(\frac{I_2}{I_1}\right)$$

where $\beta$ is the sound intensity in decibels, $I_1$ is the initial sound intensity, and $I_2$ is the final sound intensity. In most cases, the value for $I_1$ is the threshold of hearing, an intensity of $1.0 \times 10^{-12}$ W/m².

A logarithm is the exponent to which the base number must be raised to produce a given number.

Example: $10^2 = 100$
so $\log_{10} 100 = 2$

For base 10, $\log 100 = 2$

**Multiplying logs**

$(10^2)(10^3) = 10^{2+3} = 10^5$

$\therefore \log(10^2)(10^3) = \log 10^2 + \log 10^3$
$= 2 + 3 = 5$

**Dividing logs**

$\frac{10^3}{10^2} = 10^{3-2} = 10^1$

$\therefore \log \frac{10^3}{10^2} = \log 10^3 - \log 10^2$
$= 3 - 2 = 1$

EXAMPLE 8 **Calculating a decibel level**

A normal conversation involves sound intensities of about $3.0 \times 10^{-6}$ W/m$^2$. What is the decibel level for this intensity?

### *Solution and Connection to Theory*

**Given**

$I_1 = 1.0 \times 10^{-12}$ W/m$^2$ (the threshold of hearing)

$I_2 = 3.0 \times 10^{-6}$ W/m$^2$

$$\beta = 10 \log \left(\frac{I_2}{I_1}\right) = 10 \log \left(\frac{3.0 \times 10^{-6} \text{ W/m}^2}{1.0 \times 10^{-12} \text{ W/m}^2}\right) = 10 \log (3.0 \times 10^{6})$$

$$= 10(6.5) \text{ dB} = 65 \text{ dB}$$

Thus, a normal conversation at about a one-metre separation distance has a sound level of 65 dB. This number is much easier to refer to than a large number like $3.0 \times 10^{-6}$ W/m$^2$.

Table 13.2 compares the loudness of various sounds to the threshold of sound. The value of the intensity is given in pW/m$^2$ and W/m$^2$ as well as in decibels.

| **Table 13.2** **Loudness of Sounds** | | | |
|---|---|---|---|
| Sound level (dB) | Sounds | Intensity (pW/m$^2$) | Intensity (W/m$^2$) |
| 0 | Lowest audible sound for humans | 1 | $10^{-12}$ |
| 10 | Rustle of leaves | 10 | $10^{-11}$ |
| 20 | Whisper at 1 m | $10^2$ | $10^{-10}$ |
| 30 | Whisper at 30 cm | $10^3$ | $10^{-9}$ |
| 40 | Quiet room away from traffic | $10^4$ | $10^{-8}$ |
| 50 | Auto engine at 10 m | $10^5$ | $10^{-7}$ |
| 60 | Conversation at 1 m | $10^6$ | $10^{-6}$ |
| 70 | Busy traffic or 30 m from freight train | $10^7$ | $10^{-5}$ |
| 80 | Subway or very close to Niagara Falls | $10^8$ | $10^{-4}$ |
| 90 | Pneumatic drill or noisy lawn mower | $10^9$ | $10^{-3}$ |
| 100 | Motorcycle or chain saw | $10^{10}$ | $10^{-2}$ |
| 110 | Rock concert near the stage | $10^{11}$ | $10^{-1}$ |
| 120 | Threshold of pain | $10^{12}$ | 1 |
| 180 | Rocket launch pad | $10^{18}$ | $10^6$ |

**EXAMPLE 9** **Changing sound intensities**

How loud (in decibels) would the sound be for a rock concert with music intensity 2.0 W/m² at 1.0 m if the person is sitting 100 m away from the source?

### *Solution and Connection to Theory*

**Given**

For our case, $I_1 = 2.0$ W/m²     $I_2 = ?$     $r_1 = 1.0$ m     $r_2 = 100$ m

$$\frac{I_1}{I_2} = \frac{(r_2)^2}{(r_1)^2} = \frac{2.0 \text{ W/m}^2}{I_2} = \frac{(1.0 \text{ m})^2}{(100 \text{ m})^2}$$

$$I_2 = \frac{2.0 \text{ W/m}^2(1.0 \text{ m})^2}{(100 \text{ m})^2} = 2.0 \times 10^{-4} \text{ W/m}^2$$

We can now calculate decibels using

$$\beta = 10 \log\left(\frac{I_2}{I_1}\right)$$

$$\beta = 10 \log\left(\frac{2.0 \times 10^{-4} \text{ W/m}^2}{1.0 \times 10^{-12} \text{ W/m}^2}\right) = 10 \log (2.0 \times 10^8) = 10 (8.3)\text{dB} = 83 \text{ dB}$$

Thus, the person sitting 100 m away experiences a sound level equivalent to city traffic.

**Fig.13.23**  Pete Townsend of The Who

Not all rock concerts are as tame as the one described in Example 9. Back in the 1970s, when concerts were becoming louder and louder, The Who set a dubious record of blasting music at 120 dB at 40 m from the stage.

The sound produced was equivalent to standing only 60 m from a jet taking off. Remember that a rock concert is not a short event. Pete Townsend (Fig. 13.23), a member of The Who, suffered permanent ear damage as a result of a career of playing loudly.

**Fig.13.24**  Sound Intensity

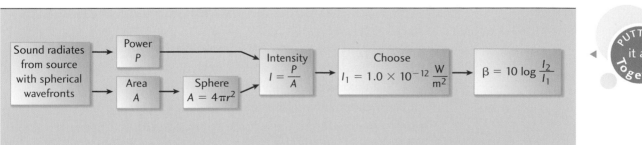

1. Why do we use a logarithmic scale to describe the range of sound intensities we can hear?

2. By what factor does the sound increase or decrease when the listener moves
   a) twice as far away from the source?
   b) 5.3 times as far away?
   c) 3 times closer?
   d) 0.3 times as far away?

3. What is the intensity of sound for the following decibel values?
   a) 100 dB      b) 20 dB      c) 55 dB      d) 78 dB

4. How many times louder or softer than a sound level of 30 dB is a sound at
   a) 50 dB?      b) 10 dB?      c) 85 dB?      d) 0.5 dB?

## Human Hearing Threshold

If the hearing threshold in both ears at 500 Hz is 35 dB or worse, you probably need hearing aids. A whisper in a quiet library is 30 dB. There are devices available now that can give the user an 80 dB or more peak gain. (Physically, every 6 dB increase represents a doubling of sound pressure. Perceptually, every 10 dB increase sounds twice as loud.)

Compare this increase to the old trumpet hearing aids of the 1800s. Alexander Graham Bell was working on developing hearing aids when he invented the telephone.

**Fig.13.25A**                    **Fig.13.25B**

5. Research the difference in characteristics between older versions of hearing aids (amplified all sounds) and current models (Fig. 13.25).

6. Research **assistance devices** such as the TTY and TDD devices available to the hearing impaired.

7. Research the state of development of **cochlear implants**. Are researchers getting closer to producing artificial hearing?

# ▶ 13.5 Doppler Effect

When a racing car passes you as you sit in the stands, you hear the familiar VVRRrrrrr<sub>rrroooom</sub> sound, where the pitch of the sound seems to drop as the car passes by you. That sound is heard anytime two objects pass each other with different velocities while emitting sounds. In the mid 1800s, Christian Doppler, an Austrian physicist, explained this phenomenon.

**Fig.13.26**  1 and 2 hear the same sound. No change in wavelength occurs when the source is at rest.

In order to formulate an equation for this phenomenon, we start with the assumption that the medium in which sound travels (air) is stationary.

**Case 1 — The ambulance is stationary.** As shown in Fig. 13.26, the waves move out uniformly and are heard by both person 2 standing in front of the ambulance and person 1 standing behind it. Because the waves move symmetrically, the wavelength observed by both people is the same.

**Case 2 — The ambulance is moving.** Figure 13.27 shows that the sound's wavefronts are bunching up in the direction of motion. The wavelengths approaching person 2 ahead of the ambulance are now getting smaller. Person 2 now senses more wavefronts per unit time than she did when the ambulance was not moving. This increased rate of arrival is just the increase in frequency, so she hears a higher-pitched sound.

For person A behind the car, the effect is reversed. The sound wavefronts spread out as the source moves away from the listener. This motion increases the wavelength and the listener detects fewer wavefronts arriving per unit time. The resulting drop in frequency is heard as a lower-pitched sound.

It should be noted that the Doppler effect occurs only if the speed of the moving source is less than Mach 1.

**Fig.13.27**  Observers in front and behind a moving sound source hear a different frequency

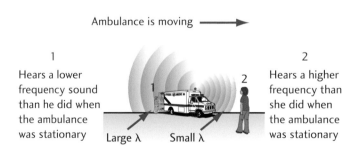

Ambulance is moving →

1
Hears a lower frequency sound than he did when the ambulance was stationary   Large λ   Small λ

2
Hears a higher frequency than she did when the ambulance was stationary

## Moving Source Equation — Approaching the Listener

For this derivation, refer to Fig. 13.28. An object moving towards an observer covers a distance of $v_o t$, where $t$ is time of travel and $v_o$ is the speed of the object. The standard sound wave from the non-moving object is $\lambda_1$. The new sound wave, $\lambda_2$, is smaller by the distance $v_o t$. Thus

$$\lambda_2 = \lambda_1 - v_o t$$

Since each successive wave is produced in a time $T$, the period of the wave, we can write our equation as

$$\lambda_2 = \lambda_1 - v_o T$$

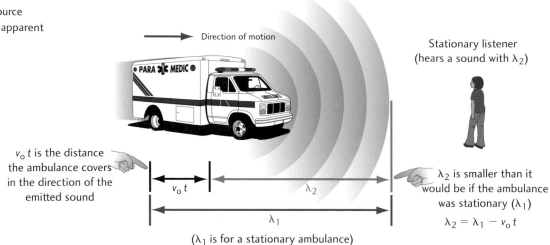

**Fig.13.28** As the sound source approaches the listener, the apparent wavelength decreases

Direction of motion

Stationary listener (hears a sound with $\lambda_2$)

$v_o t$ is the distance the ambulance covers in the direction of the emitted sound

$v_o t$

$\lambda_2$

$\lambda_2$ is smaller than it would be if the ambulance was stationary ($\lambda_1$)

$\lambda_2 = \lambda_1 - v_o t$

$\lambda_1$

($\lambda_1$ is for a stationary ambulance)

Remember that $v = \lambda f$, so the frequency ($f_2$) perceived by the listener is

$$f_2 = \frac{v_{\text{sound}}}{\lambda_2}$$

Substituting into the expression for $\lambda_2$, we obtain

$$f_2 = \frac{v_{\text{sound}}}{\lambda_1 - v_o T}$$

Now use

$$\lambda_1 = \frac{v_{\text{sound}}}{f_1} \quad \text{and} \quad T = \frac{1}{f_1}$$

Substituting again for $\lambda_1$ and $T$, we obtain

$$f_2 = \frac{f_1 v_{\text{sound}}}{(v_{\text{sound}} - v_o)}$$

We now use the subscript $s$ to denote sound. The equation becomes

$$f_2 = \frac{f_1 v_s}{v_s - v_o}$$

The difference in frequencies, $f_2 - f_1$, is referred to as the **Doppler shift**.

EXAMPLE 10 **The apparent frequency of an approaching car sounding a horn**

The Batmobile is approaching Batgirl at a speed of 140 km/h while sounding its horn. Calculate the apparent frequency of the horn heard by Batgirl if the sound has a frequency of 500 Hz. Assume a speed of sound of 344 m/s.

**Fig.13.29**

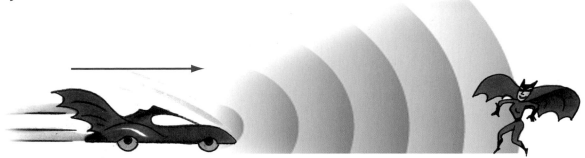

*Solution and Connection to Theory*

**Given**

$v_s = 344$ m/s    $v_o = 140$ km/h $= 38.9$ m/s    $f_1 = 500$ Hz    $f_2 = ?$

$$f_2 = \frac{f_1 v_s}{v_s - v_o}$$

$$= \frac{500 \ s^{-1}(344 \text{ m/s})}{344 \text{ m/s} - 38.9 \text{ m/s}}$$

$$= 564 \text{ Hz}$$

The frequency perceived by Batgirl is 564 Hz, which is greater than the emitted frequency and therefore has a higher pitch.

## Moving Source Equation — Moving Away from the Listener

For the source moving away, the term for the approaching source, $\lambda_2 = \lambda_1 - v_o T$, changes to

$$\lambda_2 = \lambda_1 + v_o T$$

The equation for apparent frequency of a moving source is the same as that for the approaching source except for the *plus sign* in the denominator.

$$f_2 = \frac{f_1 v_s}{v_s + v_o}$$

**EXAMPLE 11**    **The apparent frequency of a receding car sounding a horn**

If the sound of the horn has a frequency of 500 Hz, calculate the apparent frequency heard by Robin if the Batmobile is travelling at 140 km/h away from him. Assume a speed of sound of 344 m/s.

If the *person* approaches or moves away from a sound source instead of the source moving relative to the person, the Doppler effect still occurs, but with a subtle difference. In this case, the wavelength of the sound does not change, but the number of wavelengths encountered per unit time by the moving person is different than if the person was stationary. This situation produces a slightly different formula,

$$f_2 = f_1 \left( 1 \pm \frac{v_o}{v_s} \right)$$

where $v_o$ is the speed of the observer. Note that the perceived frequency is different for this case.

**Fig.13.31**

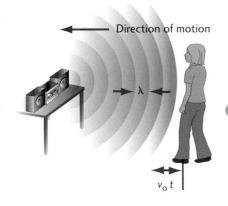

Direction of motion

$\lambda$

$v_o t$

**Fig.13.30**

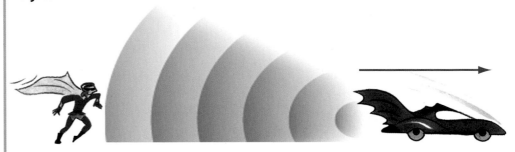

### Solution and Connection to Theory

**Given**

$v_s = 344$ m/s  $\quad v_o = 140$ km/h $= 38.9$ m/s  $\quad f_1 = 500$ Hz  $\quad f_2 = ?$

$f_2 = \dfrac{f_1 v_s}{v_s - v_o}$, since the source is moving away from the listener.

$$f_2 = \frac{500 \text{ s}^{-1}(344 \text{ m/s})}{344 \text{ m/s} + 38.9 \text{ m/s}} = 449 \text{ Hz}$$

The frequency perceived by Robin is 449 Hz, which is less than the emitted frequency and therefore has a lower pitch.

Both conditions can be rolled into one equation by using the $\pm$ sign, where + *indicates a receding source* and − *indicates an approaching source.*

$$f_2 = \frac{f_1 v_s}{v_s \pm v_o}$$

**Fig.13.32**   Summary of Doppler Effect

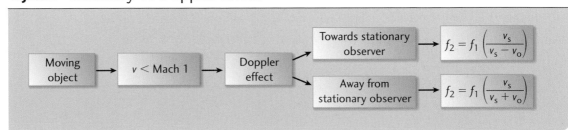

1. Explain why the Doppler effect occurs only if the sound-emitting object is moving relative to the listener.
2. If you have studied the light unit, how is the Doppler effect for sound different from that for light?
3. Calculate the apparent frequency heard by a person if a car travelling at 110 km/h emits a sound with frequency 450 Hz. Assume that the car is moving
   a) away from the listener.
   b) toward the listener.

## Animals with Sonar, Part II: A Very Sophisticated Animal

The sonar used by bats has a wavelength comparable to the size of their prey. The emitted pulses are 0.001 s in duration and are of a frequency too high for humans to hear. To find how far away its prey is, the bat interprets the time it takes for its emitted signal to return. The location of the insect is determined by comparing the slight time difference for the returning signal to reach each of the bat's ears. The bat uses the Doppler effect, caused by the regular rhythm of the prey's wings, to determine whether the insect is travelling towards or away from it. It distinguishes edible prey from other objects by the apparent pitch changes in the sound generated by the prey's wings as the prey moves towards or away from the bat (Fig. 13.33).

4. Calculate the distance between a moth and a bat if the air temperature is 14°C and the sonar took 0.11 s to return to the bat.
5. How would a bat know that a leaf blowing in the wind was not prey?
6. Researchers catch bats in thin nets. Why don't the bats detect the nets?

**Fig.13.33**

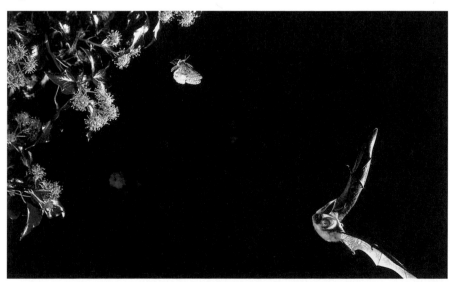

# 13.6 The Characteristics of Hearing

## Method of Hearing

Fig.13.34   The human ear

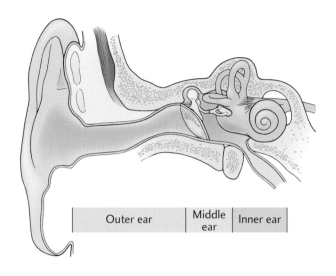

Anatomically, the ear is divided into three sections: the outer, middle, and inner ear (Fig. 13.34).

Fig.13.35   The outer ear

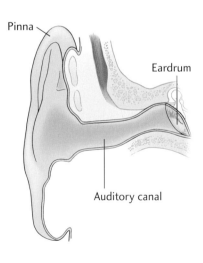

**Outer Ear** (Fig. 13.35), **Sound Collector**. The pinna directs sound from in front of us into our ears. This way, we do not have to turn our heads each time someone speaks to us. The sound is then directed down the canal to the middle ear. The size of the canal is ideal for amplification in the range around 2800 Hz.

**Middle Ear** (Fig. 13.36), **Transference Station**. The sounds vibrate the eardrum, which transmits the vibrations through the three small bones (hammer, anvil, and stirrup) attached to it. This stage creates another small amplification. The smallest bone in the body, the stirrup, is located here, measuring about 3.5 mm.

The middle part of the ear is connected by way of the **Eustachian tube** to the throat. When you need to equalize the pressure on both sides of the eardrum, such as during ascent or descent in a plane, you open the tube by swallowing (or chewing gum). Infections and colds can also block up this passage, leading to muffled hearing and ear pain.

**Inner Ear** (Fig. 13.37), **Sorting Station**. When the vibrations reach the **cochlea**, they set the cochlear fluid in motion. The cochlea contains a series of fine hairs (over 20 000 of them!). The size of the hairs dictates the ease with which they move. The hairs near the entrance of the cochlea are activated by higher frequencies, whereas hairs further inside the cochlea are activated by lower frequencies. The motion triggers nerve cells at the base of the hairs, thereby sending a signal to the brain.

**Fig.13.36** The middle ear

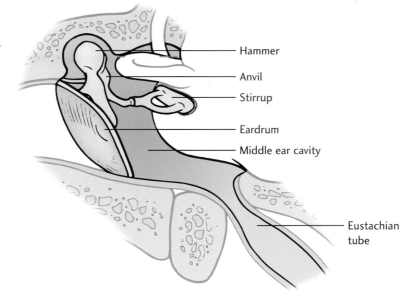

- Hammer
- Anvil
- Stirrup
- Eardrum
- Middle ear cavity
- Eustachian tube

**Fig.13.37** The inner ear

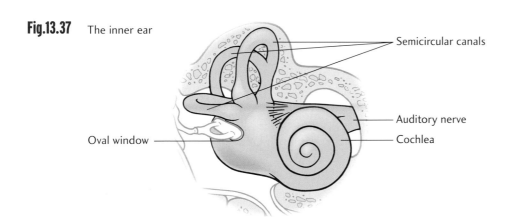

- Semicircular canals
- Auditory nerve
- Cochlea
- Oval window

Damage to the inner ear is permanent, causing deafness (recall Pete Townsend of The Who, Fig. 13.23). Sudden loud bursts of noise can destroy the ability of the cochlea hairs to transmit vibrations to the dural nerves. However, other ear damage, such as eardrum ruptures, can be repaired.

Children prone to ear infections may have fluid buildup behind the eardrum, causing severe pain, and, in extreme cases, rupturing the eardrum. "Tubes" are often surgically placed through the child's eardrum to equalize the pressure in the middle ear, allowing the fluid to drain down the Eustachian tube.

## Sensitivity

The human ear is a remarkable sensing device. From the intensity section (13.4), we learned that the ear has a wide range of sensitivity ($10^{-12}$ W/m² to over 1.0 W/m², corresponding to 0 dB to 120 dB). However, this sensitivity is dependent on the frequency of the emitted sound.

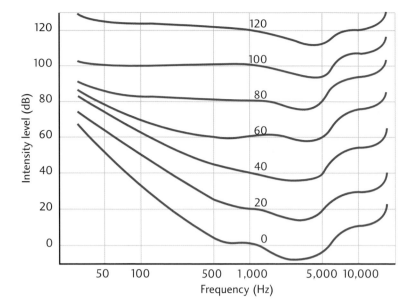

**Fig.13.38** Sensitivity levels of the human ear at different frequencies

**Tinnitus** is a ringing sensation in the ears. It is an early felt condition associated with long-term exposure to loud music. Loss of hearing occurs when the tiny hair cells in the inner ear are damaged from repeated exposure to loud sounds. The mechanism of damage is much like the effect of walking on grass. When you walk on the grass only occasionally, it has a chance to recover. But if the grass is trampled frequently, it loses its ability to spring back and becomes permanently damaged.

| Noise Exposure Times (maximum per day) | |
|---|---|
| Level (dB) | Time (h) |
| 80 | 8 |
| 95 | 4 |
| 100 | 2 |
| 105 | 1 |
| 110 | $\frac{1}{2}$ |
| 115 | $\frac{1}{4}$ |

From the graph in Fig. 13.38, you can see that

1. the range of frequencies we hear is about 25 Hz to 19 000 Hz. Higher frequencies have a higher pitch.
2. the ear is most sensitive to sounds around 2800 Hz because the intensity of audible sound at this frequency drops to 0 dB.
3. as the loudness of the sound increases, the ability to hear at different frequencies becomes roughly the same. You can see this effect because the curves on the graph become more and more level across the graph.
4. generally speaking, we are more sensitive to higher-pitched sounds. The intensity of sound at lower frequencies must be greater in order for us to hear it.

In summary, we can say that our ears are more sensitive to middle frequencies than to high or low frequencies if the sound level is low.

When we listen to music through stereo systems, we can compensate for the different sensitivities at different loudnesses by adjusting the bass, midrange, and treble controls. When the sound becomes very loud, our frequency response becomes relatively equal and the adjustments are for personal taste only.

**White noise** is so called because it has a fairly steady intensity over a broad range of frequencies. White noise (nondescript background noise) can cause hearing damage more quickly than music at the same decibel level. In industries where workers are exposed to sound intensity levels of 85 dB or more, ear protection is required by law in many jurisdictions. Prolonged exposure at this intensity will damage the ear. The Walkman can be harmful because of its proximity to the ear. Although it doesn't seem loud, it can easily deliver 100 dB of sound to the eardrum. The sound doesn't have a chance to use the $\frac{1}{r^2}$ law to decrease the intensity of the music before it enters the ear canal.

# 13.7 Applications — Ultrasonics

The human range of hearing extends from about 25 Hz to 19 000 Hz. Any frequencies below the lower limit are referred to as **infrasonic**. Any frequencies occurring past the upper limit are referred to as **ultrasonic**. However, the hearing range for other animals is often quite different (see Table 13.3).

## Sonar — Echo Finding

**Sonar** stands for **so**und **n**avigation **a**nd **r**anging. This process is used to determine the depth of water under a boat or ship. It can also be used to find sunken objects like ships, or fish, and is used by many fishing enthusiasts today.

Ultrasonic sounds aimed into the water are emitted by a device called a **transducer**. The sounds travel downward until they hit something and reflect back. The time it takes for the sound to return to the surface determines the depth of the object or the bottom of the water body.

| Table 13.3 Ranges of Hearing for Animals | | |
|---|---|---|
| Animal | Frequency range (Hz) | |
| | low | high |
| Dog | 15 | 50 000 |
| Cat | 60 | 65 000 |
| Porpoise | 150 | 150 000 |
| Bat | 1000 | 120 000 |
| Moth | 3000 | 150 000 |

**Fig.13.39** An echo sounder emits impulses, then records the echoes. The time between the two events is converted to metres.

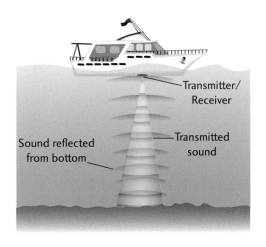

Transmitter/ Receiver

Transmitted sound

Sound reflected from bottom

The transducer is usually a type of crystal that exhibits **piezo-electric properties**. These crystals generate a small electric charge when pressure is applied to them. The amount of current generated by the crystal is proportional to the force applied. One can also reverse this effect. By applying a current at a particular frequency of the crystal, you can force the crystal to vibrate. Thus, the crystal can act like a receiver and an emitter.

## Industrial Applications

### Reflectoscope

A **reflectoscope** is a device used to find flaws in materials such as tires and castings. It sends out short bursts of ultrasound into a material. The piezo-electric crystal acts like both a transmitter and a receiver. Between bursts, the current to the crystal is turned off and the reflecting vibrations are picked up by the crystal and changed back into electrical signals. Any flaws in the material show up as variations on a homogeneous background.

### Emulsifiers

High-frequency soundwaves can cause liquids that normally would not mix to emulsify. An example of an emulsion is milk, where fat globules are in suspension in the milk. In industry, metal alloys can be made using this process. Metals are mixed and blasted by ultrasound waves, causing the metals to stay mixed until they cool and harden.

### Cleaners

Ultrasound techniques are used to clean gems and other materials. They can also be used to cause particles such as dust and smoke to clump together. This technique is useful in pollution control in large factories. Ultrasound can weld certain plastics, disinfect and clean metal instruments, and is used inside measuring devices that monitor such properties as size, pressure, or density of substances.

### Humidifiers

A recent use of ultrasound is to create a fine mist from a storage unit of water. The mist is cool to the touch and thus can be placed in children's bedrooms in order to humidify the air (Fig. 13.40).

**Fig.13.40**  An ultrasonic humidifier

## Medical Applications

### Diagnostics

For diagnostic purposes, sounds in the range of 1–10 MHz are used by doctors. A transducer is placed in contact with a person's skin. The sound waves travel into the body and are reflected back by different organs. Although the range of speeds in various tissues is very close in value, high-resolution detection systems can discern the differences between muscle and fat tissue, even though speeds of transmission in tissues vary by a few percent only.

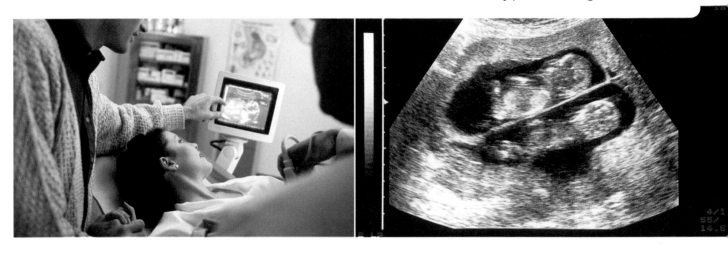

It takes only about 50 ms for the ultrasound signal to be detected, allowing for a real-time image of the inside of the body to be displayed on a monitor. The low power of the transducer ($3 \times 10^{-3}$ W/cm$^2$) ensures that no damage is done to the body.

The same techniques are used to study the heart (echocardiography). Because we are dealing in real time, cardiologists can be alerted to any pumping problems in the heart valves during tests or surgery.

In the field of obstetrics, two-dimensional imaging is used to get a real-time view of the fetus. The ultrasonic method is preferred because it does no harm to the growing fetus. The uterus of the mother, filled with amniotic fluid, is an ideal medium for the transmission of sound. This image of the fetus is used to detect problems, measure size, keep track of its development, and determine the child's gender (Fig. 13.41).

## Surgery

Ultrasound is now used to break up kidney stones into smaller pieces so that they can be passed without great discomfort. This technique is much less stressful on the patient, who normally would have to undergo a painful operation. The medical system also benefits economically because no post-surgical stay in hospital is required by the patient.

## Sound Absorption and Traffic Barriers

If a tree falls in the forest and no one is around, does it make a sound? The answer to this question is both "yes" and "no." The tree's fall generates the repetitive compressions and rarefactions of air molecules around it, but the true definition of sound requires that it stimulate the auditory nerve. The same applies to noise. Noise is any unwanted sound; therefore, it needs someone to not only detect it, but to also decide that he or she doesn't want it.

In general, there are two types of noise control. Active noise control requires a complicated system of electronics. Passive noise control refers to the more traditional system of reflectors and sound buffers. Active controls require a system of microphones, electronics, and speakers to record and produce a sound wave that is complementary (opposite) to the noise. When superimposed, the two sound waves cancel each other out, eliminating the unwanted noise. The complex nature of most sounds and the complicated and expensive active noise control systems make them impractical for widespread use.

**Fig.STSE.13.1** A roadway noise barrier

Traffic may be one of the biggest contributors to urban noise pollution. Although zoning restrictions often prevent residential construction near major roads, the use of passive roadway noise barriers (Fig. STSE.13.1) is the method of choice for controlling traffic noise in most urban settings.

Figure STSE.13.2 illustrates how the barrier creates a sound wave shadow that provides a shield from the noise. One interesting problem with these barriers is caused by the diffraction of sound waves: the top of the noise barrier can act like an acoustic antenna. This effect is avoided by building the barrier with randomly staggered tops, as shown in Fig. STSE.13.1.

**Fig.STSE.13.2** The path of reflected and diffracted sound waves

Ongoing research is providing alternative materials to construct barrier walls. One promising material, both environmentally and economically, is crumb rubber. Crumb rubber, made of recycled car tires, appears to be non-toxic and environmentally stable.

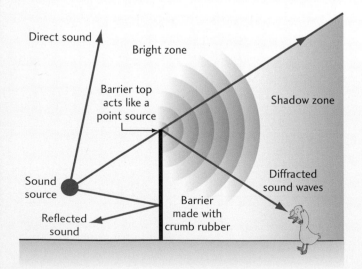

Noise pollution affects our quality of life because it can interfere with communication, sleep, recreation, work, and even the learning environment in our schools. Consistent exposure to noise of 85 dB (e.g., a portable household vacuum cleaner) or higher can cause permanent hearing loss.

## Design a Study of Societal Impact

High-density housing in urban areas often has homes quite close to one another and in areas where noise can be a problem. New subdivisions constructed near a major airport in Southern Ontario have signs posted that warn potential buyers of the risk (Fig. STSE.13.3).

Should these people be compensated for their noise exposure? Are there sections of their sales contract that relate to the noise situation?

Many people use portable music players for cassettes and CDs, or MP3 players. More than ever, students are now tempted to do homework or even attend classes while listening to music. Review current research on the effect of noise or background music on attention and school performance.

## Design an Activity to Evaluate

Evaluate the ability of different materials to block or dampen sound. Perform a correlation study by placing a sound source speaker on one side of a material barrier and a microphone with a oscilloscope on the other. Measure sound wave amplitude as a dependant variable when changing the thickness of the sound-dampening material. Test different types of materials.

## Build a Structure

Design a sound-proof box. Insert a microphone into the box. Monitor it using an oscilloscope to determine differences in the sound amplitude inside the box as it is subjected to external sound.

## You should be able to

*Understand Basic Concepts:*

- Define transverse and longitudinal waves, giving examples of each.
- Define "cycle," "period," "frequency," and "amplitude."
- Explain the relationship between the state of matter and the speed of sound.
- Calculate the speed of a wave in different media using the wave equation.
- Find the speed of sound in air given the temperature in °C.
- Change the speed of sound in m/s to a Mach number.
- Describe how a sound barrier is formed and its consequences.
- Calculate the intensity of sound at different distances from a source.
- Describe how the decibel system works for sound intensity.
- Convert sound intensity levels between different units and give examples.
- Explain the Doppler effect and calculate changes in frequency for moving sources and observers.

*Develop Skills of Inquiry and Communication:*

- Draw, measure, and interpret the properties of waves such as phase, frequency, and amplitude changes.
- Design and conduct an experiment to determine the speed of sound in various media such as hydrogen, helium, air, and carbon dioxide.
- Analyze the speed of sound experiment and determine factors that could affect the agreement of experimental (empirical) values with theoretical ones.

*Relate Science to Technology, Society, and the Environment:*

- Describe the process of hearing.
- Describe various hearing problems and evaluate the effectiveness of possible corrections.
- Describe applications of ultrasound.
- Relate the aspects studied in this unit to possible careers in fields involving sound.
- Describe how the knowledge of the properties of waves is applied to building acoustical noise barriers.
- Describe how animals such as bats, some birds, and dolphins produce and receive ultrasonic, infrasonic, and audible sounds, and how they use them.
- Identify sources of noise in our environment and explain how these noises are reduced by the use of acoustical noise reduction methods.

## Equations

$$T = \frac{1}{f}$$

$$v = \lambda f$$

$$v = 332 + 0.6T$$

$$f_2 = f_1 \frac{v_s}{(v_s \pm v_o)} \quad (+ \text{ receding}, - \text{ approaching})$$

$$I = \frac{P}{4\pi r^2}$$

$$\frac{I_1}{I_2} = \frac{r_2^2}{r_1^2}$$

$$\beta = 10 \log \left(\frac{I_2}{I_1}\right)$$

## Conceptual Questions

1. Why can't sound be a transverse wave when moving through air?

2. If all sound is produced by vibrating objects, do all vibrating objects produce sound?

3. If the speed of sound is 332 m/s, does a particle of air necessarily move at this speed?

4. Describe what causes the air to vibrate for common, everyday sounds.

5. As ice melts, what happens to the speed of sound passing through it?

6. If light travels forever in space, why does sound die off in air?

7. When a person inhales helium, his or her voice sounds high. There is a gas, $SF_6$, which, if inhaled, causes the voice to sound low. Explain how this effect occurs. ($SF_6$ gas is heavier than air, so it's not a good idea to try inhaling it because it will fill up your lungs and cause some breathing problems.)

8. Does a music note of frequency 440 Hz have the same wavelength in water as it does in air?

9. If you are in the water, what do you have to do to hear a beaver slap its tail twice? (Note: The beaver slapped its tail only once.)

10. How is the wavelength of sound affected as the temperature decreases?

11. How can air create a barrier that is "solid" enough to stop planes from penetrating?

12. When you snap a towel, a reasonably sharp "crack" is heard. For one brief moment, the end of the towel is moving at greater than the speed of sound. What causes the "crack"?

13. Can you tell how far away a plane is by observing it, then hearing the sound?

14. Does a pilot singing very loudly in a plane travelling at Mach 2 form a sound barrier in the cockpit? Can he hear his own singing?

15. Is 0 dB an absolute or a relative value?

16. Is it possible to have sounds with an intensity level of −1 dB?

17. In the Doppler effect, the assumption is that air is stationary. What complications arise if this isn't true?

18. When a racing car passes you, do you hear the Doppler effect if you also are moving but not as fast? Does the direction you are moving in make a difference to the sound you hear?

19. If you are moving in the same direction and with the same speed as an object generating a siren sound, will you hear the Doppler effect?

20. Account for the different shapes of ears of various animals to the role hearing plays in their lives.

21. If sound travels faster in solids than in air, why does wax buildup in the ear cause hearing problems?

22. Why is listening to Walkmans more harmful than listening to monster sound systems even though the power output of the monster systems is 50 times greater than that of the Walkman?

## Problems

### ▶ 13.1 Introduction to Wave Theory

23. Use Fig. 13.42 to find
   a) the wavelength.
   b) the period.
   c) the amplitude.
   d) the peak-to-peak value (crest to trough).
   e) the frequency.

**Fig. 13.42**  For this problem, note that there are two different scales used (*d*(m) and *t*(s)).

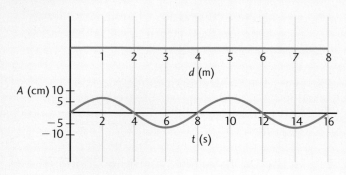

**24.** A tuning fork's tines vibrate 250 times in 2.0 s. Find
  **a)** the frequency of vibration.
  **b)** the period of vibration.

**25.** There are six classes in one day. If all the classes take 6.5 hours each day, find the
  **a)** frequency of the classes occurring each day.
  **b)** period of the classes.

**26.** The frequency of a note is 440 Hz. Find the wavelength of the sound given that the speed of sound is
  **a)** 332 m/s.  **b)** 350 m/s.  **c)** 1225 km/h.

**27.** The frequency of a tuning fork is 1000 Hz. If the wavelength is 35 cm, find the speed of sound in
  **a)** m/s.      **b)** km/h.

**28.** Gravity waves are still being searched for by astrophysicists. These waves travel at the speed of light ($c = 3.0 \times 10^8$ m/s). If the expected frequency is about 1600 Hz and the size of a football field is 250 m, how many football fields long is the wavelength of a gravity wave?

**29.** If $\frac{\lambda}{4}$ is 0.85 m and the frequency is 125 Hz, find
  **a)** the wavelength.
  **b)** the period of the wave.
  **c)** the velocity of the wave.

**30.** Find the period and velocity for the following frequencies if the wavelength is 0.50 m:
  **a)** 0.30 Hz        **b)** 400 s$^{-1}$
  **c)** 30 cycles/s    **d)** 5.0 kHz
  **e)** 102.1 MHz

**31.** Find the frequency and velocity given that the wavelength is 75 cm for the following periods:
  **a)** 0.020 s        **b)** 15.0 ms
  **c)** 2.0 min        **d)** 0.6 h

**32.** You are shouting in a monotone voice with a frequency of 440 Hz. Your friend is 300 m away. If the speed of sound is 344 m/s, how many wavelengths occur between you and your friend?

▶ **13.2 The Transmission and Speed of Sound**

**33.** Calculate the time it would take for sound to travel through 2000 m of the following substances, given the velocity of sound through the substance:
  **a)** Helium (972 m/s)
  **b)** Water (1 450 m/s)
  **c)** Steel (5 130 m/s)
  **d)** Glass (4700 m/s)

**34.** Calculate the wavelength in the following substances if the frequency is 1000 s$^{-1}$ and the speed of sound in the medium is given:
  **a)** Lead (1 230 m/s)
  **b)** Hydrogen (1 267 m/s)
  **c)** Water (5250 km/h)
  **d)** Air (1 234 km/h)

**35.** Calculate the speed of sound in air for the following temperatures :
  **a)** 0°C        **b)** 25°C
  **c)** 30°C       **d)** −15°C

**36.** What is the wavelength of the sound produced by a bat if the frequency of the sound is 90 kHz on a night when the air temperature is 22°C?

37. How far away is a storm if you hear the sound of thunder 7.0 s after the lightning flash on a day when the air temperature is 31°C?

38. Determine the depth of water if an echo using sonar returns in 870 ms and the speed of sound in water is 5300 km/h.

39. If it takes 0.8 s for your voice to be heard at a distance of 272 m, what is the temperature of the air?

40. If you stand on top of a hill overlooking a lake and shout, how long is the lake if an echo is heard 2.0 s later on a day when the air temperature is 21°C?

41. The air temperature is 20°C. You are swimming underwater when you hear a boat noise. Then, 3.5 s later, you hear a crash. If the speed of sound in water is 1 450 m/s, how long after the crash does your friend on the dock beside you hear the crash?

42. On a hot summer night (32°C), you are listening to a rock group in a stadium 350 m away. A friend of yours is sitting in an air-conditioned house across the country, listening to the broadcast on the radio. If the signal travels 3000 m up to a satellite that retransmits it, who hears the concert first ($c = 3.0 \times 10^8$ m/s)?

43. How many times more wavelengths occur in air than in water for an air temperature of 10°C if the speed of sound in water is 5 220 km/h and the frequency of sound is 500 Hz?

### 13.3 Mach Number and the Sound Barrier

44. Calculate the Mach number for the following speeds of sound. State whether the speed is subsonic or supersonic. Assume the speed of sound in air to be 332 m/s:
    a) 664 m/s          b) 306 m/s
    c) 140 km/h         d) 7171 km/h

45. Calculate the Mach number for sound, given the temperature and the speed:
    a) 332 m/s at 30°C
    b) 340 m/s at −10°C
    c) 6000 km/h at 13°C
    d) 6000 km/h at −13°C

46. How far has a plane travelled from the point at which you hear the sound of a sonic boom if the plane is travelling at Mach 2.2 at an altitude of 8000 m and the average air temperature for the sound is 15°C? It took 3.40 s to hear the sonic boom.

47. Assume you visit a world where the atmosphere is made of hydrogen (the planet is massive and holds onto this gas). Your spacecraft can fly at Mach 20 on Earth, as measured by sound at 5°C. On this planet, what is your Mach number if the speed of sound in hydrogen is 1 267 m/s?

48. What is the Mach number for a shuttle if it starts re-entry after travelling around Earth in 1.495 h at an orbital radius of $6.73 \times 10^6$ m? Assume that the air temperature is −30°C.

### 13.4 Sound Intensity

49. Given a sound intensity of $6.0 \times 10^{-6}$ W/m², find the intensity at the following distances from the source:
    a) The distance from the source doubles.
    b) The distance from the source quadruples.
    c) The distance from the source is halved.
    d) The distance from the source decreases by a third.

50. At close proximity, rustling leaves have a sound intensity of about $1.2 \times 10^{-11}$ W/m². At what distance is the sound at the threshold of hearing ($1.0 \times 10^{-12}$ W/m²)?

51. If the surface area that sound travels through is 5.5 m² and the source produces a sound power of $3.0 \times 10^{-3}$ W, find the intensity of the sound at the surface.

**52.** If the sound intensity drops to $4.8 \times 10^{-5}$ W/m$^2$ in Problem 51,
a) what area does the sound intercept?
b) what is the ratio of sound intensities?
c) how much farther has the sound travelled?

**53.** Find the logs of the following values:
a) 100     b) 1000     c) 0.01
d) $3.5 \times 10^{-4}$   e) $5.67 \times 10^6$
f) 1          g) 0

**54.** Given the log value, find the ratio $\left(\frac{I_2}{I_1}\right)$ that, when logged, produces the given quantity (take antilogs):
a) 2       b) 6       c) $-2$
d) $-6$    e) 3.5    f) 0.35

**55.** Knowing $\beta = 10 \log \frac{I_2}{I_1}$, how many times larger or smaller is $I_2$ compared to $I_1$ given that $\beta =$
a) 1?      b) 4?      c) $-1$?
d) $-3$?    e) 2.5?    f) 0.5?

**56.** How many times greater in intensity is the threshold of pain (120 dB) than
a) normal conversation (60 dB)?
b) a whisper (20 dB)?
c) a rock concert (110 dB)?
d) 30 m from a freight train (75 dB)?

**57.** At one point in the room, the sound intensity is $3.5 \times 10^{-6}$ W/m$^2$. If you move twice the distance away, find
a) the sound intensity at the new distance.
b) the decibel difference between the intensities.

**58.** A hearing aid increases the sound intensity level, thereby allowing a person to hear better. For the following decibel increases, by how much does the intensity of sound increase?
a) 30 dB     b) 22 dB     c) 18.9 dB

**59.** A refrigerator lightbulb uses 25 W of power. A pneumatic jack hammer produces a sound intensity of 110 dB. How many jack hammers would you need so that the sound power could light one lightbulb, assuming 100 % conversion of sound energy?

**60.** A rock concert produces sounds at 120 dB, measured 2.0 m away. How far back should you be in order to listen to the music at 100 dB?

**61.** A person has a threshold of hearing of 5 dB. Another person has a threshold of hearing of 25 dB. Which person has better hearing and by how much?

**62.** You and your friend have bought stereo systems. Your stereo has a signal-to-noise ratio of 50 dB, your friend's stereo has a signal-to-noise ratio of 60 dB. Who has the better system and by what factor?

**63.** If you could add the intensities of conversations between two people (65 dB), how many of them would you need to duplicate the sound intensity of a rock concert (120 dB)?

▶ **13.5 Doppler Effect**

**64.** A siren emits a sound at 1700 Hz. Assume a speed of sound of 332 m/s. What frequency would a stationary observer hear if the car with the siren is travelling at
a) 25 m/s toward the observer?
b) 25 m/s away from the observer?
c) 140 km/h toward the observer?

**65.** Repeat Problem 64, assuming an air temperature of 30°C.

**66.** How fast is a car moving and in what direction if the frequency of its horn drops from 900 Hz to 875 Hz, as heard by a stationary listener? The air temperature is 0°C.

**67.** As a racing car zooms by you, its pitch decreases by 20%. If the speed of sound is 345 m/s, how fast is the car travelling?

**68.** The sound of a racing car has its pitch decrease by 10%. If the temperature of the air is 22°C, how fast is the car travelling?

**69.** Two people hear the 1700 Hz siren of an ambulance. One person is in front and the other person is behind the ambulance. If the ambulance is travelling at 120 km/h, what is the difference in frequencies heard by the two people? Assume the speed of sound to be 333 m/s.

**70.** Refer to Fig 13.31. Find the apparent frequency a person moving at 30 m/s hears if she is moving
**a)** toward a stationary siren with frequency 1800 Hz.
**b)** away from a stationary siren with frequency 1800 Hz.

**71.** Repeat Problem 70 for a siren moving at 30 m/s and a stationary listener.

## Purpose

To study the vibrations associated with longitudinal and transverse motion as well as the decay of the amplitude with time.

## Equipment

Spring (with a relatively small spring constant)
String (1.0 m long), Mass (100 g)
Ruler, Retort stand plus clamp, Stop watch

**Fig.Lab.13.1**

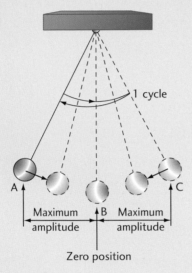

## Procedure — Pendulum

1. Tie a mass to the end of the string and attach the string to the retort stand (clamped to a desk).
2. Draw back the pendulum from the zero position and measure the value of the amplitude, as illustrated in Fig. Lab.13.1.
3. Starting at A, record the time at which the pendulum reaches points B, C, B, and A (see Fig. Lab.13.1). Repeat for three cycles.
4. Record the time for the amplitude to drop to 0.8, 0.7, 0.6, 0.5, and 0.4 of its original value.
5. Time one more cycle.

## Procedure — Spring

1. Hang a spring from a clamped retort stand and attach a mass to the end of the spring.
2. Put a ruler behind the retort stand and mark the zero position of the spring.
3. Pull the mass down and record the distance it is displaced from the zero location.
4. Starting at A, record the time at which the pendulum reaches points B, C, B, and A (see Fig. Lab.13.2). Repeat for three cycles.

5. Record the time for the amplitude to drop to 0.8, 0.7, 0.6, 0.5, and 0.4 of its original starting value.
6. Time one more cycle.

**Fig.Lab.13.2**

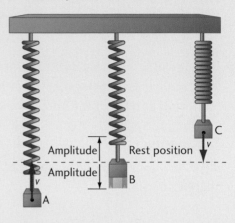

## Data

1. Assume the position to the right of zero and the position above zero to be positive. Assume the other two positions to be negative. Create a chart for the three cycles of the oscillating action for each type of oscillator.
2. Create a chart for the amplitude versus time.

## Analysis

1. Draw a graph of amplitude versus time for each oscillator for the three cycles measured.
2. Draw an amplitude-versus-time graph for each oscillator using the values obtained until it reaches 0.4 of its original value.
3. Calculate the period and frequency for each oscillator.

## Discussion

1. The two oscillators can be used to describe the actions of a source that creates either transverse or longitudinal waves. Which oscillator most likely goes with which wave action? Explain your reasoning.
2. Explain why the graph shapes are similar for each oscillator.
3. Account for the fact that the period and frequency remain constant even though the amplitude is decreasing.
4. What factors cause the amplitudes of each oscillator to decrease?
5. Is the decay of the amplitude linear?
6. What happens to sound waves as they travel over a given period of time?

# LAB 13.2 Speed of Sound

## Purpose
To calculate the speed of sound in air.

## Equipment
Resonance tube
Tuning forks (4–5 different frequencies)
Thermometer, Ruler
Water, Rubber stop

## Procedure
1. Fill the resonance tube with water so it's near the top of the tube.
2. Select a tuning fork and strike it against a rubber stop. Bring it over top of the resonance tube.
3. Slowly lower the water until a resonance is heard (loud reverberation). Record the value of the air column.
4. Repeat this procedure for the other tuning forks.
5. Measure the inner diameter of the resonance tube.
6. Record the temperature of the air in degrees Celsius.

## Data

| | |
|---|---|
| Frequency of tuning fork | Hz |
| Length of air column ($L$) | m |
| Diameter of tube ($D$) | m |
| Temperature ($T$) | °C |

## Analysis
1. Using the formula $\lambda = 4(L + 0.3D)$, calculate the wavelength for each tuning fork. This formula is a corrected formula for the first resonance length of the given tuning fork. The theory behind resonances will be explained in Chapter 14.

**Fig.Lab.13.3**

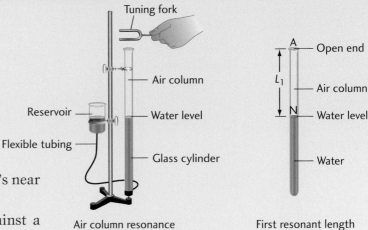

Air column resonance                First resonant length

2. Use the formula $v = \lambda f$ to calculate the speed of sound.
3. Use the formula $v = 332 + 0.6T$ to calculate the speed of sound.
4. Average the answers obtained from each equation and calculate the percent deviation. Use the temperature-dependent formula's answer as the accepted result.
5. Create a chart summarizing the two sets of calculations.

## Discussion
1. Were your values within an acceptable range? If not, find reasons for the discrepancy.
2. Sound travels faster in water than in air. In our experiment, which aspects of $v$, $\lambda$, and $f$ changed when part of the sound travelled through the water? If the speed in water is faster by a factor of four, by how much did the wavelength and the frequency change?

## Conclusion
Summarize your results.

**LABORATORY EXERCISES**

## Purpose

To calculate the speed of sound in a gas medium.

## Equipment

Hollow plastic pipe, sealed at one end
Oscilloscope (or computer and computer interface)
Sound generator (or adjustable tuning fork)
Microphone
Thermometer

## Procedure

Design and conduct an experiment to find the speed of sound in a gas medium. Gases commonly found in labs are helium, hydrogen, and carbon dioxide.

## Considerations

1. Take into account the density of the gas with respect to air when deciding on the orientation of the apparatus.

2. Use theoretical values for the speed of sound in the gas and the frequency of the tuning fork or wave generator sound used to start the experiment. Try to minimize the length of tubing used.

## Discussion

1. Look up the theoretical value of the speed of sound in the gas medium you used and compare it to the obtained value.

2. Calculate the percent deviation and discuss any differences.

3. Does the density of the gas have a direct relationship to the speed of sound in the gas?

4. Can any of these gases be used in the original speed of sound experiment?

# More than Meets the Ear

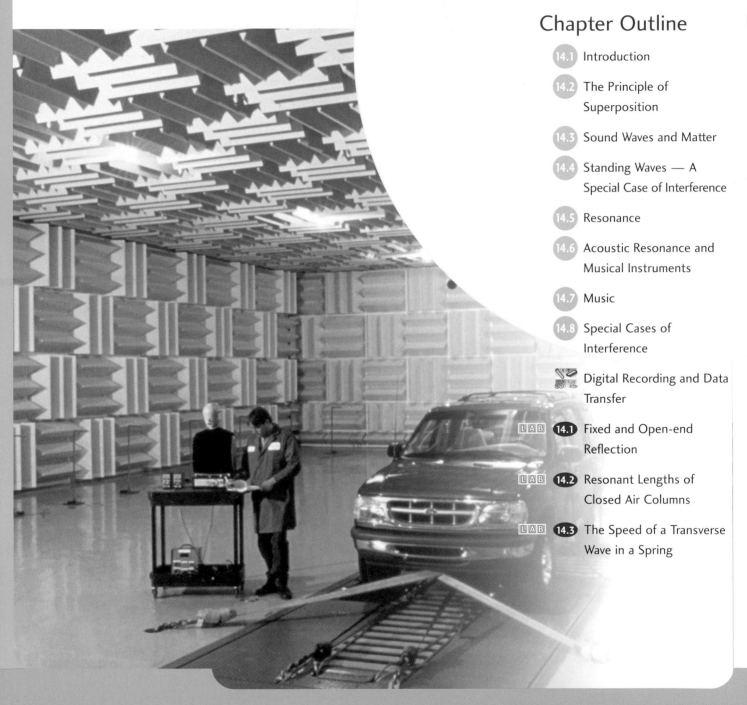

**By the end of this chapter, you will be able to**
- describe how standing waves are formed in different media according to the principle of superposition
- relate the wave characteristics of frequency, amplitude, and overtones to pitch, loudness, and quality of sounds
- explain how resonance produces sound in musical instruments

## 14.1 Introduction

So far, our study of sound has involved a basic understanding of frequency and wavelength. We have defined frequency, period, and amplitude, and we have studied the factors that affect the speed of a sound wave. We have examined the intensity of a sound wave and used the Doppler effect to describe what happens when a sound source moves. We have even examined how we hear particular sounds. There are many different sounds, each with its own wave shape, amplitude, and frequency. Our ears pick up a diverse spectrum of sounds coming from many different sources. This chapter will use all of our previous knowledge of waves to examine how waves interact with each other and their immediate surroundings.

## 14.2 The Principle of Superposition

Sound waves are fluctuations in a medium's pressure that move away from their source. Individually, sound waves move independently through the medium. In fact, any two or more waves can pass through one another. When we hear something, we are sampling the sound waves at a particular point in space from all sound sources.

Note that even though sound waves are longitudinal waves, we often represent them as transverse waves in drawings and oscilloscopes or computer displays. Many of the same principles apply to both types of waves, and transverse waves are much easier to draw and visualize.

In our earlier discussion of waves, you were introduced to the concept of wave **interference**. Interference is the result of two or more waves meeting each other at a particular point in space at the same time. The net wave that forms at the point of interference has an amplitude that is equal to the vector sum of all wave amplitudes that come together at that point. This concept of the sum of all amplitudes is called the **principle of superposition**. Figure 14.1 illustrates how two component waves in the same place and at the same time can produce a totally different resultant wave.

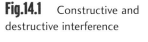
**Fig.14.1** Constructive and destructive interference

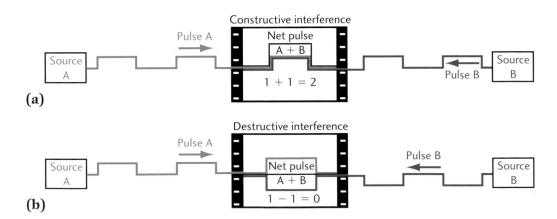

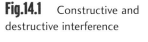

UNIT D: Waves and Sound

The sound that we hear is the overall wave sum, even though the figures show the component waves. Wave pulses can interfere and construct pulses of larger amplitude, or, if they have opposite orientations, destroy one another. The building up or increase of a wave's amplitude is called **constructive interference** and the tearing down or decrease in amplitude is called **destructive interference.** When the component waves are complex or curved, it is very difficult to predict the overall wave forms. For practice, we often use simplified square pulses to show the principle of superposition. In the next few examples, we will identify how two different waves interfere with each other according to the principle of superposition. For simplicity's sake, we will provide a "ghost image" of the two component waves, even though we don't actually see them.

**EXAMPLE 1**   **Drawing a resultant wave from component waves**

Use the **principle of superposition** to draw the resultant wave that would be visible if the two component waves, A and B, are moving as shown in Fig. 14.2.

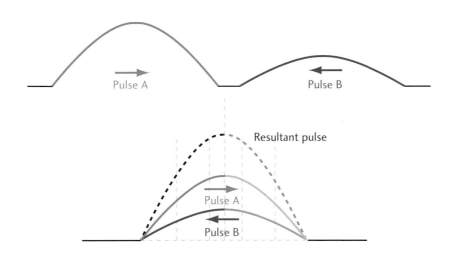

**Fig.14.2**   Add the amplitudes of pulses A and B along the vertical lines to find the amplitude of the resultant pulse

**Fig.14.3**   Applying the Principle of Superposition

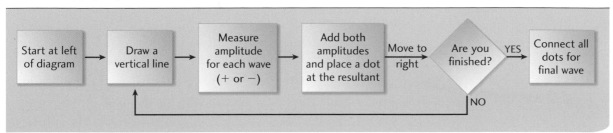

**EXAMPLE 2**  **The resultant of two pulses**

Draw the resultant wave that would be heard if pulses A and B are moving as shown in Fig. 14.4.

**Fig. 14.4**

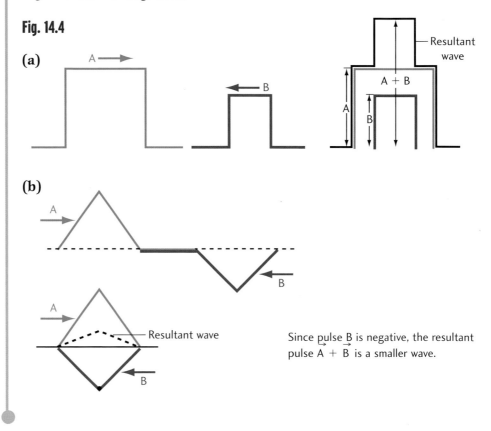

Since pulse $\overrightarrow{B}$ is negative, the resultant pulse $\overrightarrow{A}$ + $\overrightarrow{B}$ is a smaller wave.

Sound waves may come from the same source or from different sources of vibration. If they are from one source, then they have the same size, shape, and frequency. Waves from the same source can meet if they are reflected back towards their source.

1. **a)** Draw a sequence in which two square wave pulses approach, touch, overlap halfway, overlap fully, then overlap halfway again, and finally separate. Be sure to show the *resultant waves* in the sequence. The two pulses have the same amplitude and are both positive.
   **b)** Draw the same sequence but invert one pulse so it is the negative version of the other pulse.

## Active Sound Control

Note the addition of the positive and negative amplitude pulses when they are completely overlapping each other. The resultant is zero. This effect is the basis of **active sound control (ASC)**, which consists of cancelling an undesirable noise by superposing an opposite phase noise. Active noise reduction is a process that senses the unwanted *sound pollution* (noise), then generates an out-of-phase signal to cancel the disturbance. It is like generating the upside down or negative square pulse at the same time as the positive pulse was produced. Headphones used by pilots of small planes use this technology to reduce engine noise.

## 14.3 Sound Waves and Matter

Like all wave forms, sound waves can be either absorbed, transmitted, or reflected when they encounter a different type of matter.

## Absorption

**Absorption** is the process whereby the sound's energy is quickly dissipated by being transformed into other forms of energy. Absorption of sound is very important for engineers who design *sound-proof* rooms. These rooms, such as the one shown in Fig. 14.5, have walls made of a material that can absorb sound energy.

A sound-proof room, or **anechoic chamber**, is used for sound research. It can virtually eliminate the internal reflection or transmission of sound through its walls.

## Transmission

**Transmission** is the passing of sound energy from one medium to another at a medium boundary. Some of the sound energy may be absorbed in the process. Transmission causes a change in the wavelength of a wave because the sound either speeds up or slows down as it passes into the new medium. Figure 14.6 shows the relationship between the speed of sound, $v$, the wavelength, $\lambda$, and the frequency, $f$, of a sound wave as it is transmitted between two mediums.

Since $v_1 = f\lambda_1$ and $v_2 = f\lambda_2$,

$$\frac{v_1}{v_2} = \frac{f\lambda_1}{f\lambda_2} = \frac{\lambda_1}{\lambda_2}$$

The change in wavelength is directly proportional to the change in speed. Longitudinal sound waves moving from a slower to a faster medium behave much like hockey players stepping off the floor onto the ice. As their speed ($v$) increases, the distance between them ($\lambda$) also increases, but the frequency ($f$) with which they pass any point remains the same.

**Fig.14.5** An anechoic chamber is used to test for automobile noise

**Fig.14.6** The transmission of sound waves between a slow and a fast medium

Slow

$v_{water} > v_{air}$
$\lambda_{water} > \lambda_{air}$
$f_{water} = f_{air}$

Fast

EXAMPLE **3**   **Change in wavelength**

A sound wave of wavelength 0.750 m is travelling in air at 0.0°C when it hits a block of steel at the same temperature. What is the wavelength of the sound wave in steel if the speed of sound in steel is 5050 m/s?

### Solution and Connection to Theory

**Given**

$\lambda_{sound} = 0.750$ m       $T = 0.0°C$       $v_{steel} = 5050$ m/s       $\lambda_{steel} = ?$

Recall that the speed of sound in air is $v = 332 + 0.6T$.

Rearrange the equation

$$\frac{\lambda_{sound}}{\lambda_{steel}} = \frac{v_{sound}}{v_{steel}}$$

for $\lambda_{steel}$, then substitute and solve.

$$\lambda_{steel} = \lambda_{sound}\left(\frac{v_{steel}}{v_{sound}}\right)$$

$$\lambda_{steel} = 0.750 \text{ m} \frac{(5050 \text{ m/s})}{(332 \text{ m/s})}$$

The phrase "keep your ear to the ground" makes reference to the fact that sound travels faster through a solid (the ground) than a gas (air).

$$\lambda_{steel} = 11.4 \text{ m}$$

Therefore, the wavelength of sound in steel is 11.4 m.

## Reflection

Sound can be absorbed or transmitted as it meets another medium, but it can also have its energy turned back onto itself in the process of **reflection.** In reflection, the wavelength of the returning wave is not altered because there is no change in speed. However, when a sound wave is reflected at a solid boundary, the reflected wave pulse has its *phase* shifted by $\frac{1}{2}\lambda$, because its amplitude is inverted. Figure 14.7 shows how a wave crest reflected from a fixed end returns as a trough.

**Fig.14.7**   Reflection of a wave pulse at a fixed end has its amplitude inverted

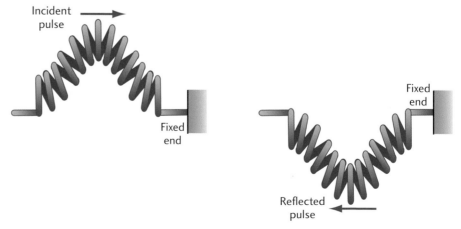

When a wave pulse reflects at a free end, as in Fig. 14.8, the wave reflects in the same phase and is not inverted. These two types of reflection will help us to understand what happens in many musical instruments.

UNIT D: Waves and Sound

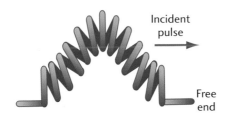

Incident pulse

Reflected pulse

Free end

Free end

**Fig.14.8** A wave pulse reflected at a free end is not inverted

**1. a)** Look up the speed of sound in oak (Table 13.1). Calculate the change in wavelength for a sound generated in air by a 250 Hz tuning fork as it enters the oak, given that the air temperature is 20°C.

**b)** Repeat the exercise in part a) for sound travelling from air to water.

An **acoustical engineer** is someone who deals with the impact of noise on people. Noise affects all of us and can induce fatigue, interrupt communication, and possibly affect safety. Noise from highways, airports, and industry is usually contained by various barriers. The design and production of shapes and materials for barriers, along with their positioning relative to noise generators and receivers, are aspects of this job.

**Fig.14.9**  **When Sound Waves Meet a Boundary**

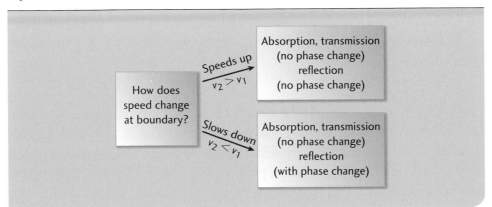

How does speed change at boundary?

Speeds up $v_2 > v_1$ → Absorption, transmission (no phase change) reflection (no phase change)

Slows down $v_2 < v_1$ → Absorption, transmission (no phase change) reflection (with phase change)

## 14.4 Standing Waves — A Special Case of Interference

One of the most important instances of wave interference occurs when a particular wave reflects back on itself (with or without phase inversion) with the same frequency, wavelength, and speed. Figure 14.10 demonstrates how two wave trains with the same characteristics interfere with each other as they meet head on.

The red and blue waves in Fig. 14.10 are approaching component waves, and the black wave shows the resultant wave pulse, calculated using the principle of superposition. The resulting wave form, called a **standing wave**, has a particular pattern, which is illustrated in Fig. 14.11.

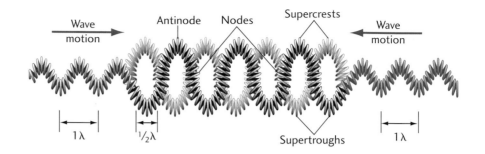

**Fig.14.11** A standing wave

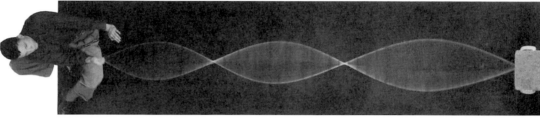

A standing wave is characterized by points in which the medium does not vibrate, called **nodes**. These nodes are interspersed between sections of medium that alternate between constructive "supercrests" and "supertroughs," called **antinodes**. In longitudinal sound waves, they are called supercompressions and superrarefactions.

Figure 14.12 illustrates that the distance between successive nodes, the **inter-nodal distance** $(d_n)$, is equivalent to one-half the wavelength of the wave source.

**Fig.14.12** Nodes are $\frac{1}{2}\lambda$ apart

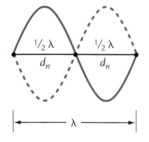

$$d_n = \tfrac{1}{2}\lambda$$

The number of inter-nodal distances is always one less than the number of nodes, just as your hand has five fingers, but only four spaces between them.

In a medium such as a guitar string, the boundaries between the string and the next medium can be considered "fixed" because a guitar string is attached at both ends. Therefore, the standing wave is terminated at each end with a node. Other mediums, such as a car antenna (Fig. 14.13), have "free ends" (attached or closed at one end only). Their standing waves terminate with an antinode.

**Fig.14.13** The wind can produce a free-end standing wave in a car radio antenna

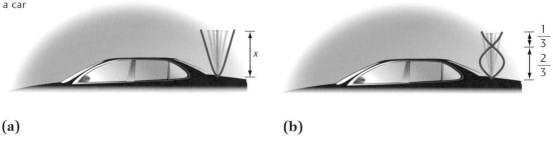

(a)                    (b)

**EXAMPLE 4**    **Standing waves in a duck pond**

A standing wave occurs in a duck pond when one duck repeatedly tries to "jump" for food, as shown in Fig. 14.14.

(a) The nodes are at every 38 cm. What wavelength of wave is our hungry duck producing?

**Fig.14.14**

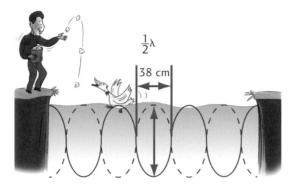

(b) If the wave speed in the pond is 0.95 m/s, how often does the duck "jump"?

*Solution and Connection to Theory*

**Given**

$d_n = 38$ cm        $v = 0.95$ m/s        $f_{duck} = ?$    $\lambda = ?$

(a) $d_n = \frac{1}{2}\lambda$        $38$ cm $= \frac{1}{2}\lambda$        $\lambda = 2(38$ cm$) = 76$ cm

Therefore, the wavelength of the duck's wave is 76 cm or 0.76 m.

(b) $v = f\lambda$

Rearranging the equation and solving for $f$,

$$f = \frac{v}{\lambda} = \frac{0.95 \text{ m/s}}{0.76 \text{ m}} = 1.25 \text{ Hz}$$

Therefore, our duck jumps for food 1.25 times every second.

**EXAMPLE 5**    **Wavelength and speed of a standing wave**

A standing wave has a distance of 45 cm between four consecutive nodes. What is the wavelength of the wave? What is the speed of the wave in the medium if the frequency of the source is 30 Hz?

**Fig.14.15**

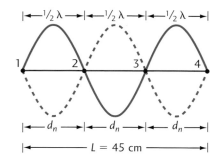

## Solution and Connection to Theory

### Given

$L = 45$ cm $\qquad f = 30$ Hz $\qquad \lambda = ?$ $\qquad v = ?$

There are four nodes, so there must be three inter-nodal distances. The length of the wave is therefore

$$L = 3d_{\mathrm{n}} = 3\left(\tfrac{1}{2}\lambda\right)$$

$$\lambda = (L)\tfrac{2}{3} = (45 \text{ cm})\tfrac{2}{3} = 30 \text{ cm}$$

Therefore, the wavelength of the standing wave is 30 cm.
For the speed,

$$v = f\lambda = 30 \text{ Hz}(30 \text{ cm}) = 900 \text{ cm/s}$$

From the measured wavelength and frequency, the speed of the wave is 900 cm/s or 9.0 m/s.

1. State the conditions needed to produce standing waves.
2. **a)** A standing wave is produced in a vibrating car antenna as the car moves along a slightly rough highway. The wave has three nodes in a distance of 30 cm. Calculate the wavelength of the standing wave.
   **b)** Assume that the wave's frequency is 20 Hz. Calculate the velocity of the wave.

## 14.5 Resonance

In the last section, we found that under the right conditions, a standing wave can be formed in certain mediums such as a guitar string. Strings with fixed ends may vibrate with one large loop (antinode) between them. This implies that the string has a specific frequency with which it can vibrate.

The lowest frequency of a string is called its **fundamental frequency** or **first harmonic**, $f_0$. Higher frequencies of the string are integer multiples of the fundamental frequency, $2f_0$, $3f_0$, etc. They are called **harmonics** (second, third, etc.) or **overtones** (first, second, third, etc.). (See Fig. 14.16.)

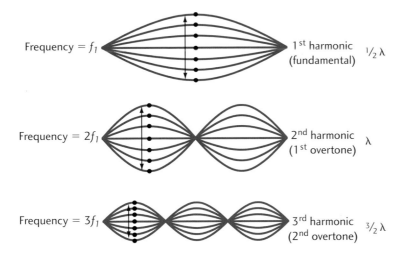

Frequency = $f_1$    1st harmonic (fundamental)   $\frac{1}{2}\lambda$

Frequency = $2f_1$   2nd harmonic (1st overtone)   $\lambda$

Frequency = $3f_1$   3rd harmonic (2nd overtone)   $\frac{3}{2}\lambda$

**Fig.14.16**   The first three harmonics of a vibrating string

## Mechanical Resonance

On a swing, if you want to swing with greater and greater amplitude, you have to push yourself at the right time in order to match your push frequency with the natural frequency of the swing.

> **Mechanical resonance** is the vibrating response of an object to a periodic force from a source that has the same frequency as the natural frequency of the object.

Figure 14.17 uses a speaker and a tuning fork to illustrate the basic concepts of mechanical resonance. The tuning fork has a natural resonant frequency with which it vibrates. The speaker, if tuned to emit the same frequency, will cause the tines of the tuning fork to oscillate. If the speaker is turned off after a few moments, we would hear the tuning fork continue to sound as if it had been struck. One of the most famous examples of mechanical resonance was the collapse of the Tacoma Narrows Bridge (Washington State, 1940), shown in Fig. 14.18.

**Fig.14.17**   The speaker causes the tuning fork to vibrate

$f_{speaker}$   $f_{tuning fork}$

$f_{speaker} = f_{tuning fork}$

**Fig.14.18**   Mechanical resonance in the Tacoma Narrows Bridge (Washington State, 1940)

The bridge had a design flaw that gave it a natural frequency that was coincidentally similar to the frequency of the wind gusts at that particular spot. Large amplitude oscillations were caused in the bridge structure by mechanical resonance and the structure crumbled under the stress. Figure 14.19 summarizes other examples of mechanical resonance.

**Fig.14.19**  Further examples of mechanical resonance

| Example of Mechanical Resonance | Photo |
|---|---|
| **(a) Rocking a car out of an ice rut**<br><br>If the people pushing the car and the driver pushing down on the accelerator do so at the natural rocking frequency of the car, it rocks back and forth with ever-increasing amplitude until it can finally be pushed out of the rut. |  |
| **(b) Pushing a child on a swing**<br><br>Push a child on the swing at the correct frequency, always at the same point in the cycle, and the child's amplitude of swinging increases dramatically. |  |
| **(c) Pendulum clocks**<br><br>For hundreds of years, people depended on the constant natural frequency of a swinging pendulum to control the speed of a clock. Today, the source of vibration is often a quartz crystal. |  |

### An Example of Resonance

The frequency at which a person walks can coincide with the resonance frequency of water swishing back and forth in a bucket. If you carry two buckets of water while walking, the amplitude of the wave action builds up and your leg will get wet. However, if your walking frequency doesn't match the resonant frequency of the water in the buckets, the water forms little surface ripples and becomes more stable.

For the following resonance situations, explain what is happening and suggest a solution for getting rid of the resonance.

1. **a)** A truck drives down your street and the windows of your house rattle.
   **b)** Soldiers marching in step across a long bridge cause it to vibrate up and down with an ever-increasing amplitude.
   **c)** The low hum of large motors in a factory cause workers' internal organs, like the heart, to vibrate, making the workers feel sick.

**d)** A tuning fork vibrating at 250 Hz causes another tuning fork with the same frequency to also vibrate.

**e)** A sharp note maintained by a singer shatters a thin-walled glass.

**2.** Find other examples of resonance and explain how the resonance can be eliminated.

*The Sweet Spot*

Anyone who has ever hit a ball using a baseball bat knows the effect of a stinger: the feeling in your hands caused by the vibrating bat after impact with the ball. In some cases, the whole arm is jarred, and in other instances, the bat may break. We have also experienced the smooth, effortless hit. The point of contact where this type of hit occurs is called the "sweet spot."

If the bat hits the ball at a node (point of destructive interference), the bat doesn't excite any resonance modes and hence doesn't vibrate. This hit is smooth and effortless. If the bat hits the ball at a maximum (antinode), then a corresponding resonance mode is excited and the bat vibrates, causing the bat to "sting" the hands. In many hits, the duration of bat-ball contact is enough to excite the fundamental and second resonance modes, both with roughly equal amplitudes (illustrated in Fig. 14.20B). The ideal spot to hit the ball is about halfway between the nodes of each vibration (the sweet spot). At this spot, each resonance mode has a tiny amplitude, thus creating an effect similar to hitting the ball at a pure node.

**3.** Speculate on the difference in energy transfer to the ball when the bat hits the ball at the sweet spot as opposed to away from the sweet spot, especially at an antinode.

**4.** Research the different materials that baseball bats are made of. How would the material affect the resonance of the bat?

**5.** Research the various ways in which a bat is "doctored." Do these techniques change the location of the sweet spot on the bat?

**Fig.14.20A** Joe Carter after hitting a home run in the final game of the 1993 World Series

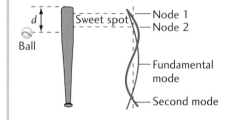

**Fig.14.20B** The sweet spot

# 14.6 Acoustic Resonance and Musical Instruments

Acoustic resonance is the process responsible for the sound waves that come from various musical instruments. Like mechanical resonance, the instrument is tuned to a particular natural frequency. When stimulated by a source of vibration that has the same frequency, a standing resonant wave is set up in the instrument and large amplitude oscillations result. We hear these oscillations as the characteristic "note" that is being played. The best way to examine acoustic resonance is to look at two different types of musical instruments that support standing waves in different ways. We will look at wind instruments and stringed instruments that support standing waves in air columns and strings respectively.

# Wind Instruments — Standing Waves in Air Columns

**Fig.14.21** A bottle acts like a closed air column

If you have ever taken a breath and blown air over the opening of a pop bottle to make a sound like a fog horn then you have experienced resonance in air columns (see Fig. 14.21).

**Wind instruments** include traditional brass or woodwind instruments, such as a trumpet or clarinet. Figure 14.22 illustrates how the vibration source for a brass instrument is the musician blowing air through vibrating compressed lips. A thin sliver of wood, called a **reed**, does the same for a woodwind.

**Fig. 14.22**   Vibrations in a brass instrument

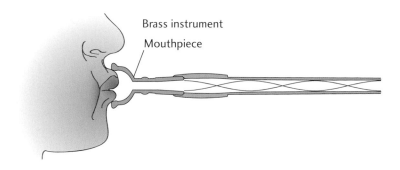

No matter what the source of vibration, these instruments are nothing more than elaborate air columns in which a standing wave is formed. It is important to note that it is virtually impossible to model the behaviour of longitudinal sound waves with pictures. For all intents and purposes, longitudinal wave compressions and rarefactions will be modelled with crests and troughs respectively, using transverse waves. Figure 14.23 uses a tuning fork to show how standing waves can be set up in open and closed air columns. Note that sound waves reflect at closed and open ends in the same way that waves in springs reflect at fixed and free ends.

**Fig.14.23**   The relationship between transverse and longitudinal waves

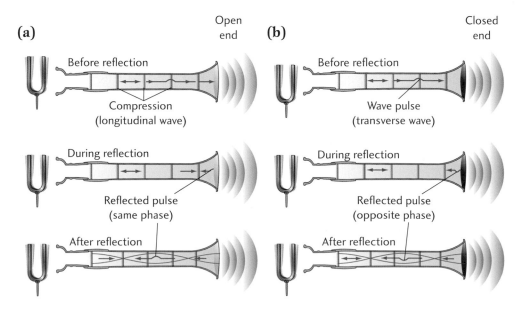

The waves that are produced migrate from the source to the open end of the air column, where some of their energy is transmitted. Much of the wave energy is reflected back inside the air column, without any phase change. This type of reflection is the same as that witnessed in solid materials, such as the car antenna (see Fig. 14.13). In closed air columns where the sound wave meets a "fixed" end, there is reflection in the opposite phase. Either type of reflected wave meets more waves from the source. Acoustic resonance is achieved when a standing wave is formed inside the air column and the entire instrument begins to vibrate. Figure 14.24 illustrates how standing waves look in open and closed air columns.

**Fig.14.24** Resonant lengths and frequencies for open and closed air columns

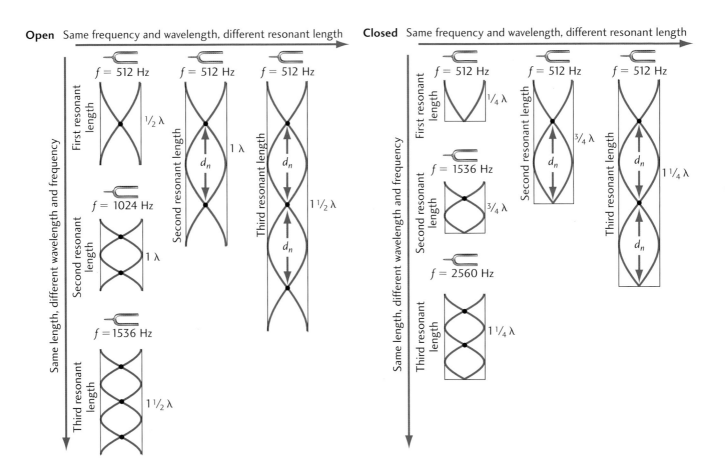

From the **know your "knodes"** rule, you can easily see that when standing waves are created, only a few wavelengths are possible. This means that the air column is also tuned to resonate with only a few different frequencies. If we recall that the internodal distance for any standing wave, $d_n$, is equal to $\frac{1}{2}\lambda$, then the specific resonant lengths of the air column can be compared to the wavelength, as shown in Table 14.1.

**KNOW YOUR "KNODES"**

Standing wave patterns have a node at any closed end and an antinode at any open end of the medium in which they travel.

**Table 14.1**
**Lengths of Air Columns**

| Resonant length | Number of nodes ($n$) | Closed Air Column | | Open Air Column | |
|---|---|---|---|---|---|
| | | Number of internodal distances | Length of column in wavelengths ($\lambda$) | Number of internodal distances | Length of column in wavelengths ($\lambda$) |
| First | 1 | $\frac{1}{2}$ | $\frac{1}{4}\lambda$ | 1 | $\frac{1}{2}\lambda$ |
| Second | 2 | $\frac{3}{2}$ | $\frac{3}{4}\lambda$ | 2 | $1\lambda$ |
| Third | 3 | $\frac{5}{2}$ | $\frac{5}{4}\lambda$ | 3 | $\frac{3}{2}\lambda$ |
| Fourth | 4 | $\frac{7}{2}$ | $\frac{7}{4}\lambda$ | 4 | $2\lambda$ |
| General statement | Based on $n$ | $\frac{2n-1}{2}$ | $\frac{(2n-1)\lambda}{4}$ | $n$ | $\frac{n}{2}\lambda$ |

**EXAMPLE 6**  **Finding wavelength**

Recall that the distance between consecutive nodes, $d_n$, is $\frac{1}{2}\lambda$.

An air column that is open at both ends is 1.50 m long. A specific frequency is heard resonating from the column. What is the longest wavelength and its associated frequency that could be responsible for this resonance? The speed of sound is 345 m/s.

### Solution and Connection to Theory

**Given**

The longest wave occurs at the first resonant length, where $n = 1$.

Therefore, $L = \frac{1}{2}\lambda$

**Fig. 14.25**

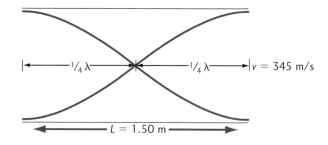

$\frac{1}{2}\lambda = 1.50 \text{ m} = 2(1.50 \text{ m}) = 3.00 \text{ m}$

Therefore, the maximum wavelength is 3.00 m.

$v = f\lambda$

$f = \dfrac{v}{\lambda} = \dfrac{345 \text{ m/s}}{3.00 \text{ m}} = 115 \text{ Hz}$

Therefore, the frequency of this wave is 115 Hz.

EXAMPLE 7    Finding frequency

A closed air column resonates at two consective lengths of 94.0 cm and 156 cm. If the speed of sound is 350 m/s, what is the resonant frequency of the air column?

### *Solution and Connection to Theory*

#### Given

$L_1 = 94.0$ cm     $L_2 = 156$ cm     $v = 350$ m/s

The difference in length between any two resonant lengths is always $\frac{1}{2}\lambda$.

$\frac{1}{2}\lambda = L_2 - L_1 = 156$ cm $- 94.0$ cm $= 62$ cm or 0.62 m

$\lambda = 2(0.62$ m$) = 1.24$ m

Finally, $f = \dfrac{v}{\lambda} = \dfrac{350 \text{ m/s}}{1.24 \text{ m}} = 282$ Hz

Therefore, the resonant frequency of the column is 282 Hz.

**Fig.14.26**   Solving Problems With Air Columns

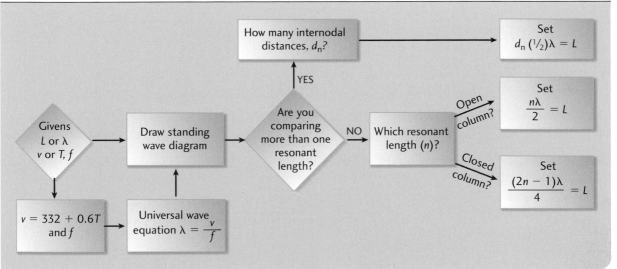

Wind instruments change their frequency in two ways. They can have the lengths of their air columns adjusted so they are tuned to different fundamental frequencies, or they can have the source vibrate at another resonant frequency for a particular air column length. In brass instruments, such as a trumpet (Fig. 14.27A) or tuba, the musician pushes valves that open passages to more tubing, which effectively lengthens the instrument. A trombone (Fig. 14.27B) has a free-moving slide that allows the musician to continually adjust the length of the air column and frequency of the sound.

**Fig.14.27A** Valves change the air column length in a trumpet

**Fig.14.27B** A trombone has a free-moving slide that allows you to change the air column length

Woodwind instruments, like the clarinet, the oboe, and the saxophone, vary their air column length by uncovering holes in the body or **bore** of the instrument. Figure 14.28 shows how an open hole in the instrument makes the internal pressure of the air in the air column equal to the atmospheric pressure at that point, causing an antinode to be formed at that length. An antinode here acts to shorten the instrument's air column and increase the frequency of its sound.

**Fig.14.28** An open hole changes the length of the open air column

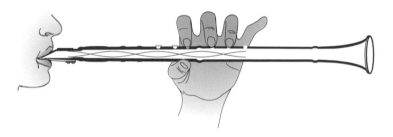

Flutes and piccolos work in much the same manner, but the vibration is caused by the interaction of moving air from the breath of the musician and the air inside the mouthpiece.

**Fig.14.29** Standing waves in strings with a node at each end

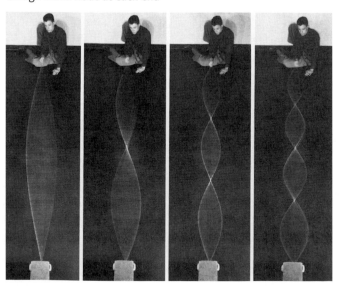

## Stringed Instruments — Standing Waves in Strings

Stringed instruments, such as guitars and violins, resonate by having a standing wave set up in the string. Figure 14.29 outlines the possible ways that standing waves occur in strings. Remember that a node must appear at each end of the string because the string is fixed at both ends.

The resonant wavelengths of strings have a similar pattern to those of open air columns. A string resonates when its length is equivalent to $\frac{1}{2}\lambda$, $\lambda$, $\frac{3}{2}\lambda$, $2\lambda$, and so on.

Achieving different frequencies with strings is more complicated than with air columns. There are four variables that affect the frequency of a string. They are length, tension, diameter, and density. Table 14.2 summarizes how each variable affects a string's overall frequency.

**Table 14.2**
**Table of Proportionality of Variables for Strings**

| Variable | Proportionality | Description | Comparative equation |
|---|---|---|---|
| Length (L) | $f \propto \dfrac{1}{L}$ | If the length is halved, the frequency doubles. Frequency increases when the length decreases. | $\dfrac{f_1}{f_2} = \dfrac{L_2}{L_1}$ |
| Tension (T) | $f \propto \sqrt{T}$ | Frequency varies directly as the square root of the tension. Frequency increases when the tension increases. If tension increases by a factor of four, the frequency doubles. | $\dfrac{f_1}{f_2} = \dfrac{\sqrt{T_1}}{\sqrt{T_2}}$ |
| Diameter (d) | $f \propto \dfrac{1}{d}$ | Frequency varies inversely as the diameter. Frequency increases when the diameter of a string decreases. If the diameter is halved, then the frequency doubles. | $\dfrac{f_1}{f_2} = \dfrac{d_2}{d_1}$ |
| Density (ρ) | $f \propto \dfrac{1}{\sqrt{\rho}}$ | Frequency varies inversely as the square root of the density. Frequency increases when density decreases. If the density is quartered, then the frequency doubles. | $\dfrac{f_1}{f_2} = \dfrac{\sqrt{\rho_2}}{\sqrt{\rho_1}}$ |

**EXAMPLE 8**   **A guitar string**

A guitar string of length 0.80 m has a frequency of 375 Hz. When it is shortened to 0.60 m, what is its new frequency?

*Solution and Connection to Theory*

**Given**

$L_1 = 0.80$ m      $L_2 = 0.60$ m      $f_1 = 375$ Hz      $f_2 = ?$

Rearrange the equation

$$\frac{f_1}{f_2} = \frac{L_2}{L_1}$$

$$f_2 = f_1 \left(\frac{L_1}{L_2}\right)$$

$$f_2 = 375 \text{ Hz} \left(\frac{0.80 \text{ m}}{0.60 \text{ m}}\right) = 500 \text{ Hz}$$

Therefore, the new frequency of the string is 500 Hz.

EXAMPLE 9

A string has an original tension of 150 N. What new tension must be applied to the string to have it vibrate with a frequency exactly twice that of the original?

### Solution and Connection to Theory

**Given**

$$T_1 = 150 \text{ N} \qquad f_1 = f_2 \qquad T_2 = ?$$

If $f_2$ is double the original, then $f_2 = 2f_1$.

$$\frac{f_1}{f_2} = \frac{\sqrt{T_1}}{\sqrt{T_2}}$$

$$T_2 = T_1\left(\frac{f_2}{f_1}\right)^2 = 150 \text{ N}\left(\frac{2f_1}{f_1}\right)^2 = 600 \text{ N}$$

Therefore, the new tension would have to be 600 N.

**Fig.14.30**  Solving Standing Waves in Strings

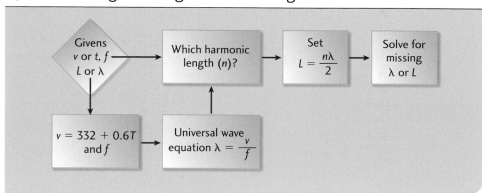

String instruments, such as acoustic guitars and violins, create sound from their vibrating strings. The rest of the instrument, i.e., the entire body and the air inside it, serves to amplify the sound made by the strings because it resonates to the string frequency. The quality of the sound depends greatly on the shape and the materials from which the resonance box is made. The way the instrument resonates is what makes its sound "music to our ears."

**Fig.14.31** Solving Problems With Guitar Strings

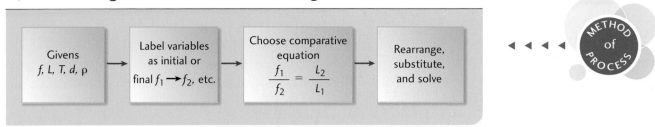

1. An open air column has a length of 1.2 m. The air temperature is 20°C.
   a) Find the wavelengths of the first, third, and sixth resonances that can be generated in the air column.
   b) Find the frequencies associated with these resonances.
2. Repeat Question 1 for a closed air column.
3. A guitar string vibrates at 400 Hz and has a length of 0.8 m. Find the new frequency if
   a) the string is lengthened to 0.9 m.
   b) the string is replaced with another string, the density of which is greater by a factor of two.
   c) the tension in the string is decreased by a factor of 0.4.
   d) the string is replaced with another string, the diameter of which is twice as large.

## 14.7 Music

So far, we have discussed the topic of sound in a very clinical fashion. We know what sound is and how various sounds are produced in a few musical instruments. However, we have not examined what differentiates sound from music. The main difference between music and generic sounds or noise is the structure of the sound wave.

An **oscilloscope** depicts complex longitudinal sound waves as transverse waves. The oscilloscope plots the variation in the electric signal versus time from a microphone that samples the sound. Figure 14.32 shows two oscilloscope tracings, one of noise and the other produced by a violin.

The violin's tracings have a regularly re-occurring pattern of curved sections. The noise tracings, on the other hand, are random, sharp fluctuations.

Three characteristics of waves that are used to describe music and musical tones are pitch, loudness, and quality.

**Fig.14.32** The difference between music and noise

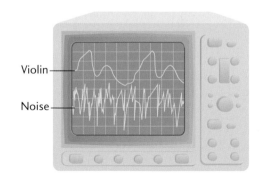

Violin

Noise

## Pitch

**Pitch** is the highness or lowness of a musical note. A higher pitch has a higher frequency. Figure 14.33 illustrates how pitch and frequency are related.

If the pitch of a sound is increased by one octave, the frequency is doubled. On a musical scale, the C above middle C, for example, has twice the frequency of middle C.

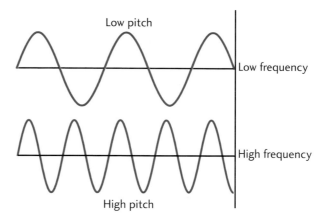

**Fig.14.33** Pitch and frequency are directly related

## Loudness

**Loudness** is related to the amplitude of a sound wave. The greater the amplitude, the higher the volume of the sound. Figure 14.34 shows this relationship.

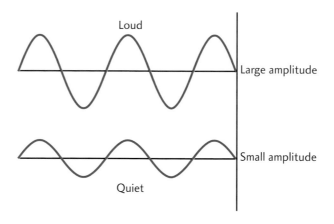

**Fig.14.34** Loudness and amplitude are related

## Quality

**Quality** has to do with the complexity of the wave form. It is the degree of richness of a sound, such as that produced by a symphony orchestra. Recall that a string can vibrate with a fundamental frequency, $f_o$, as well as higher harmonics or overtones of frequency $2f_o$, $3f_o$, and so on (recall Fig. 14.16). Figure 14.35 shows two waveforms of similar frequency to highlight the differences between a pure tone and a rich, high-quality tone.

Quality makes a difference to the way a tone is heard. The more harmonic frequencies that are present at one time in a sound, the richer the quality of the tone. One string can vibrate at several frequencies at once. When a piano key is struck, it vibrates several strings for each note, which improves the quality of the sound.

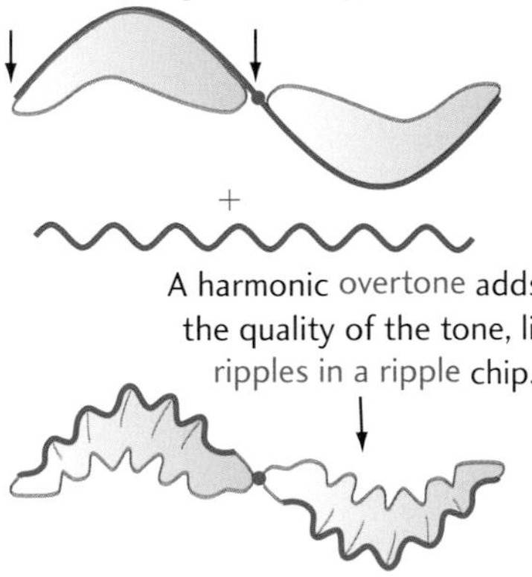

A regular potato chip is like half the wavelength of a single wave.

+

A harmonic overtone adds to the quality of the tone, like ripples in a ripple chip.

**Fig.14.35**  Richer, higher-quality sounds have more overtones

Follow the instructions given below to draw a simple sound wave form by adding the fundamental to the first overtone (first harmonic to the second harmonic).

1. **a)** Draw two cycles of a wave with wavelength 4 cm and amplitude 5 cm. On top of this wave, draw another wave with wavelength 2 cm and amplitude 5 cm.

   **b)** To define the final wave form, find the points on both waves where only one of the waves has zero amplitude. Place dots (in a different colour) on the other wave, directly above these points. The amplitude of the final wave is the non-zero amplitude at these points.

   **c)** Find the points where both waves cross. The amplitude of the final wave at these points is double the amplitude at the points of intersection. Place your dots accordingly.

   **d)** Find the points where the two waves cancel. The amplitude of the final wave at these points is zero, so place your dots on the zero line.

   **e)** Find the maximum amplitude points (troughs and crests) of both waves. Add the amplitudes of the two waves together at these points and place your dots at the sum values. (Remember that amplitude is positive and negative.)

   **f)** Draw the resultant wave by connecting the dots.

# 14.8  Special Cases of Interference

There are many other cases where interference of sound waves can cause very interesting effects.

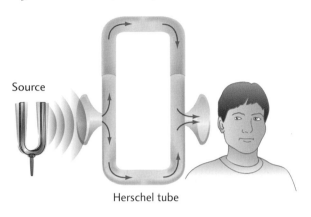

**Fig.14.36A**  Interference in a Herschel tube

Source

Herschel tube

## Herschel Tube

The Herschel tube (Fig. 14.36A) is a device that splits the sound waves from a single source into two paths of different lengths.

The sound wave in the longer path lags behind the other wave. When it is finally reunited with its "sister" wave, they interfere according to the principle of superposition. If the longer section was $\frac{1}{2}\lambda$ longer than the other section, then every compression of one wave would meet a rarefaction of the other wave, resulting in total destructive interference and silence.

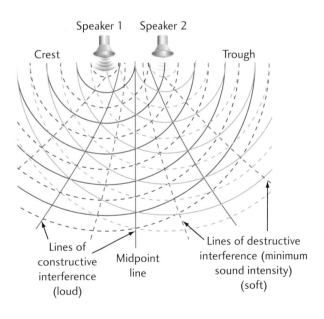

**Fig.14.36B**  Interference of two speakers sounding the same frequency

Speaker 1    Speaker 2

Crest                          Trough

Lines of constructive interference (loud)

Midpoint line

Lines of destructive interference (minimum sound intensity) (soft)

## Side-by-side Speakers

Sound waves from two speakers sitting side by side, as shown in Fig. 14.36B, would produce the same type of wave interference pattern as long as they were both of the same frequency. The dotted lines in Fig. 14.36B show the places where there would be total destructive interference. If you walked across the area in front of these speakers, the sound intensity would fluctuate between loud and soft as you passed through these regions. This effect is very similar to the interference pattern produced by the two identical sources generating water waves in Fig. 12.27.

## Single Tuning Fork

Figure 14.37 outlines the patterns of interference that occur when a simple tuning fork is struck.

The sound waves coming out of the tuning fork at 90° to each other are out of phase. This effect produces regions of minimum sound intensity at the corners where the compressions and rarefactions meet, resulting in a quieter sound.

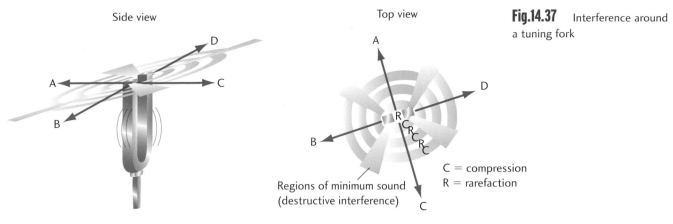

**Fig.14.37** Interference around a tuning fork

C = compression
R = rarefaction

Regions of minimum sound
(destructive interference)

## Beat Frequency

When two notes of slightly different frequency are sounded together, a complicated wave form results. Figure 14.38 shows the resultant wave form (b) that is created when the two original waves (a) interfere according to the principle of superposition.

**Fig.14.38** Beats formed from two slightly different frequencies

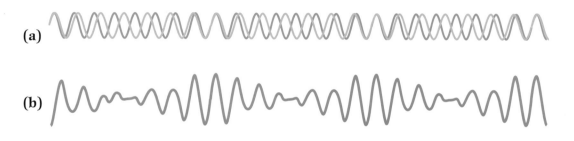

**(a)**

**(b)**

The result is a pulsating sound in which the sound intensity alternates between loud and soft at a specific frequency. Figure 14.39 examines the beat frequency for two frequencies, 2 Hz and 4 Hz, as they are played together.

**Fig.14.39** Interference of a 2 Hz and 4 Hz signal produces two beats per second

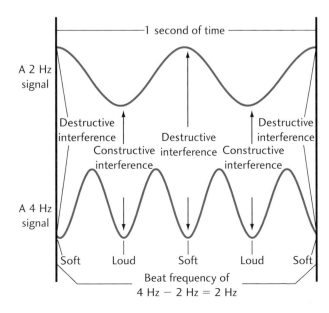

**Beat frequency** refers to the frequency of a pulsating noise, and not the frequencies of any of the tuning forks emitting the sounds.

The beat frequency is related to the two original frequencies by the formula

$$\text{beat frequency } (f_B) = |f_2 - f_1|$$

The beat frequency ($f_B$) is the absolute value of the difference between the two original frequencies. Piano tuners use beats to tune pianos. When a piano key and a tuning fork are struck together and no beats are heard, the tuner knows that key is in proper tune. The absence of beats indicates that the string and the tuning fork are vibrating at the same frequency.

---

**EXAMPLE 10**  **Tuning a piano**

A piano tuner strikes a 256 Hz (middle C) tuning fork and middle C on a piano. She hears 20 beats in 5.0 s. What are the possible frequencies of the out-of-tune note?

*Solution and Connection to Theory*

**Given**
$f_1 = 256$ Hz    # of beats = 20 cycles    $t = 5.0$ s    $f_2 = ?$

To find the beat frequency,

$f_B = \dfrac{20}{5.0 \text{ s}}$    $f_B = 4.0$ Hz

$f_B = |f_2 - f_1|$

$f_2 = f_B + f_1$    or    $f_B - f_1$

$f_2 = 256$ Hz $+ 4.0$ Hz    or    $256$ Hz $- 4.0$ Hz

$f_2 = 260$ Hz or 252 Hz

Therefore, the two possible frequencies of the note are 260 Hz and 252 Hz.

**1.** Two vibrating tuning forks make 12 beats in 4.0 s. If one tuning fork is 1000 Hz, what are the possible frequencies of the other tuning fork?

◄  ◄  ◄  ◄

### The Human Voice

The human voice consists of such complex waveforms, that they are only now being reproduced artificially, with only moderate success. Artificial voice technology, consisting of a voice synthesizer and a computer actuator, is used by individuals who have lost the ability to speak because of ailments such as throat cancer, ALS (Amyotrophic Lateral Sclerosis or Lou Gehrig's Disease), and strokes. The field of voice engineering is expanding rapidly due to the highly sophisticated microcomputer chips being developed. In the near future, a robotic voice will sound very similar to a human voice.

Stephen Hawking, one of the greatest scientific minds in history, was diagnosed with ALS at the age of 21. Not given much hope of surviving more than five years, he is still going strong at the age of 59, making breakthrough discoveries in astrophysics and the nature of time and the universe. He is confined to a wheelchair and uses his limited muscle control to activate a synthesizer in order to communicate. He once said, "I try to lead as normal a life as possible, and not think about my condition, or regret the things it prevents me from doing, which are not that many."

**2.** Research how the human voice produces its complex range of sounds.

**3.** Stephen Hawking is just one of many individuals with handicaps who have risen above their disability. Research three other individuals who have not allowed a physical disability to keep them from pursuing their interests.

**Fig.14.40**   Stephen Hawking

## Digital Recording and Data Transfer

The digital era is upon us. Analog recordings on vinyl records or magnetic media, such as cassette and video tapes, are being replaced by digitally recorded tapes, CDs (compact disks), and DVDs (digital video disks). Even standard analog-based cellular phones are being replaced by digital mobile phones.

All recordings begin as a simple electric wave. The electric voltage increases and decreases, as shown by the pink wave in Fig. STSE.14.1. Analog recording devices make an impression on the surface of the vinyl record or tape that matches the fluctuation in electric voltage coming from the source. On a vinyl record, the higher the voltage, the narrower the groove cut into the surface. When the record is played, a needle, which is a very narrow piezo-electric crystal, is dragged through the groove. A piezo crystal is a unique substance that produces an electrical potential or voltage when pressure is applied to it. As the size of the groove changes, so does the "recorded" voltage. Dust, dirt, scratches, and surface deterioration, however, result in poor recording quality.

Cassette tapes or other magnetic media, like analog videotapes, store the fluctuation in voltage as a fluctuation in the magnetic strength on the tape. Often, noise from the tape recorder's motor or the tape sliding by the heads is also recorded. The tape player heads detect the changing magnet strength and convert it into a voltage that is amplified and output to the speakers. The magnetic strength of these tapes deteriorates with time or when brought near other magnets.

The major advance with digital recordings is that the size of the electrical voltage is coded as a number by an analog-to-digital converter (ADC). The digital numbers represent the changes in voltage versus time. Data is transmitted or stored with no deterioration in its quality, and no addition of any extraneous

**Fig. STSE.14.1**

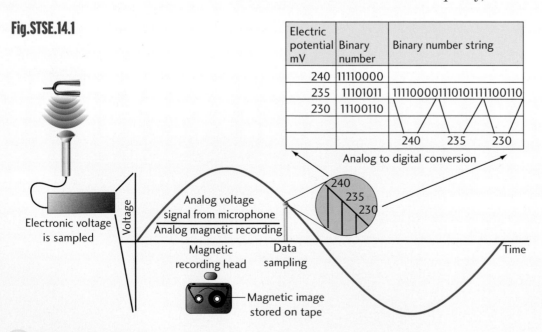

| Electric potential mV | Binary number | Binary number string | | |
|---|---|---|---|---|
| 240 | 11110000 | | | |
| 235 | 11101011 | 111100001110101111100110 | | |
| 230 | 11100110 | | | |
| | | 240 | 235 | 230 |

Analog to digital conversion

**Digital data string**
magnetically or optically recorded

1
0

Electronic voltage is sampled

Voltage

Analog voltage signal from microphone
Analog magnetic recording

Magnetic recording head

Data sampling

240
235
230

Time

Magnetic image stored on tape

noise. When the information is decoded with a digital-to-analog converter (DAC), the information recovered is exactly the same as that which was stored. Because the stored data is numerical, it may be manipulated mathematically to filter it or change it as desired. For example, each successive number multiplied by a decreasing value results in an audio recording that fades to silence.

The benefits of digital coding, recording, and data transmission include crisp, clear recordings and images, as well as low-power worldwide transmission of information in real time. However, digital communication has also brought us increased dependance on Internet and satellite technology as well as the ability to make perfect duplicates of pirated music. Like all technology, digital technology is not without its problems.

## Design a Study of Societal Impact

Many computer users have CD burners that can make exact duplicates of music or data stored on compact disks without any deterioration or change from the original recording. How does the use of these products affect the royalty-based wages of people who create the original work?

Digital satellite signals for television, radio, mobile phones, and the Internet now use less power because the information in the signal is more important than the strength of the signal. What positive health and environmental effects may result from this change?

## Design an Activity to Evaluate

Evaluate the quality of a sound as it passes through different electronic devices. Record the same sound on computer, cassette tape, through a walkie talkie, a cellular phone, and a regular phone. Use a microphone to capture the sound time spectrum on a computer data interface or by videotaping an oscilloscope.

Figure STSE.14.2 is an image of the binary signal sent into outer space for extraterrestrials to decode in the SETI (Search for Extraterrestrial Intelligence) project. Research the SETI project and decode this message the way an extraterrestrial might.

**Fig.STSE.14.2**

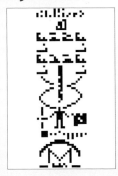

## Build a Structure

Use a spreadsheet to combine a data signal with a set of noise data (from your teacher). Pass the data file to another group. Its task is to find and remove the noise. Do this activity by trial and error, or research mathematical tools, such as fourier transformers, to filter out the noise signal.

**You should be able to**

*Understand Basic Concepts:*

- Define the principle of superposition and predict the shapes of overall waveforms created from two or more component waves.
- Describe the process of absorption, transmission, and reflection of sound waves.
- Describe and solve problems related to how speed, wavelength, and frequency of a sound wave change when moving from one medium to another.
- Define and identify examples of constructive and destructive interference.
- Relate the type of phase change that occurs in a wave at both fixed and free ends.
- Describe the principle of superposition in the development of standing waves.
- Solve problems involving standing waves, frequency, wavelength, and speed of sound in air columns and strings.
- Define the term "mechanical resonance" and apply it to acoustic resonance in air columns, strings, and their related musical instruments.
- Describe how instruments, including air column and string instruments, can affect a change in the pitch and quality of the note heard.
- Describe and explain the characteristics of a musical sound.
- Explain how a pulsating beat frequency is produced when two sounds of slightly different pitch are played together.

*Develop Skills of Inquiry and Communication:*

- Measure and draw various transverse waveforms and describe what would happen to the frequency, wavelength, and speed of a wave as it passes from one medium to another.
- Interpret the results of experiments designed to highlight the conditions necessary to produce resonance in air columns.

*Relate Science to Technology, Society, and the Environment:*

- Apply technology, like that of a soundproof room, to the study of sound produced by automobiles.
- Describe how the knowledge of physics is important for an acoustic engineer in sound and noise management and a civil engineer designing new structures.
- Outline how mechanical resonance is related to rocking a car out of an ice rut, the sweet spot of a baseball bat, and pushing a child on a swing.
- Evaluate the effectiveness of sound reproduction and transmission technology, such as cell phones and digital sound recorders (computer).

**Equations**

$$\frac{\lambda_1}{\lambda_2} = \frac{v_1}{v_2}$$

$$d_n = \frac{1}{2}\lambda$$

$$L = \frac{(2n - 1)}{4}\lambda \text{ (closed air column)}$$

$$L = \frac{n}{2}\lambda \text{ (open air column)}$$

$$\frac{f_1}{f_2} = \frac{L_2}{L_1}$$

$$\frac{f_1}{f_2} = \frac{\sqrt{T_1}}{\sqrt{T_2}}$$

$$\frac{f_1}{f_2} = \frac{d_2}{d_1}$$

$$\frac{f_1}{f_2} = \frac{\sqrt{\rho_2}}{\sqrt{\rho_1}}$$

$$f_B = |f_2 - f_1|$$

## Conceptual Questions

1. Describe some cases of mechanical resonance that have not been discussed in the text. Be sure to use the specific physics terminology.

2. Apparently, some singers can shatter a wine glass with their singing voice. To which topic is this ability related? What qualities would a singer's voice need to have to be able to shatter glass?

3. Your car's rearview mirror vibrates only when you drive at a certain speed. Explain.

4. When your car is stuck in an ice rut, the principle of resonance could be used to help you out. Explain how a few well-timed pushes could move a heavy car.

5. Explain how beat frequency can be used to tune an instrument.

6. Sound is caused by a vibration. In each of the following cases, describe what is vibrating:
   a) Blowing over a pop bottle
   b) A drum
   c) An organ
   d) A piano
   e) A knock on the door

7. When filling your car with gasoline, in the last few seconds before filling the tank, a noise with a rising pitch comes from the tank. Explain.

8. Some guitar strings are either wound with extra material or are made from different substances. Explain why this would affect the pitch of different strings.

9. A car muffler is a closed chamber made up of open tubes of various lengths for the exhaust gases to pass through. Describe how the principle of superposition can be used with these "air columns" to reduce the noise of the car's exhaust system.

## Problems

▶ **14.2  The Principle of Superposition**

10. Use the principle of superposition to determine the resulting wave pulse when the two pulses meet each other, as shown in Fig. 14.41.

**Fig.14.41**

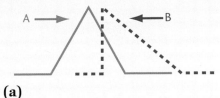

**(a)**

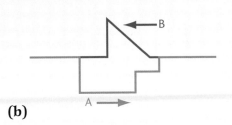

**(b)**

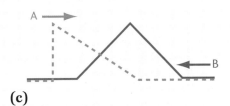

**(c)**

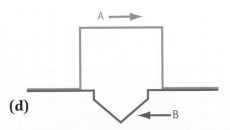

**(d)**

11. Explain why an oscilloscope, a device that displays a transverse wave, is used to study sound, which is a longitudinal wave.

12. With a quick sketch of an oscilloscope, illustrate
   a) a transverse wave of wavelength 4 cm and amplitude 1.5 cm.

**b)** a wave with half the frequency of a).

**c)** Sketch a) as a longitudinal wave.

13. In your notebook, draw a simple sketch of a wave form that illustrates the characteristics of sound indicated in each box in Fig. 14.42. Start with a single wavelength. Under each sketch, write a brief description of the waveform you have drawn.

**Fig.14.42**

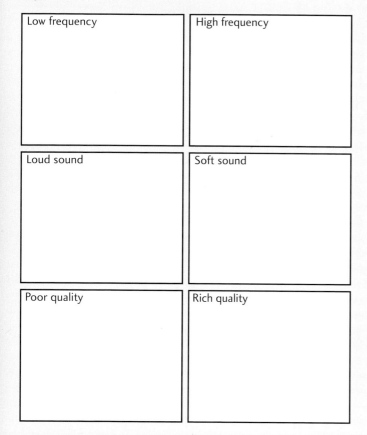

| Low frequency | High frequency |
| Loud sound | Soft sound |
| Poor quality | Rich quality |

14. Explain the role of harmonics in the quality of a musical note.

15. Why is a xylophone built with removable bars if they can't be interchanged?

16. A big gravel truck rumbles by your house, causing your window to vibrate enough to make a loud tone. Explain what is happening.

### 14.3 Sound Waves and Matter

17. A sound wave of speed 341 m/s and a wavelength of 0.33 m enters a low-pressure area where the speed decreases to 335 m/s. What is the resulting wavelength?

18. Use the parameters given in Problem 17 to calculate the frequency of each wave. Explain why listening to an outdoor concert does not affect the pitch of the sound heard by the audience.

### 14.4 Standing Waves — A Special Case of Interference

19. A xylophone bar resonates with a particular sound because a standing wave has been set up in it. The bar behaves like an open air column because each end is free to vibrate. A 20.0 cm bar resonates with its fifth resonant length at 22.0°C. What is the frequency that is heard?

20. Using Fig. 14.43, draw a transverse standing wave between the speaker and the wall that would result from the sound reflections. Assume that the air temperature is 30°C and the speaker generates a 175 Hz note.

**Fig.14.43**

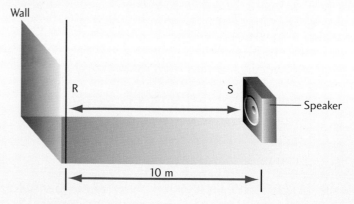

## 14.5 Resonance

**21.** If pendulum 1 in Fig. 14.44 is set in motion, which of the other three pendulums would also move? What principle is at work here?

**Fig.14.44**

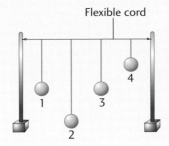

Flexible cord

## 14.6 Acoustic Resonance and Musical Instruments

**22.** An air column that is open at both ends has a distance of 24.0 cm from one resonant length to another. What is the wavelength of sound that is in resonance with this tube? How would the wavelength be affected if the tube was closed at one end?

**23.** Water is slowly drained out of a tube until the air column is 8.0 cm long. A loud sound is then heard.
   **a)** What is the wavelength of the sound that is produced by resonance?
   **b)** How long would the tube have to be for the same note to resonate at the third resonant length?

**24.** A tuning fork vibrating with a frequency of 950 Hz is held near the end of an open air column that has been adjusted to its first resonant length at 25.0°C.
   **a)** What is the speed of sound in the room?
   **b)** What is the wavelength of the sound produced?
   **c)** How long is the tube in centimetres?

**25.** A 1024 Hz tuning fork is held up to a closed air column (closed at one end and open at the other) at 30.0°C. What is the minimum length of an air column that would resonate with this frequency?

**26.** Organ pipes, open at one end, resonate best at their first resonant length. Two pipes have length 23.0 cm and 30.0 cm respectively.
   **a)** What is the wavelength of the sound emitted by each pipe?
   **b)** What are the respective frequencies if the speed of sound is 341 m/s?
   **c)** What is the air temperature in this church?

**27.** One of the tubes in Pan's flute measures 10 cm from one open end to the other. The air temperature is 20.0°C.
   **a)** What is the fundamental wavelength of the note that is heard?
   **b)** What is the corresponding frequency?

**28.** A tuning fork was sounded over an adjustable closed air column. It was found that the difference between the second and fifth resonant length was 90.0 cm. What was the frequency of the tuning fork if the experiment was done in a lab with air temperature 25.0°C?

**29.** Hollow tube chimes are made of metal and are open at each end. These columns resonate best at their third resonant length. One chime is 2.5 m long and the air temperature is 25.0°C.
   **a)** What is the speed of sound?
   **b)** What is the wavelength of the sound produced?
   **c)** What is the frequency of the sound that is heard?

**30.** A guitar string is struck and found to have a frequency of 2048 Hz. If both the tension and the length are doubled, what is the new frequency of the string?

**31.** A string that is 90.0 cm long with a diameter of 0.75 mm and a tension of 60.0 N has a frequency of 1000 Hz. What new frequency is heard in each of the following situations?
   **a)** The length is increased to 100.0 cm.
   **b)** The tension is increased to 80.0 N
   **c)** The diameter is increased to 0.77 mm.
   **d)** Both factors in parts a) and b) are done together.

**32.** A fundamental frequency of 550 Hz is played on a guitar string.
  **a)** What is the first harmonic frequency of the string?
  **b)** The tension of the string is doubled. What is the new fundamental frequency of the string?

**33.** The distance between the first and third nodes of a standing wave in a violin string is 4.0 cm.
  **a)** Draw a scale diagram to illustrate the string.
  **b)** What is the wavelength of the sound wave that is produced?
  **c)** What is the frequency of the note that is heard if the speed of sound is 345 m/s?

**34.** A string under a tension of 170 N has a frequency of 300 Hz. What will its frequency become if the tension is increased to 340 N?

**35.** Two steel strings of equal diameter and tension have a length of 0.75 m and 0.95 m respectively. If the frequency of the first string is 250 Hz, what is the frequency of the second string?

## 14.7 Music

**36.** The note C ($f$ = 512 Hz) is played on a piano. Calculate the frequencies that would correspond to this note's second, fourth, and fifth harmonics.

## 14.8 Special Cases of Interference

**37.** Calculate the beat frequencies that are heard when the following pairs of frequencies are sounded together:
  **a)** 312 Hz and 300 Hz
  **b)** 852 Hz and 857 Hz
  **c)** 1024 Hz and 1000 Hz

**38.** Liona Boyd, a famous Canadian guitarist, tunes her guitar's A string with a 440 Hz tuning fork. Beats are heard at a frequency of 4 Hz. To give herself more information, Ms. Boyd wraps a piece of masking tape around one of the tuning fork tines and continues tuning. This time, a beat frequency of 5 Hz is heard. Is more information required to find the specific frequency of the string? What are the possible frequencies of the string? In each case, what should Ms. Boyd do to tune the string?

**39.** A 512 Hz tuning fork is struck with another tuning fork and beats are heard with a beat frequency of 3 Hz. What are the possible frequencies of the unknown tuning fork?

## LAB 14.1  Fixed and Open-end Reflection

### Purpose

To examine the way in which pulses are reflected at fixed and open-end springs.

### Safety Consideration

Take care that the two people holding the spring don't let go of it. If the spring snaps, it could hurt someone.

### Equipment

Masking tape
Piece of paper
Stopwatch
"Slinky" spring or rope
4 m long string

### Procedure

1. Stretch the spring or rope out on the floor between two people at a comfortable length of 5–8 m. Place a small piece of masking tape on the spring near the centre. With one person holding one end rigidly, have the person at the other end send a transverse pulse down the length of the spring with a rapid sideways motion to one side and back to the centre. Describe the motion of the tape.

2. Repeat Step 1 with a longitudinal pulse, produced by a rapid forward-and-back motion of the end of the spring.

3. Stretch the spring or rope out on the floor between two people to a comfortable length of about 5–8 m. Place a folded piece of paper (like a "tent") on the floor next to the rigidly held end of the spring, as shown in the diagram, on the same side of the spring that a pulse is to be sent.

4. With a rapid sideways motion, send a pulse down to the rigidly held end of the spring. Watch for any movement of the tented paper to note which way the reflected pulse emerges. If no motion in the paper is observed, then place the paper on the other side of the spring and try to send another pulse.

5. Compare the size of the reflected pulse's amplitude by setting the "tented" piece of paper at different distances from the spring and sending pulses down.

### Fig.Lab.14.1

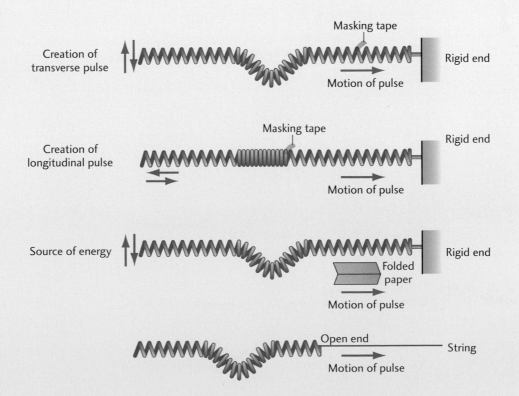

6. Simulate an open-ended reflection by tying a piece of string to the spring. Send a transverse pulse down from one end of the string and observe the way the pulse reacts at the string-spring interface (this is an approximated "open end"). Note on which side the reflected pulse emerges.

## Data

Be sure that all your qualitative answers to the procedure questions are recorded neatly.

## Uncertainty

Any distances that are noted or measured for this lab are only to give a qualitative comparison of the wave pulse amplitudes before and after reflection.

## Analysis

When a wave pulse is reflected on the opposite side of the incident pulse, it is said to be "out of phase." A pulse that is reflected on the same side of the incident pulse is said to be "in phase."

## Discussion

1. Describe the motion of the spring's particles as they transmit
   a) a transverse pulse.
   b) a longitudinal pulse.
2. What conditions cause an incident wave pulse to be reflected out of phase or in phase?
3. Was any wave transmitted at the string-spring interface? If so, on what side did it transmit compared to the incident pulse?

## Conclusion

Make a concluding statement that summarizes what goes on at an open end and a fixed end of a spring/string. Your statement should consider both the amplitude and direction of each transmitted and reflected pulse.

# LAB 14.2 Resonant Lengths of Closed Air Columns

## Purpose
To measure and compare to accepted values the lengths of closed air columns that resonate with a known frequency.

## Safety Considerations
1. Be sure to clean up any spilled water. It could be hazardous for those walking in the room.
2. Sound all tuning forks on a rubber hammer or rubber stopper and not on a solid desk top. Improper sounding of the tuning forks can cause damage.

## Equipment
Thermometer, Metre stick
Two tuning forks (minimum 512 Hz)
Rubber hammer or stopper
Golf tube (tubes that separate golf clubs in a golf bag)
Large transparent graduated cylinder (to contain the entire golf tube)
Alternative: A sliding piston air column from a scientific supply company

**Fig.Lab.14.2**

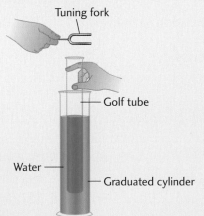

Tuning fork
Golf tube
Water
Graduated cylinder

## Procedure
1. Prepare a data table from the guidelines given below.
2. Set up the lab equipment as shown in Fig. Lab.14.2. Be sure that the water you use (if you are using water) is as close as possible to room temperature. Leave the water such that it may equilibrate to achieve room temperature.
3. Measure the room temperature.
4. Strike one of the tuning forks and hold it over the top end of the tube. Slowly draw the tube out of the water and listen for the first resonant point. You will hear it when the intensity of the tone reaches a sudden peak.
5. Measure the length of the air column from the surface of the water to the open end and record this measurement as your first resonant length.
6. Strike the tuning fork again and draw the tube farther out of the water to find the second and third resonant lengths.
7. Repeat Steps 5–6 for another tuning fork that has a different frequency.

## Data
Measure the first, second, and third resonant lengths in centimetres for two different tuning forks. Measure the room temperature.

## Uncertainty
Assign both instrumental and procedural uncertainties to all the measured quantities. The metre stick should have an associated overall uncertainty of about ±2 mm. The thermometer should have the typical uncertainty of ±0.1 of the smallest division.

## Analysis
1. Calculate the speed of sound at the temperature you measured using the equation $v_s = (332 \text{ m/s} + 0.6T)$
2. Use your value for the speed of sound and the frequency of each tuning fork to calculate the wavelengths of the two sound waves.
3. Use the equation $L = \frac{(2n - 1)\lambda}{4}$ to predict the resonant wavelengths.

## Discussion
1. Compare the six calculated and measured resonant lengths to see how well they agree. Did you hear every resonant point that you were supposed to?
2. Based on your comparisons, can you attribute any of your measured lengths to different resonant points?
3. Why might your group have found extra resonant lengths where they didn't fit?

## Conclusion
Write a concluding statement that summarizes whether or not your experimental data corresponded to theoretical values, taking into account experimental uncertainty.

LABORATORY EXERCISES

## Purpose

To measure the speed of a transverse wave in a spring, string, or rope under conditions of changing tension and frequency.

## Safety Consideration

Take care that the two people holding the spring don't let go of it. If the spring snaps, it could hurt someone.

## Equipment

"Slinky" spring or wave demonstration spring (5–8 m long)
Rope (about 5–8 m long)
Metre stick, Stopwatch, Masking tape

## Procedure

1. Stretch the spring or rope out on the floor between two people to a comfortable length of 5–8 m. Place a piece of masking tape on the floor at each end of the spring.
2. Measure the length of the spring/rope by finding the distance between the two pieces of masking tape.
3. One person holding the spring/rope should begin moving the end side to side until a standing wave is created and can be sustained.
4. Time the "wave maker" with the stopwatch for about 20 seconds as he/she counts the number of full cycles that he/she is producing.
5. Record the number of loops or antinodes that were present in the spring/rope during the experiment as well as the number of cycles that were completed in the time measured.
6. Change the speed of your oscillations to create a different number of "loops" or antinodes in the spring and repeat the measurements to eventually find the speed of the waves.

## Fig.Lab.14.3

7. Repeat this procedure again for a different tension in the spring (new length) or a different material, such as a rope.

## Uncertainty

Record the time from the stopwatch with an appropriate uncertainty that represents the timer's reaction reflexes. The length of the spring should only be recorded to ±0.05 m due to the way in which the length was measured and the fluctuation in length during the oscillations.

## Analysis

1. Calculate the length of each "loop" or antinode by taking the length of the spring/rope and dividing it by the total number of antinodes that were visible during the oscillations.
2. Calculate the frequency of the wave oscillations using the number of oscillations and the total time taken.
3. Find the speed of the waves for each case in the spring/rope using the universal wave equation, $v = f\lambda$.

## Discussion

1. Which type of apparatus transmitted waves at a faster rate?
2. Which apparatus transmitted waves faster, a tight spring or a loose spring?
3. Was there a detectable difference, beyond a reasonable margin of uncertainty, in the speed of the wave when a different frequency was used?

## Conclusion

Make a concluding statement that addresses the purpose of this lab. This statement should summarize your findings about the effects of a change in the speed of a wave in a medium when the frequency or medium is adjusted.

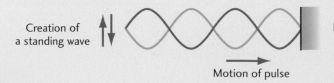

Creation of a standing wave

Rigid end

Motion of pulse

# Electricity and Magnetism

# UNIT E: Electricity and Magnetism

Hydro lines, wires, extension cords, computers, toasters, TVs, microwaves, calculators, traffic lights, streetcars, subways, lights, heaters ... the list is endless. You are surrounded by and immersed in electricity, the power source of our technological world.

Where do we get our electricity? Looking beyond the plug in the wall, this unit will provide you with a complete overview of the science behind electricity and the technology needed to provide it to you. In Canada, large electrical generating stations create most of our electricity. What source of energy provides power to the generating stations? Some generating stations are powered by the energy of falling water; others burn coal, oil, or natural gas; and some use the energy released during a nuclear reaction. Each of these energy sources comes with an environmental "cost." Ecosystems are changed or destroyed by the construction of a dam, global warming increases with the burning of fossil fuels, and half a century after building the first nuclear power stations, we still have not solved the problem of what to do with the radioactive waste. While conservation is the most effective way to lower the environmental cost of generating electricity, researchers are continually searching for more efficient and Earth-friendly power-generating technologies.

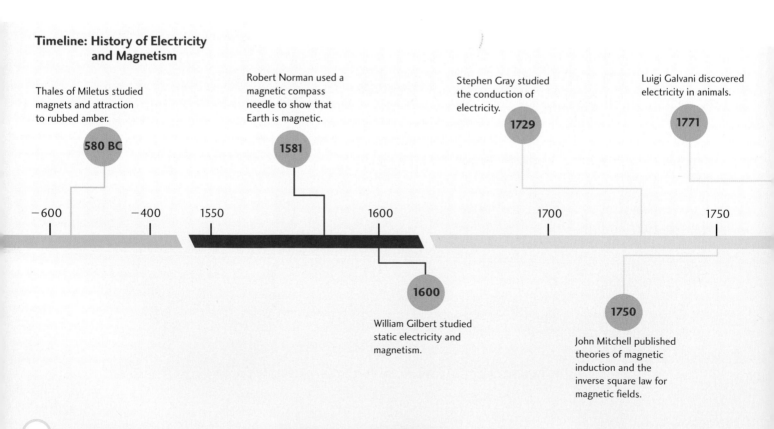

## Timeline: History of Electricity and Magnetism

Thales of Miletus studied magnets and attraction to rubbed amber.
**580 BC**

Robert Norman used a magnetic compass needle to show that Earth is magnetic.
**1581**

Stephen Gray studied the conduction of electricity.
**1729**

Luigi Galvani discovered electricity in animals.
**1771**

−600    −400    1550                    1600                    1700                    1750

**1600**
William Gilbert studied static electricity and magnetism.

**1750**
John Mitchell published theories of magnetic induction and the inverse square law for magnetic fields.

How are all these forms of energy transformed into electricity that can turn on a light? How is electricity transported to where it is needed? These are just a few of the interesting questions that will be addressed in the following chapters.

In this unit, you will also have an opportunity to study magnetism. Do you understand how an object becomes magnetized? Why is it that when you break a magnet in half, instead of getting one broken magnet, you get two smaller functioning magnets? This unit will also investigate electromagnetism, the combination of electricity and magnetism. An electrical current flowing through a coiled wire creates a magnetic field. Conversely, a magnet moving inside a coiled wire creates an electrical current. Many products you use every day contain electromagnets. Can you think of any? If you are stuck for an answer, here's a hint: "Use a lifeline and phone a friend."

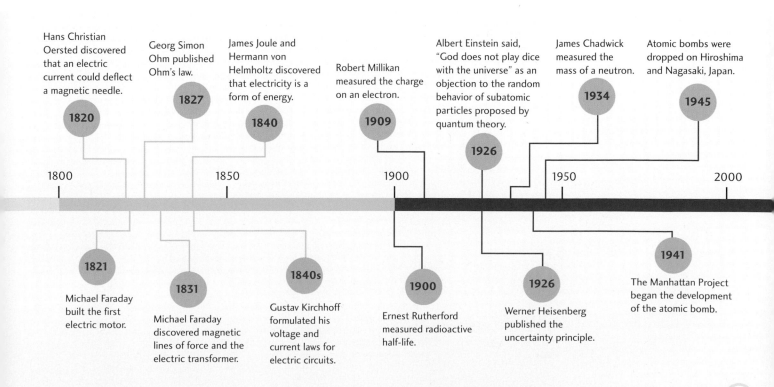

Hans Christian Oersted discovered that an electric current could deflect a magnetic needle.

**1820**

Georg Simon Ohm published Ohm's law.

**1827**

James Joule and Hermann von Helmholtz discovered that electricity is a form of energy.

**1840**

Robert Millikan measured the charge on an electron.

**1909**

Albert Einstein said, "God does not play dice with the universe" as an objection to the random behavior of subatomic particles proposed by quantum theory.

**1926**

James Chadwick measured the mass of a neutron.

**1934**

Atomic bombs were dropped on Hiroshima and Nagasaki, Japan.

**1945**

1800          1850          1900          1950          2000

Michael Faraday built the first electric motor.

**1821**

Michael Faraday discovered magnetic lines of force and the electric transformer.

**1831**

Gustav Kirchhoff formulated his voltage and current laws for electric circuits.

**1840s**

Ernest Rutherford measured radioactive half-life.

**1900**

Werner Heisenberg published the uncertainty principle.

**1926**

The Manhattan Project began the development of the atomic bomb.

**1941**

# Electrostatics

## Chapter Outline

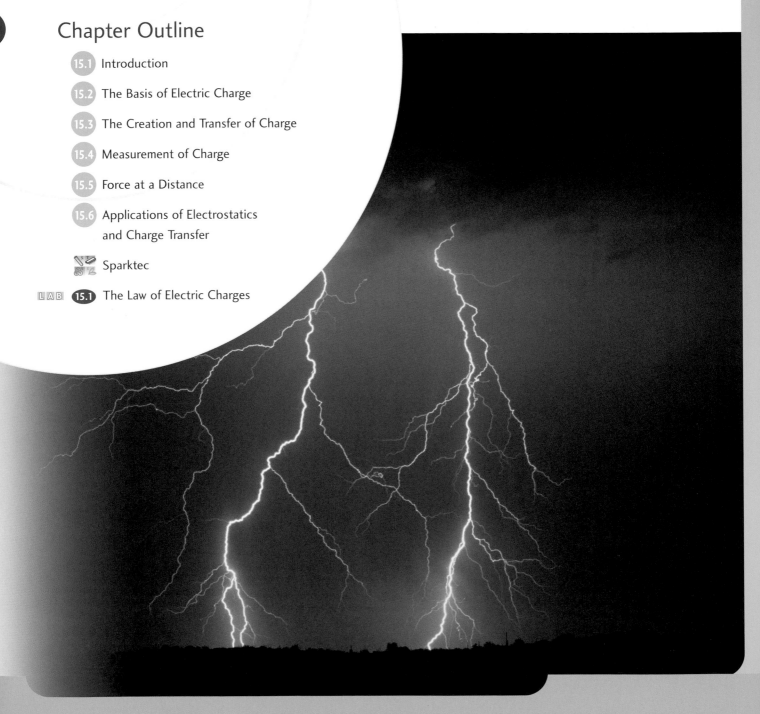

**By the end of this chapter, you will be able to**
- define the law of electric charges and use it to explain how charge is transferred
- use a field map to predict force at a distance for electric fields
- relate how electrostatics is involved in today's technology

# 15.1  Introduction

Have you ever tried to turn your radio on during a power failure to get a weather report and wondered for a moment why it didn't work? Many of us take for granted the role that electricity has in our lives. Devices such as televisions, CD players, computers, and now even telephones all depend on a constant supply of electricity to our household. In these next few chapters, we will examine the nature of electricity, how it is generated, and the way in which it is linked to technological development. In this chapter, we will discuss **electrostatics**, or electricity at rest.

# 15.2  The Basis of Electric Charge

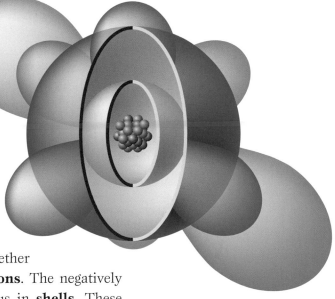

**Fig.15.1**  A model of an atom

Shuffling across a carpet on a dry winter's day can be a shocking experience. Twenty-five hundred years ago, Greek philosophers found that amber rubbed with fur attracts small particles like sawdust and bits of straw. The Greeks thought that the amber was somehow alive. Today, we explain this effect as the transfer of parts of atoms. The study of electricity has revealed a great deal about atoms and has lead to the development of much of our current technology. Figure 15.1 is a simplified version of our current model of an atom.

Atoms have three component parts, each with its own electric state, called **charge**. The positively charged **protons** are clustered together in the atomic **nucleus** together with neutral (no electric charge) particles called **neutrons**. The negatively charged particles called **electrons** surround the nucleus in **shells**. These mobile electrons are the particles transferred from fur to amber to create attractive forces, as the Greeks had observed. The name for amber in Greek is *elektron*. In his experiments, Benjamin Franklin noted the opposite electrical nature of amber and fur. He designated amber as having a negative charge and fur as having a positive charge. When any objects that possess these charged states are placed near each other, they experience forces of attraction or repulsion. These two different charges follow the **law of electric charges**.

A **model** is a physical or mental representation of a phenomenon or process that cannot be shown otherwise.

---

**Law of electric charges**

Opposite charges attract each other.
Like charges repel each other.
Charged objects attract neutral objects.

---

The law of electric charges has led to the invention of a device that allows us to detect electric charge, the electroscope. Figure 15.2 illustrates a typical electroscope and how it works to detect charge. The excess charge that is distributed evenly throughout the electroscope pushes apart two loosely held metal foil leaves.

If the number of positive (+) and negative (−) charges is equal, the charges cancel each other out, leaving no overall charge. If one type of charge is in excess, then the object is left with that overall charge. Figure 15.3 shows how a particular material can end up with an excess positive or negative charge.

**Fig.15.2** Excess negative charge can be detected with an electroscope

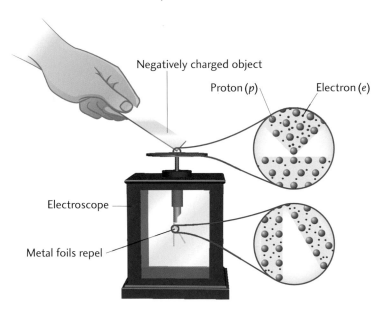

Negatively charged object

Proton (*p*)  Electron (*e*)

Electroscope

Metal foils repel

**Fig.15.3** Objects become charged by transferring electrons

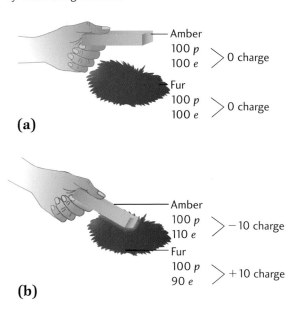

Amber
100 *p*
100 *e*  ⟩ 0 charge

Fur
100 *p*
100 *e*  ⟩ 0 charge

**(a)**

Amber
100 *p*
110 *e*  ⟩ − 10 charge

Fur
100 *p*
90 *e*  ⟩ + 10 charge

**(b)**

Since the positively charged protons are locked in the nucleus, **all net charges on objects are due to a deficit or excess of electrons**. When an atom or a piece of matter has an excess of electrons, its net charge is *negative*. When it has a deficit of electrons, its net charge is *positive*.

**Fig.15.4  How Charges are Achieved**

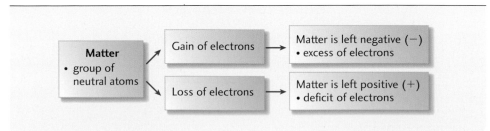

**Matter**
• group of neutral atoms

Gain of electrons → Matter is left negative (−)
• excess of electrons

Loss of electrons → Matter is left positive (+)
• deficit of electrons

# 15.3 The Creation and Transfer of Charge

An object can obtain a charge by any of three methods: **friction**, **contact**, and **induction**.

## Charging by Friction

When two different substances are rubbed together, there is a net transfer of electrons from one material to the other. Each material has its own characteristic attractive force that holds the electrons around the atom in place. When rubbed together, as shown in Fig. 15.5, the energy of friction moves electrons from the object that has the weakest force of attraction. Table 15.1 lists some common substances in order of increasing attraction for electrons.

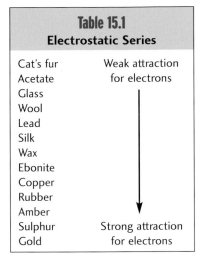

**Table 15.1**
**Electrostatic Series**

| | |
|---|---|
| Cat's fur | Weak attraction |
| Acetate | for electrons |
| Glass | |
| Wool | |
| Lead | |
| Silk | |
| Wax | |
| Ebonite | |
| Copper | |
| Rubber | |
| Amber | |
| Sulphur | Strong attraction |
| Gold | for electrons |

**Fig.15.5**

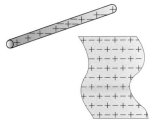

**(a)** Neutral glass rod and wool cloth

**(b)** Rubbing rod and wool cloth together transfers electrons from glass to wool

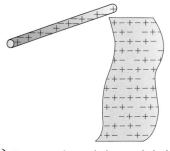

**(c)** Separate charged glass and cloth

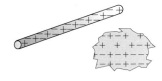

**(d)** Charged rod attracts neutral paper

---

**EXAMPLE 1    Fatal attraction**

What are the charges of wool and ebonite when they are rubbed together?

### Solution and Connection to Theory

Referring to the electrostatic series in Table 15.1, ebonite has the stronger attraction for electrons, so it would receive electrons from the wool. Therefore, the wool would become positive and the ebonite would be negative.

**Fig.15.6**   Charging by Friction

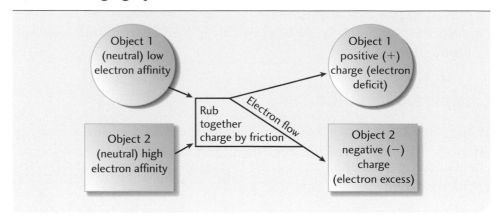

## Charging by Contact

Once something is charged either positively or negatively, it tends to lose its excess charge to another object if they come into contact. Figure 15.7 points out that excess electrons in a negatively charged object move to a neutral body, leaving it with a negative charge (Fig. 15.7(a)). A positively charged object will draw electrons out of a neutral object, leaving it positively charged (Fig. 15.7(b)).

**Fig.15.7**   Charging by contact with a charged glass rod

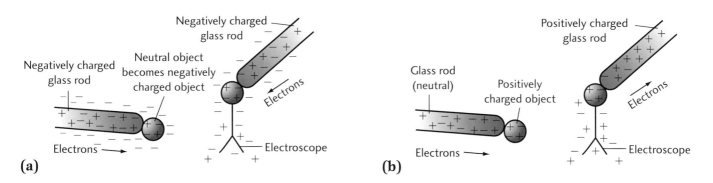

## Charging by Induction

When a charged object is brought close to an object without physical contact, the charged object will **induce** a movement of electrons in the uncharged object. If the object to be charged is attached to a **grounding source** (a pool of excess electrons, such as your hand), as shown in Fig. 15.8, the object will take on or off-load electrons to the ground. Removal of the ground makes the charge flow irreversible, leaving the object with the opposite charge from the originally charged source.

**Step 1:** Bring a positively charged object close to the electroscope with no contact. The electrons are attracted up, which creates an induced positive charge on the leaves of the electroscope.

**Fig.15.8** Charging an electroscope negatively by induction

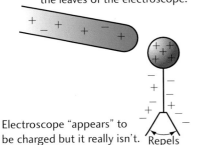

Electroscope "appears" to be charged but it really isn't.

**Step 2:** Ground the electroscope by touching it to provide charge to "balance" the induced charge.

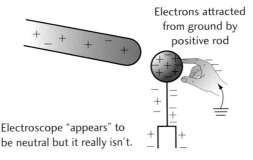

Electrons attracted from ground by positive rod

Electroscope "appears" to be neutral but it really isn't.

**Step 3:** Move the grounding source (your hand) away to leave excess electrons on the electroscope.

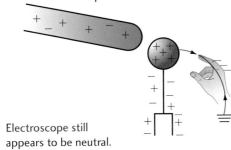

Electroscope still appears to be neutral.

**Step 4:** Remove charged object. The electroscope is left with the opposite charge of the original object.

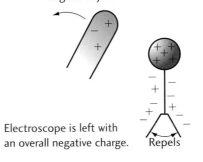

Electroscope is left with an overall negative charge.

**Fig.15.9** Charging by Contact or Induction

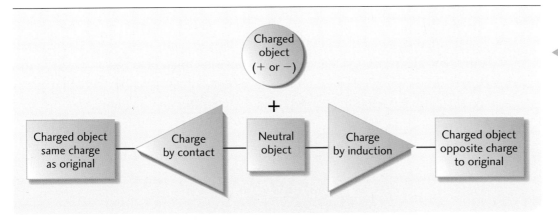

## Electrical Discharge

An excess of either charge means that the charges will experience a force of repulsion that pushes them as far away from each other as possible. This excess is what causes static electric shock, forcing electrons to be passed from object to object. The same force of repulsion is responsible for the massive charge flow that takes place in a lightning discharge. Excess charge is built up in the atmosphere by friction, not unlike your socks on the carpet. The

**Fig.15.10** Lightning is rapid charge transfer

friction between air currents and water droplets or ice crystals in cloud formations causes a separation of charges. If the charges become large enough, the spectacular discharge to Earth we see as lightning may result, as illustrated in Fig. 15.10.

The chance of a lightning strike can be greatly reduced if we can prevent charge separation. A **lightning rod**, such as the one shown in Fig. 15.11, doesn't attract lightning, but allows excess charge in the atmosphere to be slowly transferred to the ground.

**Fig.15.11** A lightning rod prevents a lightning strike

**Fig.15.12** A Van de Graaf generator simulates a lightning strike

Lightning can be simulated in the physics lab by using a device that transfers electrons by friction, the Van de Graaf electrostatic generator. Figure 15.12 shows how the electric motor drives a rubber belt that picks up electrons by friction and deposits them in the metal sphere.

**(a)**

**(b)**

UNIT E: Electricity and Magnetism

When enough electrons build up in the sphere, which represents the upper atmosphere in a lightning storm, the resulting repulsion of like negative charge causes electrons to be repelled from the sphere in a fashion similar to a lightning bolt.

Many safety systems use a grounding mechanism that provides a path for excess electrons to flow to the ground, or that allows a deficit of electrons to be neutralized by transferring electrons from the ground. Materials made up of atoms with loosely bound electrons that can be easily transferred to neighbouring atoms are called **conductors**. Other materials have atoms with tightly held electrons that are not transferred anywhere. These materials are called **insulators** and are often used to protect people or property from electric shock. Figure 15.13 illustrates how both insulators and conductors are used in modern wiring. The copper in the telephone cable *conducts* electrons, and the outer plastic coating *insulates* the surroundings from electron transfer. These wires make perfect "electron tunnels" that allow transfer of charge from one place to another, but keep the effects of the environment out.

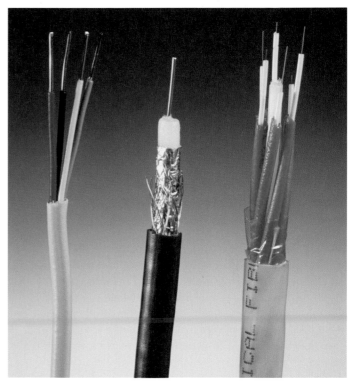

**Fig.15.13** Telephone, coaxial, and fibre optic cables

1. State the rules of reaction between positives and negatives. Is there another force that behaves similarly?
2. How do neutral objects interact with charged objects? Explain the processes.

◄ ◄ ◄ ◄

## Neutral Objects

A neutral object (its total charge is zero) doesn't mean that the object has no charge. In fact, a neutral object is a dynamic system of balance. It has the same number of positive charges as negative charges. Because they are in balance, we cannot detect them. Similarly with white light. White light is composed of many colours, each having a different wavelength. As long as all the colours are present, we see white light and not its component colours.

# 15.4 Measurement of Charge

Early studies of electricity required scientists to quantitatively measure amounts of electric charge. Because it's impossible to count individual electrons, scientists grouped electrons into "bundles" containing more or less equal amounts of electrons. One bundle of electrons or **charge**, symbolized by $Q$, was given the unit name of coulomb (C), after **Charles de Coulomb**, a French scientist and inventor (1736–1806). This approach is similar to consistently filling an egg carton with a dozen eggs, but not knowing that there are 12 eggs in a dozen. In 1911, Robert Millikan performed his famous **oil drop experiment**. He estimated that the number of electrons in one coulomb of charge is $6.25 \times 10^{18}$.

**Fig.15.14**  In 1911, American scientist R.A. Millikan succeeded in measuring the charge on a single oil droplet. A droplet of radius $10^{-6}$ m falls through the air at a constant speed and picks up a charge by contact with an ion. The droplet then falls between two brass plates. The upper plate is connected to a battery that gives the plate a charge opposite to that on the droplet. Because the droplet is charged, it can be acted on by an electric force. The electric force causes the droplet to move upwards. When the battery is switched off, the droplet falls. If the distance and time of the droplet's motion are known, its speed can be calculated. If we know the calculated speeds, the voltage of the battery, and the properties of oil and air, we can determine the charge on the oil droplet.

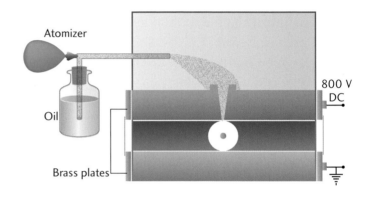

The overall charge on an object may be determined by the equation

$$Q = Ne$$

where $Q$ is the amount of charge in coulombs,
$N$ is the total number of electrons in either deficit or excess, and
$e$ is the charge on an electron, $1.602 \times 10^{-19}$ C.

To convert between charge and number of electrons,

$1 \text{ C} = 6.25 \times 10^{18} \, e$ or
$1 \, e = 1.602 \times 10^{-19}$ C

---

**EXAMPLE 2**  **Static cling**

Jordan put her wool socks and a silk shirt together in a tumbling clothes dryer after washing them. When she took them out, she noticed that the wool sock and whatever was left of the silk shirt were stuck together because of an electrostatic force of attraction. If $3.7 \times 10^{24}$ electrons were transferred between the wool and the silk, what is the amount of charge on the silk shirt?

UNIT E: Electricity and Magnetism

### Solution and Connection to Theory

**Given**

$N = 3.7 \times 10^{24}$ electrons     $Q = ?$

The charge on the silk is a result of the transfer of electrons. Whatever the amount of charge is on the silk, the wool has the same amount, only of opposite charge. One would be due to an excess of $3.7 \times 10^{24}$ electrons and the other would be due to a deficit.

$$Q = Ne$$
$$= 3.7 \times 10^{24} \, \cancel{e} \, \frac{(1.602 \times 10^{-19}\,C)}{\cancel{e}}$$
$$= 5.9 \times 10^{5}\,C$$

Therefore, the charge on either the wool or the silk is $5.9 \times 10^{5}$ C.

In Table 15.1, we see that wool is higher on the list than silk. We know that the wool would lose electrons and silk would gain them. Therefore, the wool has a charge of $+5.9 \times 10^{5}$ C and the silk has a charge of $-5.9 \times 10^{5}$ C.

If any two of these materials come into contact, electrons are passed from the item with a weak attraction for electrons to the one with the higher attraction for electrons. The electron receiver becomes negative and the electron donor becomes positive.

1. What is the fundamental charge carrier? Which charge is the mobile one? How do you produce a net positive and a net negative charge?
2. **a)** How many coulombs are there in one fundamental charge?
   **b)** How many charges are there in one coulomb?
3. State the law of conservation of electric charge. What other conservation laws do you know?
4. How is charge transferred from one object to another? What dictates which way the charge moves?

## 15.5 Force at a Distance

In Chapter 4, we learned that a force is defined as a push or pull on an object. One difference between the forces we have studied and electrostatic forces is that electrostatic forces can occur between charged objects that are some distance from one another. These forces are said to work "at a distance." In general, the farther apart the charges, the weaker the forces between them.

When we wish to describe our position in relation to certain geographical areas, we use a map. To describe the forces that exist in areas around electrostatic charges, we use a **field map**. A field map describes an **electric field**, the space around a single charge or an array of charge(s) in which electric forces act.

A **field** is a volume of three-dimensional space in which a certain property or quantity is distributed.

**Fig.15.15** A field map analogy

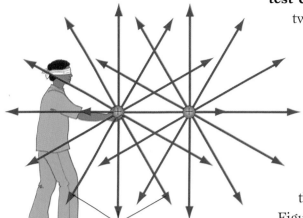

Field map

The quantity that is distributed in an electric field is **force**. If a positive **test charge** is placed inside the electric field of another charge, the two charges will experience a force of attraction or repulsion. Just as your road map helps you choose the direction in which you should travel, a field map tells you not only the strength of a force, but also the direction in which it will act.

The "hot/cold" game is a good analogy for mapping out a field structure. One person is blindfolded and sets out to find an object. He or she walks around the room, and his or her distance from the object is mapped by others shouting "warmer" or "colder," depending on whether the person is getting closer or farther away from the object. Figure 15.15 illustrates how an electric field relays its information to us in a similar way.

The closer the positive test charge (analogous to the blindfolded participant) comes to the positive object, the stronger the repulsive force becomes. The field map shows the relative value of force strength based on how close the **field lines** in the map are to each other. The direction of the field lines (as shown by the arrows) shows the direction of the force. The "warmer"

**Fig.15.16** Field maps around different charge configurations

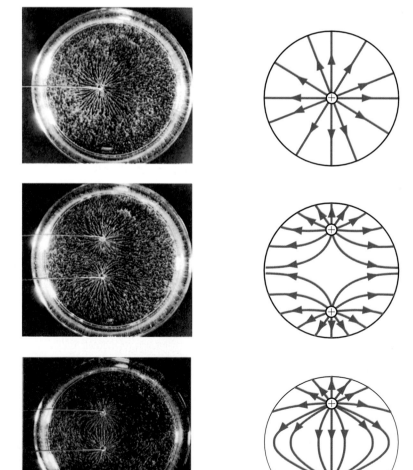

**(a)** Single positive charge

**(b)** Equal like charges

**(c)** Equal and opposite charges

the test charge is to the charged object, the closer together the field lines. By convention, the arrows on the lines of force indicate the direction a positive test charge would take if placed at that spot in the electric field. Figure 15.16 shows examples of field maps around charges. Each line represents the path of a positive test charge if it were placed in the field and released.

Other forces that act at a distance include magnetic forces (see Chapter 17) and the force of gravity (see Chapter 5). These two force fields are illustrated in Fig. 15.17.

**Fig.15.17**  Magnetic and gravitational fields. The arrows indicate the direction(s) of motion of objects in that field.

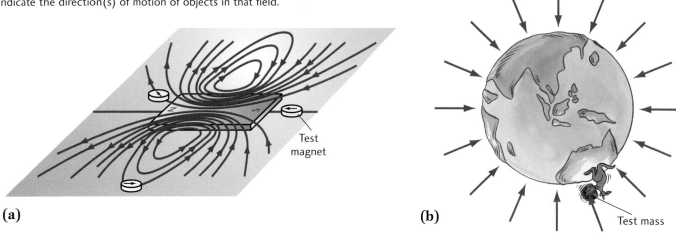

**(a)**

**(b)**

Test magnet

Test mass

◄  ◄  ◄  ◄  ◄

APPLYING the Concepts

1. What other forces act without contact?
2. How does the magnitude of the electrostatic force vary with distance? Does any other force act the same way?
3. Compare the electrostatic force to the gravitational force.

# 15.6  Applications of Electrostatics and Charge Transfer

The concepts of force at a distance and static electric charge have many practical applications. Table 15.2 describes many examples of how electric force at a distance and electrostatics may be applied.

## Table 15.2
### Applications of Electrostatic Forces

| Application and description | Schematic diagram | Photo |
|---|---|---|

**(a) Electrostatic Precipitator** Exhaust gases enter the precipitator cylinder that is made of a grounded metal conductor. A centrally placed, highly charged secondary conductor ionizes the gases (splits them into charged particles) and electrical "lightning-like" discharges occur. The solid and liquid ions are repelled to the outer wall, where they are neutralized and collected. The resulting cleaner gases are released through the top.

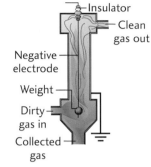

Insulator
Clean gas out
Negative electrode
Weight
Dirty gas in
Collected gas

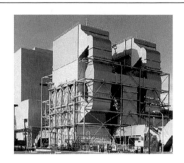

**(b) Electrostatic Air Cleaner** The particles in air are ionized (given an electrostatic charge) by corona wires as they enter the air cleaner at one end. The collecting plates at the other end have an opposite charge to the particles, which are attracted and gathered there. Cleaner, particle-free air is then forced back out of the unit.

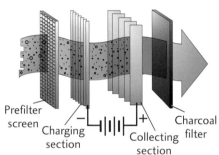

Prefilter screen
Charging section
Collecting section
Charcoal filter

**(c) Electrostatic Painting** The item to be painted is given a positive charge and the paint is given a negative charge as it leaves the spray nozzle. The paint is electrostatically attracted to the area being painted.

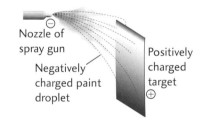

Nozzle of spray gun
Negatively charged paint droplet
Positively charged target

**(d) Bug Zapper** A black light attracts flying insects through a highly charged mesh screen. A grounded central core means that the bugs are hit by tiny lightning bolts when they enter the zapper.

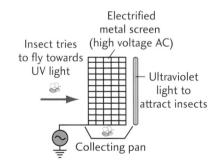

Electrified metal screen (high voltage AC)
Insect tries to fly towards UV light
Ultraviolet light to attract insects
Collecting pan

BK -40

**(e) Photocopier** The drum, which is coated with selenium, is positively charged. An image of an original document is shone on the drum, leaving the areas that received bright light (the non-print areas) neutral. The remaining areas, which are still positively charged, pick up negatively charged toner (made of carbon and carried by plastic beads) in the shape of the print. Positively charged paper rolls over the drum, attracting the negatively charged toner. The sheet is then heated to "set" the image on the paper.

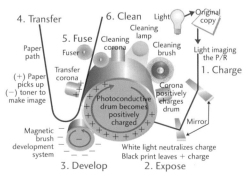

4. Transfer
6. Clean
Light
Original copy
Cleaning lamp
5. Fuse
Cleaning corona
Cleaning brush
Paper path
Fuser
Light imaging the P/R
Transfer corona
1. Charge
(+) Paper picks up (−) toner to make image
Photoconductive drum becomes positively charged
Corona positively charges drum
Magnetic brush development system
Mirror
White light neutralizes charge
Black print leaves + charge
3. Develop
2. Expose

Xerox 1050 Series
Perfect Fit Copiers

The force of repulsion between electrons causes electrons to flow through conductors, creating current electricity. Current electricity is what runs all our modern conveniences on which we're so dependent. In the next chapter, we will study the concept of current electricity so that we can understand how it has become such an important commodity for modern living.

1. Describe the differences between charging by induction and charging by contact.
2. Describe the hydrogen atom in terms of the electrostatic force and the force of gravity. Which force dominates? Why? (You may wish to look up the mass of an electron and proton.)

## Ink Jet Printers

The inkjet printer uses charged plates and ink droplets, which get charged by the plates as they leave the print head. The drops are extremely small ($1 \times 10^{-4}$ m in diameter) and travel relatively quickly towards the paper (65 km/h). A computer connected to a sensor in the print head detects areas with print on the original document. As the drops pass by the charging plates, the plates are turned OFF, thereby allowing the spray of ink to fly directly onto the paper. When the sensor detects areas without print, the computer turns the plates ON, thereby charging the drops of ink. The charged deflection plates attract the unwanted drops, which go into a reservoir (Fig. 15.18A).

**Fig.15.18A**

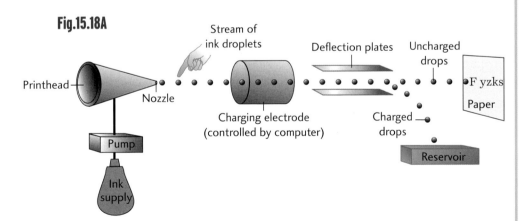

**Fig.15.18B**

These machines need constant upkeep and maintenance. A college course trains students to become technicians in this area.

3. Compare the resolution and speed of the ink jet printer, the laser printer, and the dot-matrix printer.
4. The photocopy machine also uses electrostatics through a process called **xerography**. Use Table 15.2 to explain how a photocopier works. Draw a block diagram illustrating the process.

## Sparktec

**Fig.STSE.15.1** The Sparktec SPK-8000

Can physics triumph over chemistry to protect property and the environment? Sparktec Environmental Inc. of Stoney Creek, Ontario, thinks that it can. This Canadian company has developed a device that generates a pressure wave in fluids using a high-voltage spark. The device, shown in Fig. STSE. 15.1, is the Sparktec plasma sparker (SPK-8000). Like a car spark plug, it produces a spark with a direct current voltage of about 8 000 V for short time periods. The spark produces the usual ultraviolet light and ozone gas ($O_3$). When submerged in water, it also produces a high-energy pressure wave, which can be used in water management and treatment systems.

The infestation of zebra mussels in the Great Lakes region has created serious problems for industries that maintain water intake systems. Water intake systems can become blocked by zebra mussels as well as other natural organic growth, as shown in Fig. STSE. 15.2 and 15.3. As Sparktec's pressure wave travels down the pipe system (Fig. STSE.15.4), it dislodges the zebra mussels and other debris. Field tests (Fig. STSE.15.5) have shown excellent results.

The current practice is to clean the pipes using chlorine, which poses a health hazard. At an estimated maximum of $200 per year, the cost of running a Spartec device seems very reasonable, as it requires only a standard 120/240 V electrical service.

Sparktec is currently testing the effectiveness of using the system to kill fecal streptococci and more resilient bacteria, such as cryptosporidium, in municipal water treatment applications. Although this system shows much promise, there may be resistance to its widespread acceptance as a physics alternative to a traditional chemical application.

**Fig.STSE.15.2** Zebra mussels

**Fig.STSE.15.3** A zebra-mussel-encrusted intake pipe

| Power Consumption of the SPARKTEC Pulsed Power Sparker | | | | |
|---|---|---|---|---|
| Voltage (V) | Energy (kWh/year) | Average power consumption during discharge cycle (W) | Maximum power consumption during discharge cycle (W) | Estimated yearly cost of energy |
| 6000 | 1224 | 140 | 280 | $61.20 |
| 7000 | 1666 | 190 | 380 | $83.30 |
| 8000 | 2177 | 314 | 629 | $108.85 |
| 9000 | 3401 | 388 | 776 | $170.05 |

**Fig.STSE.15.4** A pressure wave travels down the pipe

## Design a Study of Societal Impact

The most feared spark is, of course, lightning. What devices are currently on the market that could either prevent lighting from striking or at least manage/control the strike? What would be the environmental or social impacts if lightning was not controlled?

Research the physics behind voltage surge suppressors. Contact insurance companies to find out how much money is spent annually to replace electronic equipment that has been damaged by electrical surges.

Taking preventative measures would have been much cheaper than fixing the zebra mussel problem. What other environmental disasters could we minimize or prevent by acting sooner?

**Fig.STSE.15.5** The difference Sparktec can make

## Design an Activity to Evaluate

Sparks are used as ignition devices in many natural gas and propane burning appliances such as barbecues. Obtain an old hand-held piezo-electric barbecue lighter and take it apart. Mount each piece in an appropriate spot on a display board with appropriate labels to explain to others how this simple device works. Use the piezo-electric cell from the dismantled barbecue lighter or a compression piezo-electric cell from a scientific supply company. Set up the cell (from whatever source) by attaching either end of the two electric leads to a voltmeter (analog, digital, or the voltmeter setting on a computer data interface. Be sure to check that the device may register or not be damaged by high voltages.).

Conduct a correlation study of the electric potential (voltage) that can be created across the spark gap versus the force that is applied to compress the cell.

Conduct a similar study of potentials created across the spark gap of a standard two-cycle engine spark plug. The engine can be cranked by hand after the voltmeter leads are attached, or the spark plug could be set off in the physics lab using a standard tesla coil. Variables that could be adjusted could be spark gap, relative humidity, etc.

**Fig.STSE.15.6** The spark unit of an SPK-8000

## Build a Structure

Build a Sparktec-like prototype device from the basic materials of a dismantled barbecue lighter. The basic components could also be fabricated after researching the design of electronic camera flashes. If students are successful at creating a reliable underwater spark, a competition could be started to see which design team could create the best/strongest pressure wave.

**You should be able to**

*Understand Basic Concepts:*

- Describe the current model of the atom and outline the role of each subatomic particle in the net electric charge on an object.
- Compare and contrast the function of conductors and insulators and outline their role in the transmission of electrical energy.
- Outline the steps to successfully charging an object by either friction, contact, or induction.
- Relate how the repulsion of electrons is the basis of current electricity.
- Define concepts and units relating to electrostatic charges and simple field theory such as electric charge, coulomb, and electric field.
- Describe and illustrate the three-dimensional properties of an electric field, including its shape, direction, and strength.
- Model the concept of force at a distance, with examples.

*Develop Skills of Inquiry and Communication:*

- Design and conduct an experiment to verify the law of electric charges.
- Verify physical data that have been accepted by the scientific community, such as the electrostatic series, through experimentation.
- Analyze experimental observations to verify personal predictions about experimental outcomes.

*Relate Science to Technology, Society, and the Environment:*

- Analyze the operation of various technological devices, such as an electroscope, an electrostatic air cleaner, a bug zapper, a photocopier, and an ink jet printer, and identify the principles of electrostatics in each.
- Relate how the acceptance of certain conventions, such as positive and negative electric charge (the coulomb), are important in the scientific community.
- Recognize how electrostatic discharges are being used to provide environmental and financial benefits to traditional chemical water treatment.

**Equations**

$Q = Ne$

## Conceptual Questions

1. Using atomic theory, explain why electrons move from one substance to another, such as when acetate is rubbed with silk.

2. A new solid material developed for the International Space Station is being tested for its electrostatic properties. In a series of steps, describe how you would test this material to determine its rightful place in an updated electrostatic series.

3. A computer technician is always warned to touch the metal body of a computer before touching any electronic parts. What does touching the computer body do to prevent static electric damage to the circuits?

4. We often "ground" our electric appliances by attaching a wire from the appliance to the ground so that excess charge can be deposited there. How does this safety measure work? Why do we not have to worry about Earth picking up a static electric charge?

5. Why are we more susceptible to building up electrostatic charges when the weather is very dry? What time of year would static shocks be most frequent?

6. When you refuel your boat at a marina, the attendant usually touches the fuel delivery nozzle to the metal edge of the boat's fuel inlet before adding any gasoline. Why?

7. If an electric field is set up by charging a single negative point charge, how would you describe the field shape around this charge? Sketch this field shape.

8. If you were to double the charge value on a test object that is used to map out an electric field, what would happen to the strength of the electric field at each test point?

9. Using an electric field map, how can you tell the difference between regions where there is a weak electric field and a strong electric field?

## Problems

### 15.2 The Basis of Electric Charge

10. Which parts of the atom are represented by positive signs and by negative signs?

11. What is the charge on each of the following?
    a) A normal atom of oxygen
    b) An electron
    c) A nucleus
    d) A neutron
    e) A proton

12. Several items are listed below along with the circumstances that could have left them with a charge. For each example, state which item would have a positive or a negative charge because of a deficit or excess of electrons.
    a) A piece of rubber rubbed with silk
    b) The silk from part a)
    c) An acetate sheet rubbed with cat's fur
    d) Glass rubbed with wool

13. A piece of amber is rubbed with fur.
    a) What type of charge is on the amber?
    b) What kinds of particles are transferred to the amber?

14. A glass rod is suspended from a string and charged by rubbing it with a piece of silk.
    a) After rubbing, what type of charge is on each material?
    b) What should happen if the silk is brought close to the glass rod?

15. At a birthday party, a balloon is rubbed on someone's hair and brought close to a ribbon on a party decoration. The ribbon was repelled by the balloon. What type of charge is on the ribbon?

**16.** State whether each of the following is an electric conductor or an insulator and give a reason why.
  **a)** Plastic food wrap
  **b)** A lightning rod
  **c)** Your plastic comb
  **d)** A party balloon stuck to a wall
  **e)** A car's tire if you are caught in a lightning storm
  **f)** The rubber belt on a Van de Graaf electrostatic generator

**17.** The CN Tower in Toronto is a prime location for lightning strikes. Why? What did the engineers have to do to protect people and property from lightning damage?

▶ **15.3 The Creation and Transfer of Charge**

**18.** Summarize the steps involved in charging a balloon positively by induction.

▶ **15.4 Measurement of Charge**

**19.** What is the function of an electroscope?

**20.** A metal leaf electroscope is touched by a positively charged strip.
  **a)** What type of charge will register on the electroscope? What causes this process?
  **b)** What will happen to the leaf (or leaves) of the electroscope? Why?
  **c)** What will happen to the leaves of the electroscope if the overall system is grounded?

**21.** A wire passes a charge of 15.0 C. How many electrons pass through the wire?

**22.** Small charges, such as those passed between people when a static electric shock is mistakenly given, are measured in small units called $\mu C$ (microcoulombs). A shock of 1.1 $\mu C$ was passed from one student to another in a dry physics classroom. How many electrons does this amount represent?

**23.** With a deficit of $4.0 \times 10^{11}$ electrons, what is the charge on an electroscope?

**24.** A glass rod with a charge of $5.4 \times 10^8$ electrons touches another insulator so that all of the excess electrons are shared equally. What is the final charge on the glass rod?

**25.** An atom is known to have a nucleus with a positive charge of $2.4 \times 10^{-12}$ C. How many electrons does this atom have?

**26.** Draw two circles in your notebook, about 5 cm apart, and label them both with $(-)$ negative signs. Use the concept of placing test charges on the page to map what the electric field would look like.

**27.** How would the field map change if the charge on the left was tripled?

**28.** Draw two parallel lines in your notes to represent two parallel metal plates, one positive and the other negative, about 2 cm apart. Map the electric field between the plates.

▶ **15.6 Applications of Electrostatics and Charge Transfer**

**29.** Assume that you are asked to spraypaint a metal fence. How can static electricity help you avoid wasting paint?

**30.** The ease with which we can photocopy has environmental consequences. Discuss some of the ways that the extensive use of photocopiers has affected our lives. You might consider land fill, recycling programs, and indoor air quality.

## LAB 15.1 The Law of Electric Charges

### Purpose

To examine the attraction and repulsion of electrostatic charges.

### Safety Consideration

Note: Use two small pieces of putty or masking tape to secure any ebonite or glass rods to the watch glass so they do not roll off and break.

### Equipment

Two small watch glasses, Two polyethylene strips
Two acetate strips, Two ebonite rods
Two glass rods, Woolen cloth
Cotton cloth, Silk cloth, Fur

### Fig.Lab.15.1

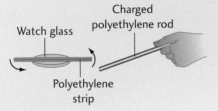

Watch glass • Charged polyethylene rod • Polyethylene strip

### Procedure

1. Prepare a data chart similar to Table Lab.15.1.
2. Use the electrostatic series table in the textbook to predict what will happen to the electroscope in each case (attraction or repulsion). Also predict the type of charge on the test material in each case.
3. Set up an electroscope by taking a polyethylene strip and rubbing it with wool. Then place it on a watch glass, as shown in Fig. Lab.15.1.
4. Rub another strip of polyethylene with wool and use it as a "test material." Bring it close to one end of the electroscope and observe what happens. The electroscope should rotate one way or another on the desk, showing a force of attraction or repulsion.
5. Rub the polyethylene with wool again, then use the wool as a test material.
6. Rub an acetate strip with cotton (or wool) and bring it close to the polyethylene electroscope.
7. Create another electroscope from an acetate strip rubbed with cotton.
8. Repeat the experiment using the test materials in the order listed in the table.
9. Repeat the entire experiment twice more, using ebonite, glass, fur, and silk as shown in the table.

| Table Lab.15.1 Testing the Electrostatic Series | | | | | |
|---|---|---|---|---|---|
| Electroscope material (watch glass) | Charged test material | Observation repulsion/attraction | | Charge on test material (+) or (−) | |
| | | Prediction | Actual observation | Prediction | Actual observation |
| Polyethylene (wool) | Polyethylene (wool) | | | | |
| Polyethylene (wool) | Wool (polyethylene) | | | | |
| Polyethylene (wool) | Acetate (cotton/wool) | | | | |
| Acetate (cotton/wool) | Acetate (cotton/wool) | | | | |
| Acetate (cotton/wool) | Cotton/wool (acetate) | | | | |
| Acetate (cotton/wool) | Polyethylene (wool) | | | | |
| Ebonite (fur) | Ebonite (fur) | | | | |
| Ebonite (fur) | Fur (ebonite) | | | | |
| Ebonite (fur) | Glass (silk) | | | | |
| Glass (silk) | Glass (silk) | | | | |
| Glass (silk) | Silk (glass) | | | | |
| Glass (silk) | Ebonite (fur) | | | | |

## Discussion

1. What effect do like charges have on one another?
2. What effect do unlike charges have on one another?
3. a) State which objects became positively charged and the circumstances of the change.
   b) State which objects became negatively charged and the circumstances of the change.
   c) Did any objects remain neutral?
4. What problems occurred when your analysis involved an attraction of the electroscope?

## Conclusion

The electrostatic series is based on Benjamin Franklin declaring that amber became negative when rubbed with fur. In a brief paragraph, describe the implications on this experiment if Franklin had set the convention by declaring that glass becomes negative when rubbed with silk.

# Current Electricity and Electric Circuits

**By the end of this chapter, you will be able to**

- explain how current, voltage, and resistance deliver electrical power to a load
- summarize the ways in which electrical energy is supplied from various sources
- use Kirchhoff's laws to quantitatively predict how current and voltage are distributed in series and parallel circuits

# 16.1 Introduction

Electrons in a static state have energy, but they are far more useful when they are made to transfer their energy. Electric current involves electrons repelling one another and passing through a conductor. Energized electrons, directed by a conductor, allow energy to be used to power many devices.

**Fig.16.1**    A water-electricity circuit analogy

**Fig.16.2**    Electron flow in a conductor is like water flow in a pipe

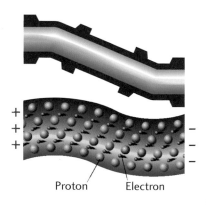

Proton          Electron

# 16.2 Current

In Fig. 16.1, the pumping station provides the water with gravitational potential energy, pumping it up into the water tower. The water loses this energy as it is piped through the sprinkler and back to its point of origin.

In an electric circuit, an energy source provides electrons with energy. Conductors transport the electrons to where the electron energy is transferred, then back to the source to be re-energized.

Figure 16.2 illustrates that a conductor carries charge in a way similar to the way in which pipes carry water. The flow of charge is called **electric current**. In this figure, electrons flow through a conductor.

> **Current** is **the rate of charge flow** and is given the symbol $I$. Current is the total amount of charge moving past a point in a conductor divided by the time taken.
>
> $$I = \frac{Q}{t}$$

where $I$ is the current in amperes (A), $Q$ is the charge in coulombs (C), and $t$ is the time in seconds.

The base unit for current is C/s, which is given the derived name of **ampere** (A), after André Marie Ampère (1775–1836). One ampere is one coulomb of charge moving through a point in a conductor every second. As with any equation, it can be used in various ways to calculate certain circuit parameters.

---

**EXAMPLE 1**    **Current and charge**

How much current flows through a hair dryer if 1400 C of charge pass through it in 2.25 minutes?

***Solution and Connection to Theory***

**Given**
$Q = 1400$ C          $t = 2.25$ min          $I = ?$

$$t = 2.25 \text{ min} \left( \frac{60 \text{ s}}{1 \text{ min}} \right) = 135 \text{ s}$$

$$I = \frac{Q}{t} = \frac{1400 \text{ C}}{135 \text{ s}} = 10.4 \frac{\text{C}}{\text{s}}$$

Therefore, the current through the hair dryer is 10.4 A.

## EXAMPLE 2    Charge and current

Your night light uses a 7 W light that draws about $6.0 \times 10^{-2}$ A of current. How much charge passes through this bulb in 8.0 hours?

### Solution and Connection to Theory

**Given**

$I = 6.0 \times 10^{-2}$ A $= 6.0 \times 10^{-2} \dfrac{\text{C}}{\text{s}}$        $t = 8.0$ hours        $Q = ?$

$$T = 8.0 \text{ h} \left( \frac{60 \text{ min}}{1 \text{ h}} \right) \left( \frac{60 \text{ s}}{1 \text{ min}} \right) = 2880 \text{ s}$$

To convert hours to seconds, you can also multiply by 3600 s/h.

$$Q = It = 6.0 \times 10^{-2} \frac{\text{C}}{\text{s}} (2880 \text{ s}) = 1.7 \times 10^2 \text{ C}$$

Therefore, the charge through the light bulb is $1.7 \times 10^2$ C.

## EXAMPLE 3    Electron flow

How many electrons have passed through the night light in Example 2? The charge on one electron is $1.602 \times 10^{-19}$ C.

### Solution and Connection to Theory

**Given**

$Q = 1.7 \times 10^3$ C     $e = 1.602 \times 10^{-19}$ C

$Q = Ne$

$$N = \frac{Q}{e} = \frac{1.7 \times 10^3 \text{ C}}{1.602 \times 10^{-19} \text{ C}} = 1.1 \times 10^{22} \text{ electrons}$$

**EXPONENT MATH**

Taking the multiplier and power parts separately, you get

$$\frac{1.7}{1.602} = 1.1$$

$$\frac{10^3}{10^{-19}} = 10^{3-(-19)} = 10^{22}$$

## Direction of Current Flow

It is now well understood that current is a flow of negatively charged electrons repelling one another. Historically, current flow was thought to move from the positive (+) terminal to the negative (−) terminal of any power supply. The model of positive charge flow is called **conventional current** and it is still used today. In this text, we will consider current as the flow of electrons.

Benjamin Franklin thought that the positive terminal had an excess of electricity and the negative terminal had a deficit of electrons. From this perspective, it only made sense that current flowed from a positive to a negative region. If you prefer to think of electron flow, then most of the concepts covered in this book will make sense.

To keep track of the direction of electron current flow, a coloured wiring convention is used in which black represents the negative terminal and red represents the positive terminal of any power supply. Therefore, we will think of current as flowing from the black negative (−) terminal to the red positive (+) terminal.

## Measurement of Current

The measurement of current, as we will discover in our labs, can be quite tricky. Like a turnstile that counts the number of passengers entering the subway, our device to measure current must be an integral part of the circuit. An **ammeter** (a current-measuring device) must be wired so that all current flows through it. In all cases, the conductor must be rewired so that the current runs serially through the ammeter. The ammeter must be an excellent conductor so that no energy is lost due to its addition to the circuit.

In **DC** or **direct current**, the current flows in a single direction from the power supply through the conductor to a **load**, such as a light bulb or other device that uses energy, and back to the power supply, as shown in Fig. 16.3. In **alternating current (AC)**, the electrons periodically reverse the direction of their flow. This reversal is carried out with the help of magnetic forces, which we will discuss in Chapter 17.

For electric current to flow, it must have a complete path from the negative side of the power supply to the positive side. This path of current is called a **circuit** and is required for any electrical device to work properly.

The latest digital ammeters are very forgiving if you forget about the correct red–black wiring convention or push too much current through them. Table 16.1 lists some of the problems and the safe use of these ammeters.

**Fig.16.3** A typical series circuit (a) and schematic (b)

**Safety tip.** When you are disconnecting wires in the lab, be careful! High current causes sparks.

**(a)**

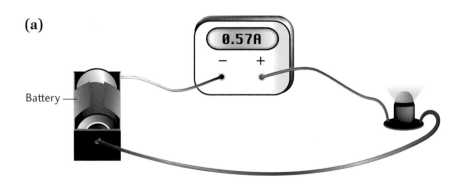

**(b)**

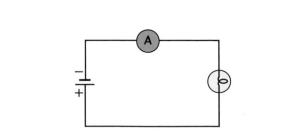

UNIT E: Electricity and Magnetism

## Table 16.1
### Ammeter Safety

| Problem | Analog meter | Digital meter | Safe solution |
|---------|--------------|---------------|---------------|
| Too much current passes through the meter for its current setting. | Wires, other internal mechanisms may burn out. The fuse may burn out. **Fig.16.4A** | An error or a null display. There may be no damage. A fuse may burn out. **Fig.16.4B** | Check setting of meter before powering up the circuit. Always choose a higher current setting than required. |
| Meter leads are connected in reverse. | Analog needle is "buried" below zero on the meter. Internal damage may result. | A negative sign is displayed in front of the current value. | Follow coloured wiring conventions. Electrons out of (−) and into (+). |

## Drawing Circuits

To help us understand circuits, we need a way to illustrate them in a quick and simple fashion. Figure 16.5 is a legend of many circuit symbols and what they represent. We will begin to draw circuits using the items in this table as a standard.

**Fig.16.5** Circuit symbols

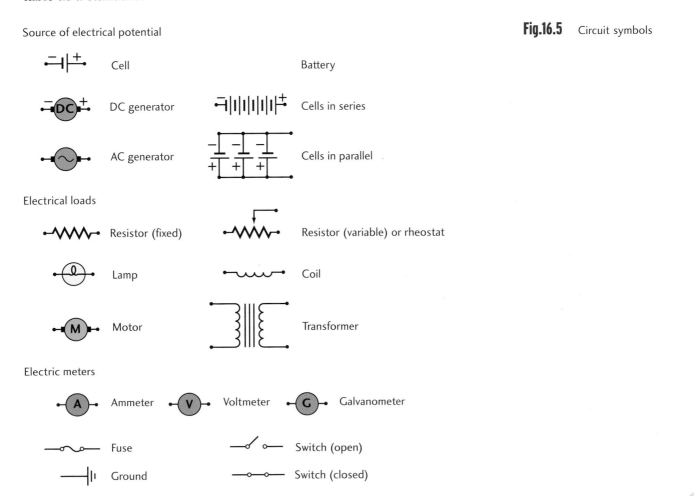

Source of electrical potential

- Cell
- Battery
- DC generator
- Cells in series
- AC generator
- Cells in parallel

Electrical loads

- Resistor (fixed)
- Resistor (variable) or rheostat
- Lamp
- Coil
- Motor
- Transformer

Electric meters

- Ammeter
- Voltmeter
- Galvanometer
- Fuse
- Switch (open)
- Ground
- Switch (closed)

1. How is current different from a static charge build-up? What causes electron flow? If you have already studied energy (Chapters 7 and 8), use principles discussed there to explain why charges move.
2. Calculate the current produced for
   a) a light bulb with $1.0 \times 10^5$ C of charge passing through the filament for 2.5 hours.
   b) an electroscope with a surplus of $2.2 \times 10^{10}$ electrons that discharges completely in 0.6 s through a person's finger.
3. a) How long would it take to pass 700 C of charge through a toaster drawing 10 A of current?
   b) How many electrons pass through the toaster during this time?
4. What is the difference between conventional and electron current flow?

# 16.3 Electrical Potential

Charge does not flow on its own. We saw previously that excess of any one charge causes a force of repulsion. A complete circuit also allows the excess charge to "see" a region of charge deficit at the power supply.

In the same way that the bicycle in Fig. 16.6 possesses gravitational potential energy at different heights in a gravitational field (recall force at a distance), an electric charge has a certain amount of electrical potential energy because of the electric field set up by the power supply.

Work had to be done on the bicycle to increase its gravitational potential energy. Similarly for the charge in the circuit. Work is done by the power supply to increase the electrical potential energy of each coulomb of charge from a low to a high value. As the charge flows through the load, its energy decreases.

**Fig.16.6** Gravitational and electrical potential energy

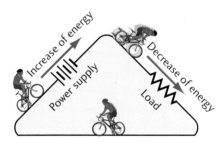

In some textbooks, the equation is $V = \dfrac{W}{Q}$, where $W$ is the work.

> The electrical potential energy for each coulomb of charge in a circuit is called the **electric potential difference** (V),
>
> $$V = \frac{E}{Q}$$
>
> where $E$ is the energy required to increase the electric potential of a charge, $Q$. Potential difference is often called **voltage**.

The unit for electric potential difference is the volt, named after Count Alessandro Volta (1745–1827).

> One volt (V) is the electric potential difference between two points if one joule of work (J) is required to move one coulomb (C) of charge between the points.

**Potential difference and energy**

What is the potential difference across an air conditioner if 72 C of charge transfer $8.5 \times 10^3$ J of energy to the fan and compressor?

***Solution and Connection to Theory***

**Given**

$Q = 72$ C     $E = 8.5 \times 10^3$ J     $V = ?$

$$V = \frac{E}{Q}$$

$$V = \frac{8.5 \times 10^3 \text{ J}}{72 \text{ C}}$$

$$V = 1.2 \times 10^2 \text{ V}$$

Therefore, the potential difference or voltage in the air conditioner is $1.2 \times 10^2$ V.

**Energy and potential difference**

A static electric shock delivered to a student from a "friend" transfers $1.5 \times 10^1$ J of electrical energy through a potential difference of 500 V. What is the quantity of charge transferred in the spark?

***Solution and Connection to Theory***

**Given**

$E = 1.5 \times 10^1$ J     $V = 500$ V     $Q = ?$

$$V = \frac{E}{Q} \quad \therefore Q = \frac{E}{V}$$

$$Q = \frac{1.5 \times 10^1 \text{ J}}{500 \text{ V}}$$

$$Q = 0.03 \text{ C}$$

Therefore, the charge transfer between the "friends" is 0.03 C.

**Fig.16.7** Delivering electrical energy

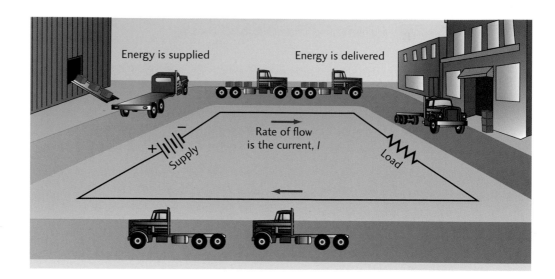

Energy is supplied

Energy is delivered

Rate of flow is the current, $I$

Supply

Load

Recall that

$V = \dfrac{E}{Q}$ and $I = \dfrac{Q}{t}$

so $E = VQ$ and $Q = It$

Therefore, $E = VQ$

$\qquad = VIt$

A practical analogy may help you to understand how electric current, energy, and potential are related. In the product delivery system in Fig. 16.7, each cell in the loading line adds a package of energy to a coulomb "truck." Just as trucks deliver products to a store over a road, so a circuit delivers energy to a load. In electricity, the carrier of the energy is a coulomb of charge, which delivers its energy cargo in joules per coulomb. A store requires a certain amount of goods to be delivered. The amount delivered depends on the size of the trucks' loads and their speed. So, too, for an electric circuit. The energy delivered to the load depends on the potential (energy per charge) and the rate at which the charge is delivered (the current). The energy transferred by charge flow is

$$E = VIt$$

where $E$ is the energy in joules, $V$ is the potential difference in volts, $I$ is the current in amperes, and $t$ is the time in seconds.

**EXAMPLE   6    Electrical energy**

One 1.5 V (AA) battery runs a portable MP3 player that draws $5.7 \times 10^{-3}$ A of current for about six hours before it runs out. How much energy does the battery transfer?

*Solution and Connection to Theory*

**Given**

$V = 1.5$ V $\qquad I = 5.7 \times 10^{-3}$ A $\qquad t = 6$ h $\qquad E = ?$

$t = 6\,\cancel{h}\left(\dfrac{3600\text{ s}}{1\,\cancel{h}}\right) = 21\ 600$ s

$E = VIt = 1.5$ V$(5.7 \times 10^{-3}$ A$)(21\ 600$ s$) = 185$ J

Therefore, the battery transfers 185 J of energy.

EXAMPLE 7 **Potential difference and energy**

A coffee maker draws about 5.0 A of current for 270 s using $1.6 \times 10^5$ J of energy. What is the potential difference across the coffee maker?

***Solution and Connection to Theory***

**Given**

$I = 5.0$ A $\qquad t = 270$ s $\qquad E = 1.6 \times 10^5$ J $\qquad V = ?$

$E = VIt$

Rearrange the equation for $V$.

$$V = \frac{E}{It} \qquad V = \frac{1.6 \times 10^5 \text{ J}}{5.0 \text{ A}(270 \text{ s})} \qquad V = 119 \text{ V}$$

The potential difference across the coffee maker is 119 V.

## Measuring Potential Difference

Potential difference between any two points can be measured using a **voltmeter**. As illustrated in Fig. 16.8, a voltmeter must be connected **in parallel** with a load in the circuit in order to compare the potential before and after the load.

The voltmeter must have a large resistance—that is, it must be a much poorer conductor than the load to which it is connected, so that the measurement by the voltmeter will divert a minimal current from the circuit.

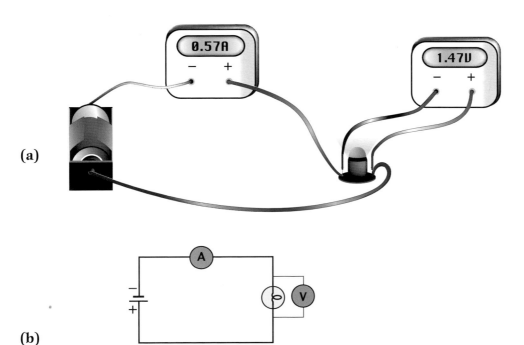

**(a)**

**(b)**

**Fig.16.8** The connection of a voltmeter in a circuit

1. Explain the difference between current and voltage.

2. You go to a store to buy a 12 V car battery. All the batteries are 12 V, but they differ in cranking amps. What should you look for in a winter battery?

3. **a)** A 12 V car battery delivers $1.3 \times 10^4$ J of energy to the starter motor. How much charge does it deliver?

   **b)** How many electrons does the battery transfer?

   **c)** Given that you keep the key turned for 2.5 s (time to turn the motor over in order to start the car), how many amps are delivered to the starter motor?

4. Lightning transfers charge between a charged cloud and the ground. If the voltage difference between the two is $1.3 \times 10^8$ V and $3.2 \times 10^9$ J of energy is transferred, find

   **a)** the total charge moved between the two potential energy surfaces.

   **b)** the number of electrons making up the charge.

   **c)** the current delivered if the lightning stroke takes 25 microseconds to hit the ground.

### Career Alert!

Meteorologists (people who study weather) require a large amount of physics training. The study of storms and their formations requires knowledge about electricity, sound (acoustics to describe thunder production), energy (transfer of energy and convection systems), forces (describing the effects of lightning), and pressure.

## ▶ 16.4 Supplying Electrical Potential Energy

Electrical energy always originates from some other form of energy. Electrical energy is a kind of medium of exchange for obtaining energy from easily produced forms to the forms we need. There are many different devices for converting energy from some other form to electrical potential energy. The original form may be chemical, mechanical, thermal, or light energy. Table 16.2 lists some of the common sources of electrical energy.

| Table 16.2 Sources of Electrical Energy | |
|---|---|
| **Source process** | **Common applications** |
| Voltaic cells | Chemical potential energy is released during a reaction as electrons are driven between two different metals. E.g., common dry cell batteries for portable electric devices |
| Piezo-electricity | Quartz and Rochelle salt crystals create small electric potential when mechanical force or stress is applied to them. E.g., phonograph cartridges, barbecue spark starters |
| Thermoelectricity | Two pieces of different metals joined together and subjected to temperature differentials transfer thermal energy to electric potential energy in what is called a **thermocouple**. E.g., gas appliance pilot light safety system: current keeps gas valve open as long as flame is lit |
| Photo electricity | Light energy absorbed by electrons of certain metals causes charge flow. E.g., satellite and international space station power supply, calculator power supply |
| Electromagnetic induction in generators (see Chapter 18) | Kinetic energy of water or steam forces conductors to rotate in a magnetic field. E.g., hydro-, nuclear-, fossil-fuel-powered electric generators |

# 16.5 Resistance—Ohm's Law

The amount of current flow in a circuit, and therefore the amount of energy transferred to any useful device, depends on two things: (1) the potential difference of the power supply (the amount of push) and (2) the nature of the pathway through the loads that are using the electric potential energy. We have already discussed potential energy in detail, so we must now turn our attention to the electrical characteristics of the pathway through the load.

Compare the two simple circuits in Fig. 16.9. The only difference between the two in the electrical sense is that the broader path in (a) allows the current to pass through the load much more easily than the narrower path in (b).

The push on the charge (potential difference) is the same, but the pathways are very different. The overall result is that the more difficult the path, the more opposition there is to flow. The measure of this opposition to flow is called electrical **resistance**. To define resistance more quantitatively, we must experiment with the circuit by measuring the quantities of potential difference across the load and the current passing through it. This way, we can indirectly develop a quantitative measure of resistance.

**Fig.16.9** The pathway makes a difference

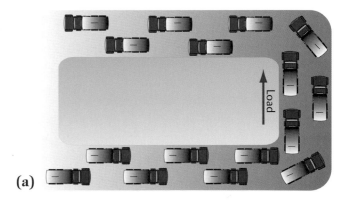

**(a)**

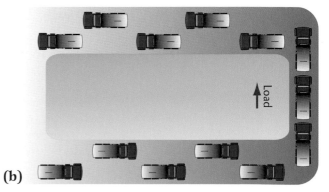

**(b)**

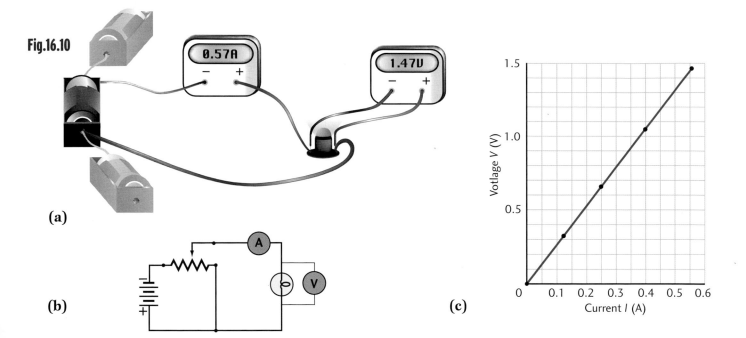

**Fig. 16.10**

(a)

(b)

(c)

| Table 16.3 | | |
|---|---|---|
| I (A) | V (V) | $\frac{V}{I}$ (Ω) |
| 0 | 0 | – |
| 0.12 | 0.31 | 2.6 |
| 0.25 | 0.64 | 2.6 |
| 0.40 | 1.04 | 2.6 |
| 0.57 | 1.47 | 2.6 |

Ω is the capital Greek letter Omega.

The circuit illustrated in Fig. 16.10(a) and schematized in 16.10(b) allows us to experiment with the electrical potential across a load. The idea is to see how much current flows over a load when the potential difference is varied. Figure 16.10(c) shows that the graph of voltage vs. current is a straight line and the slope of the graph, the $\frac{V}{I}$ ratio, is constant. Therefore, the slope and the $\frac{V}{I}$ ratio must represent the resistance of the load because the resistance remained unchanged in the experiment.

$$R = \frac{V}{I},$$

where R is the **resistance** in volts/ampere, which is given the derived unit of ohm (Ω), after Georg Simon Ohm (1787–1854).

V is the potential difference in volts (V) and I is the resulting current in amperes (A).

In general, Ohm found that the $\frac{V}{I}$ ratio was constant for a particular resistor. This ratio is called Ohm's law. The steps in the process of developing **Ohm's law** (or any other linear equation) are shown in Fig. 16.11.

**Fig. 16.11** Generating the Linear Equation for Ohm's Law from Data

METHOD of PROCESS ▶ ▶ ▶ ▶

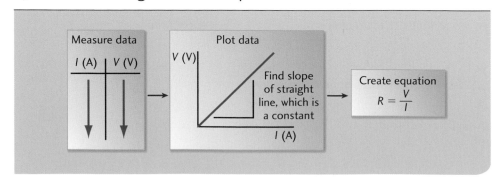

UNIT E: Electricity and Magnetism

The amount of current flowing through a resistor varies directly as the amount of potential difference applied across the resistor as long as other variables, such as temperature, are controlled. There is a resistance of 1 Ω when 1 A of current flows with a potential difference of 1 V across a resistor.

## EXAMPLE 8  Calculate current

An electric stove element is connected to a 240 V supply and has a known resistance of 19.8 Ω. What current will this element draw?

### *Solution and Connection to Theory*

**Given**

$V = 240$ V $\qquad R = 19.8$ Ω $\qquad I = ?$

$V = IR \qquad \therefore I = \dfrac{V}{R}$

$I = \dfrac{240 \text{ V}}{19.8 \text{ Ω}}$

$I = 12.1$ A

Therefore, the current that the element will draw is 12.1 A.

## EXAMPLE 9  Calculate resistance

What is the resistance of a 1200 W hair dryer that draws about 10 A from a 120 V circuit?

### *Solution and Connection to Theory*

**Given**

$I = 10$ A $\qquad V = 120$ V $\qquad R = ?$

$V = IR \qquad \therefore R = \dfrac{V}{I}$

$R = \dfrac{V}{I}$

$= \dfrac{120 \text{ V}}{10 \text{ A}}$

$= 12$ Ω

Therefore, the hair dryer has a resistance of about 12 Ω.

EXAMPLE 10 **Electrical caution**

An electric belt sander that was designed for a 120 V circuit to draw about 11.0 A was accidentally plugged into a 240 V line. The sander operated for about five seconds until it burned out. (a) What is the resistance of the sander? (b) What current did the sander draw from the 240 V line?

***Solution and Connection to Theory***

**a) Given**

$V_1 = 120$ V $\qquad I_1 = 11.0$ A $\qquad R_1 = ?$

$$R_1 = \frac{V_1}{I_1}$$

$$= \frac{120 \text{ V}}{11.0 \text{ A}}$$

$$= 10.9 \ \Omega$$

The sander has a resistance of 10.9 Ω.

**b) Given**

$V_2 = 240$ V $\qquad R_1 = 10.9 \ \Omega \qquad I_2 = ?$

$$I_2 = \frac{V_2}{R_1}$$

$$= \frac{240 \text{ V}}{10.9 \ \Omega}$$

$$= 22.0 \text{ A}$$

A current of 22.0 A is twice the capacity of the wiring in the sander.

## Factors that Determine Resistance

You have seen that a thinner wire has a larger resistance than a thicker one. Other properties of conductors also affect their resistance. The resistance of a conductor depends on its length, cross-sectional area, the material it is made of, and its temperature. Table 16.4 describes how these four factors affect resistance. The formulas show the ratio of the resistances of two conductors with different values for each factor.

## Table 16.4
### Factors that Affect Resistance

| Factor | Description | Proportionality |
|---|---|---|
| Length | The longer the conductor, the greater the resistance. | If the length is doubled, then the resistance is doubled $\frac{R_1}{R_2} = \frac{L_1}{L_2}$. |
| Cross-sectional area | The larger the cross-sectional area or thickness of the conductor, the less resistant it has to charge flow. | If the cross-sectional area is doubled, the resistance goes to half of its original value $\frac{R_1}{R_2} = \frac{A_2}{A_1}$. |
| Type of material | Some materials are better conductors than others. The general measure of the resistance of a substance is called the **resistivity**. Resistivity has units $\Omega \cdot m$. | If the resistivity $(\rho)$ is doubled, then the resistance is also doubled. $\frac{R_1}{R_2} = \frac{\rho_1}{\rho_2}$ |
| Temperature | Since moving charge is impeded by molecules, greater molecular motion at higher temperatures tends to increase the resistance. | An increase in temperature of the conductor usually contributes to an increase in the resistance, but not for all substances. |

---

### EXAMPLE 11  Resistance of aluminum wire

A 200 m piece of aluminum wire has a resistance of 1.7 $\Omega$. What is the resistance of a 50 m portion cut from it?

#### *Solution and Connection to Theory*

**Given**

$L_1 = 200$ m $\qquad R_1 = 1.7\ \Omega \qquad L_2 = 50$ m $\qquad R_2 = ?$

$$\frac{R_1}{R_2} = \frac{L_1}{L_2}$$

$$R_2 = R_1\left(\frac{L_2}{L_1}\right)$$

$$R_2 = 1.7\ \Omega\left(\frac{50\ \text{m}}{200\ \text{m}}\right) = 0.42\ \Omega$$

Therefore, the resistance of the 50 m piece of wire is 0.42 $\Omega$.

---

### EXAMPLE 12  Resistance and cross-section

How would the cross-sectional area of a 50 m piece of aluminum have to be changed to give it the same resistance as the 200 m piece in Example 11?

### Solution and Connection to Theory

**Given**

$R_1 = 0.42 \; \Omega$ $\qquad$ $A_1 = A_1$ $\qquad$ $R_2 = 1.7 \; \Omega$ $\qquad$ $A_2 = ?$

$$\frac{R_1}{R_2} = \frac{A_2}{A_1}$$

$$A_2 = A_1 \left( \frac{R_1}{R_2} \right)$$

$$A_2 = A_1 \left( \frac{0.42 \; \Omega}{1.7 \; \Omega} \right) = 0.25 A_1$$

Since area $= \pi r^2$, the 50 m wire would have to be about half the radius ($\sqrt{0.25} = 0.5$) in order to make its resistance the same as that of the 200 m wire.

1. Use the values $V = 120$ V, $I = 10.6$ A, and $R = 11.3 \; \Omega$ to create three problems, using each variable as the unknown.
2. Calculate the new resistance of a copper wire if
   **a)** the wire is cut from a length of 200 m ($R = 1.1 \; \Omega$) to a length of 35 m.
   **b)** if the cross-section of the wire is changed by a factor of 0.24.
3. By connecting an extension cord to an electrical load, such as a heater, you increase the total resistance of the system. Suggest why the resistance in the extension cord should be small, and possible problems that could arise from using one. Should the wire have a large or small cross-section in order to keep the resistance down to a minimum?

The **gauge number** of a wire indicates its cross-sectional area. A wire that has a small gauge number has a large cross-sectional area. Similarly, a small cross-section has a large gauge number.

### Superconductivity Part 1: Transmission Lines

Superconductivity is the ability of a material to conduct electricity without heat loss due to electrical resistance. The first superconductors became superconducting only at low temperatures (near 0 K or $-270\,°$C). In recent years, high-temperature superconducting materials, known as HTSs, have exhibited these properties at temperatures as high as 140 K ($-133\,°$C). This property saves on cooling costs to keep the material at the required temperature.

The promise of superconductors is transmission lines that carry electricity without energy loss. This ability would reduce the cost of producing electricity as well as the space occupied by supply lines (Fig. 16.12). Currently, there is a global race to produce a wire material that can carry currents of 100–1000 A (called the critical current, $I_c$) at the highest possible temperature without losing its superconductive properties.

**Fig.16.12**

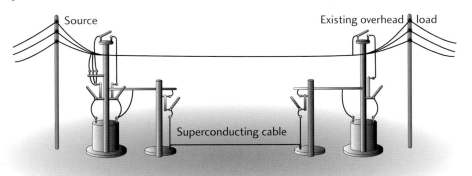

Source       Existing overhead load

Superconducting cable

4. Search the Web to find the highest temperature reached by a super-conducting material to date. Does it currently have any practical uses?

5. Research the possible improvements in computer technology as a result of superconductivity.

# 16.6 Series and Parallel Circuits

Now that we know how to relate current, potential difference, and resistance in simple circuits, we can examine the different ways in which those circuits can be combined. The two simplest ways to connect conductors and loads are illustrated in Fig. 16.13. In a **series circuit**, the loads are connected one after another in a single path, whereas in a **parallel circuit**, they are side by side.

Each arrangement affects the way in which potential difference and current act in the various parts of the circuit. Gustav Robert Kirchhoff (1824–1887) studied the way each of the circuit parameters behaved in series and parallel circuits. His research led to the publication of the laws of both current and voltage, called Kirchhoff's laws.

**Fig.16.13**    Simple series and parallel circuits

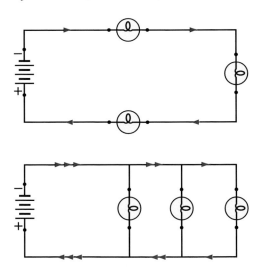

> **Kirchhoff's current law** The total amount of current into a junction point of a circuit equals the total current that flows out of that same junction.

In Fig. 16.14, three branches meet at one junction point and two branches leave another junction point so that $I_1 + I_2 + I_3 = I_T = I_4 + I_5$.

> **Kirchhoff's voltage law** The total of all electrical potential decreases in any complete circuit loop is equal to any potential increases in that circuit loop.

**Fig.16.14**    An illustration of Kirchhoff's current law

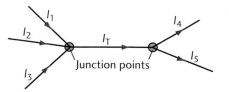

**Fig.16.15** An illustration of Kirchhoff's voltage law

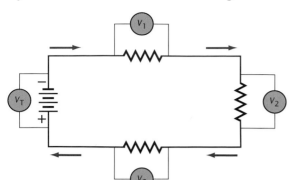

In Fig. 16.15, the potential increase, $V_T$ is equivalent to the sum of all the potential losses so that $V_T = V_1 + V_2 + V_3$.

Kirchhoff's laws are particular applications of the laws of **conservation of electric charge** and the **conservation of energy**. In other words, in any circuit, there is no net gain or loss of electric charge or energy.

**EXAMPLE 13** **Kirchhoff's laws in a series circuit**

Figure 16.16 shows a simple series circuit. Use Kirchhoff's voltage and current laws to find the values of the missing voltage ($V_2$) and current ($I_3$).

**Fig.16.16** A simple series circuit

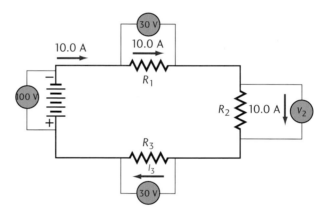

*Solution and Connection to Theory*

**Voltage** According to Kirchhoff's voltage law, this series circuit has one voltage increase of 100 V. This voltage must be distributed so that the sum of all voltage drops for each individual series resistor must equal this value. Therefore,

$$V_T = V_1 + V_2 + V_3$$

so $V_2 = V_T - V_1 - V_3$

$$= 100 \text{ V} - 30 \text{ V} - 30 \text{ V}$$
$$= 40 \text{ V}$$

**Current** According to Kirchhoff's current law, this series circuit has no real junction point, so it has only one path of flow. Therefore,

$$I_T = I_1 = I_2 = I_3 = 10 \text{ A}.$$

EXAMPLE 14 **Kirchhoff's laws in a parallel circuit**

Figure 16.17 shows a simple parallel circuit. Use Kirchhoff's voltage and current laws to find the values of the missing voltage ($V_2$) and current ($I_3$).

*Solution and Connection to Theory*

**Voltage** According to Kirchhoff's voltage law, this parallel circuit has one voltage increase of 30 V. This increase must be met by the same decrease for each of the three different parallel resistor paths. Therefore, $V_T = V_1 = V_2 = V_3$, so the voltage drop across any of the three parallel resistors is 30 V, no matter what their resistances are.

**Fig.16.17** A simple parallel circuit

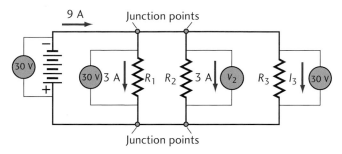

**Current** According to Kirchhoff's current law, this parallel circuit has four junction points (circled in Fig. 16.17), one at the top and bottom of each branch, to resistors 1 and 2. The sum of the current entering these junctions must equal the sum of the current exiting them.

Therefore, $I_T = I_1 + I_2 + I_3 = 9A$,

so $I_3 = I_T - I_1 - I_2 = 9\ A - 3A - 3A$

$\qquad = 3A$

In Examples 13 and 14, we had a simple case of a series or a parallel circuit with three resistors. In practice, however, circuits are more complicated combinations of both series and parallel elements. We can determine the overall resistance of series or parallel circuit elements by applying both Ohm's law for resistance and both of Kirchhoff's laws.

## Resistances in Series

Referring to Fig. 16.16 again, we find that all current must first pass through resistor 1, then 2, and so on. The voltage drops across each resistor. The sum of the voltage drops gives the overall voltage drop in the circuit.

$$\text{From Kirchhoff's law,} \quad V_T = V_1 + V_2 + V_3$$

$$\text{From Ohm's law,} \quad I_T R_T = I_1 R_1 + I_2 R_2 + I_3 R_3$$

$$\text{But from Kirchhoff's law,} \quad I_T = I_1 = I_2 = I_3 = I$$

$$\text{The currents factor out;} \quad \cancel{I} R_T = \cancel{I} R_1 + \cancel{I} R_2 + \cancel{I} R_3$$

$$\text{therefore,} \quad R_T = R_1 + R_2 + R_3$$

For the more general case where you have more than three resistors, the equation can be generalized as

$$R_T = R_1 + R_2 + R_3... + R_N$$

where $N$ is the total number of series resistors in the circuit.

> **EXAMPLE 15**   **Resistors in series**

If the values of all the resistors in a series circuit are the same, the overall resistance can be determined by

$$R_T = NR$$

where $N$ is the total number of resistors and $R$ is the resistance of each individual resistor.

What is the series equivalent resistance of 10 $\Omega$, 20 $\Omega$, and 30 $\Omega$ resistors connected in series?

### Solution and Connection to Theory

$$R_T = R_1 + R_2 + R_3$$

Therefore, $R_T = 10\ \Omega + 20\ \Omega + 30\ \Omega = 60\ \Omega$

## Resistances in Parallel

Referring to Fig. 16.17 again, we find that the total current must split and distribute itself among all of the available circuit paths.

From Kirchhoff's law,     $I_T = I_1 + I_2 + I_3$

From Ohm's law,     $\dfrac{V_T}{R_T} = \dfrac{V_1}{R_1} + \dfrac{V_2}{R_2} + \dfrac{V_3}{R_3}$

But from Kirchhoff's law,     $V_T = V_1 = V_2 = V_3 = V$

The voltages factor out;     $\dfrac{\cancel{V}}{R_T} = \dfrac{\cancel{V}}{R_1} + \dfrac{\cancel{V}}{R_2} + \dfrac{\cancel{V}}{R_3}$

therefore,     $\dfrac{1}{R_T} = \dfrac{1}{R_1} + \dfrac{1}{R_2} + \dfrac{1}{R_3}$

If the values of all the resistors in a parallel circuit are the same, the overall resistance can be determined by

$$\frac{1}{R_T} = \frac{N}{R}$$

$$\therefore R_T = \frac{R}{N}$$

where $N$ is the total number of resistors and $R$ is the resistance of each individual resistor.

For the more general case where you have more than three resistors, the equation can be generalized to

$$\frac{1}{R_T} = \frac{1}{R_1} + \frac{1}{R_2} + \frac{1}{R_3} \cdots + \frac{1}{R_N}$$

where $N$ is the total number of parallel resistors in the circuit.

EXAMPLE 16 **Resistors in parallel**

What is the parallel equivalent resistance for a 25 Ω, 40 Ω, and a 10 Ω resistor, wired in parallel?

*Solution and Connection to Theory*

$$\frac{1}{R_T} = \frac{1}{R_1} + \frac{1}{R_2} + \frac{1}{R_3}$$

$$\frac{1}{R_T} = \frac{1}{25\ \Omega} + \frac{1}{40\ \Omega} + \frac{1}{10\ \Omega}$$

$$\frac{1}{R_T} = \frac{(40\ \Omega)(10\ \Omega) + (25\ \Omega)(10\ \Omega) + (25\ \Omega)(40\ \Omega)}{(25\ \Omega)(40\ \Omega)(10\ \Omega)} = \frac{1\ 650\ \Omega^2}{10\ 000\ \Omega^3}$$

$$\therefore R_T = \frac{10\ 000\ \Omega}{1\ 650} = 6.1\ \Omega$$

Note how the units cancel correctly.

Example 16 can be done much faster with the $\frac{1}{X}$ key on your calculator. Simply key each parallel resistor value followed by the $\frac{1}{X}$ key as you add them up. After you press the equal (=) sign for the sum, don't forget to press the $\frac{1}{X}$ key one more time for the final answer.

1. Calculate the total resistance for the following:
   **a)** Three resistors, each 20 Ω, connected in series
   **b)** Three resistors, each 20 Ω, connected in parallel
   **c)** Three resistors, each 20 Ω, connected in parallel, which are then connected to three resistors, each 20 Ω, connected in series.
2. For resistors of 10 Ω, 15 Ω, and 20 Ω, two of the resistors are connected in parallel and one resistor is connected in series. Calculate the possible total resistance values.
3. **a)** What happens to a string of light bulbs connected in series if one light bulb goes out?
   **b)** What happens to a string of light bulbs connected in parallel if one light bulb goes out?
4. A 1.0 Ω resistor is hooked up to a 1.0 × 10⁶ Ω resistor in a) series b) parallel. For each situation, calculate the total resistance and explain the dominance of one resistor in the total value.

### Three-way Light Bulbs

Three-way light bulbs, which have three different light intensity settings, have two filaments of different resistance connected in parallel. Each filament can be turned on separately, or they can both be turned on at the same time, thus producing three different light intensities.

## 16.7 The Circuit Analysis Game

The distribution of current and electric potential energy loss in a circuit is determined by the way the circuit is designed and the overall resistance of certain circuit branches. The study of how the circuit parameters of current and voltage are distributed in a circuit is called **circuit analysis**. What follows is a simple set of rules to a game, similar to a crossword, but even more fun.

The game board consists of a circuit (Fig. 16.18) with numerous unknown parameters.

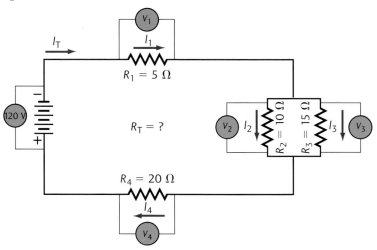

**Fig.16.18** A sample circuit for analysis

The object of the game is to find all the missing parameters in the circuit, such as the following:

Total current, resistance, and voltage $(I_T, R_T, V_T)$
The voltage across each resistor $(V_1, V_2, V_3, V_4)$
The current through each resistor $(I_1, I_2, I_3, I_4)$
The resistance of each resistor $(R_1, R_2, R_3, R_4)$

The score card for the game is provided in Table 16.5. We will fill it in as we go. The initial given values are marked in **bold**.

| | | Table 16.5 | |
|---|---|---|---|
| | | **Score Card for Circuit Analysis Game** | |
| Circuit Item | V (V) | I (A) | R (Ω) |
| Resistor ($R_1$) | [6]19.4 | [5]3.87 | [1(a)]**5** |
| Resistor ($R_2$) | [7]23.2 | [8]2.32 | [1(a)]**10** |
| Resistor ($R_3$) | [7]23.2 | [8]1.55 | [1(a)]**15** |
| Resistor ($R_4$) | [6]77.4 | [5]3.87 | [1(a)]**20** |
| Total Resistance ($R_T$) | [1(a)]**120** | [4]3.87 | [3]31 |

Note: The superscripted numbers represent the order in which the calculations are to be performed.

**The winner of the game** is the first person to complete the score card with written proof of all entries.

## Rules and Strategies of the Circuit Analysis Game

1. a) Fill in all known quantities.
   b) Fill in any "buried" known quantities. These quantities are the ones you can assume at a glance from Kirchhoff's laws, like the fact that any resistor in line with $I_T$ has the same value.
2. Reduce any parallel element to a series equivalent.

**Fig.16.19**   A series-equivalent circuit

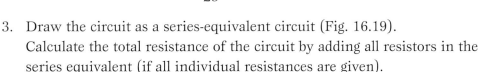

$$\frac{1}{R_{2-3}} = \frac{1}{R_2} + \frac{1}{R_3}$$

$$\frac{1}{R_{2-3}} = \frac{1}{10\ \Omega} + \frac{1}{15\ \Omega} = \frac{25\ \Omega}{150\ \Omega^2}$$

$$R_{2-3} = \frac{150\ \Omega}{25} = 6\ \Omega$$

3. Draw the circuit as a series-equivalent circuit (Fig. 16.19). Calculate the total resistance of the circuit by adding all resistors in the series equivalent (if all individual resistances are given).

$$R_T = R_1 + R_{2-3} + R_4$$

$$R_T = 5\ \Omega + 6\ \Omega + 20\ \Omega = 31\ \Omega$$

4. Use $V = IR$ to find any missing variable if you are given any two out of three parameters in a row. We now have a $V_T$ and an $R_T$.

$$I_T = \frac{V_T}{R_T} = \frac{120\ \text{V}}{31\ \Omega} = 3.87\ \text{A}$$

5. According to Kirchhoff's current law, all series resistors have the same current,

$$\therefore I_1 = I_4 = I_{2-3} = I_T = 3.87\ \text{A}$$

6. If you have two out of three knowns in a row on the score card,

$$V_1 = I_1(R_1) = 3.87\ \text{A}(5\ \Omega) = 19.4\ \text{V}$$

$$V_4 = I_4(R_4) = 3.87\ \text{A}(20\ \Omega) = 77.4\ \text{V}$$

7. Voltages (Kirchhoff's voltage law for series and parallel circuits) Here, $V_2 = V_3$ by Kirchhoff's voltage law. The sum of all individual voltages must equal the total voltage.

$$\therefore V_2 = V_3 = V_{2-3} = V_T - V_1 - V_4 = 120\ \text{V} - 19.4\ \text{V} - 77.4\ \text{V} = 23.2\ \text{V}$$

8. Two out of three knowns in a row. Check after every step.

$$I_2 = \frac{V_2}{R_2} = \frac{23.2 \text{ V}}{10 \text{ }\Omega} = 2.32 \text{ A}$$

$$I_3 = \frac{V_3}{R_3} = \frac{23.2 \text{ V}}{15 \text{ }\Omega} = 1.55 \text{ A}$$

You just won the game! You can be sure by going back and double-checking the answers on the score card.

## Other strategies that you could use

1. Current splitting (with parallel elements):

    If the current that is entering the parallel resistors (usually the total current, $I_T$) and the resistor values are known, try this method to see how the current is split between the two resistors.

    Given two resistors, $R_2 = 10 \text{ }\Omega$ and $R_3 = 15 \text{ }\Omega$, more of the total current, $I_T$, would flow through the smaller resistor, $R_2$. The current would be split between the two resistors proportionally, based on their resistance values, as shown below (see also Fig. 16.20).

$$I_2 = I_T \text{ (the resistance ratio)}$$

**Fig.16.20**

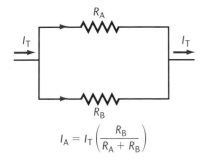

$$I_A = I_T\left(\frac{R_B}{R_A + R_B}\right)$$

$$I_2 = I_T\left(\frac{R_3}{R_2 + R_3}\right) = 3.87 \text{ A}\left(\frac{15 \text{ }\Omega}{10 \text{ }\Omega + 15 \text{ }\Omega}\right) = 3.87 \text{ A}\left(\frac{15}{25}\right) = 2.32 \text{ A}$$

The **resistance ratio** for any resistor is $= \left(\dfrac{\text{opposing resistor}}{\text{sum of both resistors}}\right)$

Of course, $I_3$ would be easily found by subtracting from the total:

$$I_3 = I_T - I_2 = 3.87 \text{ A} - 2.32 \text{ A} = 1.55 \text{ A}$$

**Tips from the coach** Don't let the rounding "throw you off your game." Someone else may have slightly different answers, especially if he or she used a different strategy than you did.

2. Series-equivalent resistors

    Find the voltage drop across any parallel element by using the series-equivalent resistance and the total current.

$$V_{2-3} = V_2 = V_3 = I_{2-3}(R_{2-3})$$

$$V_{2-3} = V_2 = V_3 = 3.87 \text{ A}(6 \text{ }\Omega)$$

$$V_{2-3} = V_2 = V_3 = 23.2 \text{ V}$$

**Tips from the coach** Remember that using current-splitting or series-equivalent resistors will take you on a different route to win the game.

Like any game, it is not who wins that is important, but rather how the game is played. This attitude is also true for circuit analysis. The most important object is to play the game by trying out the individual strategies to finish the problem. Like any game, you will need lots of practice. The practice for these problems appears at the end of the chapter.

**Fig.16.21** Summary of Series and Parallel Circuits

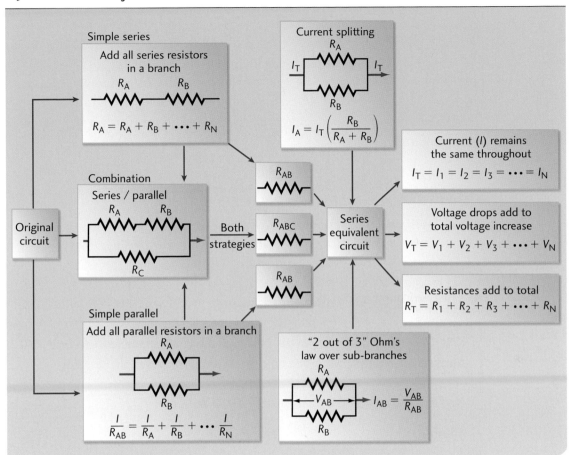

Simple series

Add all series resistors in a branch

$R_A \quad R_B$

$R_A = R_A + R_B + \cdots + R_N$

Current splitting

$R_A$

$I_T \qquad I_T$

$R_B$

$I_A = I_T \left( \dfrac{R_B}{R_A + R_B} \right)$

Combination

Series / parallel

$R_A \quad R_B$

$R_C$

Original circuit

Both strategies

$R_{AB}$

$R_{ABC}$

$R_{AB}$

Series equivalent circuit

Current ($I$) remains the same throughout

$I_T = I_1 = I_2 = I_3 = \cdots = I_N$

Voltage drops add to total voltage increase

$V_T = V_1 + V_2 + V_3 + \cdots + V_N$

Resistances add to total

$R_T = R_1 + R_2 + R_3 + \cdots + R_N$

Simple parallel

Add all parallel resistors in a branch

$R_A$

$R_B$

$\dfrac{I}{R_{AB}} = \dfrac{I}{R_A} + \dfrac{I}{R_B} + \cdots \dfrac{I}{R_N}$

"2 out of 3" Ohm's law over sub-branches

$R_A$

$\leftarrow V_{AB} \rightarrow \qquad I_{AB} = \dfrac{V_{AB}}{R_{AB}}$

$R_B$

1. A 5.0 V power supply is hooked up to resistors with values of 10 Ω, 15 Ω, and 20 Ω. Calculate the voltage across each resistor and the current through it for the following resistor combinations:
   a) All the resistors are in series.
   b) All the resistors are in parallel.
   c) Two of the resistors are connected in parallel with one connected in series. Do all the combinations.
2. Explain Kirchhoff's laws using your results from Question 1.

APPLYING the Concepts

## 16.8 Power in Electric Circuits

Recall that **power** is the rate at which work is done. In the case of electric circuits, power is the rate at which electrical energy is passed on to various circuit loads. For each particular load, a coulomb (1 C) of charge is the energy carrier, and the electric potential is the amount of energy (1 V = 1 J/C) that the charge is carrying. Therefore, the amount of power dissipated in the load depends on how fast the charge arrives at the load.

From Chapter 7, recall that $P = \dfrac{E}{t}$

and from Section 16.3, $E = VIt$

Then, $P = \dfrac{E}{t} = \dfrac{VIt}{t}$

$P = IV$

where $I$ is the current in amperes (A), $V$ is the potential difference in volts (V), and $P$ is the power in watts (W).

There are two other formulas for power:

$$P = IV, \text{ but } V = IR. \text{ Therefore, } I = \frac{V}{R}$$

$$\therefore P = IV = \frac{V}{R}(V)$$

$$\therefore P = \frac{V^2}{R}$$

$$P = IV, \text{ but } V = IR$$

$$\therefore P = I(IR)$$

$$= I^2R$$

The unit for power is the watt, which must come out of the units for both current and voltage:

$$P = IV$$

In unit format,

$P$ = A (current) × V (voltage)

$$= \frac{\cancel{C}}{s} \text{ (current)} \times \frac{J}{\cancel{C}} \text{ (voltage)}$$

$$= \frac{J}{s} = W \text{ (power)}$$

We now have three tools to calculate power, depending on the givens in your problem:

$$P = IV$$

$$P = \frac{V^2}{R}$$

$$P = I^2R$$

### EXAMPLE 17   Household power

What is the maximum power that can be drawn from a standard 120 V household circuit that has a circuit breaker (or fuse) of 15 A?

#### Solution and Connection to Theory

**Given**

$V = 120$ V          $I = 15$ A          $P = ?$

$P = IV$

$P = (15 \text{ A})(120 \text{ V})$

$P = 1800$ W

Therefore, the maximum power on any 15 A fused/breakered circuit is 1800 W.

### EXAMPLE 18   Power to the amp

Calculate the power rating of a stereo amplifier (not the speaker power) if it is plugged into a standard 120 V outlet and has a resistance of 120 Ω.

#### Solution and Connection to Theory

**Given**

$V = 120$ V          $R = 120$ Ω          $P = ?$

$$P = \frac{V^2}{R}$$

$$P = \frac{(120 \text{ V})^2}{120 \text{ }\Omega}$$

$$P = 120 \text{ W}$$

Therefore, the power rating of the stereo is 120 W.

**EXAMPLE 19**  **Power in the current**

How much power is dissipated in a circuit with a 15 $\Omega$ resistor that draws a current of 10.0 A?

**Solution and Connection to Theory**

**Given**

$R = 15 \text{ }\Omega$ $\qquad$ $I = 10.0 \text{ A}$ $\qquad$ $P = ?$

$P = I^2R$

$P = (10.0 \text{ A})^2(15 \text{ }\Omega)$

$P = 1500 \text{ W}$

Therefore, the power dissipated in the circuit is 1500 W.

1. Calculate the power produced by a 12 V battery charger if it delivers
   a) 10 A in the fast-charge mode. $\qquad$ b) 2 A in trickle-charge mode.
2. a) A portable heater, rated at 1 kW, is plugged into a 120 V outlet. How many amperes of current will it draw?
   b) Will it burn out if it is plugged into a 220 V circuit?
3. a) For Question 2, calculate the amount of charge delivered in 1.0 minutes.
   b) Calculate the number of electrons in that amount of charge.
   c) Find the energy delivered by the heater.
   d) What is the resistance of the heater?

# 16.9 The Cost of Electricity

Every month, we buy electrical energy from an electric power company, such as BC Hydro or Ontario Power Generation. The SI unit for energy is the joule, but this unit is so small, that buying energy by the joule would not make much sense. Imagine that your monthly electricity bill stated that you used 4 500 000 000 J at $ 0.000 000 022 per joule. The bill would be for $99, but you can see how silly this unit of energy is in this case. As a result, a more convenient unit for buying and selling electricity has been chosen. This unit is the kilowatt hour (kWh). It is best understood by reviewing the power equation, rearranged for energy $E = Pt$, where $P$ is in kilowatts and $t$ is in hours. Your electricity bill would now read 1250 kWh of energy at $0.08 for every kilowatt hour. The bill is still for $99, but both the unit for energy and the rate are in more reasonable units. One way of thinking about it is to consider that every joule of electrical energy has a certain value in kilowatt hours. The conversion factor between the two units is given below.

$$\text{SI equivalent of 1 kWh}$$

$$1 \text{ kWh} = 1 \times 10^3 \frac{\text{J}}{\text{s}} \times 1 \text{ h} \times \frac{3600 \text{ s}}{1 \text{ h}}$$

$$= 3.6 \times 10^6 \text{ J}$$

A value of $0.082 or 8.2¢/kWh is a reasonable estimate for cost, but other pricing structures may exist and change regularly.

The way to calculate the cost is summarized by the relationship

Total cost = $P$ (in kW) × time (hours) × rate (cost/kWh)

### EXAMPLE 20    Energy costs money

The person in control of your household cheque book has been remarking that you should not be leaving so many unattended lights on in the house. You accidentally leave your overhead room light, with three 100 W light bulbs in it, on while you go off to school for a period of nine hours. How much money would this little accident cost your family?

### *Solution and Connection to Theory*

**Given**

$P = 3 \times 100$ W          $t = 9$ hours          rate = $0.082/kWh

The equation for cost is

Cost = $P$ (in kW) × time (hours) × rate (cost/kWh)

The power must be converted into units of kilowatt hours and the time must be quoted in hours.

$$\text{Cost} = (3 \times 100 \text{ W}) \frac{1 \text{ kW}}{1000 \text{ W}} \times 9 \text{ h} \times \$0.082/\text{kWh}$$

Cost = $0.22 or 22¢

If this memory lapse were a regular occurrence for each school day of the month (about 20 days), then the total cost would be ($0.22/day × 20 days) $4.40, a considerable sum, especially if you consider that it is for only one month of the school year.

**Fig.16.22** Transfer of Energy in Electric Circuits

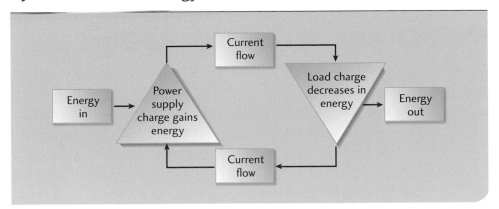

1. **a)** A dryer uses 15 A of current at 240 V for 1.2 h. How much will it cost to do the laundry if the charge for electricity is 8.2 ¢/kWh?
   **b)** If your computer uses 2.5 A at 120 V, how much does it cost to use for 1.2 h?
2. How much does it cost to run
   **a)** a 0.3 kW furnace motor that turns on for 12 minutes 25 times a day?
   **b)** eight 60 W light bulbs, operating for an average of 6.4 hours per day?
   **c)** a 15 Ω toaster plugged into a 120 V outlet once a day for 3.0 minutes?
   **d)** a 15 A drier plugged into a 240 V outlet that runs for 55 minutes seven times a month?
   **e)** a refrigerator for one day if it draws 2.0 A from a 120 V source that turns on for 10 minutes every hour?

Assume that the cost of electricity is 8¢/kWh.

## Electric Current and the Human Body

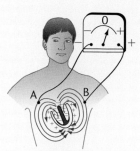

**Fig.STSE.16.1** Current flow around a partially depolarized heart

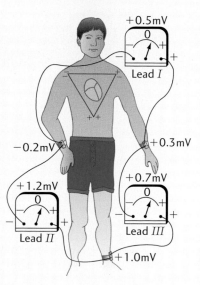

From computers to calculators, toasters to TVs, electricity is not only all around us, but also inside us! Electricity is an essential part of the human body's functioning. Your nervous system sends signals through your body using electricity. Nerve cells are conductors that electrically depolarize (lose their charge difference) and then re-polarize to control every aspect of our sensation and movement. Figure STSE.16.1 shows current flowing around a partially depolarized heart.

Many products and procedures have been developed that measure or send electricity through your body. Some of them play an important role in life-sustaining medical treatments and procedures. For example, **electrocauterization** is a process that uses a spark from an electric current to control severe bleeding by burning tissue to create a seal. Doctors measure the heart's electrical activity using an **electrocardiograph**. Voltage is measured between leads placed at three different locations on the body, known as Einthoven's triangle, shown in Fig. STSE.16.2. An **electrocardiogram** (Fig. STSE.16.3) is a graph of the voltage fluctuations plotted against time. When the heart's natural electric currents are disrupted during a myocardial infarction or heart attack, doctors reset its natural rhythm by applying a high-voltage shock from a **cardiac defibrillator**.

Law-enforcement agencies take advantage of the electrical capabilities of the body with the use of polygraph devices (lie detectors). Polygraphs use an electric current to measure the electrical resistance of a person's skin. As an alternative to deadly weapons for apprehending criminals, some police forces are now using Taser guns (Fig. STSE.16.4). A Taser gun uses compressed air to fire two fish-hook-tipped wires into the victim. Fired at close range, the fish hooks act as electrical leads that can deliver a shock of 50 000 V using only 26 W of power. One jolt is enough to disrupt the motor impulses and incapacitate a perpetrator.

**Fig.STSE.16.2** Einthoven's triangle and ECG

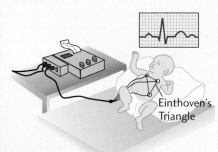

**Fig.STSE.16.3** An electrocardiogram

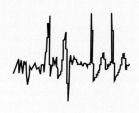

**Fig.STSE.16.4** A police Taser gun

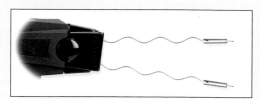

## Design a Study of Societal Impact

How can knowledge of physics be useful to a doctor or a polygraph operator? What career opportunities are there for someone knowledgeable in the physics of electricity?

Galvanic skin response meters are often used in conjunction with other devices, such as blood pressure and heart rate monitors in polygraphy or lie detection. Write an essay that addresses the question of whether a lie detector test is accurate, reliable, and valid. Which jurisdictions currently admit polygraph tests in a court of law? Has anyone ever fooled a lie detector?

Prepare a biography of actor Christopher Reeve who has a spinal cord injury. What obstacles still need to be overcome in spinal cord research before he would have a chance of walking again?

## Design an Activity to Evaluate

Use a galvanic skin response meter to perform a correlation study of skin resistivity. Record data from one individual at different times of the day and under different circumstances. Develop an experimental protocol that controls variables and addresses the issue of consistency.

Study the galvanic skin response (GSR) of several people using the same variables. Perform a statistical analysis to determine if any valid predictions can be made for using the device on an individual.

## Build a Structure

Build your own galvanic skin response meter following the directions provided in Fig. STSE.16.5 or of your own design.

**Fig.STSE.16.5A** Galvanic skin response sensor

Aluminum foil
Hook side
Wire — Sticky side — Sticky side
Loop side
3/4 in
3/4 in
3.5 in

**Fig.STSE.16.5B** A simple polygraph

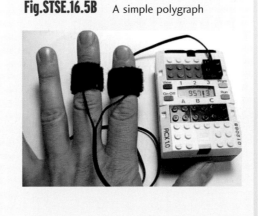

## You should be able to

*Understand Basic Concepts:*

- Define and describe the concepts and units of electric current, electric potential difference (voltage), resistance, and electrical power.
- Use graphical methods to determine the equation and units for Ohm's law of resistance.
- Compare how electric current is distributed in both series and parallel circuits.
- Describe and differentiate between the two conventions of electron (−) and electric (+) current flow, recognizing that electric current flow is preferred.
- Relate the transfer of energy in a circuit pathway to the manufacture and delivery of goods.
- State how electric energy may be supplied in a circuit.
- List the factors that affect the resistance of an electrical load and use proportionality equations to predict the results of their changes to the overall resistance.

*Develop Skills of Inquiry and Communication:*

- Use both an ammeter and a voltmeter to measure the current and voltage in different parts of electrical circuits.
- Design and analyze combination series and parallel circuits on paper to quantitatively predict the potential difference (voltage), current, and resistance of all circuit elements using Kirchhoff's laws and Ohm's law.
- Design and conduct an experiment to verify the validity of Kirchhoff's current and voltage laws for series, parallel, and combination circuits.
- Illustrate and interpret on the basis of experimental data how Ohm's law applies to a circuit and its component parts.

*Relate Science to Technology, Society, and the Environment:*

- Analyze and describe the role of electric currents and potential with respect to the human body.

- Describe how electric current can be used for the apprehension of criminals and their prosecution in a court of law.
- Outline some practical applications of electric current and potential in the medical field.
- Analyze the different units that are used in electricity sales and estimate the cost of running certain electrical appliances.

## Equations

$$I = \frac{Q}{t}$$

$$V = \frac{E}{Q} = \frac{W}{Q}$$

$$E = VIt$$

$$V = IR$$

$$\frac{R_1}{R_2} = \frac{A_2}{A_1}$$

$V_T = V_1 + V_2 + V_3$　from Kirchhoff's law (series)
$I_T = I_1 = I_2 = I_3$　from Kirchhoff's law (series)
$R_T = R_1 + R_2 + R_3 \ldots + R_N$ (series)
$R_T = N(R)$ (series)
$I_T = I_1 + I_2 + I_3$　from Kirchhoff's law (parallel)
$V_T = V_1 = V_2 = V_3$　from Kirchhoff's law (parallel)

$$\frac{1}{R_T} = \frac{1}{R_1} + \frac{1}{R_2} + \frac{1}{R_3} \ldots + \frac{1}{R_N} \text{ (parallel)}$$

$$R_T = \frac{R}{N} \text{ (parallel)}$$

$$P = IV$$

$$P = \frac{V^2}{R}$$

$$P = I^2R$$

$$\text{Cost} = P \text{ (in kWh)} \times t(\text{hours}) \times \text{rate (cost/kWh)}$$

## Conceptual Questions

1. In many portable battery powered devices such as CD players, the batteries are inserted end to end.
   a) Are these batteries installed in series or in parallel?
   b) If a standard AA battery has a voltage of 1.5 V, what is the voltage requirement of a device that needs two batteries?
   c) What is the electrical benefit of a device that requires batteries side by side in parallel?

2. A student wants to think of current flow as negatively charged electrons moving through a wire, but her teacher states that current direction is defined as the direction of positive charge flow because of historical convention. Briefly describe what is meant by "convention" and include at least two other examples of where a historical convention is used in society today.

3. Many electronic devices will not guarantee that their products will work at extreme temperatures. Which components would be most affected by extreme temperatures?

4. Boosting a car using someone else's battery for cold weather starting requires the combination of two batteries. Are these batteries connected in series or parallel? Explain.

5. What type of circuit is used exclusively in our homes for all lighting and outlets, series or parallel? Describe at least two observations that could be used to back up your answer.

6. The new Christmas mini-lights come with a warning that a burnt-out light must be replaced immediately or a fire hazard may result. What does this warning imply about the way in which these lights are wired? What observation about series or parallel circuits must be overlooked in order for your previous answer about circuit type to make sense? (Some of these mini-lights have an internal shunt that keeps the series circuit active even if the filament burns out.)

7. You and your friend are having a friendly disagreement. You do not know which of your two unmarked resistors has the greatest resistance. The only way to settle this disagreement is to go into the lab and get experimental data. Draw a graph of the potential difference versus the current for each resistor on the same axis. In doing so, explain how you could tell from this graph which of you was right.

8. Why is energy consumption in your home measured in kilowatt hours and not in joules? Show by proper unit analysis that a kilowatt hour is a unit of energy.

## Problems

### 16.2 Current

9. How long does it take for a current of 9.3 mA to transfer a charge of 12 C?

10. How much charge is transferred by a current of 0.80 A in 19 minutes?

### 16.3 Electrical Potential

11. What is the potential difference between two points if $2.0 \times 10^3$ J of work is required to move 1 C of charge between the two points?

12. What is the potential difference between two points when a charge of 65 C has $2.50 \times 10^2$ J of energy supplied to it as it moves between the points?

13. What is the energy of a proton accelerated through a potential difference of 500 kV? The charge on one proton is $1.6 \times 10^{-19}$ C.

**14.** How much energy is transferred to a radio if a current of 0.40 A runs through it for 1.5 minutes, with a potential difference of 115 V?

**15.** What is the potential difference across a curling iron if there is a current of 2.5 A through it that transfers 9 360 J of energy to the curling iron in 32 s?

**16.** How much energy is dissipated over a 2.5 minute period when a current of 5.0 A runs through a potential difference of 80 V?

**17.** A microwave at a potential difference of 120 V uses 50 000 J of energy during the 60 s it is on. What is the current through the microwave?

**18.** An electric saw operates at a potential difference of 120 V and draws a current of 9.5 A. If it takes 40 s to make a cut, calculate the amount of electrical energy used by the saw in that time.

**19.** An electric motor is used to do the $2.30 \times 10^4$ J of work needed to lift an engine out of a car. If the motor draws a current of 3.2 A for 30 s, calculate the potential difference across the motor.

**20.** In a lightning discharge, 45 C of charge move through a potential difference of $10^8$ V in $3.0 \times 10^{-2}$ s. Calculate
   **a)** the current represented by the lightning bolt.
   **b)** the total energy released by the lightning bolt.

**21.** How much energy is gained by an electron accelerated through a potential difference of $2.5 \times 10^4$ V?

**22.** How much energy is required to run a leaf blower if it draws 13 A from a 117 V outlet for 10.0 min?

▶ **16.5 Resistance—Ohm's Law**

**23.** A voltmeter connected across the ends of a stove heating element indicates a potential difference of 120 V when an ammeter shows a current through the coil of 6.0 A. What is the resistance of the coil?

**24.** A TV remote control has a resistance of 9.2 Ω and is connected to two AA batteries with a potential difference of 3.0 V. What is the current through the remote control?

**25.** What is the potential difference across a computer power supply with a resistance of 50 Ω if the motor draws a current of 2.2 A?

**26.** A 100 Ω wire resistor has its length doubled. What is its new resistance?

**27.** A 500 Ω wire resistor is compared to the resistance of the same material but of half its radius. What is the resistance of this wire?

**28.** Resistivity is given by the equation $\rho = \frac{RA}{L}$. What is the resistance of a 100 m piece of copper with a diameter of 1.0 mm? (The resistivity of copper is $1.7 \times 10^{-8}$ Ω·m.)

▶ **16.6 Series and Parallel Circuits**

**29.** A string of Christmas tree lights with 25 bulbs connected in series draws a current of 3.8 A from a 120 V source. Find
   **a)** the total resistance of the string of lights.
   **b)** the resistance of each light.
   **c)** the potential difference across each light.

**30. a)** What is the resistance of a coffee maker that draws a current of 5.0 A from a 117 V source?
   **b)** What resistance would have to be added in parallel with the same coffee maker to increase the current to 15.0 A?

**31.** Calculate the total resistance in each of these cases:
   **a)** 20 Ω, 30 Ω, and 60 Ω in series

**b)** 8 Ω, 6 Ω, and 48 Ω in parallel

**c)** A combination of 4 Ω and 9 Ω connected in parallel, in series with another combination consisting of 4 Ω and 12 Ω connected in parallel with each other.

**32.** How many 60 Ω resistors must be connected in parallel to draw a current of 10.0 A from a 120 V source?

**33.** The potential difference across a resistor is 50.0 V when the current through it is 5.0 A. What resistance must be added in series with the resistor to reduce the current by half?

**34.** A portable mobile phone is designed to operate at a potential difference of 5.0 V and a current of 0.200 A, but the only source available has a potential of 12.0 V. What resistance must be added in series with the phone to make it operate?

▶ **16.7** The Circuit Analysis Game

**35.** Examine these circuits and find all of the missing circuit parameters. For each one, remember to use the circuit analysis game score card. Let's play Circuit Analysis!

|       | V (V) | I (A) | R (Ω) |
|-------|-------|-------|-------|
| $R_1$ |       |       |       |
| $R_2$ |       |       |       |
| $R_3$ |       |       |       |
| $R_T$ |       |       |       |

**a) Fig.16.23**

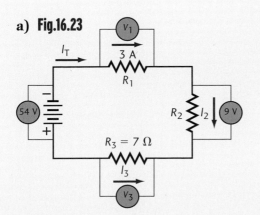

**b) Fig.16.24**

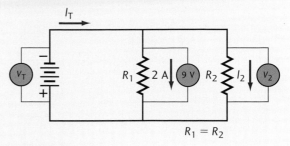

$R_1 = R_2$

**c) Fig.16.25**

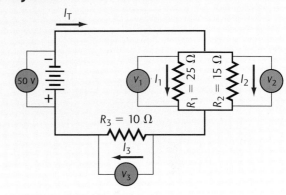

**d) Fig.16.26**

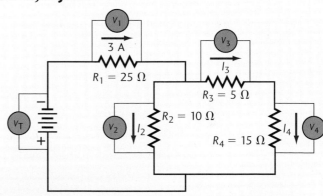

**e) Fig.16.27**

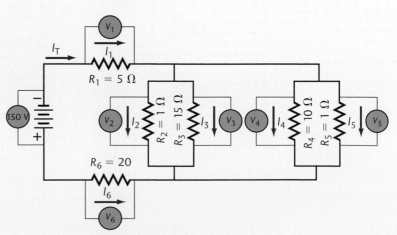

**f) Fig.16.28**

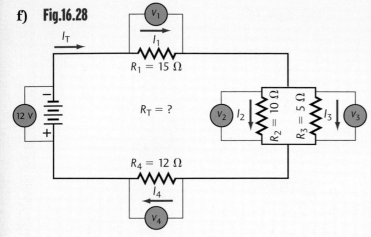

## 16.8 Power in Electric Circuits

**36.** Calculate the power dissipated by each of the following:

a) An electric stove drawing 13.0 A from a 240 V source

b) A frying pan that draws 11.0 A and has a resistance of 11.6 $\Omega$

c) A 2057 $\Omega$ night light plugged into a 120 V source

**37.** a) What maximum power can be used on a 120 V circuit with a 15 A fuse?

b) How much more current can safely be drawn from a 120 V outlet fused at 15 A if a 600 W curling iron and a 1200 W hair dryer are already operating in the circuit?

**38.** A 1.2 kW iron that normally operates on a 120 V circuit is plugged into a 240 V outlet.

a) What current is the iron really supposed to draw?

b) What current will it draw when connected to 240 V?

c) What power will it use on 240 V?

d) What will happen to the iron when it is plugged into this 240 V circuit?

## 16.9 The Cost of Electricity

**39.** An automotive hoist motor draws 3.5 A from a 120 V source and operates for an average of nine minutes every hour in an eight-hour day. Calculate the annual cost of operating the hoist motor if the average cost of electrical energy is 8.2¢/kWh.

**40.** Four sets of Christmas lights, each holding 25 bulbs, are set up for a Christmas display. These 7 W bulbs were lit from 8:00 PM to 12:00 AM every night from December 1 to January 10. If the average cost of electrical energy is 8.2¢/kWh, how much will this Christmas display cost to light?

## Purpose

To quantitatively verify Kirchhoff's current and voltage laws for series, parallel, and simple combinations circuits.

## Safety Consideration

Be sure to follow the teacher's instructions in order to avoid personal injury and equipment damage.

## Equipment

DC power supply

Resistors of various resistance values (100 Ω or above)

Several alligator clip patch cables (both black and red)

Two digital or analog multimeters

## Procedure

1. Prepare a lab prediction/data table, as shown in Table Lab.16.1.
2. Wire the circuit, including the voltmeter, as shown in either Fig. Lab.16.1 or Fig. Lab.16.2, depending on the type of circuit you are examining.
3. Remove the power supply from the circuit and then use the second multimeter as an ohmmeter to measure the resistance of the entire circuit. One at a time, remove each resistor from the circuit and measure its resistance. Record all four resistance values in the data table.

4. Reconnect the entire circuit and apply a voltage to the circuit with the power supply. Be careful not to change the setting on the power supply at any time after any measurements are being taken.
5. Use the voltmeter connected to the circuit to measure the voltage across the power supply terminals. Record in the voltage data table.
6. Use the free black lead of the voltmeter to register the electrical potential on either side of each resistor. Subtract the voltage (potential difference) across each resistor and record it in the column "Measured" of the data table.

**Fig.Lab.16.1**

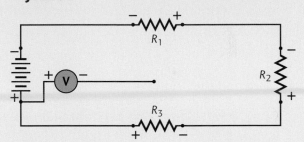

**Fig.Lab.16.2**

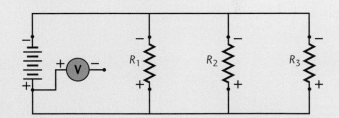

| Table Lab.16.1 | | | | | | | |
|---|---|---|---|---|---|---|---|
| Circuit Element | Voltage (V) | | Current (A) | | Resistance (Ω) | | |
| | Calculated | Measured | Calculated | Measured | Calculated | Measured | |
| Resistor 1 | | | | | | | |
| Resistor 2 | | | | | | | |
| Resistor 3 | | | | | | | |
| Resistor 4 | | | | | | | |
| Total Circuit Value | | | | | | | |

7. Reconfigure the multimeter to act as an ammeter. Carefully break the circuit at the power supply and at each resistor, one at a time, and insert the ammeter into the circuit in series. Measure the current flowing through each part of the circuit. Record these four current values in the data table.

## Uncertainty

Assign an appropriate instrumental uncertainty to each of your measured values.

## Analysis

1. Calculate the total resistance of the circuit by using the appropriate resistance summation formulae from the individual measured resistance values. Record this value in the chart.

2. Use Ohm's law $(V = IR)$ to calculate the expected current through the entire circuit based on the measured voltage and the calculated resistance from the previous step. Record this value in the chart.

3. Use both Kirchhoff's current and voltage laws to calculate the expected currents and voltages for each individual resistor. Record these values in the chart.

## Discussion

1. Compare all of the measured values with their calculated counterparts. Are any of these values the same, within experimental uncertainty?

2. What reasons would you give for the difference between the measured and calculated total circuit currents?

3. Suggest a change in the experimental procedure or other measurements that could be taken to conduct a more valid test of Kirchhoff's laws.

## Conclusion

Write a concluding statement that addresses the purpose of this lab. Were Kirchhoff's current and voltage laws verified within experimental uncertainty?

# Magnetism and Electromagnetism

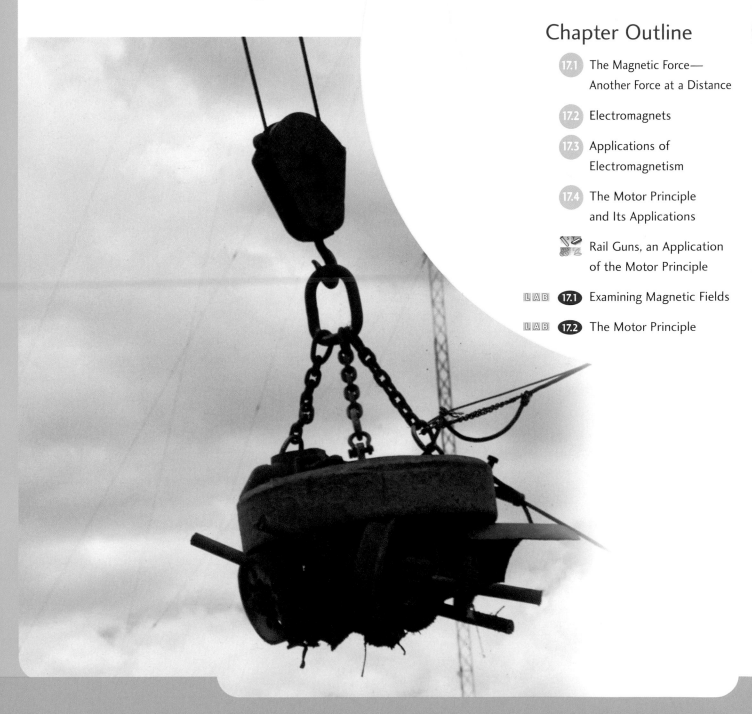

**By the end of this chapter, you will be able to**

- explain how the concept of force at a distance applies to a magnetic field
- describe how current flow can create electromagnets
- outline the relationship between magnetism and electromagnetism
  in creating many practical devices, including electric motors

581

## 17.1 The Magnetic Force—Another Force at a Distance

**Fig.17.1** Repulsion by like magnetic poles makes the magnets float

When it's time to order a pizza, where do you find the phone number? You usually look either in the telephone book, or on the refrigerator. Those small pieces of advertising, picture frames, and decorations on the fridge are all held onto your metallic refrigerator door by magnetic forces. The magnetic force, as illustrated by the floating magnet in Fig. 17.1, is another example of a force that acts at a distance. A **magnetic field** is the distribution of a magnetic force in the region of a magnet. We can apply the same field theory to magnets as we did to electrostatic forces. As with electric fields, there are two different magnetic characteristics, labelled **north** and **south**, that are responsible for magnetic forces. Figure 17.2 illustrates the law of magnetic forces.

> Similar magnetic poles, north and north or south and south, *repel* one another with a force at a distance. Dissimilar poles, north and south, *attract* one another with a force at a distance.

**Fig.17.2** The law of magnetic forces

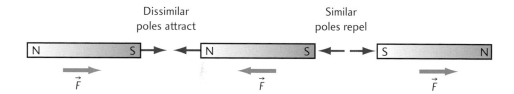

By looking at the way solid iron from lava flow is magnetized, geophysicists have deduced that the direction of Earth's magnetic field has changed from time to time.

This law is the basis for magnetic forces that act in devices such as fridge magnets as well as Earth's magnetic field. To map a magnetic field, we use a **test compass**, instead of the test charge we used in electrostatics. Field lines show the direction in which the *north seeking pole* of this test compass would point at that point in space.

**Fig.17.3** A field shows direction of force

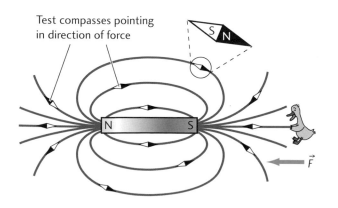

Test compasses pointing in direction of force

Figure 17.3 shows how a field shape can be mapped around a simple bar magnet with the use of many small test compasses. The magnetic field is so intricate that it is often better demonstrated by carefully spreading iron filings near a magnet. Figure 17.4 uses iron filings to show magnetic fields.

Earth acts like a giant permanent magnet, producing its own magnetic field. Figure 17.5 illustrates Earth's magnetic field as well as how a compass responds to this field for navigating the globe. It is suggested that Earth's magnetic field is produced

**(a)**

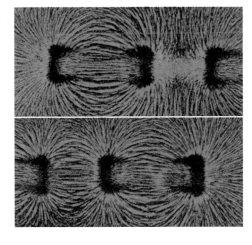

**Fig.17.4**   Visualizing 3D magnetic fields with iron filings

**(b)**

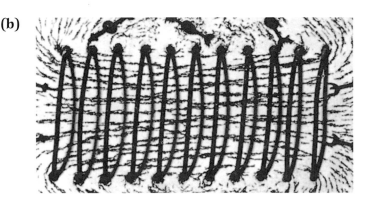

**Fig.17.5**   Earth's magnetic field

because of the flow of hot liquid metals inside Earth. This theory will make much more sense after we study the process of electromagnetic induction in the next chapter.

The interesting thing about magnetic forces is that they don't act just between two magnets. The magnet in Fig. 17.6 attracts certain metals that are not magnets. These metals are iron, nickel, and cobalt, or mixtures of these three. Collectively, they are called the **ferromagnetic metals**. In fact, it appears that all magnets are made up of these materials. A magnet will demonstrate that dimes and quarters are ferromagnetic, but that newer nickels and pennies are not.

Ferromagnetic elements have an atomic structure that seems to make them strongly magnetic. Think of magnetic materials as composed of a lot of smaller magnets in what is called the **domain theory of magnets**.

**Fig.17.6**   A magnet attracts ferromagnetic metals

> **Domain Theory** All large magnets are made up of many smaller and rotatable magnets, called **dipoles**, which can interact with other dipoles close by. If dipoles line up, then a small **magnetic domain** is produced.

Figure 17.7 illustrates how a nickel can be magnetized and attracted to a magnet when domains line up.

Although this theory does not explain how magnetic forces are generated, it helps to explain various interesting facts about the way magnets behave. Some of them are described in Table 17.1.

**Fig.17.7**   A pre 1982 nickel is magnetized by another magnet

Randomly pointing domains

Domains in same direction

N

Canadian nickels used to be made of nickel, but are now made of a copper–nickel alloy that is 75% copper and not ferromagnetic. Pennies used to be mostly copper; since 1997, they are mostly zinc.

| Table 17.1 | |
|---|---|
| **Explaining Magnetic Properties** | |
| Observation | Explanation with domain theory |
| **Magnetic induction** Ferromagnetic materials can be magnetized. Earth magnetizes railroad tracks and construction girders. | Domains that are pointing in random directions can be aligned if they are placed in a large field with a fixed direction. |
| **Demagnetization** Ferromagnetic materials can lose their magnetic strength. | Domains could lose their order and point in different directions, causing a dilution and overall weakening of the magnet. |
| **Reverse magnetization** The polarity of magnets can be reversed. | A large magnetic field pointing in the opposite direction causes all the domains to line up with the new field, reversing the overall magnetic polarity. |
| **Breaking of a large magnet** into smaller ones | In all the pieces, the domains still line up, so each acts like its own magnet. |
| **Maximum strength** A magnet can become only so strong and no more. | Once all the domains are aligned, there is no way to increase the magnet's strength any further. |

The strip on the back of your credit card stores your information and personal identification number along its length as a magnet of fluctuating strength.

Magnets are used in many places in society, but there are many applications where permanent magnets are impractical because they are of a set strength that can deteriorate over time. Also, they are always on and can never be shut off. In the next few sections, we will discuss how scientists were able to overcome these problems to produce strong, dependable, adjustable-strength magnets that you can shut off at will. These electromagnets are extremely useful in modern technology.

1. What are the similarities and differences among magnetic fields, electric fields, and gravitational fields?
2. Explain how two magnets are formed when one magnet is broken in two. How does this effect prove that a magnetic **monopole** does not exist?
3. How is the fact that magnetic field lines always form closed loops another way of saying that a magnet always has a north and a south pole?

## 17.2 Electromagnets

Force at a distance, the common element between electrostatics and magnetism, directed the research of many scientists, among them William Gilbert and Hans Christian Oersted. Much of their time was spent trying to find a link between the two forces. Oersted made an important discovery, summarized in Oersted's principle:

**Oersted's Principle** Charge moving through a conductor produces a circular magnetic field around the conductor.

Oersted's principle is illustrated in Fig. 17.8.

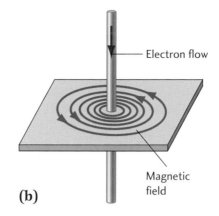

**Fig.17.8**   Oersted's principle

Electron flow

Magnetic field

**(a)**

**(b)**

Mapping the magnetic field allows you to predict the direction of the electromagnetic force from the current. Scientists have developed several hand signs to help you predict how magnetic forces act. They are called **left-hand rules** because they involve using your left hand. In general, these rules are like physical formulas because they allow you to take certain known factors and predict one unknown factor. Figure 17.9 shows how the **first left-hand rule for conductors** can be applied to Oersted's principle. In all, there are three left-hand rules. The first left-hand rule for conductors using Oersted's principle is abbreviated as LHR#1.

**Left-hand rule #1 for conductors** Grasp the conductor with your left hand such that the thumb points in the direction of electron (−) current flow. The curved fingers point in the direction of the circular magnetic field around the conductor.

**Fig.17.9**   Left-hand rule #1 (LHR#1)

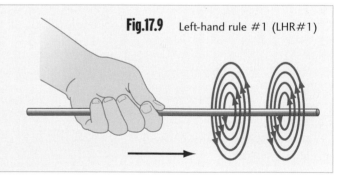

The examples given below will demonstrate how the first left-hand rule can be used to predict the direction of the magnetic field around a straight conductor.

**EXAMPLE 1**   **Using LHR#1**

a) In Fig. 17.10(a), given the direction of the current, find the direction of the magnetic field.

b) In Fig. 17.10(b), given the direction of the magnetic field, find the direction of the current.

**Right-hand rule #1 (RHR#1) (for conventional current flow)**

Grasp the conductor with the thumb of the right hand pointing in the direction of conventional, or positive (+), current flow. The fingers point in the direction of the magnetic field.

**Fig.17.10**

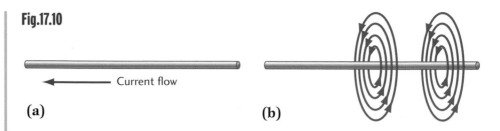

Current flow

**(a)**        **(b)**

### Solution and Connection to Theory

a) Using LHR#1, arrange your left hand so the thumb points in the direction of the current. The magnetic field points in the direction of your curled fingers, as shown in Fig. 17.11(a).

b) Use LHR#1 to curl your left hand around the conductor, with fingers pointing in the direction of the magnetic field. As shown in Fig. 17.11(b), your thumb points in the direction of the electron current flow.

**Fig.17.11**    Using LHR#1

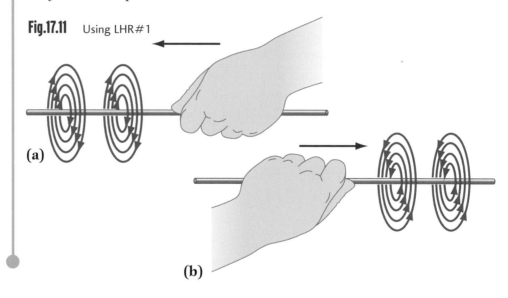

**(a)**

**(b)**

**Fig.17.12**    The magnetic field around a coiled conductor or **solenoid** is like that of a bar magnet

Now we can turn our magnet on and off when current flow through the conductor is interrupted, but the magnetic field produced is weak and circular. The next step in making the magnet more practical is to make it stronger and to straighten out its field to resemble that of a bar magnet. It may seem strange, but to straighten the curved magnetic field around a straight conductor, scientists curved the conductor, as shown in Fig. 17.12.

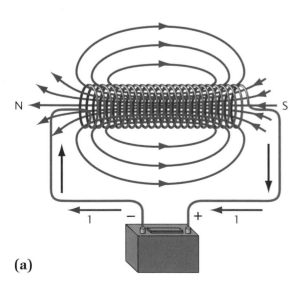

**(a)**

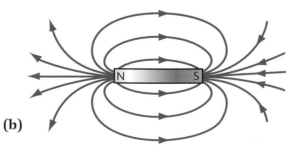

**(b)**

If the wire is coiled, the individual field lines fall on top of each other, thereby strengthening the overall field. Coiling the wire in a linear cylinder also straightens out the field. Figure 17.13 summarizes a **second left-hand rule for coils**.

---

**Left-hand rule #2 for coiled conductors** Grasp the coiled conductor with the left hand such that the curled fingers point in the direction of the electron (−) current flow through the conductor. The thumb points in the direction of the magnetic field within the coil. Outside the coil, the thumb represents the north (N) end of the electromagnet produced by the coil.

**Fig.17.13** Left-hand rule #2 (LHR#2) for coils

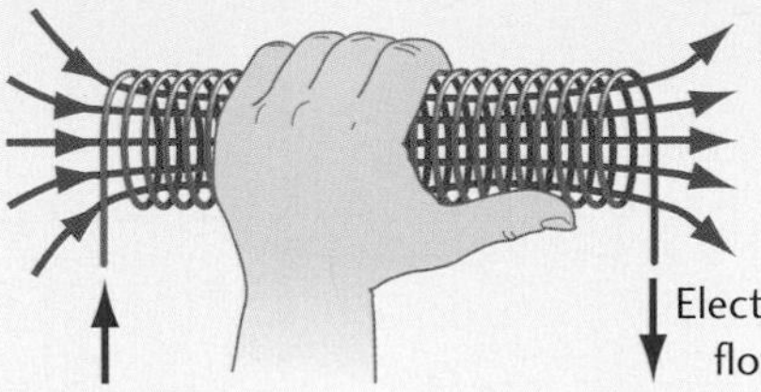

Electron flow

---

LHR#2 predicts the relationship between the direction of electron flow in a coil and the direction of the magnetic field at the end of the electromagnet.

We now have the ability to create a magnet that acts like a bar magnet but that can be turned off when it needs to be. The other advantage of this **electromagnet** is that the strength of the magnetic field ($B$), and therefore the magnetic force that it can produce, can be adjusted by changing some of the factors that affect the magnet's strength. These factors are summarized in Table 17.2.

**Right-hand rule #2 (RHR#2) (for conventional current flow)**

Grasp the coil with the right hand, with curved fingers pointing in the direction of conventional, or positive (+), current flow. The thumb points in the direction of the magnetic field, which is the north (N) end of the electromagnet produced by the coil.

| | Table 17.2 | |
|---|---|---|
| | **Factors that Determine the Strength of an Electromagnet** | |
| Factor | Description | |
| Current in the coil<br><br>$B_2 = B_1\left(\dfrac{I_2}{I_1}\right)$ | The greater the current flow, the greater the field strength. Strength *varies directly* as the current in the coil. | |
| Number of turns in the coil<br><br>$B_2 = B_1\left(\dfrac{n_2}{n_1}\right)$ | The greater the number of coils, the greater the field strength. Strength *varies directly* as the number of turns in the coil if the current is constant. | |
| Type of material in the coil's centre<br><br><br><br>$B_2 = B_1\left(\dfrac{\mu_2}{\mu_1}\right)$ | The more ferromagnetic the material within the coil, the greater the magnet's strength. Iron is one of the better materials to use.<br><br>Strength *varies directly* as the measure of the ferromagnetic properties (magnetic permeability, $\mu$) of the core material. | |
| Size of coil | The smaller the diameter of the coil, the stronger the magnetic field. | |

The term *varies directly* means that if one variable is increased, then the other is also increased by the same proportion. For example, if you double one variable, then the other variable is also doubled.

The magnetic field strength, $B$, is measured in units called **tesla (T)**. 1 T is the magnetic field strength when a 1 m long conductor, carrying a current of 1 A, crosses a magnetic field at 90°, experiencing a magnetic force of 1 N.

$$1\ T = \frac{1\ N}{A \cdot m}$$

> ## EXAMPLE 2 A magnetic field's strength

a) What happens to the strength of the magnetic field around a coil if the current through the conductor is increased from 1.0 A to 2.5 A?

b) What would happen to the field strength if the number of turns in the coil of the electromagnet were reduced by half and the current remained the same?

### Solution and Connection to Theory

**a) Given**

$$I_1 = 1.0 \text{ A} \qquad I_2 = 2.5 \text{ A} \qquad B_1 = B_1 \qquad B_2 = ?$$

Use the relationship for a direct proportionality.

$$B_2 = B_1 \left( \frac{I_2}{I_1} \right)$$

$$B_2 = B_1 \left( \frac{2.5 \text{ A}}{1.0 \text{ A}} \right)$$

$$B_2 = 2.5 B_1$$

Therefore, the new magnetic field strength is equal to 2.5 times the initial one.

**b) Given**

$$n_1 = n_1 \qquad n_2 = \tfrac{1}{2} n_1 \qquad B_1 = B_1 \qquad B_2 = ?$$

Once again, use the relationship for a direct proportionality.

$$B_2 = B_1 \left( \frac{n_2}{n_1} \right)$$

$$B_2 = B_1 \left( \frac{\tfrac{1}{2} n_1}{n_1} \right)$$

$$B_2 = \tfrac{1}{2} B_1$$

Therefore, the new field strength would be $\tfrac{1}{2}$ of the original.

**Fig.17.14** Creation of Magnetic Fields Around Current-carrying Conductors

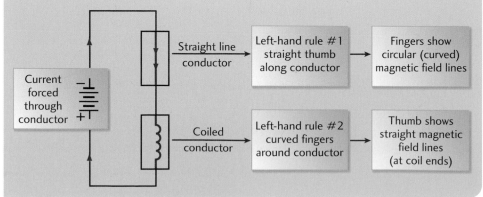

UNIT E: Electricity and Magnetism

1. State the two left-hand rules. What is the difference between the left- and right-hand rules?
2. What would happen to the magnetic field strength of a coil if
   a) the number of coils was increased from 2000 to 3000 windings?
   b) the current through the coil was increased from 3.0 A to 3.7 A?
   c) the permeability of the core was increased by a factor of two?
   d) the core size was increased by a factor of three?
   e) What is the overall strength change in the electromagnet if all these changes were made?

# 17.3 Applications of Electromagnetism

One purpose of research in electromagnetism was to produce a strong and adjustable magnet with maximum flexibility for engineers to apply in new technology. Table 17.3 summarizes some important applications of electromagnets.

**Table 17.3**
**Uses of Electromagnets**

| Description | Schematic | Photo |
|---|---|---|

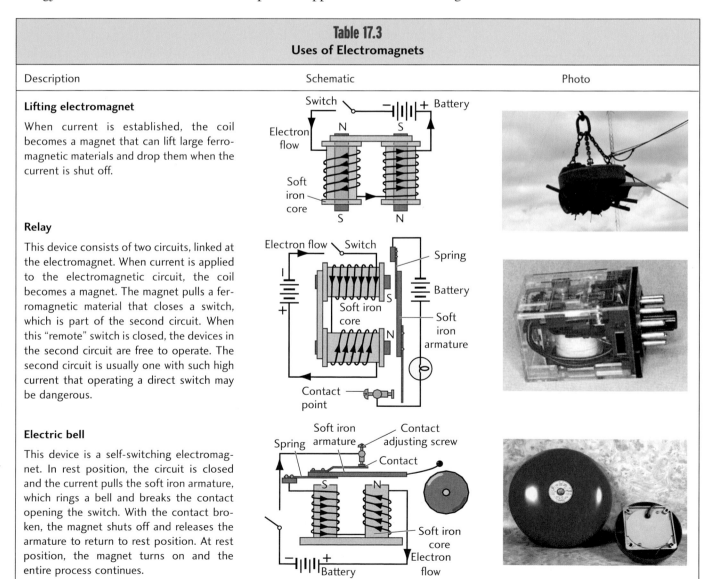

**Lifting electromagnet**

When current is established, the coil becomes a magnet that can lift large ferromagnetic materials and drop them when the current is shut off.

**Relay**

This device consists of two circuits, linked at the electromagnet. When current is applied to the electromagnetic circuit, the coil becomes a magnet. The magnet pulls a ferromagnetic material that closes a switch, which is part of the second circuit. When this "remote" switch is closed, the devices in the second circuit are free to operate. The second circuit is usually one with such high current that operating a direct switch may be dangerous.

**Electric bell**

This device is a self-switching electromagnet. In rest position, the circuit is closed and the current pulls the soft iron armature, which rings a bell and breaks the contact opening the switch. With the contact broken, the magnet shuts off and releases the armature to return to rest position. At rest position, the magnet turns on and the entire process continues.

**Fig.17.15** Drawing Field Maps

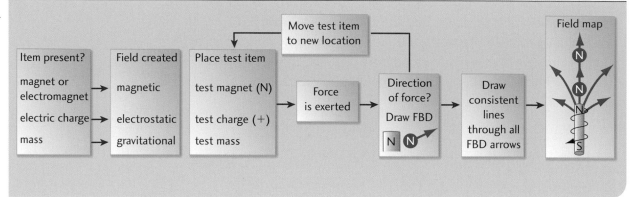

## 17.4 The Motor Principle and Its Applications

**Fig.17.16A**

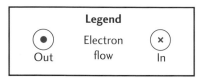

The invention of a completely adjustable magnet set the stage for scientists, such as Michael Faraday (1791–1867), to take the technology one step further. Faraday was the first person to create a device that used an electromagnet with permanent magnets to apply a directed force. The device was the first **electric motor**, which used the **motor principle** to apply this force in a continuous fashion. The motor principle involves a force produced on conductors when two magnetic fields interact, as shown in Fig. 17.16B.

**Fig.17.16B** When two fields interact

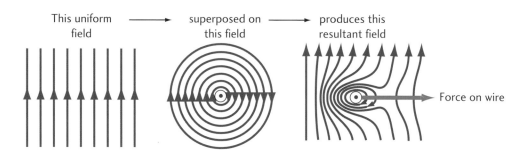

Now we can give the true definition of an ampere, which is based on the magnetic field around a conductor.

**One ampere** is the current through two parallel conductors, placed 1 m apart in a vacuum, that exert a force of $2 \times 10^{-7}$ N on each other for each metre of their length.

Two magnetic fields interact with one another to produce a force. If the conductor that carries a current cuts through an existing magnetic field, it experiences a force perpendicular to both the conductor's charge flow and the external magnetic field. The strength of this force depends on the strength of the external magnetic field and the current through the conductor.

Physicists must be able to consistently predict the direction of the force on the current-carrying conductor. The easiest way to remember the direction of force is to apply the **left-hand rule for the motor principle**, LHR#3.

**Left-hand rule #3; The motor principle** Open
your left hand so that your fingers point in the
direction of the magnetic field (from north to
south). Rotate the hand so that the thumb points in
the direction of electron (−) current flow. The orientation of the palm indicates the direction of the
force produced.

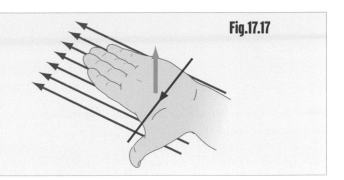

Fig.17.17

**Fig.17.18**  Left-hand Rule #3: The Motor Principle

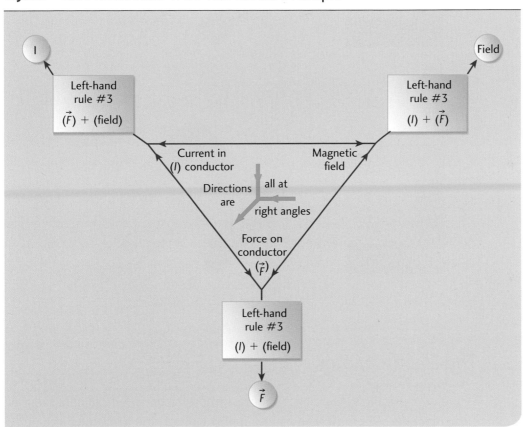

---

**EXAMPLE 3**    **Using LHR#3**

For the diagrams in Fig. 17.19, use the third left-hand rule for the motor
principle to show the unknown direction of the specified quantity.

### Solution and Connection to Theory

a) Here, the current direction and the magnet poles (field direction) are
   given. LHR#3 predicts the direction of force on the conductor (out of
   the magnet and to the right), as shown in Fig. 17.20(a).

**Right-hand rule #3 (RHR#3)
(for conventional current flow)**

Adapt LHR#3 by pointing the thumb
of the right hand in the direction of
positive (+) current flow. The rest of
the rule remains the same.

b) With the current direction and force given, LHR#3 predicts the direction of the magnetic field. Therefore, we can determine the polarity of the magnet, north at the bottom and south at the top, as shown in Fig. 17.20(b).

When the cross-section of a conductor is shown, a dot (•) represents electron current flowing out of the page, toward you. An X represents current flowing into the page.
The • and X notation for current flow relates to the two ends of an arrow. The dot (•) represents the point of the arrow coming towards you. The X represents the feathered fletching of the arrow moving away from you.

**Fig. 17.19**

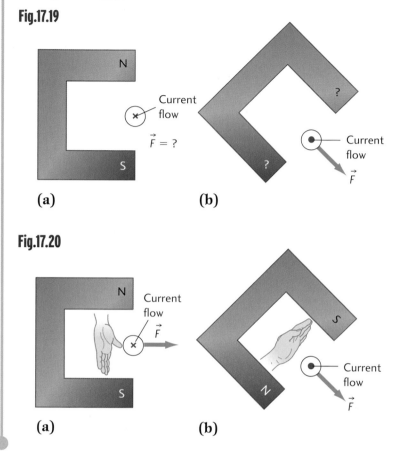

**Fig. 17.20**

## The Electric Motor

The motor principle describes the force produced between a magnet and an electromagnet. The most important application of this principle is the electric motor, a device that directs electric force full circle, without stopping part way. Figure 17.21 shows a simple St. Louis motor, an electric motor built from a few simple parts.

This basic direct-current (DC) motor has been adapted to make it safe, efficient, and cost-effective. In a DC motor, the electromagnet in the armature changes its polarity once every rotation. This polarity change is made because the split-ring commutator reverses the current flow in the armature. Figure 17.22 illustrates how an AC motor works using alternating current (AC). Because of the way it is generated, AC reverses its direction before it enters the motor. The current enters through two slip rings contacted by brushes. This way, an AC motor can take advantage of the natural current reversal of an AC circuit and not require a commutator.

**Fig.17.21** A simple electric motor

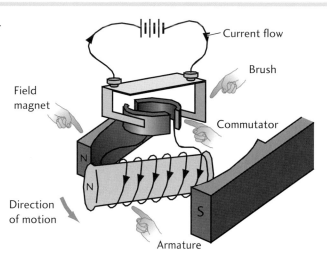

1. The current moves into the top curved, split-ring commutator (A) and is fed to the armature (coiled electromagnet) through the brushes. Applying the left-hand rule, the upper-left end of the armature is north. Repulsion from the field magnet rotates the armature clockwise.

2. The north and south ends of the armature are attracted to the opposite poles of the field magnet. Rotation continues until the brushes meet the split of the commutator.

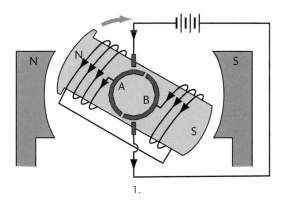

1.

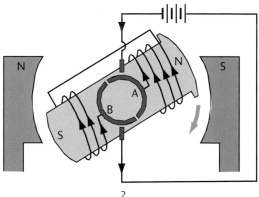

2.

3. The commutator split directs the current to the bottom commutator (B), causing a current-direction and magnetic-pole reversal in the armature. Once again, the upper-left-hand armature is north and the entire cycle begins again.

4. The continuous current flow reversal in the armature (due to the commutator) is responsible for the continuous operation of an electric motor.

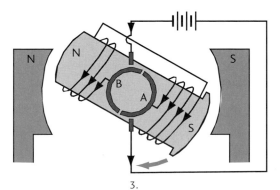

3.

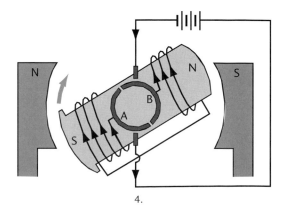

4.

**Fig.17.22** Alternating current (AC) enters a motor through slip rings

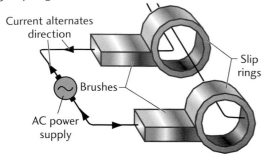

Current alternates direction

Brushes

AC power supply

Slip rings

**Fig.17.23** An AC (St. Louis) motor

In this AC motor, the current changes direction 60 times every second (in North America), which causes the polarity to change at the same rate in the armature. The AC motor can be made more reliable with slip rings instead of a split-ring commutator. Electric motors have many applications.

## Other Applications of the Motor Principle

The term "motor principle" refers to the way in which a force can be exerted on a current-carrying conductor passing through a magnetic field. The resulting force produced by the motor principle can be put to practical use in many ways. Table 17.4 outlines other uses of the motor principle.

| Table 17.4 |
| --- |
| **Applications of the Motor Principle** |

| Description |
| --- |

**Analog Galvanometer or Ammeter**

Used to measure even small electric currents, this device acts very much like an electric motor. A coil of wire connected to the test leads is surrounded by a horseshoe magnet. When current flows in the coil, it exerts a force characterized by the motor principle. The soft iron core and the attached pointer rotate against the force of the control spring.

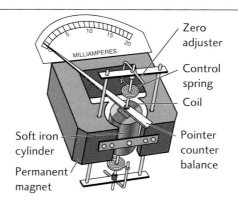

Zero adjuster

Control spring

Coil

Pointer counter balance

Soft iron cylinder

Permanent magnet

A moving-coil galvanometer

**Loudspeaker**

A loudspeaker reproduces sound waves by using the alternating current produced from the electronic sound signal. This oscillating current causes a sympathetic alternating of the loudspeaker's electromagnet. The alternating magnetic field reacts to the existing permanent magnet, resulting in oscillations in the paper cone. The oscillations produce the longitudinal sound waves we hear.

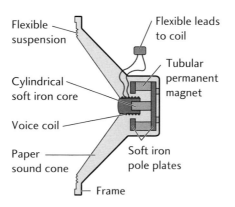

Flexible suspension

Flexible leads to coil

Cylindrical soft iron core

Tubular permanent magnet

Voice coil

Paper sound cone

Soft iron pole plates

Frame

A loudspeaker

1. Sketch a situation where the net force on a current-carrying wire is straight down, as you view your page from the top. Draw in the magnetic field lines of the permanent magnet and that of the conductor. Use field interactions to explain why the wire is forced downward.

2. Sketch the configurations needed to produce a net force
   a) up.
   b) to the right.
   c) to the left.
   d) of zero on a current-carrying wire.

## Superconductors Part 2: Maglev Trains

Superconductors were introduced in Chapter 16. Along with the property of conducting electricity with no resistive losses, these materials repel surrounding magnetic fields. This phenomenon is shown in the photo of magnets floating above a superconductor (Fig. 17.24A). The principle behind it is used in Maglev (magnetic levitation) trains, which float above the rails and can exceed speeds of 547 km/h.

There are three components to the Maglev rail system: a large electrical power source, metal coils lining the track, and guidance magnets attached to the undercarriage of the train. What is different about this system is the lack of an engine in the train. Instead, the coils in the track or guideway create a system of magnetic fields that pull and push the train. The constantly changing current in the coils changes the magnetic fields around the coils. The magnetic fields are arranged so that the train gets pulled from the front and pushed from the back.

As a result of magnetic levitation, the train floats 1 to 10 cm above the track. Levitation reduces track friction, allowing the train to reach remarkable speeds of over 500 km/h, twice as fast as most commuter trains and almost 70% the speed of a Boeing-777 commercial plane. The rail journey takes about the same time as a flight because of the ease of processing passengers and loading and unloading the train. If the power goes off and the levitation force is lost, the train settles down onto conventional wheels.

3. Pick a distance between two major cities and calculate the time it takes to fly from one place to another. Add processing time for tickets and loading of baggage (use typical times for airports). Then calculate the time it would take to go by Maglev train. Estimate the processing time it takes to get on a train. Remember that in most cases, you can bring your luggage on board yourself.

4. Research the current state of Maglev trains, especially in Japan, Germany, and the USA. Find out if there are any plans to build such systems in Canada. Relate the cost of constructing and maintaining such a system to that of conventional flight systems.

**Fig.17.24A**   Magnets float above a superconductor

© ISTEC, Tokyo, Japan. All rights reserved.

**Fig.17.24B**

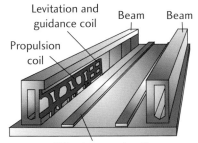

Levitation and guidance coil
Beam    Beam
Propulsion coil
Wheel support path

**Fig.17.24C**   A Maglev train

# Rail Guns, an Application of the Motor Principle

There has been much progress in the development of electric motors and related technology since the days of Oersted and Faraday. For example, the motion picture *Eraser*, starring Arnold Schwarzenegger, shows the potential of one application of the motor principle, the rail gun. A rail gun is an electromagnetic gun (Fig. STSE.17.1). Parallel rails, with electric current flowing up one side and down the other, create a magnetic field perpendicular to the rails. The magnetic field points out of the page in our diagram.

**Fig.STSE.17.1**  A simplified diagram of a rail gun

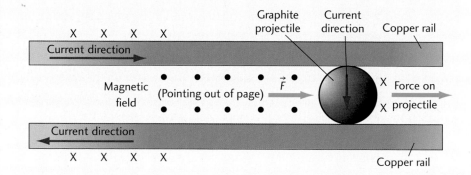

If current also passes through the projectile, the magnetic field around the projectile will force it up the rail and out of the gun, as described by the left-hand rule for the motor principle. With the fingers of the left hand pointing out of the page parallel to the magnetic field (left side of the projectile), the thumb points down the page, in the direction of current flow through the projectile. The palm then shows the direction of the force that launches the projectile.

Research on rail guns began in the 1980s with then President Ronald Reagan's Strategic Defense Initiative (SDI), also known as "Star Wars." The idea behind SDI was to use large ground- and satellite-based weapons, including rail guns, to shoot down incoming enemy missiles. When the Cold War ended, so did much of the research on these weapons. In 2001, President George W. Bush revived a new missile defense system. This program is known as NMD or the National Missile Defense program. It is estimated that rail guns need a launch speed of about 12 km/s. Thus far, some rail guns have been developed that can launch at about half that speed, with many compounded problems. Of the great amounts of power required, much of it is lost to heat. Also, the strong repulsive force between the rails can destroy the weapon.

Scientists are also developing non-military uses for rail guns. Achieving launch velocities greater than Earth's escape velocity would allow rail guns to launch satellites into orbit without the need for more expensive and environmentally damaging rockets. Rail guns are also being tested as a way to fire frozen hydrogen pellets into the core of a nuclear fusion reactor. Positive results could mean cheaper and more environmentally friendly sources of electrical energy than we currently have.

While still in the experimental stages, applications of rail guns show great promise. For now, the only place rail guns work is in the movies.

## Design a Study of Societal Impact

Electric and magnetic fields created by electronic equipment and electrical transformers are under investigation as potentially causing cancer and other negative health effects. Review current research on causes of cancer. Is the occurrence of cancer higher among people who live near hydro transmission lines or regularly use products such as cellular phones, waterbed heaters, and computers?

## Design an Activity to Evaluate

Evaluate the performance of an electric motor using either a commercially available motor kit or one of your own design. Measure changes in the rotation speed of the armature as you vary conditions, such as changing the number of armature coils, the input voltage, and the resistance.

## Build a Structure

Build an electric motor you designed or improve the design of an electric motor from a kit. Test your motor by connecting it to a crank that winches a mass (container of water). The best motor is the one that can lift the largest weight or provide the most power by lifting a weight the fastest.

Build an electromagnet of your design or improve the design of an electromagnet from a kit. The best electromagnet will be able to lift the greatest weight.

Attempt to build a rail gun launcher using a metal I-beam curtain-rod and curtain rod pulley rollers.

## SPECIFIC EXPECTATIONS

**You should be able to**

*Understand Basic Concepts:*
- Describe the three-dimensional properties of magnetic fields and relate them to the concept of force at a distance.
- Illustrate and describe the magnetic field produced around a straight and a coiled (solenoid) conductor.
- Analyze and predict the direction of the magnetic field produced when current flows through a straight or coiled (solenoid) conductor using both the left- and right-hand rules.
- State the motor principle and explain the factors that affect the force on a current-carrying conductor in a magnetic field.
- Use the left- and right-hand rules to illustrate the resulting motion of a conductor in a magnetic field.

*Develop Skills of Inquiry and Communication:*
- Design and carry out experiments using iron filings and compasses that identify and describe the various properties of magnetic fields.
- Illustrate and interpret the shape and structure of magnetic fields from their visible effects on iron filings or compasses.
- Design and construct a device that uses the principles of electromagnetism, such as a rail gun.
- Outline how some scientific conventions, such as conventional (positive (+)) current flow may become outdated upon further experimentation and discovery.

*Relate Science to Technology, Society, and the Environment:*
- Analyze and describe the operation of an electric motor, rail gun, Maglev train, or other system based on electromagnetism or the motor principle.
- Identify the historical developments of technology involving electric motors and electromagnets.

**Summary of Left-hand Rules**

*LHR#1 (conductors)*
  Thumb of left hand points in direction of electron current flow, fingers point in direction of circular magnetic field around conductor.
*LHR#2 (coiled conductors)*
  Curled fingers of left hand point in direction of electron current flow, thumb points in direction of magnetic field within coil.
*LHR#3 (motor principle)*
  Fingers of open left hand point in direction of magnetic field (north to south), thumb points in direction of electron current flow, palm indicates direction of force.

## Conceptual Questions

1. Summarize the law of magnetic forces.

2. Why does a magnet attract other, non-magnetic material?

3. What do you call the type of material that is attracted to a magnet or can be magnetized? Give at least two examples of this type of material.

4. What is strange about the north end of a compass pointing to the northern part of Earth?

5. What is meant by the domain theory of magnets? How does it explain why magnets lose their strength over time?

6. Use the domain theory to explain what happens to a magnet when it is dropped or heated.

7. How can a magnet have its polarity reversed?

8. Draw a magnetic field map around a small bar magnet. How can you tell from this field map where the field is strongest?

9. What is the left-hand rule for straight conductors?

10. How would the strength of a magnetic field around a straight conductor vary as the distance away from the conductor increases?

11. What are some of the advantages to coiling a conductor to make an electromagnet?

12. Using Oersted's principle and LHR#1, illustrate how looping a wire back on itself in a linear fashion (making a coil) will affect the overall shape and strength of the magnetic field.

13. Why does a smaller-diameter coil result in a stronger electromagnet?

14. What practical role does a piece of ferromagnetic material at the core of an electromagnet serve?

15. a) List at least three examples of where electromagnets are used in society.
    b) For each example, describe at least one safety hazard that this technology may cause or prevent.

16. Summarize the left-hand rule for the motor principle.

17. Sketch the field lines around the cross-section of two parallel wires when the current flows
    a) in opposite directions, as shown in Fig. 17.25(a).
    b) in the same direction (out of the page), as shown in Fig. 17.25(b).
    c) On each diagram, show whether the two wires will be attracted to one another or repelled.

**Fig.17.25**

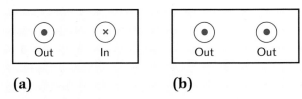

(a)                              (b)

18. Although a motor will work with a permanent field magnet, why is it preferable to make motors with two electromagnets?

19. Sketch a simple electric motor that uses an electromagnet as the field magnet.

## Problems

### 17.2 Electromagnets

20. Copy the following images into your notebook. For each current-carrying conductor, sketch a view of the magnetic field, based on the direction of current flow shown.

    a) **Fig.17.26**

**b) Fig.17.27**

**c) Fig.17.28**

**d) Fig.17.29**

**e) Fig.17.30**

**21.** Copy the following images into your notebook. For each current-carrying conductor, show the direction of electron current flow, based on the structure of the magnetic field shown.

**a) Fig.17.31**

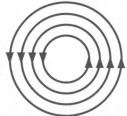

**b) Fig.17.32**

**c) Fig.17.33**

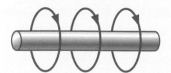

**d) Fig.17.34**

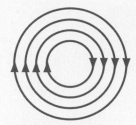

**e) Fig.17.35**

**f) Fig.17.36**

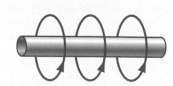

**22.** Copy the following images of a solenoid (an electromagnetic coil) into your notebook. For each current-carrying coil, sketch a view of the magnetic field around the coil, based on the direction of current flow shown. On each, label the polarity (north and south) of the electromagnet.

**a) Fig.17.37**

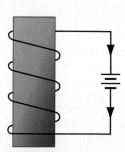

**b) Fig.17.38**

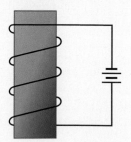

**c)** **Fig.17.39**

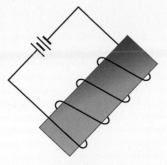

**d)** **Fig.17.40**

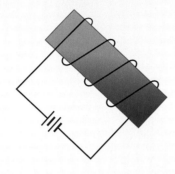

**23.** Copy the following images of solenoids into your notebook. For each coil, show the direction of electron flow that would cause the labelled magnetic polarity.

**a)** **Fig.17.41**

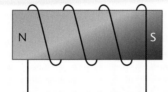

**b)** **Fig.17.42**

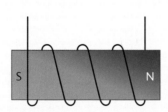

**24.** A standard electromagnet has 250 turns. When activated by a current of 1.0 A, it can lift with a force of 10 N. What would happen to the magnetic force if

**a)** the number of turns was increased to 400 without changing the length of the wire in the coil?

**b)** the current was increased by a factor of two?

**c)** the current was reduced to 0.75 A but the number of coils was changed to 500 turns without changing the length of the wire?

**25. a)** The electromagnet in a doorbell operates on a 12 V circuit with 500 turns in the solenoid. The bell had to be moved and needed more wire, which was provided by unwinding 100 turns from the solenoid. What new voltage would have to be provided to the circuit to get the doorbell to do the same job?

**b)** The electrician uncoiled 100 turns of wire and then cut them off by mistake. What voltage would be required by the doorbell now?

## 17.4 The Motor Principle and Its Applications

**26.** Copy the following images into your notebook. For all cases, indicate the field magnet poles (N or S), the current direction, field lines, and the direction of force on the conductors.

**a)** Show the direction of the magnetic field and the direction of force on the conductor in Fig. 17.43(a).

**Fig.17.43**

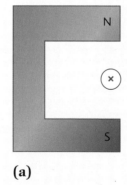

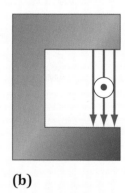

**(a)**                                    **(b)**

**b)** Show the labels of the magnetic poles and the direction of force on the conductor in Fig. 17.43(b).

**27.** Copy the following images into your notebook. For all cases, indicate the field magnet poles (N or S), the current direction, and the direction of force on the conductors.

**a)** Show the labels of the magnetic field and the direction of electron current flow through the conductor in Fig. 17.44(a).

**Figure 17.44**

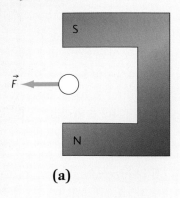

(a)

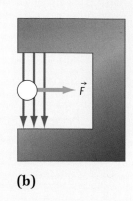

(b)

**b)** Show the labels of the magnetic poles and the direction of force on the conductor in Fig. 17.44(b).

**28.** Copy the following images into your notebook. For all cases, indicate the field magnet poles (N or S), the current direction, and the direction of force on the conductors. Show the labels of the magnetic field and the magnetic poles for each of the diagrams in Fig. 17.45.

**Figure 17.45**

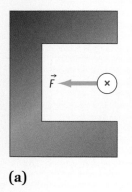

(a)

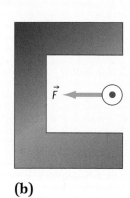

(b)

**29.** Refer to the following diagrams that involve the motor principle. For each diagram, show which way the loop would tend to turn.

**a) Fig.17.46**　　　　**b) Fig.17.47**

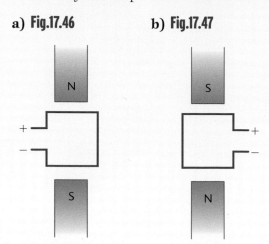

**30.** Review the following diagram of a simplified DC electric motor. Describe the path of current through the conductor, brushes, commutator, and coil by adding arrows. Identify the magnetic polarity of the armature and the rotation direction of the motor.

**Fig.17.48**

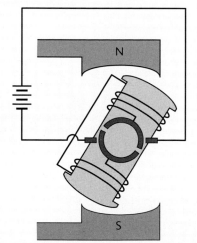

## Purpose

To trace the shape and structure of the magnetic fields around various magnets and electromagnets.

## Safety Consideration

Be careful not to spill iron filings because they can cause slivers. Be sure to keep the current low through the circuits because the wires may produce quite a bit of heat.

## Equipment

Various permanent magnets (fridge magnets, bar and horseshoe magnets, etc.)

Various electromagnets (wire-wrapped nail, simple school/homemade coil, single conductor)

Alligator clip patch wires, variable DC power supply, Knife switch

Paper and/or cardboard sheet

Blank overhead transparencies

Glycerine-filled magnetic field demonstration apparatus (if available), Iron filings

5 to 10 small test compasses

Ringstand (retort stand), Corrugated cardboard

### Fig.Lab.17.1

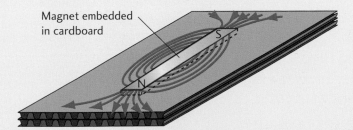

Magnet embedded in cardboard

## Procedure

Part A

1. Lay several layers of corrugated cardboard on the desk and place your permanent magnets on it.

2. Trace around each magnet with a pencil, then cut out a pocket for each magnet to sit in. These pockets should be designed so that the magnets sit flush with the top layer (see Fig. Lab.17.1). Keep these magnet holders for later labs.

3. Place a blank overhead transparency over the magnet arrays and shake some iron filings onto the transparency. Gently tap the surface of the transparency to allow the filings to be distributed evenly across its surface.

4. Place another overhead transparency on top of the iron filings in order to sandwich the loose filings. Then place several small test compasses randomly on the top transparency.

5. On the top transparency, trace estimated field lines that point toward the north ends of the test compasses using the overhead transparency marker. Follow the smooth lines defined by the iron filings. Draw enough lines to record a reasonable image of the magnetic field.

6. On the top transparency, trace the shapes of the magnets using the overhead transparency marker, then remove the transparency sheets from the cardboard. Carefully transfer the iron filings back into their original container.

**Fig.Lab.17.2**

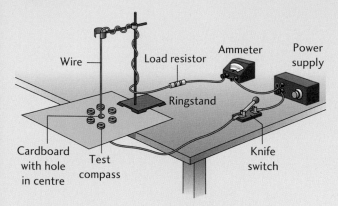

Wire — Load resistor    Ammeter    Power supply
Ringstand
Cardboard with hole in centre    Test compass    Knife switch

**Part B**

1. Set up a single conductor passing through a piece of cardboard and attach it to a variable power supply, as shown in Fig. Lab.17.2.

2. Place an overhead-transparency-and-iron-filings sandwich on the cardboard, as you did in Part A. Use blank overhead transparency sheets. Place test compasses randomly on the top overhead transparency.

3. Turn on the power supply and adjust it so that the test compasses are noticeably affected by the magnetic field. Using the overhead transparency marker, trace the magnetic field lines on the top transparency, carefully noting which way the test compasses are pointing.

4. Repeat the experiment with different types of electromagnets to see the shapes of their magnetic fields.

5. Carefully dismantle the equipment and return the iron filings to their container.

## Data

No uncertainty measurements are required here because the lab is a qualitative one.

## Uncertainty

On each overhead transparency, be sure to label the original positions and orientations of the magnets.

## Discussion

1. Where is the magnetic field strongest? weakest? Be sure to mark these extremes on the field map diagrams.

2. On each field map, draw at least one test compass and show which way it should be pointing in your field.

## Conclusion

Submit to your teacher a well-labelled field map for at least four different magnetic fields.

# LAB 17.2 The Motor Principle

## Purpose

To examine the factors that affect the magnitude and direction of force from the motor principle.

## Safety Consideration

1. To prevent a short circuit, make sure that no bare copper wires in the circuit are touching each other.
2. Be sure to have your teacher examine your experimental set-up before you turn on the power supply.

## Equipment

Two bar magnets or one horseshoe magnet
Electric magnetizer
One metre of insulated copper wire (8 to 12 gauge)
Two retort stands
Two retort stand clamps
Two #4 – #6 single-hole rubber stoppers
Several layers of corrugated cardboard sheets
Variable power supply (with ammeter/voltmeter)
One ammeter and voltmeter, if not included with variable power supply
Several alligator clip wires
One load resistor

**Fig.Lab.17.3**

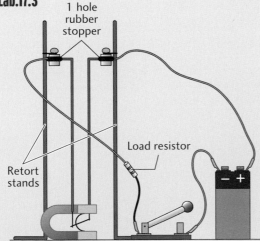

Retort stands

1 hole rubber stopper

Load resistor

## Procedure

1. Prepare an experimental record chart, as shown in Fig. Lab. 17.4. Refer to Fig. Lab. 17.5, the current-direction legend, to assign the current direction for each part of the experiment.

**Fig.Lab.17.4**

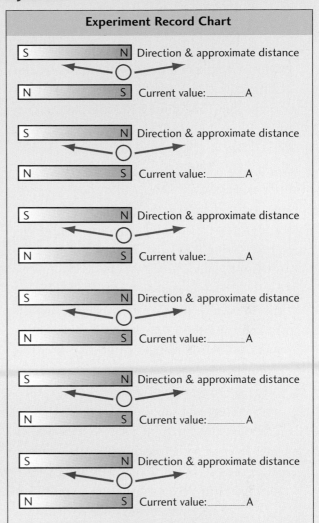

Experiment Record Chart

2. Set up the apparatus, as outlined in Fig. Lab. 17.3. Bend the wire to form a square-bottomed "U" shape that is about 20 cm wide. Carefully remove the wire insulation on the lower portion of the "U" only. Bend out and strip the insulation from two "wing-shaped" wires to rest in the rubber stoppers, as shown in the diagram.

Note: Remember to keep the bent wire to place in a kit for your teacher to use in another class.

**Fig.Lab.17.5**

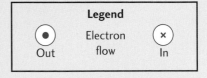

Legend

⊙ Out      Electron flow      ⊗ In

3. Arrange the entire apparatus as shown such that the horizontal bare wire passes between the separated bar magnets.

4. Stop and predict. Use LHR#3 for the motor principle to predict what will happen to the electromagnetic "swing" that you have just constructed. The wire will either swing out or in when you apply current to the circuit. Write your prediction on the record chart along with the full description of the experimental scenario.

5. Pass a direct current of less than 1 A through the circuit and note what happens to the "swing." Record the value of the current you applied.

6. Continue to experiment by recording the experimental set-up/scenario, predicting the outcome, and then noting the true results for the following variations:

a) Remagnetize the original bar magnets/ horseshoe magnet and keep all other parameters the same.

b) Increase the current flow by a factor of two and keep all other parameters the same.

c) Reverse the current flow (interchange the electrical leads at the power supply) and keep all other parameters the same.

d) Reverse the polarity of the bar magnets/ horseshoe magnet and keep all other parameters the same.

## Uncertainty

This lab is qualitative in nature, so no uncertainty measures are required.

## Discussion

1. Did the direction of force on the current-carrying conductor match with your prediction, based on LHR#3? If not, discuss with your teacher.

2. What noticeable difference occurred when
a) the magnetic field was increased?
b) the current was increased?
c) the current was reversed?
d) the magnetic field was reversed?

3. What is the purpose of the load resistor in the circuit?

## Conclusion

Make a final concluding statement that summarizes how the various parameters affect the strength and direction of the force on the current-carrying conductor.

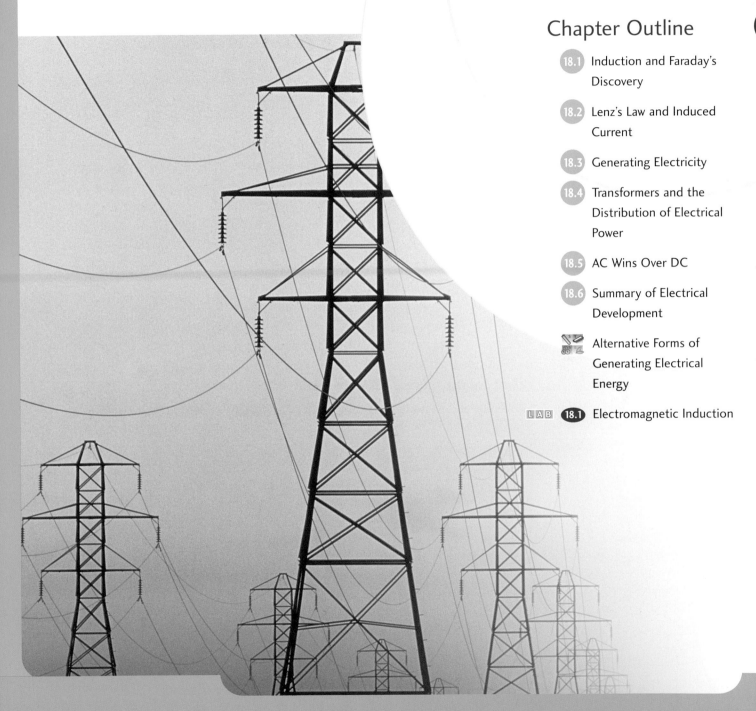

# Electromagnetic Induction and Its Applications

## Chapter Outline

### By the end of this chapter, you will be able to

- describe the integral relationship between current flow, magnetism, and electromagnetic induction, applying Oersted's and Faraday's principles
- relate the structure and function of an electromagnetic generator
- outline the differences between DC and AC in generators and transformers

# 18.1 Induction and Faraday's Discovery

In Chapters 16 and 17, we saw the importance of moving charge for transferring electrical energy and making electromagnets work for us. If moving electrons (current) in a conductor create a magnetic field, can a magnetic field be used to create current?

In 1831, Michael Faraday (1791–1867) discovered an effect that complemented Oersted's principle of a magnetic field created by a moving charge. **Faraday's law of electromagnetic induction** states:

> A magnetic field that is moving or changing intensity near a conductor *causes* or *induces* electron flow in the conductor.

**Fig.18.1**   Current flows through a conductor in a changing magnetic field

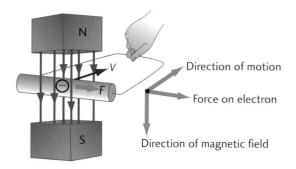

Direction of motion

Force on electron

Direction of magnetic field

Figure 18.1 illustrates how moving a conductor near a magnetic field causes a very small current to flow in the conductor.

Our knowledge of conductors and electromagnets helps us predict that coiling the wire into a helix with a smaller cross-sectional area makes a big difference in the amount of current produced.

In Fig. 18.2, our magnet causes current to flow when plunged into or pulled out of a coil of wire.

Putting the magnet into the coil pushes current in one direction, but pulling it out causes the current to move in the opposite direction. Moving the magnet in and out continuously causes the current to move back and forth continuously in what is called an **alternating current (AC)**. If you stop moving the magnet, the current also stops.

**Fig.18.2**   Coiling a conductor induces a larger current

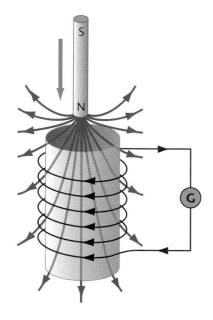

If current flow can create a magnetic field (Oersted's principle), then a moving magnetic field can, in turn, cause current to flow. Figure 18.3 shows a diagram of Faraday's iron ring apparatus that summarizes the connection between the two principles of electricity and magnetism.

**Fig.18.3**   Faraday's iron ring apparatus

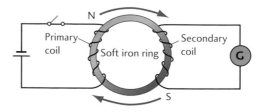

With no electrical connection between the two coils, the primary coil on the left causes the entire ring to become an electromagnet (Oersted's principle), with the north end at the top and the south end at the bottom. The ring formation simulates a north magnet entering the top of the secondary coil, which induces current to flow (Faraday's principle). Once the entire magnetic field is established, the induced current in the secondary coil stops flowing, just as it did in the coil in Fig. 18.2, when the magnet stopped moving. When the electromagnet is shut off, the current begins to flow again briefly, but in reverse, and the induced field collapses as though the north magnet was removed. This example illustrates the necessity for a constantly changing, dynamic magnetic field to keep this current flowing, even if the current alternates its direction. The iron ring apparatus is the basis for a major practical application of this technology, the **transformer**.

**Fig.18.4** Oersted's and Faraday's Principles Complement Each Other

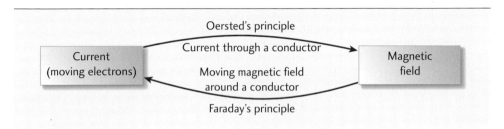

◄ ◄ ◄ ◄ CONNECTING the Concepts

1. The factors that affect the strength of a magnetic field in a solenoid (electromagnetic coil) are the number of windings, the diameter of the coil, and the permeability of the core. Faraday discovered that a changing magnetic field in the vicinity of a coil causes a current to flow. Describe how you could maximize the amount of electricity produced using these factors. (Remember that the speed at which you move the magnet is also important.)
2. Describe the difference between AC and DC and the manner in which each can be produced.
3. Why are batteries DC rather than AC?

◄ ◄ ◄ ◄ APPLYING the Concepts

# 18.2 Lenz's Law and Induced Current

If we apply the **law of conservation of energy** to **electromagnetic induction**, we realize that the electrical energy induced in a conductor must originate in some other form of energy. Figure 18.2 also illustrates that this energy might be transferred from the kinetic energy involved in the moving magnetic field. The increase in the induced current's electrical potential energy causes a decrease in the kinetic energy of the moving magnetic field. This decrease in kinetic energy is felt as an "opposition" to the moving field. The only thing that can oppose the motion of a magnetic field is another magnetic field. The electrical potential or the **electromotive force (EMF)** developed as a result of the induced current depends on the speed and strength of the inducing magnetic field and the number of turns and cross-sectional area of the induction coil.

Note the operative word in Lenz's law is to "oppose" and not "repel."

Both the induced current and the induced electric potential are related by **Ohm's law** so that

$$V = IR \quad \text{(Ohm's law)}$$
$$\therefore V_{\text{induced}} = I_{\text{induced}}R$$

German physicist Heinrich Lenz formally noted the relationship between the direction of movement of the inducing magnetic field and the direction of induced charge flow.

> **Lenz's Law** The direction of the induced current creates an induced magnetic field that *opposes* the motion of the inducing magnetic field.

Lenz reasoned that the magnetic field's motion was opposed by an induced magnetic field that was being fed by the induced current flow. The result is that you can predict the direction of current flow using the **left-hand rule #2**, as outlined in Fig. 18.6.

---

**EXAMPLE 1**  **Direction of induced current flow**

In the situations illustrated in Fig. 18.5(a) and (b), use Lenz's law to predict which way the induced current will flow in the coil.

**Fig.18.5**

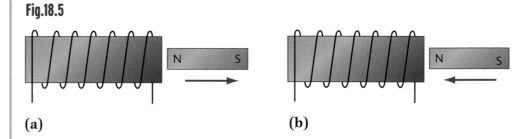

**(a)**                                    **(b)**

*Solution and Connection to Theory*

a) Lenz's law predicts that to oppose an outgoing north magnet, a south magnet must be induced at the end of the coil. In this example, the coil must be grasped with the thumb of the left hand pointing to the left, as shown. The LHR#2 for solenoids predicts that the electron current flow is as shown in Fig. 18.6(a).

**Fig.18.6**

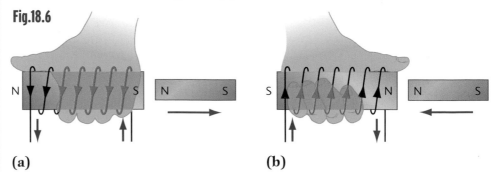

**(a)**                                    **(b)**

b) Lenz's law predicts that to oppose an incoming north magnet, a north magnet must be induced at the end of the coil. For this example, the coil must be grasped with the thumb of the left hand pointing to the right, as shown. The LHR#2 for solenoids predicts that the electron current flow is as shown in Fig. 18.6(b). This direction is exactly opposite to that in the previous question.

**Fig.18.7**  Lenz's Law and LHR#2

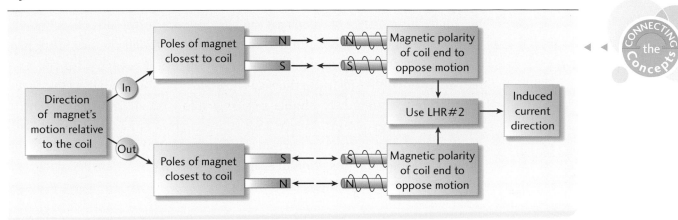

1. Draw and indicate the direction of the current flow for the following situations:
   a) A north pole entering a coil wound counterclockwise
   b) A north pole exiting a coil wound counterclockwise
   c) A south pole entering a coil wound clockwise
   d) A south pole exiting a coil wound clockwise
2. If the current induced by the motion of the magnet produced a force helping the action, what would be the implications for the law of conservation of energy?

# 18.3 Generating Electricity

Faraday's discovery, coupled with Lenz's law as a tool to predict current flow, gives us a practical device that is capable of generating electrical potential energy. This device, an **electric generator**, is made up of a permanent magnet and coils of wire, all cleverly designed to produce a continuous flow of electric current when there is an input of some rotational mechanical energy. The simplified generator, shown in Fig. 18.8, illustrates how this rotational mechanical energy can be used to generate electric current.

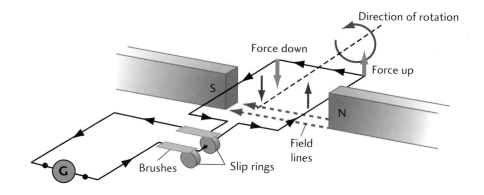

**Fig.18.8** A simplified electric generator

When rotated, the armature is pushed through the field lines of the magnet and consequently develops an induced current in the direction shown. Lenz's law dictates that the direction of current through the armature proceeds in one direction for the first half-rotation, but is reversed for the next half-rotation as the side from the right now descends on the left. If the armature rotates continuously, simple slip rings allow an alternating current to flow out of the generator. Figure 18.9 shows a standard AC generator with an armature, and a graph of current vs. the number of rotations. The graph shows how current rises and falls before it reverses direction (becomes negative) in the second half-rotation.

**Fig.18.9** A simplified AC generator

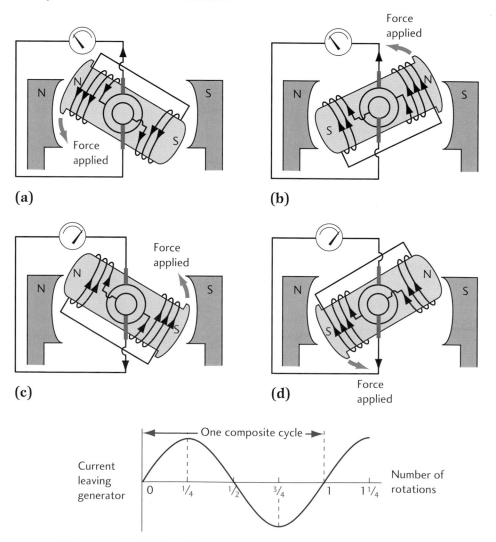

UNIT E: Electricity and Magnetism

In order to generate a direct current (DC), engineers use a split-ring commutator, the same piece of equipment required in a direct-current motor.

The commutator re-reverses the natural current flip that occurs in one cycle of generation to produce the direct current (DC).

The current is at its greatest magnitude when the conductors are breaking the inducing magnetic field at 90°.

If several separate armatures are equally spaced in the core, then the overall direct current produced is smoothed out to look more like one consistent value, as described in Fig. 18.10. The more armatures, the more efficiently one can produce electrical energy on a large scale.

In modern, large-scale generators, the rotational mechanical energy for the generator must be provided by a spinning turbine. Figure 18.11 illustrates that the turbine can be driven by the gravitational potential energy of falling water or by the expanding steam produced from either nuclear reactions or the burning of fossil fuels such as coal, oil, or natural gas.

**Fig.18.10**   DC from a generator

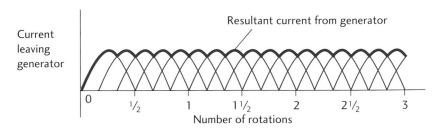

In a car, an AC generator or **alternator** produces AC, which is electronically converted to DC to charge the battery and run electric components.

**Fig.18.11**   Large-scale generators

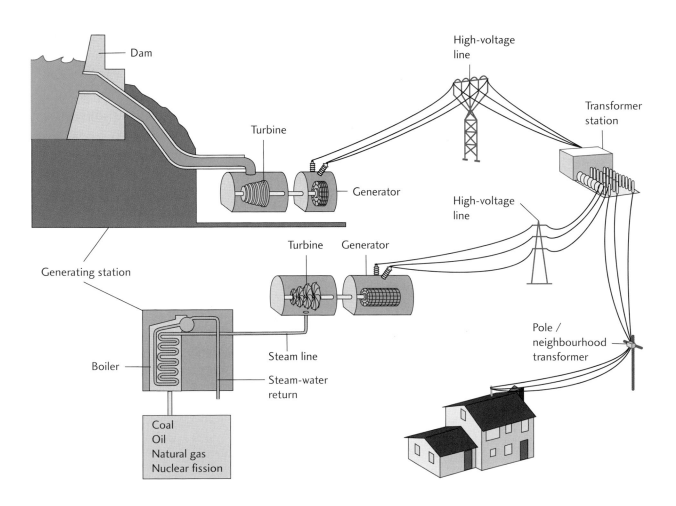

1. How are generators and motors related?
2. Compare the structural differences of the DC and AC generators, including the application of a split-ring commutator.

### Tidal Power

Tides are a storage house of energy created by the Moon's gravitational pull. The origin of tides was explained by Newton's universal law of gravity (Chapter 5).

**Fig.18.12A**   High and low tide at the Bay of Fundy

The highest tides occur in the Minas Basin, at the extremity of the Bay of Fundy in New Brunswick (Fig. 18.12A). The average tide range (high tide to low tide) in the Minas Basin is an incredible 12 m, sometimes reaching 15 m! Part of this great difference in water level is due to mechanical resonance (Chapter 14). The period of the tide motion in the Bay of Fundy is almost the same as the tidal period caused by the Moon (about 12.5 hours).

When water flows through a tidal barrage, it drops to a lower level (see Fig. 18.12B), allowing its potential energy of position to be converted to kinetic energy of motion. A turbine converts this energy to electrical energy. Depending on the type of system used, the turbines can operate either in one direction or two (at ebb tide and/or flood tide). Some tidal stations can produce 320 MW of energy.

**Fig.18.12B**

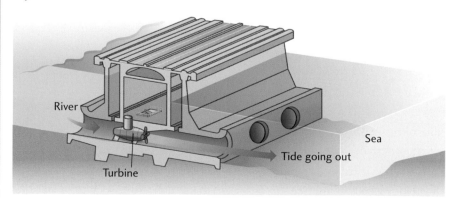

3. Research how tides are produced. Explain why there are two bulges of water (areas of high tide), one on each side of Earth, at the same time.

4. When you push a person on a swing with a constant force, the person swings higher and higher with each push. The energy of this to-and-fro motion is at a frequency that is easy for the system to absorb. Research how the tidal action of the Bay of Fundy is amplified through resonance.

5. Research two-way tidal power systems and ebb-generating systems. Compare their efficiency and cost-effectiveness.

6. What problems are associated with tidal power? Consider environmental and ecosystem concerns as well as the cost-effectiveness of these power generators.

**Fig.18.12C** The effect of the Sun and Moon on spring tides

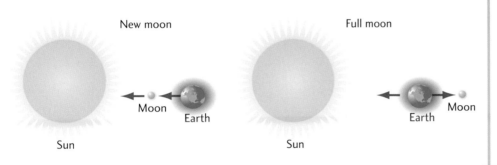

## 18.4 Transformers and the Distribution of Electrical Power

We have found that the fundamental type of current we generate is an alternating current because it requires no commutator. An electric motor needs alternating current in its armature so that it can turn continuously. To make this happen in a DC motor, a commutator is required. These are important reasons why AC current has become the standard in North America, but there is one other reason that needs to be examined. AC current is the only type of current that can be transformed from one electrical potential to another. Faraday's iron ring apparatus was the predecessor of the modern transformer, which is used to change electric potential.

The simple transformer, shown in Fig. 18.13, uses both Faraday's principle and Oersted's principle to transform current and voltage in a circuit. The primary side uses an alternating current to produce an electromagnet. The changing magnetic field in the secondary side uses Faraday's principle to produce a new alternating current. If the number of turns in the primary and secondary sides of the transformers is different, then the voltage on the primary and secondary is different. Increasing the number of turns ($N$) in the secondary compared to the primary increases the secondary voltage proportionally, i.e.,

$$\frac{V_P}{V_S} = \frac{N_P}{N_S}.$$

The overriding principle for a transformer is that the power dissipated in its primary and secondary sides must be the same. The current and electrical potential in the primary side complement each other so that their product, power, remains the same.

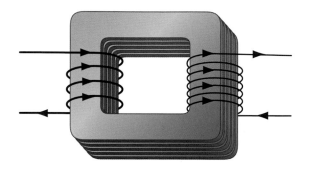

**Fig.18.13** A step-up transformer

$$P_{\text{Primary}} = P_{\text{Secondary}}$$

$$I_P V_P = I_S V_S$$

$$\therefore \frac{V_P}{V_S} = \frac{I_S}{I_P}$$

Factor in the number of turns, $N$, on the primary and secondary sides ($N_P$ and $N_S$):

$$\frac{V_P}{V_S} = \frac{I_S}{I_P} = \frac{N_P}{N_S}$$

If the number of turns in the secondary side is greater than in the primary side, then the resulting secondary electrical potential will be *stepped up*, making this a **step-up transformer**. A **step-down transformer** produces a secondary electrical potential less than that of the primary side. Of course, in both cases, whenever the electrical potential is stepped up, the current is stepped down to compensate and make the power dissipation the same for both sides. Figure 18.14 summarizes the relationship between transformer parameters.

**Fig.18.14** Voltage and Current Changes in a Transformer

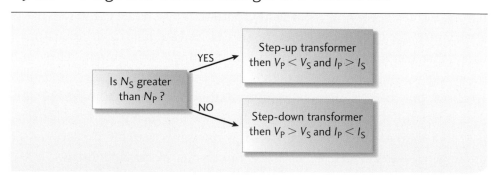

**EXAMPLE 2**  **Secondary voltage and current**

a) Figure 18.15 shows a transformer with a primary voltage of 20 V. What is the secondary voltage?

b) What is the secondary output current if the power dissipated in the transformer is 100 W?

UNIT E: Electricity and Magnetism

**Fig.18.15**

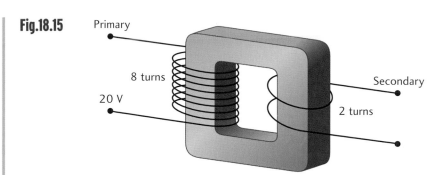

## *Solution and Connection to Theory*

### a) Given

$V_P = 20$ V     $N_P = 8$ turns     $N_S = 2$ turns     $V_S = ?$

Rearrange the transformer equation for $V_S$, substitute all variables, and solve.

$$\frac{V_P}{V_S} = \frac{N_P}{N_S}$$

$$V_S = \frac{N_S}{N_P}(V_P)$$

$$V_S = \frac{2}{8}(20 \text{ V})$$

$$V_S = 5 \text{ V}$$

Therefore, the secondary voltage is 5 V.

### b) Given

$P = 100$ W     $V_P = 20$ V     $N_P = 8$ turns     $N_S = 2$ turns     $I_S = ?$

This problem could be solved in two ways: (i) Find the primary current, $I_P$, using the power relationship, then solve for $I_S$ or (ii) use the power relationship and the secondary voltage.

$$P = I_P V_P$$

$$\therefore I_P = \frac{P}{V_P}$$

(i)     $I_P = \dfrac{100 \text{ W}}{20 \text{ V}} = 5 \text{ A}$

$$\frac{I_S}{I_P} = \frac{N_P}{N_S}$$

$$\therefore I_S = \frac{N_P}{N_S}(I_P) = \frac{8}{2}(5 \text{ A}) = 20 \text{ A}$$

(ii) $P = I_S V_S$

$$\therefore I_S = \frac{P}{V_S} = \frac{100 \text{ W}}{5 \text{ V}} = 20 \text{ A}$$

Solution (ii) has fewer steps, but it depends on evaluating the secondary voltage first.

Therefore, the secondary alternating current, $I_S$, is 20 A.

Transforming current and electrical potential are handy for running a wide range of electrical devices that all require different electrical potentials, such as radios and other types of portable electric equipment. Your CD or MP3 player, for example, may take only one AA battery. A simple transformer can be used to take your household 120 V electrical potential, step it down to 1.5 V, and convert it to DC current to eliminate the need for the battery while you are at home.

Transforming electrical potential is far more important when transmitting electrical energy from remote generating sites. The power loss over long distances is governed by the current and the overall resistance of the pathway, as given by the equation

$$P = I^2 R.$$

By lowering the current and raising the electrical potential for transmitting electricity, the amount of power loss can be greatly reduced, as illustrated in the following example.

**EXAMPLE 3**  **Power loss comparison**

Compare the power lost in transmission for a 1000 W line at 100 V to the same power on a line at 1000 V. In both cases, the resistance of the line is 1 $\Omega$.

*Solution and Connection to Theory*

**Given**

$P = 1000 \text{ W}$    $R = 1 \ \Omega$    $V_1 = 100 \text{ V}$    $V_2 = 1000 \text{ V}$

Calculate the current for $V_1 = 100$ V

$$I_1 = \frac{P}{V_1} = \frac{1000 \text{ W}}{100 \text{ V}} = 10 \text{ A}$$

$$P_1 = I_1^2 R$$

$$P_1 = (10 \text{ A})^2 (1 \ \Omega) = 100 \text{ W}$$

This is a $\frac{100 \text{ W}}{1000 \text{ W}}$ (100 %) = 10 % power loss.

Now calculate the current for $V_2 = 1000$ V.

$$I_2 = \frac{P}{V_2} = \frac{1000 \text{ W}}{1000 \text{ V}} = 1 \text{ A}$$

$$P_2 = I_2^2 R$$

$$P = (1 \text{ A})^2 (1 \ \Omega) = 1 \text{ W}$$

This is a $\frac{1 \text{ W}}{1000 \text{ W}}$ (100 %) = 0.1 % power loss.

As a result, if you transmit energy at 10 times the voltage, you reduce the power loss in the line by a factor of $\frac{10\%}{0.1\%}$, or 100 times.

Figure 18.16 shows the various stages of transformation of electric current, from its generation to its use. At the generating station, the current is stepped up to a high voltage so that it is low enough to limit the amount of power lost along its journey to the district transformer stations. At each subsequent transformer station, the voltage is stepped down until it reaches the pole or box transformer situated near the road at the edge of your property. At this last transformer, the voltage is dropped to 240 V AC for use in our homes. The 240 V is split down the middle for most common appliances in the home, but the full 240 V is reserved for higher-power applications, like the electric stove or clothes dryer.

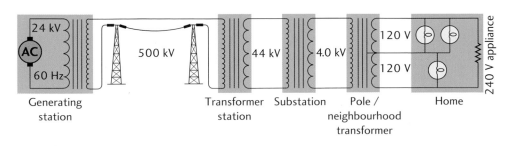

**Fig.18.16** Electrical power distribution

24 kV · AC · 60 Hz · Generating station · 500 kV · Transformer station · 44 kV · Substation · 4.0 kV · Pole / neighbourhood transformer · 120 V · 120 V · Home · 240 V appliance

1. A step-up transformer with 50 primary turns and 250 secondary turns is used to generate a current of 2.5 A at a voltage of 10 V. Find
   a) the turns ratio.
   b) the primary voltage.
   c) the primary current.
   d) the average power delivered to the secondary side.
   e) the average power of the primary side (by logic and by calculation).
   f) the resistance of the load on the output side.

2. A step-down transformer is used to convert 120 V from the wall source to an audio receiver voltage. If there is a 0.80 A current on the primary side and the turns ratio is 13:1, find
   a) the voltage across the secondary side.
   b) the current delivered to the stereo.
   c) the resistance of the stereo components.
   d) the power delivered to the secondary side.
   e) the power delivered to the primary side.

# ▶ 18.5  AC Wins Over DC

In North America, AC is supplied at a standard rate of 60 Hz. Not only is it the simplest form of current to generate because there is no commutator required, but it is transformable, minimizing power loss during transmission over long distances. In your home, electrical energy can be transformed to suit almost any voltage requirement. The standard rate of 60 cycles per second can then be used by many electrical devices in your home to keep time, such as clocks and your desktop computer.

## THE BATTLE OF THE CURRENTS

When Thomas Edison electrified New York City in 1879, he did more than invent a light bulb. He also designed the generators that supplied the electricity. Run by steam engines, the generators produced DC electricity at about 100 V. Edison's enterprises eventually became the General Electric Company, with massive investments in DC systems.

Nicola Tesla arrived in the United States in 1884, with his head full of AC inventions. After working for Edison briefly, Tesla moved to Westinghouse Corporation. There, he developed a full system of alternating-current generators, motors, transformers, and lighting. Edison was furious. His company ran ads denouncing AC as the dangerous form of electricity that was used for executions at Sing Sing prison.

In the late 1880s, financiers resolved to harness the power of Niagara Falls. In the competition for bids, Westinghouse won with Tesla's AC inventions. The first electricity from Niagara Falls was delivered to Buffalo in 1896.

# 18.6 Summary of Electrical Development

The pioneers of atomic and electrical study, from Dalton and Coulomb to Volta, probably had no idea that their work would come full circle as they created small currents from primitive batteries. Current electricity led to the development of electromagnets that offer much to society, including electric motors. Faraday's work on electromagnetic induction eventually lead to the creation of an electromagnetic generator that is capable of creating current on a grand scale, much larger than earlier scientists had ever imagined. The availability of large-scale currents led to many more applications, from simple electric lighting and heat to the intricate electronics of computers and communications technology. Figure 18.17 shows the landmarks of research in electrical energy between 1800 and 1900. Not only did this research lead to the development of the technology for generating electricity on a large scale, but it paved the way for the industrial and technological explosion in the 20th century. These early scientists were pioneers in the development of electrical technology, such as computers and communications, that would subsequently improve research in all scientific fields.

**Fig.18.17** Research and Design in Electricity and Its Applications, 1800–1900

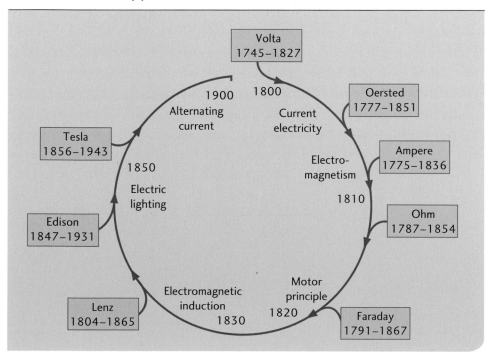

# Alternative Forms of Generating Electrical Energy

**Fig.STSE.18.1** Wind turbines

**Fig.STSE.18.2** A solar array

The demand for electrical energy is on the rise. There are two possible solutions. One way is to develop new and reliable yet inexpensive means to generate more electrical energy. The other solution involves coming up with more ways to conserve energy and decrease the overall demand so that the existing energy supply will be adequate. Although the effectiveness of conservation in meeting demand is questionable, there is no doubt that any new form of generating electrical energy must be cheap, convenient, and environmentally friendly. These issues are not always so clear cut. The "expense" for generating energy might involve factors that are not easily given a dollar value. How do you assign a monetary value to human and animal lives or the impact of relocation of communities, industries, or even entire ecosystems?

Of course, there is always the trade-off between cheap and plentiful energy at the "expense" of the environment. At present, energy is mainly generated at a central location, in large fossil-fuel-burning or nuclear facilities. Although they are capital cost intensive, they produce cheap and reliable energy for many communities. Many environmentalists place their trust in more delocalized and small-scale generating stations that might include biomass, micro hydro-electric, solar, and wind generating plants. Although these forms of generating energy appear at first glance to be sources of clean and cheap electricity, they are not without major problems that will probably limit their widespread use. Wind turbines and solar cells can produce electrical energy without releasing carbon dioxide or producing radioactive waste, but the electricity they produce is intermittent and unreliable because of the tenuous nature of wind and Sun conditions. Wind turbines and solar panel arrays, shown in Figs. STSE.18.1 and STSE.18.2, require large, expensive tracts of land in windy and sunny areas, away from trees and mountains, which are becoming harder to find, especially in heavily populated industrial countries like Japan. The type of electricity produced is of fluctuating voltage and direct current (DC) instead of the standard alternating current (AC) we are used to. It must be converted before it can be added to the main electrical system, called the **grid**. Grid connection for small, homemade wind turbines and solar cells is impractical. Any practical generation of electrical energy must be done in large complexes, such as the one in Tjaereborg, Denmark, where a two-megawatt wind turbine with a 60 m rotor diameter is installed.

The environmental benefits of some of these micro alternative energy sources is doubtful. We still need to burn fossil fuels to melt the glass and metal required to manufacture "environmentally friendly" solar cells. We need a thorough cost-benefit analysis on any newly applied technology before we can confidently claim that we have found a better way to generate energy cleanly and inexpensively.

## Design a Study of Societal Impact

Some of the best locations for wind turbines, open areas with high winds, are found along bird migration routes. One such generating station is located near Altamont Pass in California. Brainstorm a list of ways in which large-scale wind turbines might be detrimental to animals or the environment. Use current solar photovoltaic cell efficiency information to estimate the surface area of solar array required to power a typical household.

One way to ensure enough electrical energy is to lower the demand. Some companies have been involved in power conservation campaigns. What strategies have been tried to encourage the public to reduce consumption of electricity? How should the pricing structure of electricity be changed so that it would encourage conservation? How does the privatization of electrical generation (generation of electricity left to private for-profit companies) change energy conservation?

Research the Ballard® fuel cell, manufactured by the Canadian company Ballard Power Systems. This fuel cell combines hydrogen (from methanol, natural gas, petroleum, or renewable sources) and oxygen (from air) without combustion to generate electricity (see Fig. STSE.18.3).

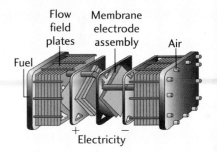

**Fig.STSE.18.3** The Ballard® fuel cell

## Design an Activity to Evaluate

Perform a data-correlation study to evaluate how the efficiency of a wind turbine changes when the blade pitch and wind speed are changed. Obtain a test turbine from your teacher or build one as part of a design project.

Perform a correlation study on a solar (photovoltaic) cell to determine the type of incident light (natural sunlight or indoor artificial light) that is most beneficial to the production of electrical energy. Examine different wavelengths and intensities of light.

## Build a Structure

Design and build a simple wind turbine that will be powered by the air flow from a standard fan. Test the efficiency of the turbine by using it to lift a reservoir of water. Determine the work done by the turbine and the power based on the time taken to lift a weight to a specified height.

Hold a design competition in which contestants use a solar cell (provided by the teacher) to power an electric vehicle. Have a solar "drag race" to see which vehicle accelerates the most.

## You should be able to

*Understand Basic Concepts:*
- Analyze and describe electromagnetic induction in qualitative terms.
- Use Lenz's law and the left- and right-hand rules to predict and illustrate the direction of electric current induced by a changing magnetic field.
- Compare DC and AC and explain why AC has become a standard in North America for household and industrial use.
- Explain the interaction of electricity and magnetism in a transformer.
- Describe the parts and operation of a step-up and a step-down transformer.
- Solve problems involving energy, power, current, and voltage on the primary and secondary coils of a transformer when the number of turns in each coil is changed.

*Develop Skills of Inquiry and Communication:*
- Design and carry out an experiment to identify the factors that affect the magnitude and direction of induced electric current in a changing magnetic field.
- Use Lenz's law and the left- and right-hand rules to predict and experimentally verify the direction of induced current flow in a conductor that is placed in a changing magnetic field.

*Relate Science to Technology, Society, and the Environment:*
- Use Lenz's law to analyze and describe the operation of an electric generator or other system that uses electromagnetic induction.
- Identify the historical developments of the technology of electromagnetic induction.
- Analyze the role of electromagnetic induction in the large- and small-scale generation of electrical energy.
- Recognize that all the different forms of generating electrical energy have both positive and negative effects on society and the environment.

**Equations**

$$\frac{V_p}{V_s} = \frac{I_s}{I_p} = \frac{N_p}{N_s}$$

## Conceptual Questions

1. Define Faraday's principle.

2. Describe at least three things that could be done to improve the electromotive force that is induced in a conductor.

3. What conditions must be met to induce current flow in a conductor?

4. Explain the relationship between Lenz's law and the law of conservation of energy.

5. Faraday's principle implies that an induced current in a coil (created by a moving magnet) creates an induced magnetic field. Explain why this induced magnetic field can't "boost" the induction process by moving the magnet, as in a motor principle.

6. A wire conductor is moved horizontally from the north pole of the field magnet to the south pole, as shown in Fig. 18.18. What is the direction of the induced current through the conductor?

**Fig.18.18**

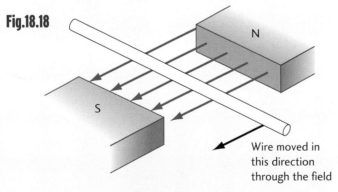

Wire moved in this direction through the field

7. Describe at least two differences between an AC and a DC generator.

8. One suggestion for a new automobile brake design is to use modified electromagnetic generators as brakes.
   a) Using the law of conservation of energy, explain how this design might work.
   b) What are some possible environmental or monetary benefits of these types of brakes in an electric car?

9. When Faraday applied a direct current to his "ring apparatus," a current flowed for only a moment in the secondary coil before it stopped. What conditions must exist in this ring apparatus for continuous current to flow? What type of current is produced?

10. Why must a transformer use only alternating current (AC)?

11. Draw a sketch of a transformer and label at least three parts. Use this diagram to summarize the relationship between current, voltage, and the number of turns on the primary and secondary coils.

12. Describe the characteristics that distinguish a step-up transformer from a step-down transformer.

13. How must electric current be altered to travel long distances without great energy loss?

14. The use of alternating current means that the electrons that power the light bulb in your room may be the same electrons that were present in the bulb when you bought it. How do these electrons get the energy to light your room if they effectively stay in the same place?

15. Give a simple but practical reason why electrical potential difference is stepped up at the generating station but stepped down several times by the time it reaches you.

## Problems

### 18.2 Lenz's Law and Induced Current

16. Sketch each of the following diagrams into your notebook. Using Lenz's law and left-hand rule #2 for solenoids (electromagnetic coils), predict the direction of the induced current flow by adding arrows to your diagrams. Add an N or S to represent the magnetic poles at each end of the coil.

**a) Fig.18.19**

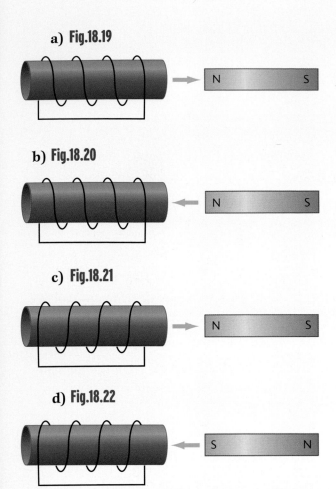

**b) Fig.18.20**

**c) Fig.18.21**

**d) Fig.18.22**

**17.** Sketch each of the following diagrams into your notebook. Using Lenz's law and left-hand rule #2 for solenoids, predict the polarity of the magnet that is being inserted or removed from the coils, as shown.

**a) Fig.18.23**

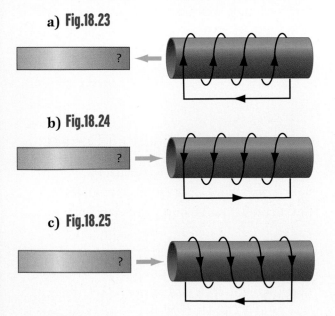

**b) Fig.18.24**

**c) Fig.18.25**

**d) Fig.18.26**

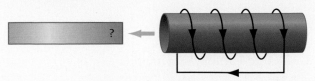

**18.** Sketch each of the following diagrams into your notebook. Using Lenz's law and left-hand rule #2 for solenoids, predict the direction in which each magnet is being moved to produce the indicated current flow.

**a) Fig.18.27**

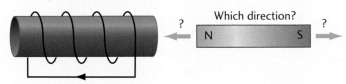

**b) Fig.18.28**

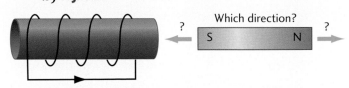

**c) Fig.18.29**

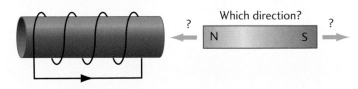

**19.** A conductor is moved up through a magnetic field, as shown in Fig. 18.30. Predict which way the current will flow inside the conductor.

**Fig.18.30**

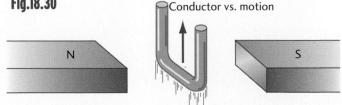

Conductor vs. motion

**20.** The "Drop Zone" is a ride at Paramount Canada's Wonderland that drops you from a great height and decelerates you safely to a stop before hitting the ground. One possible technological application of Faraday's principle and Lenz's law is in the braking mechanism of this ride. Figure 18.31 simulates the ride by using a magnet dropped into an open copper pipe.

**Fig.18.31**

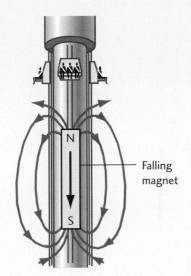

Falling magnet

**a)** In which direction would current flow in the pipe?

**b)** What shape and direction would the induced magnetic field take on?

**c)** Would this situation result in decreased acceleration of the magnet/amusement park ride? Explain.

**d)** Would the situation be any different if the magnet was dropped with the north end of the magnet down?

## 18.4 Transformers and the Distribution of Electrical Power

**21.** A transformer has 100 turns on its primary side and 600 turns on its secondary side. It is used to power an elevator motor that requires 2 A at $6.0 \times 10^2$ V. What is the potential difference and current on the primary side of the transformer?

**22.** A transformer is intended to plug into a standard 120 V household outlet to provide power for a 6 V cassette player.

**a)** If the primary coil has 1100 turns, how many turns are required on the secondary side of the transformer?

**b)** If this was a multipurpose transformer that could be switched to another secondary voltage of 3 V to power a CD player, how many secondary turns would it require then?

**23.** A primary voltage of 12 V AC was applied to the transformer illustrated in Fig. 18.32.

**Fig.18.32**

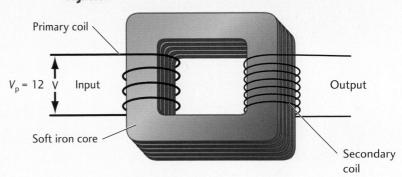

Primary coil

$V_p = 12$ V    Input

Soft iron core

Output

Secondary coil

**a)** What is the ratio of primary to secondary turns $\frac{N_P}{N_S}$?

**b)** What is secondary voltage?

**c)** Is this a step-up or a step-down transformer?

**24.** A neon lamp requires a secondary output voltage of $1.0 \times 10^3$ V at a resistance of 300 Ω. The transformer will be run from a standard 120 V outlet.

**a)** What is the power consumption of the lamp's transformer?

**b)** What is the current drawn from the primary circuit?

**c)** What is the $\frac{N_P}{N_S}$ ratio for the transformer coils?

**25.** Canadian Tire sells a device that operates on your 12 V car battery and converts the secondary output to a standard 120 V AC so that you can operate some low power household items, such as a portable personal stereo consuming 60 W.

**a)** What kind of transformer is in this device?

**b)** What must happen to your 12 V DC electricity before it is transformed to 120 V?

**c)** What is the turns ratio for this transformer?

**d)** What is the primary current?

**26.** A cellular phone battery charger has a transformer with 1150 turns on its primary side and 80 turns on its secondary side. If the charger is intended to be used on a standard 120 V line, what potential difference does the cell phone battery receive?

**27.** A step-down transformer has 750 turns on its primary side and 12 turns on its secondary side. The voltage across the primary side is 720 V.
  **a)** What is the voltage across the secondary side?
  **b)** The current in the secondary side is 3.6 A. What is the current in the primary side?
  **c)** What power is dissipated in this transformer?

**28.** A step-up transformer has 500 turns on the primary side and 15 000 turns on the secondary side.
  **a)** The potential difference in the secondary side is 3600 V. What is the potential difference on the primary side?
  **b)** The current in the secondary side is 3.0 A. What is the current in the primary side?
  **c)** What power is dissipated in this transformer?

**29.** To use North American electrical appliances in Europe, you need to take along a transformer to "adapt" to the European 240 V standard voltage (compared to our 120 V standard).
  **a)** To use your 10 A iron in the hotel room, what turn ratio must there be in the transformer?
  **b)** What current will you draw from this European circuit?
  **c)** What would happen if you plugged your iron directly into this circuit without a transformer? Explain.
  **d)** 240 V circuits exist in North America for electric clothes dryers and stoves. What safety measure must electricians adapt in order to prevent someone from mixing up these outlets?

▶ **18.5 AC Wins Over DC**

**30.** At one of our CANDU nuclear generating stations, electricity is generated at 20 kV and transmitted at 230 kV.
  **a)** What type of transformer must this be? What is its turn ratio?
  **b)** If the generator can supply only 60.0 A to the primary side of this transformer, what current must be flowing in the secondary side?

**31.** Electric transmission lines can transmit 180 kW of power with an effective resistance of only about 0.045 $\Omega$. Power of this magnitude is usually distributed at a stepped-up voltage of 1.1 kV (one kilovolt is $1 \times 10^3$ V).
  **a)** What is the effective current in the transmission wires?
  **b)** What power loss is expected with these electrical parameters?
  **c)** What percentage of the original power is lost during the transmission?
  **d)** What should be done to the potential difference on the secondary side of this transformer to reduce power loss even further? To prove your case, choose a new value for potential difference and repeat the power loss calculation.

**32.** At a new hydroelectric plant, students found out that the generators could supply 500 MW (1 MW is a megawatt or $1 \times 10^6$ W), but they were only about 89 % efficient in transferring the power from the falling water to electricity.
  **a)** What is the maximum power output that the falling water could supply at 100 % efficiency?
  **b)** This power output is due to the loss of gravitational potential energy of the water as it falls. How high must this waterfall be if power was generated by $2.0 \times 10^6$ kg of water falling every second?

# LAB 18.1 Electromagnetic Induction

## Purpose

To quantitatively measure the electric current generated by moving conductive wire through a magnetic field.

## Safety Consideration

Be careful of fingers and clothing when cutting or stripping wire with sharp wire cutters or strippers.

## Equipment

Lacquered copper wire (for motor winding)
Toilet paper tube, Wire cutters
Scissors or utility knife, Masking tape
Two bar magnets, Alligator clip connecting wires
Digital multimeter or galvanometer with a zero in the middle of the scale

**Fig.Lab.18.1**

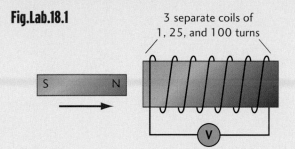

3 separate coils of 1, 25, and 100 turns

## Procedure

1. Prepare an observation data chart, similar to the one given below.
2. Wind a length of wire once around a toilet paper tube, leaving about 30 cm of excess wire so that the two wire ends can reach a multimeter or galvanometer. Slide the loop off the roll and apply some masking tape to it so it will maintain its shape.
3. Repeat the above procedure to create one coil with 25 turns and another coil with 100 turns. Be sure to label these coils with the number of coils they have so they can be used in later labs.
4. Attach the single-loop coil to the multimeter/galvanometer with a set of alligator clip wires.
5. At a slow-to-medium rate, insert the north end of a bar magnet into the centre of the coil and remove it. Repeat this motion several times. Record the approximate maximum reading from the meter and take note of the direction of the needle's movement (or the sign of the digital reading).

**Fig.Lab.18.2**

| Lab/Section/Description | Diagram | Meter reading (Current direction) |
|---|---|---|
| North end plunged into 1 coil | | |
| South end plunged into 1 coil | | |
| North end plunged into 25-turn coil | | |
| North end plunged into 100-turn coil | | |
| Two magnets—North end plunged into 100-turn coil | | |

6. Record all observations in an observation chart that includes a diagram of the direction in which the coil is wound, the magnet's motion, and the meter reading (see the sample chart).

7. Repeat Step 4 using one magnet for both the 25- and the 100-turn coil. Record all observations in the same chart.

8. Repeat the experiment again for the 100-turn coil, placing two magnets together to double the magnetic field strength.

## Uncertainty

Assign an instrumental uncertainty value for the multimeter or galvanometer. For a digital readout, it should be ±1–2 from the far right digit. Keep in mind that many digital multimeters may not read the numbers out fast enough for this lab.

## Analysis

1. Sketch a graph of the galvanometer readout vs. the number of coils (1, 25, 100).

2. On the same graph, add a curve to show what double the magnetic field looks like by plotting two data points, 0 current with 0 coils, and the value that was achieved with two magnets.

## Discussion

1. From the experiment, summarize the factors that affect the amount of current induced by the magnetic field.

2. The law of conservation of energy implies that the electrical energy generated in the coil of wire had to come from another source. What is the original source of electrical energy?

3. Lenz's law helps predict the direction of current flow in a coil. Give a simple statement of Lenz's law.

4. Refer to your lab data. Draw a simple sketch of one of the experiment sections, with appropriate labels, to show whether Lenz's law was verified in this lab.

5. Why did the induced current flow change direction?

## Conclusion

Write a concluding statement that summarizes the factors that affect the induced current formed in a coil of wire.

# Nuclear Power

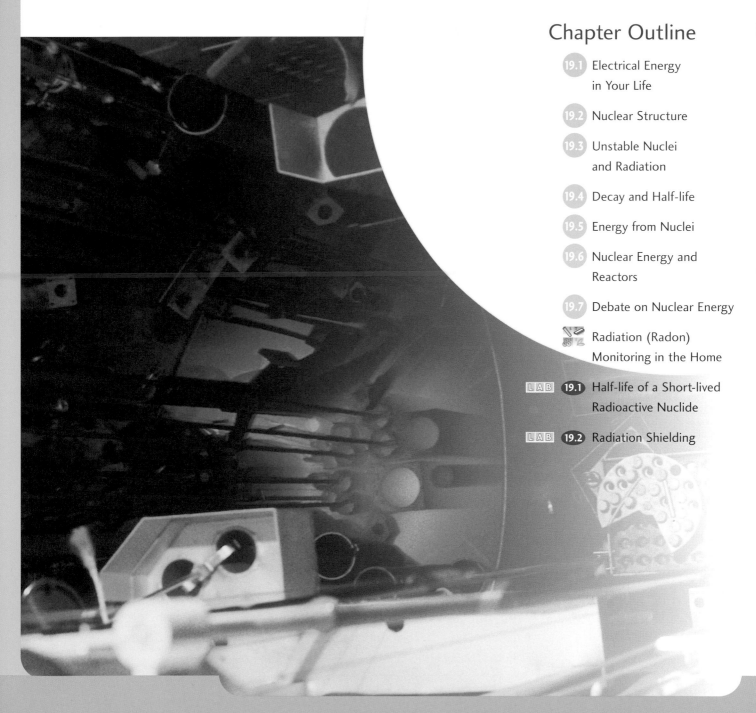

## Chapter Outline

**By the end of this chapter, you will be able to**

- describe the role of nuclear energy in Canada
- relate isotope structure to nuclear stability and radioactive decay
- describe the structure and function of nuclear (CANDU) reactors
- outline the positive and negative aspects of nuclear energy

## 19.1 Electrical Energy in Your Life

**Fig.19.1** Energy consumption and population growth in Canada

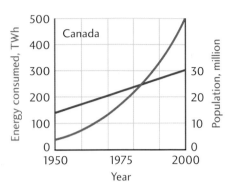

Look around you. Do you feel surrounded by electrical devices? If you are reading this book in the middle of the northern woods, perhaps not. Otherwise, there are lights or electric motors or silicon chips in almost every appliance in your home and school. To keep these appliances working requires a steady supply of electricity.

The needed supply of energy keeps getting larger. In Fig. 19.1, you can see that the population of Canada doubled between 1950 and 2000, but the graph of electrical energy consumption shows an increase of *more than ten times* in the same 50-year period. We are becoming increasingly dependent on electricity in our daily lives.

## Generating Electrical Energy from Heat

The essence of generating electrical energy is creating thermal energy to drive a steam turbine. Therefore, if we can heat water to steam, we can generate electricity. Electrical energy is derived from other forms of potential energy, such as oil, coal, natural gas, wind, falling water, etc. At the power-generating plant, all these forms of energy are converted to rotational mechanical energy that does work on a turbine by rotating its main shaft.

**Fig.19.2** Energy is transferred to a generator

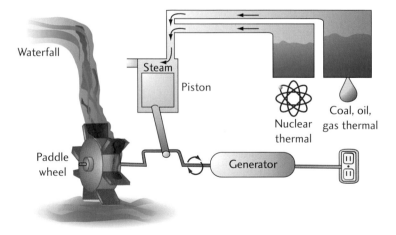

The turbine turns an electric generator that operates by way of electromagnetic induction, as we learned in Chapter 18. The generator produces electrical energy that is delivered to you via transmission lines from the generating station.

As we consume more energy, we have to provide more and more forms of the energy to keep the turbine turning.

**Fig.19.3** Relating Sources of Energy

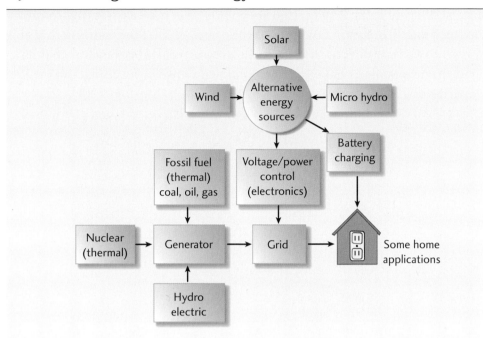

Now, think of the requirements you would like to place on those energy sources. They should be cheap, plentiful, and safe. Not only plentiful now, but also in the future. That's a tall order!

## Energy Sources

British Columbia has large supplies of hydroelectric energy. Figure 19.4 shows that hydro installations in British Columbia have increased from under 1 GW in 1950 to about 10 GW in 2001, which is more than sufficient for the needs of the province. One-third of the energy generated is sold outside its borders. The black dashed line in Fig. 19.4 shows the rate of growth of population compared with that of electricity consumption.

In addition to hydro, British Columbia has about 1 GW of installed thermal generation. The energy, supplied from natural gas, is used to boil water and the high-pressure steam drives a turbine to turn the generator. Frequently, the thermal plant is used to provide extra energy during times of peak demand, such as late on a cold December afternoon.

| Prefixes of the Metric System | | |
|---|---|---|
| Factor | Prefix | Symbol |
| $10^{18}$ | exa | E |
| $10^{15}$ | peta | P |
| $10^{12}$ | tera | T |
| $10^{9}$ | giga | G |
| $10^{6}$ | mega | M |
| $10^{3}$ | kilo | k |
| $10^{2}$ | hecto | h |
| 10 | deka | da |
| $10^{-1}$ | deci | d |
| $10^{-2}$ | centi | c |
| $10^{-3}$ | milli | m |
| $10^{-6}$ | micro | $\mu$ |
| $10^{-9}$ | nano | n |
| $10^{-12}$ | pico | p |
| $10^{-15}$ | femto | f |
| $10^{-18}$ | atto | a |

**Fig.19.4** Power generation capacity for British Columbia

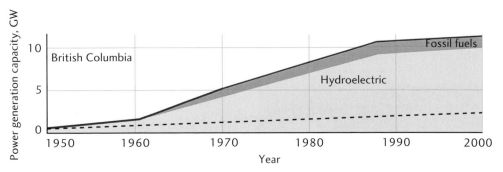

In Ontario, electrical generation also began with hydroelectric power, first at Niagara Falls. As Fig. 19.5 shows, Ontario increased its hydro installations from 2 GW to 7 GW over the last half of the 20th century, but this amount was insufficient to supply the growing demand. Several coal-powered thermal stations were built in Southern Ontario, reaching an installed capacity of 11 GW by 1980.

**Fig.19.5** Power generation capacity for Ontario

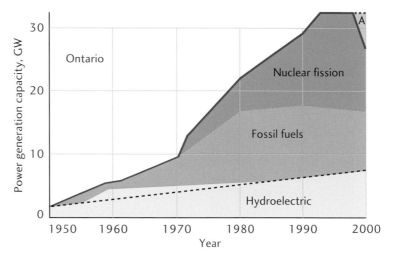

Change the unit of Canada's energy usage from terawatt-hours to the appropriate SI unit:

$$571 \text{ TWh} = (571 \times 10^{12} \text{ Wh}) \frac{3600 \text{ s}}{1 \text{ h}}$$
$$= 5.71 \times 10^{14} \times 3.60 \times 10^{3} \text{ Ws}$$
$$= 2.06 \times 10^{18} \text{ J} = 2.06 \text{ EJ}$$

In 1980, Ontario had about three times the population of British Columbia. For Ontario to have three times the installed electrical generation would require 25 GW. Hydro and thermal generators only provided 17 GW, so Ontario embarked on a program of generating electricity using energy from nuclear fission. In 1980, Ontario had 5 GW of nuclear generation, which reached a maximum of 15 GW by 1993.

Combining hydro, fossil-fuel, and nuclear energy sources, shown in Fig. 19.5, Ontario has been able to supply its customers with electrical energy at about the same rate as British Columbia. Again, the black-dashed line shows Ontario's population increase for comparison. In 1997, Ontario closed down seven older reactors at Pickering and Bruce Peninsula, causing a drop in power generation, as shown in the upper right corner of Fig. 19.5.

**Fig.19.6** Electrical energy flow in Canada

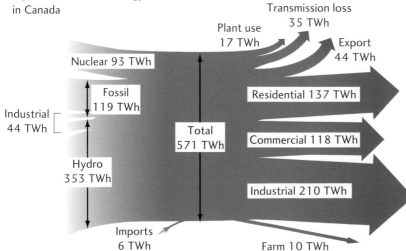

Figure 19.6 shows the flow of electrical energy from generation to consumption for a whole year in the late 1990s in all of Canada. The term "plant use" means that about 3% of the total electricity generated was used by the power-generating plants themselves.

We have suggested that energy sources should be cheap, plentiful, and safe. Before we consider our main energy sources, in light of these factors, we should demystify the most recent energy source, nuclear fission. How do you get at the energy locked deep within the nuclei of atoms?

◄ ◄ ◄ ◄ ◄

1. Draw a flowchart showing the general steps, from beginning to end, of getting electricity to your computer.
2. List the pros and cons of the various methods used to produce the energy needed to drive a turbine. Can you think of any other methods?

##  19.2 Nuclear Structure

All matter is made up of atoms. As Fig. 19.7 illustrates, atoms consist of a central nucleus with an overall positive charge surrounded by lighter, negatively charged electrons.

The nuclei of atoms contain positively charged **protons** and neutral **neutrons**. A nucleus and its constituent particles, protons and neutrons, are described by two numbers: the atomic number and the atomic mass number, which give us the details about how each nucleus is built. The **atomic number** represents the total number of protons in the nucleus and is given the symbol $Z$. The **atomic mass number**, $A$, represents the total number of protons plus the total number of neutrons. The symbol $N$ describes the number of neutrons only. The nuclear composition of an element is represented by attaching the values for $A$ and $Z$ on the left of the symbol for the element. Thus, for the gas radon, we have

$$_Z^A X \Rightarrow {}_{86}^{222}\mathrm{Rn}$$

**Fig.19.7** Model of an atom of lithium ($_3^7$Li). The nucleus is greatly enlarged to show its three protons ($_{+1}^1 p$) and four neutrons ($_0^1 n$). The neutral atom has three electrons ($_{-1}^0 e$) in two shells to balance the charge on the nucleus.

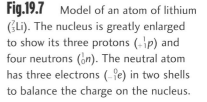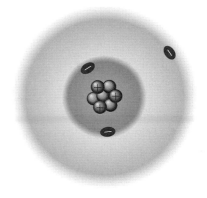

where $Z$ is the atomic number (number of protons) $\Rightarrow$ 86 for radon;
$A$ is the mass number (protons + neutrons) $\Rightarrow$ 222 for radon;
$X$ is the atomic symbol $\Rightarrow$ Rn for radon;
Number of electrons = number of protons ($Z$) $\Rightarrow$ 86 for radon;
Number of neutrons, $N = A - Z = 222 - 86 \Rightarrow$ 136 for radon.

The overall electric charge on the atom is neutral, which leads us to believe that the total positive charge of the nucleus (from the protons) is cancelled by the negative charge of an equal number of negatively charged electrons.

### EXAMPLE 1    Particles in a nucleus

An atom has a mass number of 234 and an atomic number of 90. What is the element and how many protons, neutrons, and electrons exist in this particular atom?

### *Solution and Connection to Theory*

**Given**
$A = 234$   $Z = 90$   isotope name = ?   number of protons = ?
number of neutrons = ?   number of electrons = ?

$Z$, the atomic number, is the number of protons. In a neutral atom, it also equals the number of electrons.

So, the number of protons = 90 and the number of electrons = 90.

Looking this element up on the periodic table (see inside front cover) shows that element 90 is thorium.

Since $A$ = number of protons + number of neutrons,

$N = A - Z$

$N = 234 - 90 = 144$ neutrons

Therefore, this particular isotope is thorium with 90 protons, 90 electrons, and 144 neutrons.

Just as you can purchase the same model car with different options, atoms of an element can come with different numbers of neutrons. These atoms of the same element type that have differing numbers of neutrons are called **isotopes**. Figure 19.8 shows three different versions of the same element, hydrogen. All three isotopes of hydrogen look, "taste," and act the same way in chemical compounds, but the isotopes $^2$H and $^3$H are heavier. These isotopes of hydrogen are used so much in the nuclear industry that they have special names: $^2$H is **deuterium** and $^3$H is **tritium**.

**Fig.19.8**
Three isotopes of hydrogen:
(a) $^1_1$H is normal hydrogen
(b) $^2_1$H is deuterium
(c) $^3_1$H is tritium

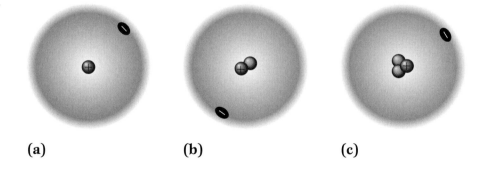

**(a)**        **(b)**        **(c)**

## 19.3  Unstable Nuclei and Radiation

The positively charged protons in nuclei tend to repel one another by the law of electric forces. The only way a nucleus can maintain some stability is to have neutrons present to dilute the repulsion and act as some sort of nuclear glue. At very short ranges, there is a **nuclear force** of attraction between a neutron and proton. The more protons there are clustered in a nucleus, the more neutrons are required to keep the nucleus from breaking apart. Each atom can contain differing numbers of neutrons, which makes some atoms more stable than others. Nuclei that have an insufficient or

UNIT E: Electricity and Magnetism

excessive amount of nuclear glue (i.e., neutrons) are not very stable. These nuclei exist in a high-energy state. In the same way that a tall, thin flower vase sitting on a table can be easily knocked over, these unstable isotopes also tend to be unstable and will break apart spontaneously.

Figure 19.9 is a graph of all possible nuclear compositions of isotopes. The horizontal axis is the atomic number, $Z$, so each number represents a particular element. The vertical axis represents the number of neutrons, $N$. The blue line represents the stable nuclei. The red areas represent naturally unstable nuclei. The pink region represents artificial unstable isotopes.

The unstable isotopes in the red region of Fig. 19.9 have too many or too few neutrons. In radioactive decay, unstable isotopes release small particles in order to reach a stable configuration with an adequate number of neutrons.

**Radiation** refers to the emissions that *radiate* away from the nucleus in the process of becoming more stable. When the nucleus changes by radiating emissions, it is said to decay. There are several ways in which a radioactive nucleus can decay and thereby reach a more stable state.

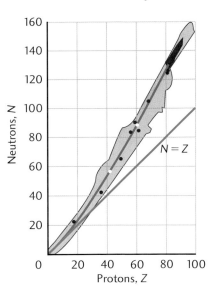

**Fig.19.9**  A chart of isotope nucleons and their stability

## Alpha Decay

The most common way for a nucleus to become more stable is by **alpha ($\alpha$) radiation**. In 1908, the **alpha particle** was identified as the nucleus of helium; that is, two protons and two neutrons. Such radiation is mostly emitted by the heaviest elements. The upper portion of Fig. 19.9 is shown in more detail in Fig. 19.10. Heavy isotopes have far more neutrons than protons, so the loss of two of each reduces the percentage of protons more than that of neutrons, thereby increasing stability. One of the earliest reactions observed by physicist Marie Curie (1867–1934) was alpha emission from radium, producing the radioactive gas, radon.

$$^{226}_{88}\text{Ra} \rightarrow {}^{222}_{86}\text{Rn} + {}^{4}_{2}\text{He} \ (\alpha)$$

Note the conservation of mass and charge in the equation. Using generic nuclear symbols, alpha decay can be summarized as

$$^{A}_{Z}\text{X} \rightarrow {}^{A-4}_{Z-2}\text{Y} + {}^{4}_{2}\text{He} \ (\alpha)$$

In short, the nucleus emits two protons and two neutrons as a helium nucleus, creating a new isotope.

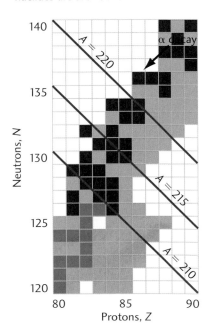

**Fig.19.10**  Chart of the nucleons (nuclear particles) of the isotopes of elements from mercury to thorium. Blue **nuclides** are stable, red nuclides are naturally radioactive, pink nuclides are artificial and radioactive.

## Beta Decay

Unstable isotopes to the left of the blue line in Fig. 19.9 have too many neutrons; there are more than enough neutrons to balance the repulsion among the protons. As a result, one of the neutrons converts to a proton plus an electron and the electron is ejected. This process is described by the reaction equation

$$^1_0n \rightarrow \, ^1_{+1}p + \, ^0_{-1}e \; (\beta^-)$$

A typical reaction of this type occurs in organic matter that has died. A small fraction of the material is carbon-14. These atoms gradually decay to nitrogen:

$$^{14}_6C \rightarrow \, ^{14}_7N + \, ^0_{-1}e$$

Notice that the $A$ and $Z$ sums balance. This kind of radiation, identified by Ernest Rutherford, is called **beta ($\beta$) decay**. With the emission of an electron, the nucleus' positive charge ($Z$) increases by one, and the nucleus becomes the next higher element in the periodic table. For example, oxygen-19 decays to fluorine-19. The generic decay equation is

$$^A_ZX \rightarrow \, ^A_{Z+1}Y + \, ^0_{-1}e \; (\beta^-)$$

Radium-226 decays to lead-206 in a sequence of nine steps, which is summarized by the relationship:

$$^{226}_{88}Ra \rightarrow 5(^4_2He) + 4(^0_{-1}e) + \, ^{206}_{82}Pb$$

In total, five alpha and four beta emissions occur in this sequence.

## Positron Emission

You may expect unstable isotopes to the right of the stable band in Fig. 19.9 to go the other way, i.e., gain a neutron. They have too few neutrons to be stable, not enough to balance the repulsion among the protons. One possible change is the decay of a proton into a neutron and a positive electron, $\beta^+$ (a **positron**).

$$^1_{+1}p \rightarrow \, ^1_0n + \, ^0_{+1}e \; (\beta^+)$$

Positrons were first detected in radioactive decay in 1933. The resulting nucleus moves down one atomic number in the periodic table. For example, when oxygen-15 emits a positron, it becomes nitrogen-15. For positron emission, the generic decay equation is

$$^A_ZX \rightarrow \, ^A_{Z-1}Y + \, ^0_{+1}e \; (\beta^+)$$

Figure 19.11 shows the details of the lower region of Fig. 19.9. Here, each coloured square represents a unique isotope. The small arrows represent three paths of change that lead to stability.

**Fig.19.11** Chart of the nucleons of the isotopes of elements from hydrogen to sodium

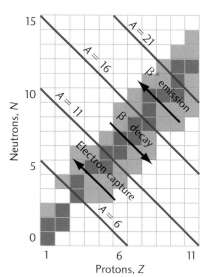

UNIT E: Electricity and Magnetism

# Electron Capture and Gamma Ray Emission

Another way for a nucleus to become less positive is to capture an electron. Adding an electron to the nucleus converts a proton to a neutron.

$$^7_4\text{Be} + \,_{-1}^{\;0}e \rightarrow \,^7_3\text{Li} + \gamma$$

Here, a beryllium nucleus converts to lithium by the capture of an electron from the inner electron orbit. However, the resulting nucleus may become "excited" by this process and emit a package of high-frequency electromagnetic radiation, known as a **gamma ($\gamma$) ray**. Gamma rays have wavelengths shorter than the X-ray range of the electromagnetic wave spectrum. Once again, this process may be summarized by

$$^A_Z\text{X} + \,_{-1}^{\;0}e \rightarrow \,_{Z-1}^{\;\;A}\text{Y} + \,^0_0\gamma$$

(electron        (gamma

capture)      emission)

---

**E X A M P L E  2**    **Radioactive decay**

For the following two decay equations, fill in the missing information.

a)  $^{222}_{86}\text{Rn} \rightarrow \,^{218}_{84}\text{Po} + \,^A_Z\text{X}$

b)  $^{239}_{93}\text{Np} \rightarrow \,^A_Z\text{X} + \,_{-1}^{\;0}e$

## *Solution and Connection to Theory*

a)  The total number of protons and neutrons on either side of the equation must be the same. For the atomic number, $86 = 84 + Z$, so $Z = 2$. For atomic mass, $222 = 218 + A$ or $A = 4$. An $A$ of 4 and a $Z$ of 2 can only mean that the missing item is $^4_2\text{He}$. This equation represents alpha ($\alpha$) decay.

b)  In this example of beta decay, the daughter nucleus must have one less neutron and one more proton than the parent nucleus. So $A$ would be the same ($A = 239$), but $Z$ would be one greater ($Z = 94$). Element 94 is plutonium (Pu), so the missing item is $^{239}_{94}\text{Pu}$.

Unstable nuclei can emit alpha particles, beta particles (and positrons), or gamma rays to become more stable. These particles and rays constitute what we call "radiation" and can do significant damage to living tissue. The characteristics of these forms of radiation are summarized in Table 19.1.

## Table 19.1
### Characteristics of Radiations

**Alpha (α) Particles**
Positively charged particles (helium nuclei) ejected at high speed with a range of only a few centimetres in air. They can be stopped by an ordinary sheet of thin aluminum foil.

**Beta (β) Particles**
Streams of high-energy electrons ejected at various speeds as high as close to the speed of light. Beta particles may be able to penetrate several millimetres of aluminum.

**Gamma (γ) Rays**
Electromagnetic radiation of very short wavelength. Their wavelengths and energies can vary. High-energy gamma rays can penetrate at least 30 cm of lead or 2 km of air.

## Other Transmutations

Alpha, beta, and gamma decay are all natural processes that take place when a nucleus stabilizes itself. Scientists have been able to cause instability in an isotope by bombarding it with protons or neutrons. Because they are charged, protons are accelerated through an electric field when they are directed at a target. In this way, protons can be temporarily added to a nucleus so scientists can study the changes the nucleus undergoes in order to stabilize itself. Some isotopes are subjected to a neutron flux in a nuclear reactor. The absence of charge in neutrons allows them to interact more easily with a target nucleus. If new neutrons are captured, a disruption occurs that will stabilize itself by undergoing some nuclear transmutations. Neutrons are used to bombard and destabilize a nucleus. Like normal decay equations, the equations in the following example may be analyzed by verifying that the atomic number ($Z$) and the atomic mass number ($A$) are balanced on both sides of the equation.

### EXAMPLE 3    Find the missing elements

Complete the following nuclear reaction equation by filling in the blank lines.

$$^{6}_{3}\text{Li} + ^{1}_{0}n \rightarrow ^{4}_{2}\text{He} + \underline{\quad}$$

***Solution and Connection to Theory***

The missing value for $Z$ can be found by comparing the values for what is given.

$Z = 3 + 0 - 2 = 1$
An atomic number of 1 means that the missing element is hydrogen.

Similarly for $A$:

$A = 6 + 1 - 4 = 3$, which means that the missing element is tritium, $^{3}\text{H}$.

1. $^{12}\text{C}$ has isotopes of $^{10}\text{C}$, $^{11}\text{C}$, $^{13}\text{C}$, and $^{14}\text{C}$. If carbon has an atomic number of 6, state the number of protons, neutrons, and electrons each isotope has.

2. For the following, state the daughter nucleus after the parent nucleus has beta-decayed:
   **a)** $^{35}_{17}\text{Cl}$    **b)** $^{212}_{82}\text{Pb}$    **c)** $^{141}_{58}\text{Ce}$    **d)** $^{227}_{89}\text{Ac}$    **e)** $^{239}_{92}\text{U}$    **f)** $^{14}_{6}\text{C}$

3. For the following, state the daughter nucleus after the parent has alpha-decayed:
   **a)** $^{238}_{92}\text{U}$    **b)** $^{226}_{88}\text{Ra}$    **c)** $^{210}_{84}\text{Po}$    **d)** $^{218}_{84}\text{Po}$

## Medical Applications of Isotopes

The use of **radioisotopes** (isotopes that are radioactive) is important in the medical field. Technicians, radiologists, doctors, and specially trained nursing staff use radiation therapy for cancer patients as well as diagnostic methods to determine the cause of an illness. The following is a partial list of radioisotopes used in medicine:

$^{60}$**Co** Commonly called the cobalt bomb, it bombards the cancer in a patient with gamma rays, destroying malignant cells.

$^{131}$**I** Used in thyroid imaging. It can also be injected into the bloodstream. The iodine naturally concentrates in the thyroid area, where it decays and kills surrounding malignant cells.

$^{51}$**Cr** Like the iodine radioisotope, chromium is injected into the body, directly into the affected area. The radiation produced by the decay of the isotope kills the malignant cells around it. In both the cases, the isotopes are short lived and the patient is not affected by the isotopes for long.

$^{198}$**Au**, $^{99}$**Tc**, $^{24}$**Na** are used as radioactive tracers.

4. For each of the radioactive isotopes listed above, find the mode of decay and the daughter nucleus produced.

**Fig.19.12** Radiation therapy machine for treating cancer

# 19.4 Decay and Half-life

If unstable nuclei destroy themselves, then they have only a limited lifetime. Figure 19.13 shows the percentage of the original sample of radium that remains over time.

The data in Table 19.2 show the pattern of decay of a radioactive sample over time.

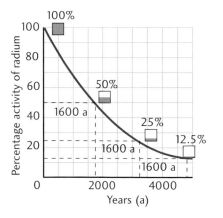

**Fig.19.13** The activity of radium over three half-lives

### Table 19.2
### Decay Data

| Time (min) | Activity (decays/s) | # of Half-lives | % Original activity |
|---|---|---|---|
| 0 | $8.00 \times 10^{13}$ | 0 | 100 |
| 10 | $4.00 \times 10^{13}$ | 1 | 50 |
| 20 | $2.00 \times 10^{13}$ | 2 | 25 |
| 30 | $1.00 \times 10^{13}$ | 3 | 12.5 |
| 40 | $0.500 \times 10^{13}$ | 4 | 6.25 |
| 50 | $0.250 \times 10^{13}$ | 5 | 3.125 |
| 60 | $0.125 \times 10^{13}$ | 6 | 1.5625 |

All the nuclei in an unstable isotope sample disintegrate in a random fashion, so the best way to examine how long they last is by statistical analysis and half-life.

## Table 19.3
### Half-lives of Common Radioactive Isotopes

| Radioisotope | Symbol | Decay | Half-life |
|---|---|---|---|
| beryllium-8 | $^{8}_{4}\text{Be}$ | $\alpha$ | $2 \times 10^{-16}$ s |
| polonium-214 | $^{214}_{84}\text{Po}$ | $\alpha$ | $1.64 \times 10^{-4}$ s |
| oxygen-19 | $^{19}_{8}\text{O}$ | $\beta$ | 29 s |
| magnesium-29 | $^{29}_{12}\text{Mg}$ | $\beta$ | 9.5 min |
| lead-212 | $^{212}_{82}\text{Pb}$ | $\beta$ | 10.6 h |
| iodine-131 | $^{131}_{90}\text{I}$ | $\beta$ | 8.04 d |
| argon-39 | $^{39}_{18}\text{Ar}$ | $\beta$ | 5.26 a |
| cobalt-60 | $^{60}_{27}\text{Co}$ | $\beta$ | 5.3 a |
| strontium-90 | $^{90}_{38}\text{Sr}$ | $\beta$ | 28.8 a |
| radium-226 | $^{226}_{88}\text{Ra}$ | $\alpha$ | $1.62 \times 10^{3}$ a |
| americium-243 | $^{243}_{95}\text{Am}$ | $\alpha$ | $7.37 \times 10^{3}$ a |
| plutonium-239 | $^{239}_{94}\text{Pu}$ | $\alpha$ | $2.44 \times 10^{4}$ a |
| uranium-235 | $^{235}_{92}\text{U}$ | $\alpha$ | $7.04 \times 10^{8}$ a |
| uranium-238 | $^{238}_{92}\text{U}$ | $\alpha$ | $4.45 \times 10^{9}$ a |
| carbon-14 | $^{14}_{6}\text{C}$ | $\beta$ | 5730 a |

**Fig.19.14**  A Geiger counter

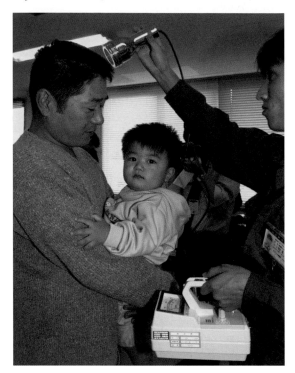

**Half-life** is the amount of time required for half of the number of unstable nuclei in an isotope to decay.

Half-life is different for different isotopes, some of which are listed in Table 19.3. Half-life can be determined experimentally by chemically analyzing a sample for the amount of isotopes present or the amount of radiation emitted from the nucleus every second, which is called the **activity** (measured in becquerels, Bq). One becquerel represents the disintegration of one nucleus per second. A radiation detector, such as a **Geiger counter** (Fig. 19.14), measures activity as it drops off over time. As the activity of a sample decays, so does the mass and number of nuclei remaining in the radioisotope.

Mathematically, radioactive decay is described by the following formulas:

$$A = A_{o}\left(\frac{1}{2}\right)^{\frac{t}{T_{\frac{1}{2}}}} \quad \text{or} \quad M = M_{o}\left(\frac{1}{2}\right)^{\frac{t}{T_{\frac{1}{2}}}} \quad \text{or} \quad N = N_{o}\left(\frac{1}{2}\right)^{\frac{t}{T_{\frac{1}{2}}}}$$

where   $A_0$, $M_0$, and $N_0$ are the initial activity, the mass, and the number of nuclei respectively.

$A$, $M$, and $N$ are the activities, the mass, and number of nuclei remaining after any time $(t)$.

$T_{\frac{1}{2}}$ is the half-life for the substance in question.

The following examples show how this formula can be applied.

EXAMPLE 4 **Calculating half-life**

The half-life of $^{90}$Sr is 28 a (a is for annum or years). If a 60.0 g sample of $^{90}$Sr is currently in a sample of soil, how much $^{90}$Sr will be present in the soil 90 a later?

**Given**

$M_o = 60.0$ g, $\quad\quad T_{\frac{1}{2}} = 28$ a, $\quad\quad t = 90$ a
$M = ? \Rightarrow M_{at\ 90\ a} = ?$

*Solution and Connection to Theory*

$$M = M_o \left(\frac{1}{2}\right)^{\frac{t}{T_{\frac{1}{2}}}}$$

$$M = 60.0\ g \left(\frac{1}{2}\right)^{\frac{90\ a}{28\ a}}$$

$$M = 60.0\ g \left(\frac{1}{2}\right)^{\frac{90\ a}{28\ a}}$$

$$M = 60.0\ g \left(\frac{1}{2}\right)^{3.214} = 60.0\ g\ \frac{1^{3.214}}{2^{3.214}} = 60.0\ g \left(\frac{1}{9.279}\right)$$

$M = 6.46$ g remaining after 90 years

Therefore, the amount of $^{90}$Sr remaining will be 6.46 g.

Decay can also be described using the exponential decay formulas

$$A = A_0 e^{-\lambda t}$$
$$M = M_0 e^{-\lambda t}$$
$$N = N_0 e^{-\lambda t}$$

where $e$ is the exponential function and $\lambda$ is the decay constant

$$\left(\lambda = \frac{0.693}{T_{\frac{1}{2}}}\right).$$

EXAMPLE 5 **The half-life of technetium**

The isotope technetium-99 has a half-life of six hours. A new sample of technetium with an initial activity of 720 Bq arrived in the lab on January 15th. How long would it take the sample to decay to one-third of its original activity?

**Given**

$T_{\frac{1}{2}} = 6$ h $\quad\quad A_o = 720$ Bq $\quad\quad t = ?$

*Solution and Connection to Theory*

The activity dropping to $\frac{1}{3}$ means that $\frac{A}{A_o} = \frac{1}{3}$, so the equation becomes

$$A = A_o \left(\frac{1}{2}\right)^{\frac{t}{T_{\frac{1}{2}}}}$$

$$\frac{1}{3} = \left(\frac{1}{2}\right)^{\frac{t}{6\ h}}$$

$$\log\left(\frac{1}{3}\right) = \frac{t}{6\ h}\ \log\left(\frac{1}{2}\right)$$

$$t = \left(\frac{\log\left(\frac{1}{3}\right)}{\log\left(\frac{1}{2}\right)}\right)(6\ h) = 9.51\ h$$

Therefore, the sample would be at $\frac{1}{3}$ activity after only 9.51 hours.

A logarithm is the exponent to which the base number must be raised to produce a given number.

Example: $10^2 = 100$
so $\log_{10} 100 = 2$

For base 10, $\log 100 = 2$

**Multiplying logs**

$(10^2)(10^3) = 10^{2+3} = 10^5$

$\therefore \log(10^2)(10^3) = \log 10^2 + \log 10^3$
$\quad\quad\quad\quad\quad\quad = 2 + 3 = 5$

**Dividing logs**

$\frac{10^3}{10^2} = 10^{3-2} = 10^1$

$\therefore \log \frac{10^3}{10^2} = \log 10^3 - \log 10^2$
$\quad\quad\quad\quad\quad = 3 - 2 = 1$

To calculate the amount of radioactive nuclei left after decay, we could also use the equation

$$N = N_0 e^{-\lambda t}$$

where $N_0$ is the number of radioactive nuclei at time $t = 0$ and $N$ is the number of nuclei left after a period of time $t$. The decay constant, $\lambda$, is equal to $\frac{0.693}{T_{\frac{1}{2}}}$ ($T_{\frac{1}{2}}$ is the half-life). The $e$ function is an exponential function and looks roughly like the curve we saw in the gravitational law when we used a negative exponent (see Fig. 5.6). The shape of the graph indicates that the decrease in the number of radioactive nuclei is not a linear one, but varies like a curve. The ratio $\frac{N}{N_0}$ represents the fraction of the total number of radioactive nuclei remaining after the decay time period. ($\frac{N}{N_0} \times 100$ gives a percent value.)

Example: A radioactive substance has a half-life of 3.83 d. If the original sample has $5.0 \times 10^5$ radioactive nuclei, how many nuclei are present after 14.6 d?

Solution: The half-life and the time are given in the same units, so we don't have to convert the units to seconds (the units cancel). First, we can calculate $\lambda$.

$$\lambda = \frac{0.693}{3.83 \text{ d}} = 0.181 \text{ d}^{-1}$$

$$N = 5.0 \times 10^5 \, e^{-(0.181) \, 14.6} = 0.071 \times 5.0 \times 10^5 = 3.6 \times 10^4 \text{ nuclei}$$

For $^{14}$C, which has a half-life of 5730 a, what percent of an unspecified initial amount is left after

**a)** 5730 a?     **b)** 12 000 a?     **c)** 120 000 a?     **d)** 1200 d?

## 19.5 Energy from Nuclei

In a chemical reaction, atoms of molecules "change partners." For example, the reaction of hydrogen with fluorine produces hydrogen fluoride (Fig. 19.15).

**Fig.19.15** A chemical reaction between hydrogen ($H_2$) and fluorine ($F_2$)

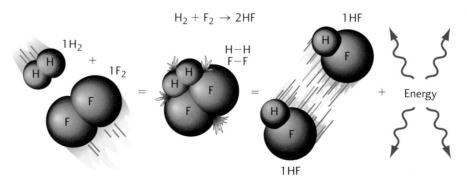

The hydrogen and fluorine molecules are held together by chemical bonds, which require energy to break. In the reaction

$$H_2 + F_2 \rightarrow 2HF$$

the constituent atoms acquire kinetic energy when the bonds between hydrogen and fluorine molecules are broken. Since less energy is needed in the bonds of HF than in the bonds of $H_2$ and $F_2$, there is a net release of energy; that is, the kinetic energy of 2HF is greater than that of the original $H_2 + F_2$. This kinetic energy registers as an increase in temperature (a production of heat). For many energetic chemical reactions, the energy produced is about 500 kJ per mole of material. The value of this amount of energy is a measure of the relative strength of the chemical bonds being broken and re-formed.

A similar release of energy, from nuclei, occurs in many nuclear reactions. In fact, one of Marie Curie's earliest observations of radium was that it was always warmer than its surroundings; not only was the radium emitting α and β particles, it was also creating heat energy.

The heat energy in nuclear reactions (and in chemical reactions) comes from a conversion of mass to energy; that is, when the energy stored in nuclei (and molecules) is released, the release is accompanied by a slight decrease in their mass. This mass decrease is called **mass defect**. It is equivalent to the amount of energy released during a reaction and can be calculated using the mass–energy equation in Chapter 9, $E = mc^2$.

One mole represents $6.02 \times 10^{23}$ nucleons.

### EXAMPLE 6    Energy in fusion

When a helium nucleus is created from isotopes of hydrogen, its mass is 0.018 u (atomic mass unit) less than the mass of the constituents. How much energy does this amount represent for 4.0 kg of helium?

The mass of any material can be determined from its atomic weight in any periodic table. For example, the atomic mass of helium is 4. Therefore, one kilomole of helium has a mass of 4.0 kg.

#### *Solution and Connection to Theory*

One kilomole of helium has a mass of 4.0 kg. Therefore, the mass defect in 4.0 kg of helium is 0.018 kg. The energy represented by that mass is given by

$E = mc^2$
where $m = 0.018$ kg and $c = 3.0 \times 10^8$ m/s.

$$E = (0.018 \text{ kg})(3.0 \times 10^8 \text{ m/s})^2$$
$$= (1.8 \times 10^{-2})(9.0 \times 10^{16} \text{ kg} \cdot \text{m}^2/\text{s}^2)$$
$$= 1.6 \times 10^{15} \text{ J}$$
$$= 1.6 \text{ PJ}$$

This 1.6 PJ of energy is about 0.08% of the electrical energy used in all of Canada for a year!

$E = mc^2$ can be used to calculate the energy released from any type of substance. This formula calculates the energy released from the mass defect, no matter what the material.

EXAMPLE 7   A big pile of TNT

Suppose the energy in Example 6 is supplied by exploding 200 kt of TNT. What fraction of the exploding TNT is represented by the conversion of mass to energy?

### Solution and Connection to Theory

For 1.6 PJ of energy, the mass converted is 0.018 kg, no matter what the nature of the conversion. The fraction of the mass of TNT converted to energy is

$$\frac{0.018 \text{ kg}}{200 \text{ kt}} = \frac{1.8 \times 10^{-2} \text{ kg}}{2.0 \times 10^{5} \text{ t}} \times \frac{1 \text{ t}}{10^{3} \text{ kg}}$$

$$= 0.90 \times 10^{-10} = 9.0 \times 10^{-11}$$

$$\approx 1 \times 10^{-10}$$

One ten-billionth is the mass converted ("lost") in a chemical explosion—less than a gram in 200 000 tonnes! By comparison, nuclear reactions involve mass conversion ranging from 1 to 7 in 1000.

**Fig.19.16**   The fission of uranium-235

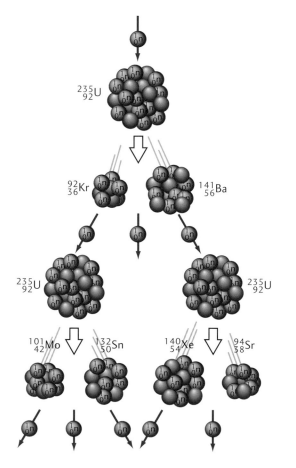

Nuclear fission and nuclear fusion are two examples of nuclear reactions in which the amount of rest energy released is so large that it may be harnessed to produce heat to drive a steam turbine to turn an electric generator.

## Nuclear Fission

In **nuclear fission,** a heavy nucleus splits into lighter atoms and releases nuclear potential energy. Although fission is a naturally occurring event, it is helped along by making the parent nucleus more unstable by adding an extra neutron. One example of a fission reaction, shown in Fig. 19.16, is the fission of a uranium-235 nucleus.

With the additional neutron, uranium-236 is so unstable that the nucleus splits apart instead of merely emitting an alpha particle or two. The resulting nuclear fragments range in atomic number from 36 to 56. A typical reaction can be represented as

$$_{0}^{1}n + _{92}^{235}U \rightarrow _{92}^{236}U \rightarrow _{56}^{141}Ba + _{36}^{92}Kr + 3_{0}^{1}n + \textbf{\textit{energy}}$$

In this case, the daughter nuclei are barium and krypton. Note that the A and Z values in the equations continue to balance.

When you skip a stone on a lake, the stone falls into the water only when it has slowed down. Similarly for neutrons. For a neutron from this reaction to be captured and begin another fission reaction, it must first be slowed down by a process called **moderation**. Once they are moderated, slow neutrons from one fission reaction may cause another fission reaction and release two or three more fast neutrons. If properly moderated, this process continues and the number of subsequent fission reactions increases at a geometric rate in a **chain reaction**. You can easily visualize a chain reaction as the effect of a series of successive doublings: 1, 2, 4, 8, 16, ... 512, 1024, ... A mere 20 steps gets you past a million. With each step taking about 10 ns, the whole event is over in less than a microsecond. In fact, 1.0 kg of uranium can be completely fissioned in 82 doublings, which would take 0.82 μs. The explosion of the atomic bomb that was used to end World War II involved a nuclear chain reaction.

If a moderator can slow down one neutron per fission, then the reaction can be sustained in a controlled fashion. Controlled nuclear fission reactions are used in **nuclear reactors**, where the immense energy can be slowly transformed into useful heat and, finally, into electrical energy.

## Fig.19.17 The Neutron Cycle in Nuclear Fission

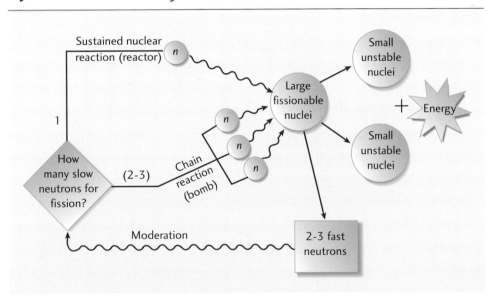

The amount of energy released in a nuclear reaction can be expressed by the energy involved in breaking or forming the nuclear bonds. This **binding energy** is a measure of the strength of the nuclear forces between nucleons. Each nucleus has a characteristic binding energy that can be expressed as a value per nucleon. The number is so tiny that we will express the quantity *per mole of nucleons*. Figure 19.18 is a graph of the binding energies in nuclei, in gigajoules per mole, vs. the number of nucleons expressed as the nuclear mass, $A$. The most stable nuclei (binding energies greater than 800 GJ/mol) have values of $A$ from 30 to 150.

**Fig.19.18** The binding energy of nuclear particles (nucleons) for the elements expressed in gigajoules of energy, plotted against the number of particles in atomic nuclei

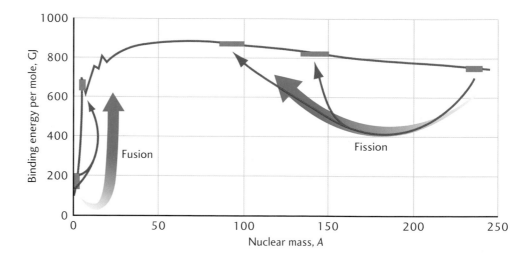

The binding energy graph in Fig. 19.18 illustrates the energetics of nuclear fission. Nuclei in the vicinity of $A = 240$ have binding energies of about 750 GJ/mol. The binding energies of the fission products average about 850 GJ/mol. The difference, 100 GJ/mol, is the energy released in a nuclear fission explosion.

### EXAMPLE 8    Energy in fission

Plutonium-239 is a readily fissionable nucleus. When plutonium fissions, what fraction of its mass is converted to energy?

### Solution and Connection to Theory

The amount of energy released in the fissioning of plutonium is about 100 GJ/mol of nucleons. A kilomole of plutonium has a mass of 239 kg; that is, there are 239 nucleons in plutonium, plus one reaction-initiating neutron. So, the energy released is $240 \times 100$ GJ/mol $\times 10^3$ mol = 24 PJ.

In Example 6, we found that the energy equivalent of 0.018 kg of any substance is 1.6 PJ. So, the mass equivalent of 24 PJ is

$$\frac{24 \text{ PJ}}{1.6 \text{ PJ}} \times 0.018 \text{ kg} = \frac{24}{1.6} \times 0.018 \text{ kg}$$

$$= 15 \times 1.8 \times 10^{-2} \text{ kg}$$
$$= 27 \times 10^{-2} \text{ kg} = 0.27 \text{ kg}$$

The fraction of plutonium converted to energy is $\frac{0.27}{240} = 0.0011$ or about 0.1 %.

Compare this answer to the result of Example 6, where the mass-energy "efficiency" of a fusion reaction is $\frac{0.018 \text{ kg}}{4.0 \text{ kg}} = 0.0045$ or 0.45 %.

# Nuclear Fusion

**Nuclear fusion** is a nuclear reaction that involves the joining or **fusion** of smaller nuclei, as illustrated in Fig. 19.19. Here, isotopes of hydrogen are smashed together to form a helium nucleus. The binding energy difference for fusion is shown at the left side of Fig. 19.18. As you can see, there is a large increase in energy. Binding energies in the range of 200 GJ/mol are overcome to produce binding energies of about 600 GJ/mol. This increase represents a production of energy of about 400 GJ/mol of nucleons, about four times the rate of energy production in nuclear fission.

In practical nuclear fusion experiments, various ways are used to force the positive nuclei of the two isotopes of hydrogen to fuse together into one helium nucleus. One typical reaction is combining deuterium and tritium:

$$_1^2H + {}_1^3H \rightarrow {}_2^4He + {}_0^1n + \textit{energy}$$

Fusion is the main source of energy production in the Sun. It involves a number of complicated cycles of nuclear reactions. One of these reactions uses carbon and nitrogen as catalysts (a catalyst speeds up a reaction, but the catalyst itself is not consumed in the reaction). Hydrogen nuclei are inserted one at a time into the cycle until

$$_1^1H + {}_7^{15}N \rightarrow {}_6^{12}C + {}_2^4He$$

Since carbon is the catalyst, the carbon nucleus will start a new cycle after the alpha particle is released. By this process, the Sun is gradually converting hydrogen to helium.

**Fig.19.19** The fusion of deuterium ($^2$H) and tritium ($^3$H)

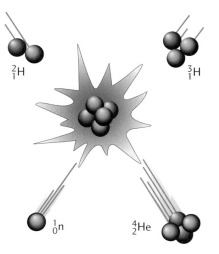

---

> ### EXAMPLE 9   How long will the Sun last?
>
> The Sun has a mass of about $2 \times 10^{30}$ kg, of which about 95 % is hydrogen and most of the rest is helium. The Sun produces energy at a rate of about $4 \times 10^{26}$ W. How long will it take for the Sun to burn out if it continues to convert energy at this rate?
>
> #### *Solution and Connection to Theory*
>
> All we need is the mass equivalent of $4 \times 10^{26}$ J/s of energy.
>
> Since $E = mc^2$,
>
> $$m = \frac{E}{c^2} = \frac{4 \times 10^{26}\ \text{J/s}}{9 \times 10^{16}\ \text{m}^2/\text{s}^2}$$
>
> $$= 0.44 \times 10^{10}\ \text{kg/s}$$

The Sun is losing mass at a rate of about $4 \times 10^9$ kg each second. To find the time remaining for the Sun, in seconds, divide the mass of hydrogen remaining in the Sun by this rate.

$$\frac{0.95 \times 2 \times 10^{30} \text{ kg}}{0.44 \times 10^{10} \text{ kg/s}}$$

$$\approx 4 \times 10^{20} \text{ s}$$

There are 8760 hours in a year $(24 \frac{h}{d} \times 365 \frac{d}{a})$, and 3600 seconds in an hour, so

$$\frac{4 \times 10^{20} \text{ s}}{8760 \frac{h}{a} \times 3600 \frac{s}{h}}$$

$$= \frac{4 \times 10^{20} \text{ s}}{3.15 \times 10^{7} \text{ s/a}}$$

$$\approx 1.3 \times 10^{13} \text{ a}$$

That's more than a trillion years. Astronomers, however, predict that some time in the next few million years, the processes driving the Sun will change form substantially, and so will the Sun.

**Fig.19.20**   Comparison of Fission and Fusion

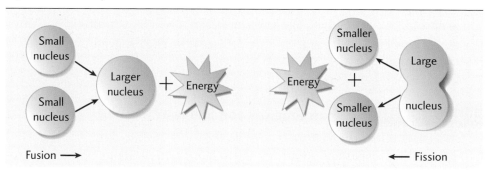

1. For the following reaction, find the amount of energy liberated in $10^{20}$ such reactions. The nuclear mass of each component is given.

$$\text{U} \quad + \quad n \quad \rightarrow \quad \text{Xe} \quad + \quad \text{Sr} \quad + 2\,(n)$$

u    (235.043924) (1.008665) (139.921620) (93.915367) 2(1.008665)

2. For the following fusion reaction, find the amount of energy liberated in $10^{20}$ such reactions:

$$^{2}\text{H} \quad + \quad ^{2}\text{H} \quad \rightarrow \quad ^{3}\text{He} \quad + \quad n$$

u    (2.014102)   (2.014102)   (3.016030)   (1.008665)

1 u = 1 amu (atomic mass unit)

UNIT E: Electricity and Magnetism

## Fusion in Stars

The process of fusion in a star creates heavier nuclei out of lighter ones. The mass difference between products and reactants is converted to energy using the famous equation $E = mc^2$. This energy is released as light and other forms of electromagnetic radiation from the star. The fusion of nuclei continues until iron is finally produced (represented by the highest point of the graph in Fig. 19.18). At this point, energy must be added in order to create heavier nuclei.

**3. a)** Where does the energy for fusion come from?

**b)** Does a star producing elements heavier than iron still generate light?

**c)** Research the different stages of a star's life in terms of temperature and fusion.

**Fig.19.21**  Phases of stars in the universe: a neutron star (arrow), a supernova, and a black hole

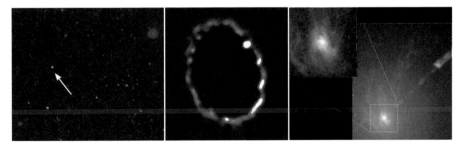

## 19.6  Nuclear Energy and Reactors

In an atomic bomb, a chain reaction starts when a sufficiently large sample of pure nuclear fuel is contained in one place long enough to moderate its own newly produced fast neutrons. This mass of material is called the **critical mass** (Fig. 19.22), the minimum amount of mass of fissionable material that can sustain a chain reaction (produce more neutrons than are lost from the surface of the material). In Fig. 9.22, the purple circles represent a uranium nucleus, and the red arrows represent the paths a neutron could take after fission. Their length shows how far a neutron travels before being captured by the next nucleus. In (a), many of the paths lead outside the mass of uranium. The mass of (b) is larger, so many neutron paths stay within the mass and will fission other nuclei. In fact, the complete fissioning of 1.0 kg of uranium in an A-bomb requires a critical mass of about 16 kg of uranium.

The resulting energy release and the accompanying destruction from one of these chain reactions is represented by the well-known mushroom cloud, shown in Fig. 19.23.

Atomic bombs, which undergo fission reactions, produce explosions equivalent to a few kilotonnes of TNT up to about 100 kt. For bigger explosions, the nuclear arms manufacturers invented the H-bomb, which derives its main energy from the fusion reaction. However, to initiate fusion requires extremely high temperatures—millions of degrees. An H-bomb

**Fig.19.22**  In sub-critical mass at (a), too many neutrons escape before colliding; in critical mass of (b), enough neutrons encounter other nuclei to maintain a chain reaction.

**(a)**

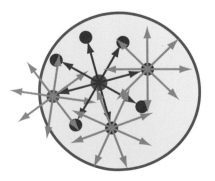

**(b)**

**Fig.19.23**

Mushroom cloud
from a nuclear blast

consists of an A-bomb, which supplies the high temperature, surrounded by several hundred kilograms of lithium deuteride, a stable solid. When the A-bomb fissions, the LiD (D = $^2$H) separates into lithium and deuterium, which undergo various nuclear fusion reactions. The result is the release of 20 Mt of energy in a superexplosion.

**Fig.19.24    Energy Sequence for a Fusion Bomb**

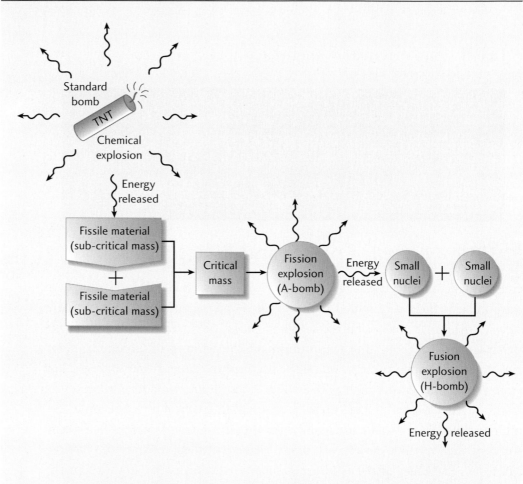

On the peaceful side, nuclear reactors are essentially complex water heaters that produce steam to drive a turbine and an electric generator. In fact, the turbines and generators used in the nuclear industry are virtually the same as those used in electricity plants that burn coal, oil, or gas. The only difference is the way in which the steam-producing heat is supplied. The best way to discover how a nuclear reactor works is to examine the basic structure and function of one of our own Canadian reactors, the CANDU reactor.

# CANDU Nuclear Power Reactor

The CANDU reactor is designed and built by Atomic Energy of Canada Limited, or AECL. The name "CANDU" is really the acronym CAN.D.U., which stands for **Can**adian, **D**euterium, **U**ranium. It signifies not only that the reactor is Canadian, but also that it uses deuterium heavy water as a moderator and uranium as a fuel. Most of the key aspects of a CANDU reactor are illustrated in Fig. 19.26.

The fuel bundle and its design geometry are also shown in Fig. 19.26. The fission reaction occurs in the fuel bundle. Heavy water, or deuterium oxide (Fig. 19.27), is used to moderate the fast neutrons in the reactor. Heavy water is chemically and physically identical to regular water, with the exception that the extra neutron in each atom of hydrogen makes it more dense.

This extra neutron makes the water especially good at slowing down fast neutrons while being able to absorb the heat produced during the reaction. The heat is carried out of the reactor by water pumps to a heat exchanger, where it is passed on to an ordinary water supply loop to avoid the possibility of radioactive products leaving the reactor area. The hot ordinary water produces steam, which turns the steam turbine and the electromagnetic generator connected to it. The steam emerging from the turbine is cooled and condensed back to water by cooling water, usually supplied from a nearby body of water, such as a lake.

**Fig.19.25** Aerial view of Pickering nuclear plant

**Fig.19.26** Parts of a CANDU nuclear reactor

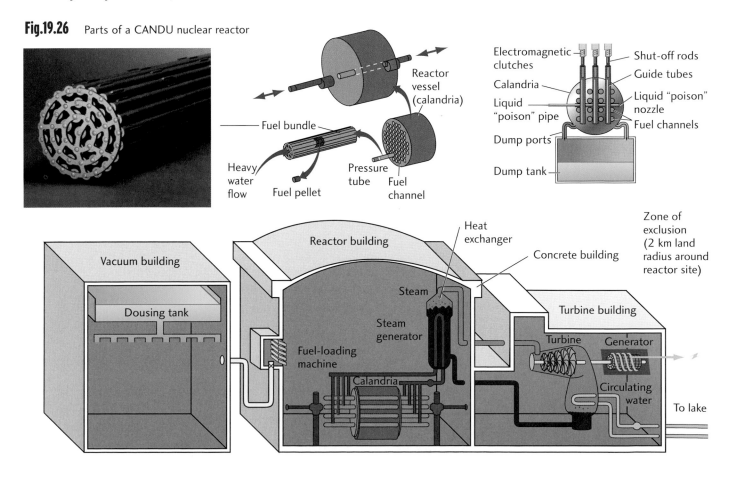

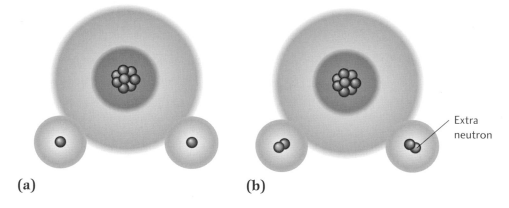

**Fig.19.27** The difference between ordinary and heavy water
(a) Ordinary water, $H_2O$
(b) Heavy water, $D_2O$

**(a)**  **(b)**

Extra neutron

**Fig.19.28** The calandria of a CANDU reactor

The CANDU reactor has many special design components that contribute to its overall safety and efficiency. The reactor core, or **calandria**, is designed with pressure tubes containing fuel bundles running horizontally through it. Heavy water at high pressure (so it won't boil) is pumped through the tubes to transfer heat to the steam generator. The calandria is filled with heavy water, which acts as a moderator to slow down free neutrons and sustain the nuclear reaction. The reactor fire that occurred at Chernobyl, near Kiev, Ukraine in April, 1986 was in the flammable moderator used in its design. The graphite moderator caught fire when the nuclear reaction got out of control, the temperature of the core rose, and the fire sent radioactive smoke into the environment. The calandria can be built to different sizes, and its design makes it possible to refuel it without shutting it down.

## Reactor Safety

Generating electricity in any way presents certain risks to life and the environment. The use of nuclear power certainly has its own risks, which are minimized with the design of certain built-in safety systems. Reactors must be cooled constantly so that excess heat will not melt any of the reactor

**Fig.19.29** Safety features that can shut down a CANDU reactor

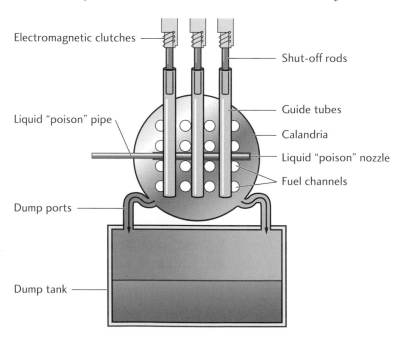

Electromagnetic clutches

Shut-off rods

Guide tubes

Liquid "poison" pipe

Calandria

Liquid "poison" nozzle

Fuel channels

Dump ports

Dump tank

components or the metallic fuel core. Although a reactor can't possibly explode like an atomic bomb, and there is no chance of a Chernobyl-like fire with a CANDU reactor, the presence of so much water has its own set of problems. Any meltdown would mean that a molten fuel core would instantaneously vaporize any water it contacts, creating a hazardous radioactive steam cloud.

A CANDU reactor is designed with at least three systems that are meant to shut down the reactor in the event of an emergency situation. These safety systems are described in Table 19.4 and illustrated in Fig. 19.29.

In the event of radioactive steam pressure build-up, the reactors are housed inside heavy, thick concrete structures that are kept at a lower air pressure than the outside atmosphere. Severe steam pressure would be handled by the activation of the vacuum building system. A low-pressure vacuum building (see Fig. 19.26) is attached to the reactor building with ductwork that transports radioactive steam there to be doused by stored water in a shower effect. Condensation of the steam would further lower the pressure and contribute to further removal of the steam from the reactor area. In addition, the reactor site is surrounded by an uninhabited two-kilometre exclusion zone.

| Table 19.4 |
| --- |
| **CANDU Safety Systems** |
| **Moderator Dump** |
| The moderator is dumped or drained from the calandria into holding tanks by gravity. More cooling water refills the calandria from above. No moderator in the calandria stops the reaction. |
| **Cadmium Control Rods** |
| Cadmium rods inserted all over the reactor core absorb slow neutrons. These rods are usually computer controlled so that the entire reactor can be kept under control. Electromagnetic releases on some of the rods cut the power and allow gravity to pull the control rods into the reactor, shutting down the reactions. |
| **Moderator "Poison"** |
| A neutron-absorbing solution containing boron can be injected into the moderator, which effectively poisons its ability to moderate neutrons by absorbing them. With no slow neutrons, the reaction would shut down, but the poisoned moderator would continue to cool the reactor. |

## Other Types of Reactors

The major United States installations, such as Three Mile Island (Fig. 19.30), are **pressurized-water reactors**, which use normal water instead of heavy water. Although their moderator is cheaper, the trade-off is that increased neutron absorption requires the use of expensive enriched uranium. Some reactors, named **fast-breeder reactors**, have been designed to "breed" more fuel as they operate, thus extending the life of the nuclear fuel. In these reactors, a layer of fuel stock, such as uranium-238, surrounds the usual reactor core. Excess fast neutrons are moderated and absorbed by the layer, creating new fuel, such as plutonium-239. One disadvantage is that the new plutonium produced is not just fuel for a reactor, but also weapons-grade material that could be attractive to terrorists.

In Britain, graphite is used as a moderator and the core is cooled by helium or carbon dioxide gas in what is called a **gas-cooled reactor**. The heat is passed to the gas, which in turn heats water to drive a steam turbine and generator.

**Fig.19.30** Pressurized-water reactors at Three Mile Island near Harrisburg, PA

# Nuclear Waste

**Fig.19.31** Dry storage of nuclear waste in concrete containers at Gentilly, QC

One of the major disadvantages of nuclear energy is the waste produced. The waste is generally categorized in three ways: high-and-low level radioactive waste, and waste heat.

Nuclear fuel has a life of about eighteen months. Spent nuclear fuel has been constantly bombarded by neutrons. The absorbed neutrons have changed much of the still-unused uranium to other highly radioactive elements, such as plutonium-239, which have lifetimes in the thousands of years. The spent fuel is removed from the reactor by remotely controlled machines and transported to another area of the reactor complex. This **high-level radioactive waste** is submerged on site in a pool of circulating water, several metres deep, where it sits cooling. After about seven years, once the radioactivity and heat of the spent fuel have decreased sufficiently, the fuel can be transferred to dry storage in concrete containers on the reactor site (Fig. 19.31).

AECL (Atomic Energy of Canada Limited) is still researching ways to store nuclear waste over several hundred years. One possibility for long-term storage is to encase the waste in a form of glass, place it in metal containers, and bury these containers at a depth of about one kilometre in shafts drilled into stable rock formations in the Canadian Shield, called **plutonic rock**. This type of rock formation appears to be very stable, and the glass and metal containment would prevent any radioactive material from entering the water table.

Low-level radioactive waste is produced from routine operation of a nuclear reactor. Protective clothing, tools, cleaning equipment, etc., may show low-level radioactivity after use. These materials are often buried at the reactor disposal sites or kept in specially designed concrete containers.

The deuterium in heavy water can capture neutrons. It picks up an extra neutron to create tritium, $^3H$, an isotope of hydrogen, which is radioactive. The tritium must be removed from the moderator or else the moderator loses its effectiveness. If a leak of heavy water from a nuclear plant occurred, the tritium in it would cause contamination.

**Waste heat** is excess heat being returned to the environment from the reactor. The condensation of steam in any electrical generation facility, including those using fossil fuels, requires large amounts of cooling water to be pumped in from a nearby lake. As a result, the lake water is returned to the lake warmer than it left. This effect is called **thermal pollution**. Although the volume of water in the lakes is so large that they are not greatly affected overall, at the local level, there is a shift in the normal distribution of aquatic species populations. For example, oxygen depletion in the general area can cause excess algae formation.

# Fusion Reactors

Fusion reactors for generating electrical energy on a large scale once looked promising. Fusion reactions are more efficient in their use of materials, and the original fuel source is as common as the hydrogen in Earth's abundant water. The waste from these reactions could be as simple as producing chemically inert helium. However, it turns out that building a safe and reliable fusion reactor on a large scale presents many problems.

Harnessing the energy of fusion in some type of reactor really amounts to harnessing the same type of energy that is fuelling the Sun. How do you contain the energy of a fusing Sun on Earth? Figure 19.32 illustrates how magnetic fields are being used to try to contain the hot gases in order to sustain a fusion reaction. Fusion can only occur at high temperature and pressure to drive together the positively charged nuclei of deuterium and tritium. Heat would decrease the gas density as the atoms ionize to plasma, a state of matter in which electrons are no longer bound to their positively charged nuclei.

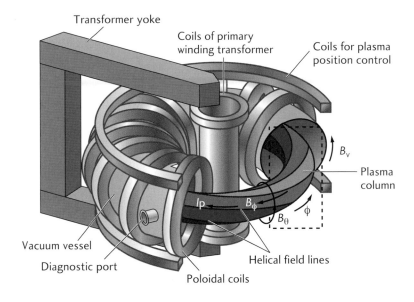

**Fig.19.32** A fusion reactor that uses a magnetic field to confine hot plasma

Another form of containment that has been a subject of ongoing research is that of **inertial confinement** (Fig. 19.33). In this example, a pellet of frozen deuterium/tritium fuel is bombarded by lasers or high-energy electron beams to increase the density of the pellet enough to raise the temperature and cause it to fuse.

In theory, all reactors that use fusion require a way to capture the liberated heat energy. A suggested system is to surround the fusion reactor with a layer of lithium-6. By capturing the energetic neutrons, which cannot be contained magnetically due to their lack of electrical charge, lithium can produce heat by undergoing yet another nuclear reaction.

$$\ce{^1_0}n + \ce{^6_3}Li \rightarrow \ce{^4_2}He + \ce{^3_1}H$$

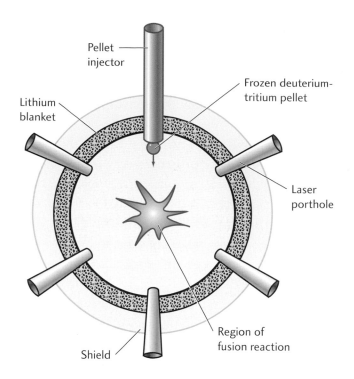

As an added benefit, the final product, tritium ($^3$H), could then be used as more fuel for the original reactor.

In 1989, chemists Stanley Pons and Martin Fleischman shocked the scientific community with claims that they had built a small-scale nuclear fusion reactor operating at room temperature. This reactor was supposed to release more energy than was required to start the reaction in a safe, low-cost process called **cold nuclear fusion**. However, their research was not widely replicated with any reliability and their research style could not stand up against the rigours of the scientific method. Today, cold fusion is still being investigated in many places. However, physicists are inclined to say that even if this "cold" process is actually producing energy, it cannot be nuclear fusion. You have to distinguish carefully between facts and explanations.

## 19.7 Debate on Nuclear Energy

Proponents of nuclear energy argue that it is a way of producing a great deal of relatively inexpensive electricity in a relatively safe manner. The debate over the safety and cost of nuclear power is a complicated one—the items in Table 19.5 barely scratch the surface. The fact is that nothing we do in life is without risk and consequences. Generating electrical energy with nuclear fission poses certain risks as well as benefits that must be fully studied before any person, government, or agency can make intelligent choices.

| | Table 19.5 | |
|---|---|---|
| | **Arguments about Nuclear Energy** | |
| Issue | For nuclear energy | Against nuclear energy |
| Demand for Electricity | The demand for electricity will keep increasing, so the way in which we generate electricity must be able to keep up. Energy conservation and alternative renewable energy technologies will only have a small effect to offset the high demand. | Energy conservation and efficiency improvements could reduce the growth rate for electricity demand while at the same time creating jobs. |
| Fuel Availability | Uranium, the fuel for nuclear fission, is indigenous to Canada, which frees us from depending on expensive importing of oil and natural gas. Using nuclear energy would make Canada more self-reliant and free from world market price fluctuations. Oil and natural gas should not be used to generate electricity because their limited supply should be reserved for transportation fuels and chemical feedstocks. | Uranium mining in Canada disturbs buried radioactive material. Exposed radioactive material is called **radioactive tailings**. It leaches into the soil and groundwater, causing radioactive contamination of sensitive ecosystems. |
| Safety | Everything we do involves risk, and there is certainly no way to generate the power that we need risk free. The safety of CANDU reactors has been proven and is a technology that is available now. Compared to other things that we do daily, the risks of nuclear power to society are extremely small given the power that is generated for everyone. | Any safety record has been based on limited operational experience. Any health and environmental effects may take years to manifest themselves, and when they do, the results are long term and catastrophic. |
| The Environment | Coal is available in Canada, but not in some provinces, and its price is steadily increasing. The use of coal presents both environmental and health concerns. Compared to burning coal, CANDU reactors are much more environmentally friendly. Operation of a reactor has a negligible impact on background radiation levels, and the highly radioactive waste that is produced does not take up much volume. Therefore, it is more easily isolated and contained. | The nature of the effects of exposure to radioactive isotopes means that any negative health and environmental effects will not be realized for years to come. The mining and milling of uranium ore leave large amounts of low-level radioactive tailings that leach into waterways close by. No permanent and safe methods for the disposal of long-lived high-level radioactive waste have been employed as of yet. Waste must be isolated from society for extremely long periods of time, putting at risk generations who have not directly benefited from the energy that created it. |
| Cost | High capital costs at the outset will be more than offset by a plenitude of safe and inexpensive power for years to come. | Nuclear power is very centralized and capital cost intensive. Quite often, the costs may be hidden due to various government subsidies. The fact that nuclear technology is very sophisticated means that this expensive, long-term investment involves much planning, long lead times, and extensive safety regulations. |

**1.** Choose and research arguments either for or against nuclear power and hold a class debate.

◀ ◀ ◀ ◀

## Radiation (Radon) Monitoring in the Home

Radon is a natural radioactive gas formed from the decay of uranium in the soil, and from radium, which exists in natural brick and some concrete materials. Tasteless, odourless, and colourless, radon can seep into your home through the foundation, and collect in high concentrations in your living areas. The US Surgeon General has identified radon as the second leading cause of lung cancer in the United States. The Environmental Protection Agency (EPA) estimates that radon is responsible for about 20 000 deaths annually. As with other causes of cancer, the effect of radon on lung cancer is even more severe for people who smoke.

Table STSE.19.1 lists the amount of radon gas measured in some British Columbia schools and private homes. The results show that this area has a problem with radon gas. For example, in Castlegar, 15% of schools and 6% of homes had a radon activity level above 750 Bq/m³. One Bq/m³ (becquerel per cubic metre) is a measure of how many radioactive decays occur per cubic metre of air volume. The Canadian guideline states that action should be taken within the year to significantly lower the amount of radon gas if the level is above 800 Bq/m³. In the United States, the EPA recommends a range of levels, starting at 150 Bq/m³, but doesn't specify a time interval for taking action.

One way to remove radon gas from a building is to ventilate the foundation. Radon gas can also be prevented from entering the basement by applying a sealer between the concrete foundation and the internal area. Both methods seem to be effective, but active ventilation is best. Ironically, we try

### Table STSE.19.1
#### Comparison of Radon Levels in Homes and in Schools

| School district | Mean radon in schools (Bq/m³) | Mean radon in homes (Bq/m³) | % of schools above 150 Bq/m³ | % of homes above 150 Bq/m³ | % of schools above 750 Bq/m³ | % of homes above 750 Bq/m³ |
|---|---|---|---|---|---|---|
| Kelowna | 26 | 85 | 4 | 7.8 | 0 | 0 |
| South Okanagan | 81 | 107 | 14 | 16.4 | 0 | 1.4 |
| Penticton | 38 | 107 | 5.6 | 16.4 | 0 | 1.4 |
| Castlegar | 100 | 240 | 38 | 41 | 15 | 6 |
| Prince George | 30 | 89 | 4.5 | 29 | 0 | 0 |
| North Thompson | 137 | 159 | 70 | 53 | 0 | 11 |
| Vernon | 57 | 74 | 5 | 9.2 | 0 | 0 |
| Nelson | 164 | 122 | 45 | 19.7 | 5 | 1.4 |
| Trail | 57 | 111 | 13 | 16.4 | 0 | 0 |

www.hlth.gov.bc.ca/rpteb/radon001.htm

to save money in the winter by insulating our houses to prevent heat loss, but in doing so, we may negatively affect our health. Alternatively, more ventilation increases the amount of fossil fuel required to heat our buildings. This increase also causes problems for our health and our environment.

## Design a Study of Societal Impact

Radon gas can be removed by adequate ventilation. But without active heat recovery ventilators, loss of heat and energy in wintertime can be a problem. Research the efficiency of current heat recovery ventilators (HRVs). Using current energy rates, calculate the cost of purchasing, installing, and operating an HRV for one year.

## Design an Activity to Evaluate

Use a Geiger detector/counter or scalar timer to perform a correlation study on the amount of background radiation in your school or home. If possible, use a commercially available radon detector (Fig. STSE. 19.1) with a quantitative readout. Evaluate different house/building conditions for background radiation/radon levels. Using Table STSE.19.1, study variables such as time of year, type of ventilation, and amount of insulation. Compare the effectiveness of sub-slab ventilation and sealing as methods for removing radon gas.

**Fig.STSE.19.1**　A radon detector

## Build a Structure

Construct a scale model of a building. Use a visible model for air contaminators, such as smoke, to study ventilation techniques. Build a battery-powered fan system to ventilate the model. Compare the effects of passive (no energy input) and active ventilation systems.

**You should be able to**

*Understand Basic Concepts:*

- Relate the source of electrical energy in a region to the geography and natural resources of that region.
- Describe the current model of an atom in terms of its constituent parts: atomic number, mass number, and the number of neutrons and electrons.
- Define the term "isotope" and identify the conditions necessary for a specific isotope to be radioactive.
- Outline the radioactive decay processes of alpha, beta, and gamma decay, electron capture, and positron emission, and illustrate how each process leads to nuclear stability. Recognize that certain transmutations can be caused artificially.
- Define the term "half-life" and relate it to the level of nuclear stability.
- Analyze decay graphs to determine half-life and apply decay equations to determine the amount of a radioactive material that will remain after a specified period of time.
- Relate in quantitative terms the link between the loss of mass in a nuclear reaction and the amount of energy released, using the equation $E = mc^2$.
- Differentiate between a fission and a fusion reaction by comparing and contrasting the mass of nuclei involved and the amount of energy released.
- Define the concept of reaction moderation and explain its role in the perpetuation of fission reactions.
- Identify the structure and function of the parts of a CANDU nuclear reactor, especially its various safety features.
- Outline the current technology of fusion reactors and describe the technical hurdles that must be overcome before they can be used to efficiently generate electrical energy.

*Develop Skills of Inquiry and Communication:*

- Demonstrate the safe handling and storage of samples of radioactive nuclides.
- Carry out experiments to determine the half-life of a short-lived radioactive nuclide.
- Design and carry out an investigation to determine the effectiveness of certain materials on the shielding of radiation from radioactive sources.

*Relate Science to Technology, Society, and the Environment:*

- Debate at least five arguments, both pro and con, related to the use of nuclear reactors to generate electrical power.
- Identify that radiation from radon gas is present in the home, school, and workplace from the naturally occurring radio-nuclides in concrete and the soil.
- Recognize that benefits to society from one technology can often be detrimental with respect to another technology.

**Equations**

$$_Z^A X \rightarrow\, _{Z-2}^{A-4} Y +\, _2^4 \text{He} \qquad (\alpha\ emission)$$

$$_Z^A X \rightarrow\, _{Z+1}^{A} Y +\, _{-1}^{0} e \qquad (\beta^-,\ electron\ emission)$$

$$_Z^A X \rightarrow\, _{Z-1}^{A} Y +\, _{+1}^{0} e^+ \qquad (\beta^+,\ positron\ emission)$$

$$_Z^A X +\, _{-1}^{0} e \rightarrow\, _{Z-1}^{A} Y \qquad (electron\ capture)$$

$$_Z^A X \rightarrow\, _Z^A X +\, _0^0 \gamma \qquad (gamma\ emission)$$

$$A = A_o \left(\frac{1}{2}\right)^{\frac{t}{T_{\frac{1}{2}}}} \text{ or } M = M_o \left(\frac{1}{2}\right)^{\frac{t}{T_{\frac{1}{2}}}} \text{ or } N = N_o \left(\frac{1}{2}\right)^{\frac{t}{T_{\frac{1}{2}}}}$$

$$A = A_o e^{-\lambda t} \quad \text{or} \quad M = M_o e^{-\lambda t} \quad \text{or} \quad N = N_o e^{-\lambda t}$$

## Conceptual Questions

1. Outline the similarities between generating electrical energy by fossil fuels (coal, oil, gas) and by nuclear processes.

2. What is meant by the term "thermal pollution" and how does it apply to most forms of electrical generation in North America?

3. We could attempt to generate electricity for all of North America using solar panels, but we don't. Describe why the choices we make for methods of generating energy must first undergo a risk/cost-benefit analysis before it can be widely used.

4. Describe the difference between a fission and a fusion reaction and give one example of each.

5. Why is it that nuclear fission does not take place in naturally occurring deposits of uranium?

6. What does the acronym CANDU stand for?

7. Using a diagram, explain the difference between regular hydrogen and deuterium.

8. Why is deuterium used in CANDU reactors?

9. How could you calm the fears of one of your friends that the nuclear reactor his mother works at could never blow up like a Hiroshima bomb or be destroyed in a Chernobyl-like accident?

10. What is the major short-term safety concern about a CANDU reactor and how is the reactor designed for this contingency?

## Problems

### ▶ 19.3 Unstable Nuclei and Radiation

11. Draw a sketch of any two isotopes of an element and write a brief paragraph to describe the similarities and differences between the two.

12. Complete the empty spots on the table below using the given information as a guide.

| Symbol | $Z$ | $A$ | $N$ | $^A_ZX$ |
|--------|-----|-----|-----|---------|
| H | 1 | | 2 | |
| Li | | | | $^7_3Li$ |
| | 6 | 14 | | $^{\phantom{0}}_6C$ |
| N | 7 | 14 | | |
| Na | 11 | | 13 | |
| Co | | | | $^{59}_{27}Co$ |
| Sr | 38 | | | $^{88}_{\phantom{0}}Sr$ |
| U | 92 | 238 | | |
| Pu | | 239 | 145 | |

13. Give the symbols for each of the following items:
    a) proton          c) neutron
    b) alpha particle  d) beta particle

14. Supply the missing information for the following nuclear reactions:
    a) $^4_2He + \_\_ \rightarrow {}^{17}_8O + {}^1_1H$
    b) $\_\_ + {}^{10}_5B \rightarrow {}^7_3Li + {}^4_2He$
    c) $^2_1H + {}^{200}_{80}Hg \rightarrow {}^{198}_{79}Au + \_\_$
    d) $^{15}_8O \rightarrow {}^{15}_7N + \_\_$
    e) $^1_0n + {}^{19}_9F \rightarrow \_\_ Ne + {}^{\phantom{0}0}_{-1}e$

**15.** Find the missing particle in each case. Determine whether the equation represents alpha or beta decay.

a) $^{210}_{82}Pb \rightarrow {}^{210}_{83}Bi + \underline{\quad}$

b) $^{214}_{83}Bi \rightarrow {}^{210}_{81}Tl + \underline{\quad}$

c) $^{133}_{55}Cs + {}^{1}_{0}n \rightarrow {}^{132}_{54}Xe + \underline{\quad}$

d) $^{230}_{90}Th \rightarrow {}^{226}_{88}Ra + \underline{\quad}$

e) $^{24}_{11}Na \rightarrow {}^{24}_{12}Mg + \underline{\quad}$

f) $^{35}_{17}Cl \rightarrow {}^{35}_{18}Ar + \underline{\quad}$

**16.** In many cases, neutrons are used to make the nucleus unstable and cause a nuclear transformation. Why is a neutron more effective than a proton at bombarding the nucleus?

## 19.4 Decay and Half-life

**17.** A 1000 Bq source of $^{24}Na$, with a half-life of 15 h, is placed into a monitoring container. How long will it take the sample to decay to an activity of 125 Bq?

**18.** A sample of $^{60}Co$ is purchased for a physics class on September 1. Its activity is $2.0 \times 10^6$ Bq. The sample is used in an experiment on June 30.

a) What activity can be expected?

b) How many days should have been allowed to go by to make the mass of the isotope $\frac{1}{64}$ of its original mass?

**19.** An archaeologist finds an oak wine cask in one of her digs. Testing the activity from the radioactive carbon-14 in the cask reveals that it is only one-quarter that of the activity coming from the modern sample of the same type of oak. How old is the sample?

**20.** Strontium-82 has a half-life of 25.0 d. If you begin with a sample having a mass of 140 g, in how many days will you have only 17.5 g of strontium-82 left?

## 19.5 Energy from Nuclei

**21.** The reaction of hydrogen with fluorine produces about 500 kJ/mol of energy.

a) How much energy is produced by the reaction of 2.0 kg of hydrogen with 38 kg of fluorine to produce 2 kmol of HF?

b) What is the mass equivalent of that amount of energy?

c) What percentage of the original mass of reactants is the mass defect?

**22.** Each day, Earth retains about 55 EJ of solar radiation, mostly in the chemical reaction of photosynthesis.

a) Calculate the mass equivalent of that amount of energy.

b) The mass of Earth is $6 \times 10^{24}$ kg. By what fraction is the mass of Earth increased annually by this solar radiation?

**23.** A CANDU reactor rated at 500 MW produces electricity at that rate, but three times as much heat. How many complete fissions of uranium per second are required to produce energy at that rate?

**24.** A CANDU reactor contains 70 kg of fissionable material. Working at the rate determined in Problem 23, what fraction of that 70 kg will be fissioned during the 550 days of fuel installation? (Fuel rods are replaced approximately every year and a half.)

## 19.6 Nuclear Energy and Reactors

**25.** Compare and contrast the features of a CANDU nuclear reactor and an American (light water) pressured-water reactor with respect to fuel, the re-fuelling process, and general operation.

26. Describe what is meant by a breeder reactor and discuss at least two of its potential benefits for the nuclear industry and for you as a consumer.

27. A country that has the ability to breed fuel for further use in a nuclear reactor can also breed fuel for other purposes. What must any government consider before selling any form of nuclear technology, including nuclear reactors, to developing countries?

28. In a CANDU nuclear reactor, the deuterium in the heavy-water moderator is constantly in a high neutron flux.
    a) Write out a nuclear reaction equation that represents the capture of a neutron by deuterium to make tritium.
    b) Why must the tritium that is created be removed from the moderator?

29. Give at least two reasons why energy generation from fission is still the nuclear method of choice for generating energy, even though fusion looks promising.

## Purpose

To calculate the half-life of a radioactive isotope.

## Safety Consideration

1. Wear latex rubber gloves when working with any radioactive substance.
2. All students must wash their hands at the end of this lab.
3. Any spillage of the radioactive eluant must be reported immediately to the teacher.
4. All eluant must be collected in a central container for proper handling and disposal.

## Equipment

Cesium-137/barium-137 minigenerator or another source that produces a short-lived radioisotope ($T_{\frac{1}{2}} < \frac{1}{4}$ of lab time)

Geiger counter (scalar timer), 10 mL beaker

### Fig. Lab.19.1

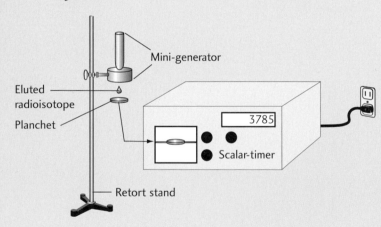

## Procedure

1. Prepare a lab data table similar to the one provided.
2. Set up the lab equipment as illustrated in Fig. Lab.19.1.
3. With the detector area free of any radioactive source, set the voltage of the scalar timer to zero and turn the detector on.
4. Start the detector and slowly increase the voltage until you see it begin to detect some of the background radiation. You have it set correctly if it registers about 5 counts in every 10 seconds. Note: If the voltage is too high,

the detector will "avalanche." This occurs when one event causes a burst of counts that are obviously increasing the visible counts very quickly. Too low a voltage will mean very few events are registered and the lab will take too long to perform.

5. Determine the background radiation level by counting the events that occur in 300 s (5 minutes). Record these values in your data table, noting that a second background count will be taken at the end of the lab.
6. Elute the minigenerator by collecting about 3 mL of the radioactive eluant into a 10 mL beaker.
7. Place the 10 mL beaker under the counter and record the count rate for one-minute intervals. Record the information for one-minute periods in the data chart as shown, being sure that you only measure for the odd-numbered time periods. Use the even-numbered time periods to record your previous data and reset the counter.
8. Repeat this procedure for at least four readings.
9. Return all the eluant to the container provided by your teacher, including any rinse water that you used to clean the beaker.

## Uncertainty

The absolute uncertainty in statistical measurements of this nature is found by taking the square root of the count. For example, a count of 4000 would have an absolute uncertainty of $\pm 63$ counts $\left(\sqrt{4000} \approx 63\right)$. If this count was registered in 60 s, the count rate would be $67 \pm 1$ counts/s $\left(\frac{4000}{60} \approx 67 \text{ and } \frac{63}{60} \approx 1\right)$.

## Analysis

1. Calculate all of the raw count rates and record their values in counts per second. Depending on the strength of your source and the absorbers you used, you may want to record the count rates in counts per minute.
2. Subtract the count rate for the background radiation and record those values, including the uncertainty.

3. Plot a graph of the corrected activity versus time. Be sure that you plot your activity at a time value that is halfway through the first, third, and fifth minute. Draw the best fit curve for all the data points.

## Discussion

1. Why did you have to plot your count rate at the half-time of any given interval?
2. Look up the half-life for the parent radioactive isotope used in this lab and compare it to the one that you calculated in this lab ($T_{\frac{1}{2}} = 2.6$ min for $^{137}$Ba).

## Conclusion

Write a concluding statement that summarizes how your experimental half-life value compared with the accepted value for your isotope, considering experimental uncertainty.

| Background Radiation | | |
|---|---|---|
| Background counts | Time(s) | Count rate (c/s) |
| | | |
| | | |
| | Average count rate | |

| Half-life Data | | | | | |
|---|---|---|---|---|---|
| Time (h) | Counts | Counting period (s) | Count rate (c/s) | Background rate (c/s) | Count rate (c/s) (corrected for background) |
| | | 60 | | | |
| | | 60 | | | |
| | | 60 | | | |
| | | 60 | | | |
| | | 60 | | | |
| | | 60 | | | |
| | | 60 | | | |

**LABORATORY EXERCISES**

## Purpose

To discover the relationship between the thickness of different shielding materials and the count rate of a Geiger counter.

## Safety Consideration

1. All sources used in this lab should be kept sealed.
2. Do not hold the sources for any extended period of time and do not place them in a pocket.
3. Return all sources to your teacher when finished.

## Equipment

Alpha-particle source
Beta-particle source
Gamma emitter
Geiger counter (scalar timer)
Variable level source housing
Stopwatch (if detector does not have a timer)
Radiation shielding sample kit (sheets of paper, glass, or copper )
Ruler

### Fig.Lab.19.2

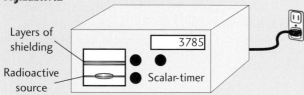

## Procedure

1. Prepare a lab data table similar to the one provided.
2. Set up the lab equipment as illustrated in Fig. Lab.19.2.
3. With the detector area free of any radioactive source, set the voltage of the scalar timer to zero and turn the detector on.
4. Start the detector and slowly increase the voltage until you see it begin to detect some of the background radiation. You have it set correctly if it registers about 5 counts in every 10 seconds. Note: If the voltage is too high, the detector will "avalanche." This occurs when one event causes a burst of counts that are obviously increasing the visible counts very quickly. Too low a voltage will mean very few events are registered and the lab will take too long to perform.
5. Determine the background radiation level by counting the events that occur in 300 s (5 minutes). Record these values in your data table, noting that a second background reading will be taken at the end of the lab.
6. Reset the counter and obtain an alpha-particle source from your teacher. **Be sure to follow all safety procedures outlined by your teacher.**
7. Place the source on the shelf at a reasonable distance from the detector such that all of the required shielding material can be applied later in the lab.
8. Start the timer and record both the count and the time for a period that is long enough to register about 500 to 1000 counts. Record this information in your data table.
9. Add a single, thin sample of an absorber that your teacher has selected to study (such as paper). Repeat Step 8 for this absorber. Continue to increase the absorber thickness, repeating Step 8 each time. Be sure to record your results. (If you do not have a radiation shielding sample kit, increase the absorber thickness by adding more layers of material.)
10. Time permitting, repeat this experiment using a different absorber or a beta source instead.

## Uncertainty

The absolute uncertainty in statistical measurements of this nature is found by taking the square root of the count. For example, a count of 4000 would have an absolute uncertainty of $\pm 63$ counts $(\sqrt{4000} \approx 63)$. If this count was registered in 60 s, the count rate would be $67 \pm 1$ counts/s $\left(\frac{4000}{60} \approx 67 \text{ and } \frac{63}{60} \approx 1\right)$.

## Analysis

1. Calculate all of the raw count rates and record their values in counts per second. Depending on the strength of your source and the absorbers you used, you may want to record the count rates in counts per minute.
2. Subtract the count rate for the background radiation and record those values, including the uncertainty.
3. For each of your absorber-source combinations, plot a graph of the background corrected count rate versus the absorber thickness.

## Discussion

1. Why is there evidence of radiation in the lab with no radioactive sources near the detector?
2. Why did you need to correct the count rate for this "background" radiation?

3. Describe the general shape of the graph that you obtained for each absorber-source combination. How does it compare with the shape of the expected graph for the decay of a substance versus time?
4. Find the "half-thickness" of each of your absorbers by interpolating a thickness value from a 50% reduced count rate (half-count) on the vertical axis.
5. Obtain the half-thickness results from all your classmates and tabulate them in such a way as to differentiate the half-thickness for each source of each material.

## Conclusion

Write a concluding paragraph that outlines which of these absorbers works the best as shielding for each type of radiation.

| Background Radiation | | |
|---|---|---|
| Background counts | Time(s) | Count rate (c/s) |
| | | |
| | | |
| | Average count rate | |

| Half-life Data | | | | | |
|---|---|---|---|---|---|
| Shelf distance (cm) | Counts | Counting period (s) | Count rate (c/s) | Background rate (c/s) | Count rate (c/s) (corrected for background) |
| | | | | | |

# Appendices

# APPENDIX A: Experimental Fundamentals

## Introduction

The reason for performing experiments lies in the need to test theories. In the research world, the experiment tests the ideas put forth by theoreticians. It can also lead to new ideas and subsequent laws as a result of the data obtained. In order to perform experiments safely, the proper use of equipment must be adhered to. The following sections outline safety concerns and the formal method of writing a scientific lab report.

## Safety

In any situation involving the use of chemicals, electrical apparatuses, burners, radioactive materials, and sensitive measuring devices, the role of safety and proper use of instrumentation is of primary importance when performing labs. There is a system, developed Canada wide, which tries to ensure workplace safety standards. **WHMIS** stands for *Workplace Hazardous Materials Information System*. This system has formulated a set of rules and symbols that recognize potential hazards and appropriate precautions when using chemicals, hazardous materials, and equipment. The following symbols, illustrated and described in Fig. A1, are the standard set of warning labels set out by WHMIS.

As well, there are a set of safety warning labels associated with household products. These are shown in Fig. A2. The symbols are referred to by the abbreviation **HHPS**, or *hazardous household product symbols*.

 Compressed gas

 Dangerously reactive material

 Flammable and combustible materials

 Biohazardous infectious material

 Oxidizing material

 Poisonous and infectious material causing immediate and serious toxic effects

 Corrosive material

 Poisonous and infectious material causing other toxic effects

**Fig.A1**   WHMIS warning labels

**Fig.A2** Hazardous household product symbols (HHPS)

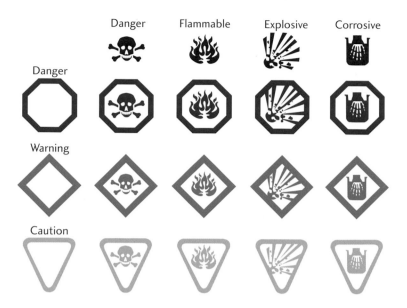

In physics at the high school level, the use of chemicals is minimal. However, the use of high-and low-voltage supplies as well as measuring and timing devices is common. Pertinent exerpts from the safety manual include:

- Fused and grounded 110–120 V outlets should be used.
- Outlets should be away from sources of flammable gases.
- A master cutoff switch should be available and accessible.
- An appropriate fire extinguisher and fire blanket should be in the room.
- High-voltage sources should be clearly marked.
- Electrical cords should be free of cuts.
- Radioactive sources should be stored in a locked cupboard.

When performing experiments, the following safety practices should be adhered to:

Experiments involving an open flame:

- Long hair should be tied back.
- Loose clothing should not be worn on experimental days. Sleeves should be rolled up.
- Do not leave the candle or burner unattended.
- Always have something under the candle to catch the wax.
- Have a beaker of water nearby in case of emergency when using candles.

Experiments involving power supplies:

- Never short out the supply.
- Keep water and wet hands away from electrical equipment, especially when using ripple tanks.
- Be aware of wires connected to high-voltage supplies. Make sure they are securely attached and not touching grounded objects.
- Always have the supply turned off when connecting it to the experimental components.
- If you're not sure, ASK!

# Lab Report

The following outline is for a general lab report. Some sections may be omitted or modified by the teacher, depending on the type of experiment and the level of experimental expertise you have developed.

**Purpose:** A statement(s) that encompasses the aim or goal of the experiment.

**Theory:** (optional) This section briefly describes the theoretical background to the experiment. It can develop or state equations to be used in the analysis as well as possible logic outcomes that are being tested. It may predict certain ideal, theoretical outcomes that will be used as comparative values against the ones obtained from the experiment.

**Diagram:** (optional) A sketch or schematic of what the experiment looks like. It can include electrical representations of set-ups, circuit drawings, and labelled diagrams of the actual physical set-up.

**Materials (Equipment):** A list of equipment and support material needed to run the experiment.

**Procedure:** (optional) In many instances, the procedure is already provided and thus need not be recopied. In cases where you have designed the experiment, the procedure becomes an important part of the lab report because it clarifies the method and reasoning behind what the experiment is set up to accomplish.

**Data:** The data section should be organized and clear. Multiple data results should be organized in a chart.

**Charts:** The standard chart is a tool for recording and reading results. The chart proper should contain data values only, without the units. Units are indicated with the headings. No calculations should be done in the chart. The start of a sample chart is shown.

**Fig.A3** Outline for a lab report

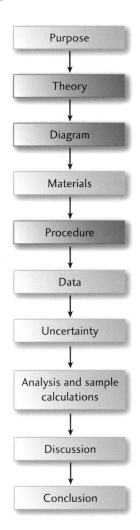

| Trial # | $m_1$ (kg) | $m_2$ (kg) | $m_3$ (kg) | $m_{total}$ (kg) | $\vec{F}_{applied}$ (N) | $\vec{d}$ (m) | $t$(s) |
|---------|-----------|-----------|-----------|-----------------|------------------------|--------------|--------|
| 1 | 1.2 | 2.0 | 4.1 | 7.3 | 71.5 | 0.6 | 0.34 |
| 2 | 1.2 | 2.0 | 5.0 | 8.2 | 80.4 | 0.6 | 0.44 |

A rough chart should be created before doing the experiment. This step helps organize your results as the experiment proceeds and allows you to easily refer back to them at a later date. A neat copy is then made for the actual report.

**Uncertainty:** This section defines the limits of the precision of the data you are collecting. It is an indicator of how accurately you can measure any event. The value is specified by the "±" sign. In some books, it is referred to as the *experimental error*. This term is somewhat misleading because it implies that you are making some kind of mistake while doing the lab. The uncertainty in a data measurement is only an indicator of the accuracy of the measuring device and the manner in which it is used.

Normally, uncertainty has two components. The ***instrumental*** part indicates the precision of the instrument. In the case of an instrument with divisions marked on it, the estimation uncertainty is ± 0.5 of a division if the divisions are very close together and hard to see in between. If there is ample space between divisions, allowing you to estimate between the lines, then ± 0.1 of a division is used. In some cases, you may use ± 0.2 of a division if the spacing between markings does not allow you to easily estimate between them. For digital readouts, the uncertainty is provided by the manufacturer.

The ***procedural*** part of the uncertainty lies in the manner you use the instrument. A 30 cm long ruler marked in mm divisions has an instrumental uncertainty of ± 0.5 mm. If you were to measure the length of the football field with it, the uncertainty would be far greater than 0.5 mm. The reason is because you must lift the ruler and place it back down. For each lift of the ruler, a repositioning or alignment uncertainty occurs, which must be taken into account. A value of 0.5 mm up to 1 mm may be assigned per lift. Timing and reflexes fall into the same category. Even though a stop watch can indicate hundredths of a second, timing an object dropped from a height of 10 cm will not have a value accurate to 0.01 s. Your reflexes are good to only 0.2 s–0.3 s because it takes a finite amount of time to press the start and stop buttons on the watch.

> The total uncertainty is the addition of the two component uncertainties.

## Statistical Deviation of the Mean

This calculation is used to obtain a scatter indicator of values that should, in theory, be the same, but are not because of factors that cannot be controlled in the experiment. For instance, if you were to roll a ball from a ramp off a table many times and measure its range from the edge of the table, you would find that the ball will land at slightly different places, even though you have made every attempt to keep the action of releasing the ball the same each time. The slight imperfections in the ball, ramp, and table all contribute to this effect. The standard deviation of the mean indicates how reproducible the event is. The value is given the Greek letter sigma ($\sigma$). The formula for standard deviation of the mean is:

$$\sigma = \sqrt{\frac{\sum\limits_{i=1}^{n} \Delta_i^2}{n}}$$

where $\Delta_i$ = |data value − average value|

$n$ is the number of data values

When the $\sigma$ (uncertainty) is quoted with the average for a set of data, the uncertainty combined with the mean will encompass 68 % of the data values. If the ± is quoted as $2\sigma$, then the range encompasses 95 % of the data values.

Example: Given the following five distances, find the average value and quote the scatter of the data in terms of one standard deviation ($\sigma$).

$d$ (m)  2.003     2.008     2.000     2.005     2.005

Average value is $\dfrac{(2.003 \text{ m} + 2.008 \text{ m} + 1.999 \text{ m} + 2.005 \text{ m} + 2.005 \text{ m})}{5}$

$= 2.004 \text{ m}$

| $\Delta$ | $\Delta^2$ | $\sum\limits_{i=1}^{5} \Delta_i^2$ | $\dfrac{\sum\limits_{i=1}^{5} \Delta_i^2}{5}$ | $\sqrt{\dfrac{\sum\limits_{i=1}^{5} \Delta_i^2}{5}}$ |
|---|---|---|---|---|
| $\lvert 2.003 - 2.004 \rvert = .001$ | $1 \times 10^{-6}$ | $4.4 \times 10^{-5}$ | $8.8 \times 10^{-6}$ | .003 |
| $\lvert 2.008 - 2.004 \rvert = .004$ | $1.6 \times 10^{-5}$ | | | |
| $\lvert 1.999 - 2.004 \rvert = .005$ | $2.5 \times 10^{-5}$ | | | |
| $\lvert 2.005 - 2.004 \rvert = .001$ | $1 \times 10^{-6}$ | | | |
| $\lvert 2.005 - 2.004 \rvert = .001$ | $1 \times 10^{-6}$ | | | |

$\therefore \sigma = 0.003$ m and we quote our average value as $2.004 \pm 0.003$ m

**Analysis and Sample Calculations:** In many experiments, a set of calculations is repetitive. In these cases, the values obtained from the calculations are summarized in table form. A sample calculation is then shown in full.

**Discussion:** In early lab reports, this section answers lab questions posed by the teacher. These questions are used to lead to an analysis and assessment of the validity of the experimental results. In cases where a comparison is made between two values or an accepted value and the experimental value, the ***percent deviation*** is used. This equation is

$$\frac{\lvert \text{accepted value} - \text{experimental value} \rvert}{\lvert \text{accepted value} \rvert} \times 100$$

or, for two values that should be the same,

$$\frac{\lvert \text{value 1} - \text{value 2} \rvert}{\lvert \text{larger value} \rvert} \times 100$$

If the percent deviation lies inside the accepted range of values based on your uncertainty assignments, then the values can be stated as being the same.

Not all experiments work successfully each time. If your results do not match the theoretical expectations, then in this section, you would discuss possible reasons for this discrepancy.

**Conclusions:** This last section is a summarizing statement of the results arrived at in the experiment. It is the bookend for the opening introductory section, the **Purpose**. This section brings together the whole intent of the experiment in terms of its degree of success.

# APPENDIX B: Manipulation of Data with Uncertainties

We first define two ways of stating uncertainty.

***Absolute uncertainty*** is the actual value of the relative and instrumental uncertainties added together. The uncertainty associated with a measurement carries the same units as the measurement.

***Relative uncertainty*** is the absolute uncertainty expressed as a percent of the data value.

## Addition and Subtraction of Data

When adding or subtracting data,
ALWAYS ADD the *absolute uncertainties* of the measurements.

Example:  $4.5 \pm 0.5$ m $+ 1.5 \pm 0.5$ m $= 6.0 \pm 1.0$ m
$4.5 \pm 0.5$ m $- 1.5 \pm 0.5$ m $= 3.0 \pm 1.0$ m

The answer always carries the largest possible uncertainty associated with it.

## Multiplication and Division of Data

When multiplying and dividing data,
ALWAYS ADD the *relative or percentage uncertainties* of the measurements.

However, before we state our final answer for a calculation, the relative or percentage uncertainty is converted back into an absolute uncertainty by ***multiplying it by the answer itself***.

Example: $(5.0 \pm 0.5$ m$) \times (2.5 \pm 0.5$ m$) = (5.0 \pm 10\%$ m$) \times (2.5 \pm 20\%$ m$)$
$= 12.5 \pm 30\%$ m$^2 = 12.5 \pm 3.8$ m$^2$

Example: Combining absolute and relative uncertainties; calculating the uncertainty of a slope.

Note: When the two types of calculations are combined, such as in a slope calculation, follow the order of operations.

***Given:*** $\vec{v}_1 = 10.0 \pm 1$ m/s $\quad \vec{v}_2 = 30 \pm 3$ m/s $\quad t_1 = 5.0 \pm 0.4$ s
$t_2 = 10.0 \pm 0.1$ s, find acceleration.

$$\vec{a} = \frac{\vec{v}_2 - \vec{v}_1}{\Delta t} = \frac{(30 \pm 3 \text{ m/s}) - (10 \pm 1 \text{ m/s})}{(10.0 \pm 0.1 \text{ s}) - (5.0 \pm 0.5 \text{ s})}$$

$$= \frac{20 \pm 4 \text{ m/s}}{5.0 \pm 0.15 \text{ s}} = \frac{(20 \pm 20\%) \text{m/s}}{(5.0 \pm 3\%) \text{s}} = 4.0 \pm 23\% \text{ m/s}$$

$$= 4.0 \pm 0.9 \text{ m/s}^2$$

# APPENDIX C: Helpful Mathematical Equations and Techniques Used in the Textbook

## Significant Figures

The number of significant digits in a value is the number of digits that are known with certainty.

These include
1. all non zero digits. Example: 1234 m
   4 significant digits
2. all embedded zeroes. Example: 1204 m
   4 significant digits
3. all trailing zeroes after a decimal. Example: 1.23400 m
   6 significant digits
4. any trailing zeroes without a decimal, if known to be measured.
   Example: 12000 m
   5 significant digits if specified or 2 significant digits otherwise

*In scientific notation, all the significant digits are included.* Thus, point 4 above becomes more obvious. Example: $1.2000 \times 10^4$ m if all the zeroes are significant and $1.2 \times 10^4$ m if the zeroes are not significant.

> When **adding and subtracting** numbers, the answer carries the least number of decimal places used in the addition or subtraction. Example: 1.2 m + 1.22 m + 1.222 m = 3.642 m, but is correctly stated as 3.6 m.

> When **multiplying and dividing** numbers, the answer carries the least number of significant digits used in the multiplication or division. Example: 1.2 m $\times$ 1.333 m = 1.5996 m$^2$, but is correctly stated as 1.6 m$^2$.

## Quadratic Formula

Given: $ax^2 + bx + c = 0$,

$$x = \frac{-b \pm \sqrt{b^2 - 4ac}}{2a}$$

If you are solving for $\Delta t$, always select the positive square root.

# Substitution Method of Solving Equations

In this method, there are two equations and two unknowns. Each equation on its own cannot provide the answer. However, by combining them through a common variable, we can obtain one equation in one unknown.

Given $m$ and $d_o$, find $f$ ($d_i$ is also unknown).
The two equations to be used are

**a)** $m = \dfrac{-d_i}{d_o}$ and **b)** $\dfrac{1}{f} = \dfrac{1}{d_o} + \dfrac{1}{d_i}$

1. Rearrange equation **a)**: $d_i = -md_o$
2. Substitute the expression for $d_i$ into equation **b)** to produce the following equation: $\dfrac{1}{f} = \dfrac{1}{d_o} + \dfrac{1}{(-md_o)}$
3. You now have only one unknown, so you can solve for $f$.

# Rearranging Equations

Many times, you find the appropriate equation, but the term to the left of the equal sign is not the one you are looking for. In this case, rearrange the equation and solve for the unknown. A guide to rearranging equations follows.

1. Move terms separated by the $+$ and $-$ first. Continue to do so until the term you are solving for is left alone on one side of the equal sign. When a term or group of terms in brackets moves across the equal sign, the sign of the term changes.
2. Separate the desired variable from other variables that are attached to it by multiplication and division. To do so, you use the opposite operation to the one that is attaching the desired variable to another one. Then, do the same thing to all the other terms on the other side of the equal sign.

Example: $\Delta \vec{d} = \vec{v}_1 \Delta t + \frac{1}{2}\vec{a}\Delta t^2$ Assume you need to solve for the acceleration.

1. Move terms first. $\Delta \vec{d} - \vec{v}_1 \Delta t = \frac{1}{2}\vec{a}\Delta t^2$
2. Separate $\vec{a}$ from $\frac{1}{2}$ and $\Delta t^2$ by dividing them out. $\dfrac{(\Delta \vec{d} - \vec{v}_1 \Delta t)}{(\frac{1}{2}\Delta t^2)} = \vec{a}$

Thus, the equation for a reads $\vec{a} = \dfrac{(\Delta \vec{d} - \vec{v}_1 \Delta t)}{(\frac{1}{2}\Delta t^2)}$ or

$$\vec{a} = \dfrac{2(\Delta \vec{d} - \vec{v}_1 \Delta t)}{\Delta t^2}$$

# Exponents

Exponents simplify multiplications of numbers.

Example: $10 \times 10 \times 10 \times 10 = 10^4$, which equals 10 000. This number can be written in scientific notion as $1.0 \times 10^4$.

Fractions or decimals are treated the same way.

Example: $\frac{1}{10} \times \frac{1}{10} \times \frac{1}{10} \times \frac{1}{10} = 0.1 \times 0.1 \times 0.1 \times 0.1 = 10^{-4}$, which equals 0.0001. This number can be written in scientific notation as $1.0 \times 10^{-4}$.

2. When an unknown is being multiplied, the same rules apply.

$A \times A \times A \times A = A^4$ and $\frac{1}{A} \times \frac{1}{A} \times \frac{1}{A} \times \frac{1}{A} = \left(\frac{1}{A}\right)^4$, which can be written as $A^{-4}$

3. Multiplication and division rules show that the exponents add and subtract respectively.

$A^n \times A^p = A^{n+p}$     Example: $10^3 \times 10^5 = 10^8$

$\frac{A^n}{A^p} = A^{n-p}$   Example: $\frac{10^3}{10^5} = 10^{-2}$. This equation could also have been written as $10^3 \times 10^{-5} = 10^{-2}$

The square root sign $\sqrt{\phantom{x}}$ can be written as the exponent $\frac{1}{2}$. Thus, $\sqrt{4}$ can be written as $(4)^{1/2} = 2$.

## Analyzing a Graph

The graph in Fig. A4 is based on pairs of measurements of a quantity $y$ (measured in arbitrary units q) with $x$ (in units p). The equation of the line is

$$y = mx + b$$

slope     $y$ intercept

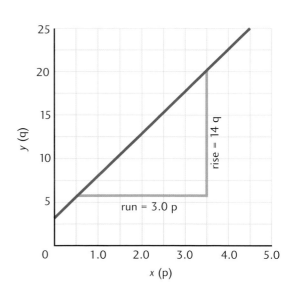

The slope of the line is

$$\text{slope} = \frac{\text{rise}}{\text{run}} = \frac{20\ q - 6\ q}{3.5\ p - 0.5\ p} = \frac{14\ q}{3.0\ p}$$

$$= 4.7\ q/p$$

The $y$ intercept of the line is 3 q. The equation of the line is

$$y = \left(4.7\,\frac{q}{p}\right)x + 3\ q$$

# APPENDIX D: Geometry and Trigonometry

**Equal angles**

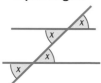

**Triangles**

$$a + b + c = 180°$$

**Similar Triangles**

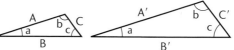

1. Angles are equal.
2. Ratios of sides are also equal. Example: $\dfrac{A}{A'} = \dfrac{B}{B'} = \dfrac{C}{C'}$

**90° Triangles**

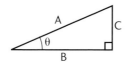

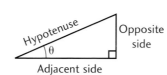

$$A^2 = B^2 + C^2$$

$$\frac{B}{A} = \left(\frac{ADJ}{HYP}\right) = \cos \theta$$

$$\frac{C}{A} = \left(\frac{OPP}{HYP}\right) = \sin \theta$$

$$\frac{C}{B} = \left(\frac{OPP}{ADJ}\right) = \tan \theta$$

**Non 90° Triangles**

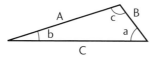

Cosine law

$$A^2 = B^2 + C^2 - 2BC \cos a$$

$$B^2 = C^2 + A^2 - 2CA \cos b$$

$$C^2 = A^2 + B^2 - 2AB \cos c$$

Sine law

$$\frac{\sin a}{A} = \frac{\sin b}{B} = \frac{\sin c}{C}$$

# APPENDIX E: Areas and Volumes

| Lengths, Areas, and Volumes |
|---|

Area of triangle with base $b$ and altitude $h$

$$= \frac{hb}{2}$$

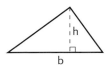

Area of trapezoid with parallel sides $a$ and $b$ and altitude $h$

$$= \frac{h(a + b)}{2}$$

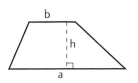

Perimeter of square with side $a$

$$= 4a$$

Circumference of circle with radius $r$

$$= 2\pi r$$

Area of circle with radius $r$ and diameter $d$ ($2r$)

$$= \pi r^2 = \frac{1}{4}\pi d^2$$

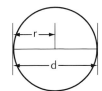

Perimeter of any other parallelogram with sides $a$ and $b$

$$= 2(a + b)$$

Area of rectangle with sides $a$ and $b$ of unequal length

$$= ab$$

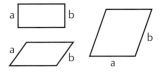

Volume of regular prism with $a$ as area of base and $h$ as altitude

$$= ah$$

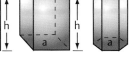

Area of square with side $a$

$$= a^2$$

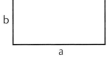

Surface of sphere with radius $r$ and diameter $d$ ($2r$)

$$= 4\pi r^2 = \pi d^2$$

Volume of sphere with radius $r$ and diameter $d$ ($2r$)

$$= \frac{4}{3}\pi r^3 = \frac{1}{6}\pi d^3$$

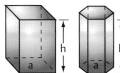

Area of any parallelogram with side $b$ and with $h$ as perpendicular distance from $b$ to side parallel to $b$

$$= bh$$

Area of rhombus with diagnostic $c$ and $d$

$$= \frac{cd}{2}$$

Volume of right cylinder with $r$ as radius of base and with $h$ as altitude

$$= \pi r^2 h$$

# APPENDIX F: Physics Nobel Prize Winners

On the Internet, you can discover the kind of physics each Nobel Prize recognized, and also more details about the recipients. See http://www.almaz.com/nobel/physics

1901 Wilhem Rontgen (1845–1923)
1902 Hendrik Lorentz (1853–1928) Pieter Zeeman (1865–1943)
1903 Henri Becquerel (1852–1908) Pierre Curie (1859–1906) Marie Curie (1867–1934)
1904 John Strutt (Lord Rayleigh) (1842–1919)
1905 Philip E. A. von Lenard (1862–1947)
1906 Joseph J. Thomson (1856–1940)
1907 Albert A. Michelson (1852–1931)
1908 Gabriel Lippmann (1845–1921)
1909 Guglielmo Marconi (1874–1937)
1910 Johannes D. van der Waals (1837–1932)
1911 Wilhelm Wien (1864–1928)
1912 Nils G. Dalen (1869–1937)
1913 Heike Kamerlingh-Onnes (1853–1926)
1914 Max von Laue (1879–1960)
1915 William H. Bragg (1862–1942) William L. Bragg (1890–1971)
1917 Charles Barkla (1877–1944)
1918 Max Planck (1858–1947)
1919 Johannes Stark (1874–1957)
1920 Charles E. Guillaume (1861–1938)
1921 Albert Einstein (1879–1955)
1922 Niels Bohr (1885–1962)
1923 Robert A. Millikan (1868–1953)
1924 Karl Siegbahn (1888–1979)
1925 James Franck (1882–1964) Gustav Hertz (1887–1975)
1926 Jean Baptiste Perrin (1870–1942)
1927 Arthur Compton (1892–1962) Charles Wilson (1869–1959)
1928 Owen Richardson (1879–1959)
1929 Louis de Broglie (1892–1987)
1930 Chandrasekhara V. Raman (1888–1970)
1932 Werner Heisenberg (1901–1970)
1933 Erwin Schrodinger (1887–1961) Paul A.M. Dirac (1902–1984)
1935 James Chadwick (1891–1974)
1936 Victor Franz Hess (1883–1964) Carl David Anderson (1905–1991)
1937 Clinton Davisson (1881–1958) George P. Thomson (1892–1975)
1938 Enrico Fermi (1901–1954)
1939 Ernest Lawrence (1901–1958)
1943 Otto Stern (1888–1969)
1944 Isador Isaac Rabi (1898–1988)
1945 Wolfgang Pauli (1900–1958)
1946 Percy Bridgeman (1882–1961)
1947 Edward Appleton (1892–1965)

1948 Patrick Blackett (1897–1974)
1949 Hideki Yukawa (1907–1981)
1950 Cecil F. Powell (1903–1969)
1951 John Cockroft (1897–1967) Ernest Walton (1903–1995)
1952 Felix Bloch (1905–1983) Edward Purcell (1912–1997)
1953 Frits Zernike (1888–1966)
1954 Max Born (1882–1970) Walther Bothe (1891–1957)
1955 Willis Lamb (1913–) Polykarp Kusch (1911–1993)
1956 William Shockley (1910–1989) John Bardeen (1908–1991) Walter Brattain (1902–1987)
1957 Chen Ning Yang (1922–) Tsung Dao Lee (1926–)
1958 Pavel Cerenkov (1904–1990) Michajlovic Frank (1908–1990) Igor Tamm (1895–1971)
1959 Emilio Segre (1905–1989) Owen Chamberlain (1920–)
1960 Donald Glaser (1926–)
1961 Robert Hofstadter (1915–1990) Rudolf Mossbauer (1929–)
1962 Lev Landau (1908–1968)
1963 Eugene Wigner (1902–1995) Maria Goeppert-Mayer (1906–1972) J. Hans D. Jensen (1907–1973)
1964 Charles Townes (1915–) Nikolai G. Basov (1922–) Aleksandr M. Prochorov (1916–)
1965 Sin-Itiro Tomonaga (1906–1979) Julian Schwinger (1918–1994) Richard P. Feynman (1918–1988)
1966 Alfred Kaster (1902–1984)
1967 Hans Bethe (1906–)
1968 Luis W. Alvarez (1911–1988)
1969 Murray Gell-Mann (1929–)
1970 Hannes Alfven (1908–1995) Louis Néel (1904–)
1971 Dennis Gabor (1900–1979)
1972 John Bardeen (1908–1991) Leon Cooper (1930–) J. Robert Schrieffer (1931–)
1973 Leo Esaki (1925–) Ivar Giaever (1929–) Brian D. Josephson (1940–)
1974 Martin Ryle (1918–1984) Anthony Hewish (1924–)
1975 Aage Bohr (1922–) Ben Mottelson (1926–) James Rainwater (1917–1986)
1976 Burton Richter (1931–) Samuel C.C. Ting (1936–)

1977 Philip W. Anderson (1923–) Nevill F. Mott (1905–) John H. Van Vleck (1899–1980)
1978 Pyotr Kapitza (1894–1984) Arno Penzias (1933–) Robert Wilson (1936–)
1979 Sheldon Glashow (1932–) Abdus Salam (1926–) Steven Weinberg (1933–)
1980 James Cronin (1931–) Val Fitch (1923–)
1981 Nicolaas Bloembergen (1920–) Arthur Schawlow (1921–) Kai Siegbahn (1918–)
1982 Kenneth Wilson (1936–)
1983 Subrehmanyan Chandrasekhar (1910–1995) William Fowler (1911–1995)
1984 Carlo Rubbia (1934–) Simon van der Meer (1925–)
1985 Klaus von Klitzing (1943–)
1986 Ernst Ruska (1906–1988) Gerd Binnig (1947–) Heinrich Rohrer (1933–)
1987 J. George Bednorz (1950–) Karl Muller (1927–)
1988 Leon Lederman (1922–) Melvin Schwartz (1932–) Jack Steinberger (1921–)
1989 Norman Ramsey (1915–) Hans Dehmelt (1922–) Wolfgang Paul (1913–1993)
1990 Jerome Friedman (1930–) Henry Kendall (1926–) Richard Taylor (1929–)
1991 Pierre de Gennes (1932–)
1992 George Charpak (1924–)
1993 Russell Hulse (1950–) Joseph Taylor (1941–)
1994 Bertram N. Brockhouse (1918–) Clifford Shull (1915–)
1995 Martin Perl (1927–) Fredrick Reines (1918–)
1996 David M. Lee(1931–) Douglas D. Osherhoff (1945–) Robert C. Richardson (1937–)
1997 Steven Chu (1948–) Claude Cohen-Tannoudji (1933–) William D. Phillips (1948–)
1998 Robert B. Laughlin (1950–) Horst Stormer (1949–) Daniel C. Tsui (1939–)
1999 Gerardus 'T', Hooft (1946–) Martinus J.G. Veltman (1931–)
2000 Zhores L. Alferov (1930–) Herbert Kroemer (1928–) Jack St. C. Kilby (1923–)

# Numerical Answers to End-of-chapter Problems

## Chapter 1

**15. a)** 1200 s, **b)** 390 min, **c)** 14.4 h,
   **d)** $1.4 \times 18^8$ s, **e)** 0.126 h,
   **f)** $6.7 \times 10^{-7}$ a

**16. a)** $2.5 \times 10^8$ µs, 250 000 000 µs,
   **b)** $2.50 \times 10^5$ m·s, 250 000 ms
   **c)** $2.50 \times 10^{-1}$ ks, 0.250 ks,
   **d)** $2.50 \times 10^{-4}$ m·s, 0.000250 Ms

**17. a)** 6.9 m/s, **b)** 41.7 m/s,
   **c)** 7.2 km/h, **d)** 180 km/h

**18. a)** 316 people, **b)** 1810 ft

**19. a)** Yes, speed of 52.9 km/h
   **b)** 2963 times slower

**21. a)** 64000 mm, **b)** 32 m,
   **c)** 32.005 m, **d)** 24 m

**22. a)** 20.5 m, **b)** 49 m, **c)** 3543.6 m,
   **d)** 30.9 km

**23. a)** 125 m [E], **b)** 75 m [N],
   **c)** 95 m [W], **d)** 95 m [N], **e)** 0

**24. a)** 28 m/s [N], **b)** 22 m/s [S],
   **c)** 33 m/s [E], **d)** 27 m/s [S]

**25.** 73 km/h, 67 km/h

**27.** Slope: **a)** km/h, **b)** no units,
   **c)** kg/m$^3$, **d)** kg/s$^2$
   Area: **a)** km·h, **b)** m$^2$, **c)** kgm$^3$,
   **d)** kgm$^2$/s$^2$

**28.** A, C, F, H: standing; B,
   G: forward motion; D,
   E: backward motion

**29. a)** I 2.5 m/s; II 0 m/s; III −1.2 m/s
   **b)** I 4500 m·s; II 6000 m·s;
   III 6750 m·s

**30.** I 2.5 m/s; II 0; III −1.2 m/s

**31.** 72 m/s; 260 km/h

**32.** 1200 km/h

**33.** 20 mm/s

**34.** −20 mm/s

**38.** slopes: **i)** 0.6 m/s; **ii)** 0.5 m/s,
   **iii)** −0.3 m/s, **iv)** −1.2 m/s

**42.** average velocity
   AB 4.3 m/s; BC 0 m/s;
   BD −3.8 m/s; AD 0 m/s;
   AE −2.1 m/s; BE −5.8 m/s

**43.** AB: slope: 0.8 m/s
   CD: slope: 0.83 m/s

## Chapter 2

**14. b)** 43 km/h, 90 km/h, 0 km/h,
   −162 km/h, −500 km/h
   **c)** 0.21 m/s$^2$, 0 m/s$^2$, −0.21 m/s$^2$,
   −0.71 m/s$^2$, 0 m/s$^2$, −0.52 m/s$^2$

**d)** 1500 m, 4500 m, 1500 m,
   −3900 m, −5600 m, −16 560 m
**e)** −18600 m
**f)** 12.5 m/s, 25 m/s, 12 m/s,
   −37 m/s, −75 m/s, −140 m/s
**g)** −26 m/s
**h)** 47 m/s

**15. a)** 10 m/s, 47 m/s, 31 m/s, −9 m/s
   **b)** 2.9 m/s$^2$, 0, −3.9 m/s$^2$,
   −4.2 m/s$^2$
   **c)** 105–145
   **d)** 0 s, 26 s
   **e)** 10 s
   **f)** 10 s–14 s, 30 s

**16.** $\vec{a} = 4.8$ m/s$^2$

**17.** $\vec{a} = -3.95$ m/s$^2$

**19. b)** 1.4 m/s$^2$; −.87 m/s$^2$, −.87 m/s$^2$,
   .20 m/s$^2$, 0.10 m/s$^2$

**20. a)** 17.5 m, 28 m, −21 m, −80 m,
   −20 m
   **b)** −75 m

**21. b)** 3.8 s
   **c)** no
   **e)** yes
   **f)** B is 28 m ahead of A

**33.** 10.2 m/s, 10.4 m/s, 9.20 m/s

**34.** 6300 m = 6.3 km

**35.** 4.2 m

**36.** 2.8 h

**37.** 72 m

**38.** 100 m

**39.** 540 s

**40.** $3.3 \times 10^{-5}$ s, 29 s

**41.** 1.3 s

**42.** 5.8 m/s = 21 km/h

**43.** 28 m/s, slowing down

**44.** 4.1 m/s$^2$

**45.** 5.5 m/s

**46.** −162 m/s$^2$

**47.** 19 m/s$^2$

**48.** −1.7 m/s$^2$

**49.** −2500 m/s$^2$

**50.** 1.5 s

**51.** 19 m/s

**52.** 9.3 m/s

**53.** −18 m/s

**54.** 10.6 s

**55.** 10 s

**56.** 38 m, 17 m/s

**57.** 22 m, 4.8 m/s

**58.** 17 m, 12 s

**59.** $-2.5 \times 10^5$ km/h$^2$

**60.** −15 m, 3.1 s

**61. a)** 4.8 m, **b)** 120 m,
   **c)** 390 m, **d)** 950 m

**62.** 4.0 m/s$^2$, 97 m

**63.** 15 m

**65.** 1300 m

**66. a)** 7.5 s, **b)** 3.8 m/s, **c)** 14 m, 23 m

**67.** 3.53 m/s$^2$

**68. a)** 15 s, **b)** 427 m, **c)** 55 m/s

## Chapter 3

**14. a)** $\vec{v}_{f_{max}} = 10$ m/s [E];
   $\vec{v}_{f_{min}} = 2$ m/s [W]

**15. a)** 0
   **b)** 0.5 km [N37°E]
   **c)** 0.5 km [W53°S]
   **d)** 2.4 km/h
   **e)** 2.4 km/h [E53°N]

**18. a)** 9.8 m/s, 20 m/s, 29 m/s, 39 m/s
   **b)** 17 m/s [R35° D],
   24 m/s [R55°D],
   32 m/s [R64°D],
   41 m/s [R70°D]

**19. a)** 0 m/s, 9.8 m/s, 20 m/s, 29 m/s
   **b)** 9.8 m/s, 9.8 m/s, 9.8 m/s,
   9.8 m/s
   **c)** 9.8 m/s [E], 14 m/s [R45°D],
   22 m/s [R64°D],
   31 m/s [R71°D]

**20.** 150 m

**21.** 140 m

**22. a)** 0.64 s, **b)** 210 m

**23.** 32 m

**24.** 2.60 m

**25. a)** land at same time
   **b)** 2.0 m

**26.** (22) 330 m/s [R1.1°D],
   (23) 45 m/s [R9.0°D]
   (24) 40 m/s [R10°D]

**27. a)** 550 m, **b)** 950 m, **c)** 100 m/s,
   **d)** 130 m/s [R48°D]

**28. a)** 14 s **b)** 1100 m
   **c)** 160 m/s [60°D]

**29. a)** 1000 m **b)** 1100 m **c)** 230 m

**30.** 8.5 m

**31.** yes

**32.** yes

**33. a)** 24 m, **b)** $t_{average} = 4.3$ s,
   **c)** 27 m/s [R53°D]

**35.** 701.5 km/h, 98.5 km/h

**36. a)** −35 km/h, **b)** 35 km/h,
   **c)** 135 km/h, **d)** 135 km/h

**37.** 28 km/h [E20°S]
**38.** 186 km/h [W36°S]
**39. a)** [S18°E] **b)** 33 km/h [S]
   **c)** 1.6 h
**40.** 220 s
**41.** 16 km/h [E22°N]
**42. a)** 3°
   **b)** 0.57 s
**43.** 280 s
**46.** $x$ component, $y$ component;
   **a)** 29 km/h, 45 km/h
   **b)** −23 km/h, 66 km/h
   **c)** 41 km/h, 13 km/h
   **d)** −35 km/h, −35 km/h
   **e)** 21 km/h, −17 km/h
**47. a)** 6.1 km/h **b)** 5.1 km/h **c)** 0
**48. a)** 71 km/h [W45°S]
   **b)** 50000 km/h² [W45°S]
**49.** $\Delta \vec{v}$ = 17 km/h [E10°S],
   $\vec{a}$ = 12000 km/h² [E10°S]
**50.** 26 m/s [E73°N]
**51. a)** $5.2 \times 10^{-3}$ m/s
   **b)** $4.9 \times 10^{-4}$ m/s² [S45°W]
   **c)** $4.9 \times 10^{-4}$ m/s² [N45°E]
**52. a)** $4.4 \times 10^{-4}$ m/s **b)** 60°
   **c)** $7.3 \times 10^{-7}$ m/s² [W60°S]
**53.** 9.6 m/s² [E60°N]
**54.** 190 km [E82°N]
**55.** 40 km [E12°N]
**56. a)** 176 m **b)** 49 m [E45°N]
   **c)** [S45°W]
**57.** $v$ = 1.2 km/h, $\vec{v}$ = 0.33 km/h
   [E45°N]
**58. a)** 130 km/h [E18°S] **b)** 7.9 h
**59. a)** 20 km/h [N21°W] **b)** 3.2 min
**60.** heading: [E21°N];
   ground speed: 28 km/h
**61.** 1.7 m/s [E]
**62. a)** [Back 12°Right]
   **b)** 3.0 m/s [Back 20°Right]
   **c)** 10 s

## Chapter 4

**19. a)** 200 N
   **b)** 5.6 N
   **c)** 8.8 N
   **d)** 280 N
**20. a)** 1.2 m/s²
   **b)** $2 \times 10^4$ m/s²
   **c)** $3.0 \times 10^{-7}$ m/s²
   **d)** 0.23 m/s²
**21.** 2900 N
**22. a)** 7500 N
   **b)** 11 m/s²
**23.** 102 kg

**24.** 756 N
**25.** $\vec{F}_{jet}$ = $1.5 \times 10^5$ N
   $\vec{F}_{jet\ fighter}$ = $1.6 \times 10^6$ N
**26.** $1.9 \times 10^4$ N
**27.** 92 N
**28.** $\vec{a}$ = −1.2 m/s² 170 g
**29.** 10900 N [S]
**30.** 0.38 m/s
**31.** 233 N
**32.** 467 N
**34.** pictures
**35. a)** 0.8 m/s²
   **b)** 1.53 m/s²
   **c)** 8.33 m/s²
**36. a)** $\vec{F}_{net}$ = 4.0 N, $\vec{a}$ = 4 m/s²
   **b)** $\vec{F}_{net}$ = 3.0N, $m$ = 1.5 kg
   **c)** $\vec{F}_{net}$ = 0, F₁ = −7.0 N
   **d)** $\vec{F}_{net}$ = 0, $\vec{a}$ = 0, $\vec{F}_1$ = 2.5 N
   **e)** $\vec{F}_{net}$ = 6.0 N, $\vec{F}_1 = F_2$ = 2.0 N
   **f)** $\vec{F}_{net}$ = 2.5 N, $\vec{F}_1$ = 8.5 N
   **g)** $\vec{F}_{net}$ = −3 N, $m$ = 0.6 kg
   **h)** $\vec{a}$ = 0, $\vec{F}_{net}$ = 0, $\vec{F}_1$ = 10 N,
   Mass can have any value
   **i)** $\vec{F}_{net}$ = $1.8 \times 10^{-2}$ N = $\vec{F}_2$
   = $3.6 \times 10^{-2}$
**37.** 1.5 m/s²
**38. a)** 1.1 m/s²
   **b)** 7.8 m/s
**39. a)** 1.4 m/s²
   **b)** 2.9 N
**40. a)** 1.2 m/s²
   **b)** 8.8 N
   **c)** 2.5 N
   **d)** 8.8 N, 2.5 N
**41. a)** 0. 42 s
   **b)** 0.59 m
**42.** 10900 N
**43. a)** −3.0 m/s²
   **b)** down
   **c)** 150 m
**44. a)** −15 N, 0
   **b)** 40 N, 40 N
   **c)** 2.5 N, −1.0 N
   **d)** 30 N, −10 N
**45. a)** 15 N [S]
   **b)** 57 N [E45°N]
   **c)** 2.7 N [W68°N]
   **d)** 32 N [W72°N]
**46.** $\vec{a}$ = 0.34 m/s² [FORWARD]
**47.** $\vec{a}$ = 0.13 m/s² [FORWARD]
**48.** $\vec{a}$ = 0.14 m/s² [E85°N]
**49.** $\vec{a}$ = 0.42 m/s² [L12°U]
**50.** $\vec{a}$ = 0.56 m/s² [R25°U]
**51. a)** $\vec{a}$ = $1.4 \times 10^{-3}$ m/s² [R3.5°U]
   **b)** $\vec{a}$ = $1.2 \times 10^{-3}$ m/s [R4.0°U]
   **c)** 0.17 m/s, 0.15 m/s

   **d)** 680 m, 770 m
**52. a)** 40°
   **b)** $F_{net_x}$ = 120 N
   **c)** 57 s
**54. b)** $\vec{a}_L$ = −0.50 m/s²
   $\vec{a}_c$ = 0.45 m/s²
**55. b)** $\vec{a}_L$ = −1.0 m/s²
   $\vec{a}_c$ = 0.89 m/s²
**56.** $\vec{a}_L$ = −0.95 m/s²
   $\vec{a}_c$ = 0.85 m/s²

## Chapter 5

**20. a)** $1.60 \times 10^{-7}$ N
   **b)** $5.2 \times 10^{-6}$ N
   **c)** 0.21 N
   **d)** $2.0 \times 10^{-10}$ N
**21.** $3.83 \times 10^8$ m
**22.** $6.2 \times 10^8$ kg
**23. a)** 668 N
   **b)** 664 N
   **c)** 107 N
**24.** $g_{Mars}$ = 3.61 m/s²
   $g_{Jupiter}$ = 24.6 m/s²
   $g_{Mercury}$ = 3.31 m/s²
**25.** $\vec{F}_{Earth}$ = 757 N
   $\vec{F}_{Mars}$ = 278 N
   $\vec{F}_{Jupiter}$ = 1890 N
   $\vec{F}_{Mercury}$ = 255 N
**26.** $r$ = $6.41 \times 10^6$
   $h$ = $3.25 \times 10^4$
**27.** $r$ = $6.32 \times 10^6$
   $h$ = $5.68 \times 10^7$ m
**28. a)** 109 N
   **b)** 20.0 N
   **c)** 2.43 N
   **d)** 48.4 N
   **e)** 0.072 N
**29. a)** 2000 N
   **b)** 32 000 N
   **c)** 1150 N
**30.** $t_{Earth}$ = 10.4 s
   $t_{Mars}$ = 5.53 s
   $t_{Jupiter}$ = 6.71 s
   $t_{Mercury}$ = 18.3 s
**31. a)** 5.82 N
   **b)** $5.82 \times 10^{-3}$ N/kg
**32.** 392 N
**33. a)** no change
   **b)** greater
   **c)** no change
   **d)** less
**34.** weight = 686 N
   $\vec{a}$ = 0.91 m/s²
**35. a)** 1300 N
   **b)** 1013 N

**36.** 0.9 N
**37.** 7.3 N
**38.** 437 N
**39. a)** 0.27 N
  **b)** 0.20 N
  **c)** does not move
**40. a)** 52 N
  **b)** 0.42 m/s$^2$
**41.** 0.89
**42.** 0.32
**43.** crate can't move (friction too large)
**44.** $\vec{F}_A > 392$ N, any $\vec{F}_A$ will start fridge moving
**45.** $\vec{F}_A > 451$ N
**46. a)** 19 N
  **b)** $-3.33$ m/s$^2$
  **c)** 1.16 m
  **d)** 0.83 s
**47. a)** 5.04 N
  **b)** 99 N
**48.** $2.26 \times 10^4$ N
**49. a)** 0.45 m/s$^2$
  **b)** 2.86 N
**50. a)** 0.27 m/s$^2$
  **b)** $\vec{F}_{T_1} = 8.8$ N
   $\vec{F}_{T_2} = 2.5$ N
**51. a)** 62 N/m
  **b)** N·m
**52. a)** 17 N
  **b)** 32 N
  **c)** 59 N
**53. a)** 0.33 m
  **b)** 0.18 m
  **c)** $1.64 \times 10^{-3}$ m
**54.** 1.68 lb
**55.** 1.2 m/s$^2$
**56.** 2900 N/m
**57.** 5200 N
**58.** 0.9 m
**59.** 3.1 m/s$^2$

## Chapter 6

**16. a)** 480 kg·m/s
  **b)** 40800 kg·m/s
  **c)** 2.3 kg·m/s
  **d)** 722800 kg·m/s
  **e)** $7.25 \times 10^{-3}$ kg·m/s
**17. a)** 2.86 kg·m/s
  **b)** 2.86 kg·m/s
**18. a)** 7000 kg·m/s
  **b)** 7000 kg·m/s
**19. a)** 84000 kg·m/s
  **b)** 84000 kg·m/s
**20. a)** 1750 Ns
  **b)** 0.3 Ns

**c)** $-230$ Ns
**21.** 0.8 m/s
**22.** 63.56 m/s
**23. a)** 1500 kgm/s
  **b)** 25 m/s
**24.** 2592 km/hr
**25.** 3.3 m/s
**26. a)** 320 N
  **b)** 32 N
**27. a)** $-370$ N
  **b)** $-1470$ N
  **c)** $-48900$ N
**28. a)** $-21800$ N
  **b)** $-19.8$ kgm/s
  **c)** $-19.8$ kgm/s
**29. a)** 168 N
  **b)** 2800 m/s$^2$
**30. a)** $-500$ kgm/s
  **b)** $-500$ kgm/s
  **c)** $-455$ N
  **d)** 2.29 m
**31.** 5.2 m/s
**32.** 9.4 m/s
**33.** 7.2 m/s
**34.** 3.1 m/s
**35.** 0.6 m/s
**36.** 0.11 m/s
**37.** 8.6 m/s
**38. a)** $1.79 \times 10^{-10}$ m/s
  **b)** 29700 m/s
**39.** $-145$ m/s
**40. a)** 44 m/s
  **b)** 52 kg·m/s
  **c)** $-52$ kg·m/s
  **d)** $1.3 \times 10^{-3}$ s
  **e)** $-4.0 \times 10^4$ N
  **f)** $1.6 \times 10^5$ m/s$^2$
**41. a)** $8.33 \times 10^4$ kg·m/s
  **b)** $-83300$ kg·m/s
  **c)** 1372 N
  **d)** 61 s
  **e)** 250 m

## Chapter 7

**12.** 62.5 J
**13.** 0 J
**14.** 0 J
**15.** $1.2 \times 10^3$ N
**16.** 1.04 m
**17.** 62 J
**18. a)** $1.1 \times 10^4$ J
  **b)** $1.1 \times 10^4$ J
  **c)** $1.1 \times 10^4$ J
**19.** $6.0 \times 10^4$ J
**20.** 25 kg

**21.** $2.0 \times 10^5$ J
**22.** $2.83 \times 10^3$ J
**23.** $1.50 \times 10^3$ W
**24.** $2.88 \times 10^6$ J
**25.** $8.3 \times 10^3$ W
**26.** 0.750 s
**27.** 0.158 m/s
**28.** $6.8 \times 10^4$ W
**29. a)** 3.00 J
  **b)** 18.8 J
**30.** 7.40 kg
**31.** 78.2 J
**32.** $4.9 \times 10^5$ J
**33.** 54 km/h
**34.** $3.9 \times 10^3$ J
**35. a)** $3.7 \times 10^3$ m/s
  **b)** $7.5 \times 10^3$ J
**36. a)** 7.00 J
  **b)** 4.85 J
  **c)** 0.81 J
**37. a)** 41 J
  **b)** 92 J
  **c)** $-10$ J
**38.** 75 %
**39.** $1.34 \times 10^4$ J, $1.71 \times 10^4$ J
**40.** 7.4 J
**41.** $E_k = 2.5 \times 10^3$ J, $E_g = 12.0 \times 10^3$ J
**42.** 457.1 m/s
**43.** 2.59 m
**44.** 34.3 m/s
**45.** 71.6 %
**46.** 0.50 m/s
**47. a)** $3.66 \times 10^3$ J
  **b)** $3.78 \times 10^3$ J
  **c)** 96.8 %

## Chapter 8

**23. a)** 373 K
  **b)** 248 K
  **c)** 0 K
  **d)** 273 K
  **e)** $-216$°C
  **f)** 27°C
**24.** $3.36 \times 10^5$ J
**25.** $2.7 \times 10^4$ J
**26.** 108°C
**27. a)** $A = 4.2$ kJ/°C
  **b)** 2.5 kJ/°C
  **c)** 2.0 kJ/°C
**28. a)** 55.1°C
  **b)** 4.8°C
**29.** $4.60 \times 10^2$ J
**30.** 88.6°C
**31.** 2.87 kg
**32.** 33 kg or 33 L

**33. a)** $1.20 \times 10^4$ J
  **b)** $2.0 \times 10^3$ J/kg°C
**34. a)** $5.62 \times 10^4$ J/kg
  **b)** $5.62 \times 10^4$ J
**35.** 5.3 kg
**36.** $4.0 \times 10^5$ J
**37.** $6.4 \times 10^5$ J
**38.** $6.7 \times 10^5$ J
**39.** lead
**40.** 0.477 kg

## Chapter 9

**21. a)** either north or south
  **b)** west
**22.** lower, middle, top
**23.** $1.01 \times 10^{-6}$ s
**24.** 229 days
**25.** yes, in 11 s
**26.** $2.99 \times 10^8$ m/s
**27.** $2.83 \times 10^8$ m/s
**28.** stationary (26 years),
  traveller (23.75 years)
**29.** $7.07 \times 10^6$ m/s
**30.** infinite amount of time
**31.** 2.2 m tall
**32.** $1.2 \times 10^{-6}$ m
**33.** $5.4 \times 10^2$ kg
**34.** 0.14 m
**35. a)** 0.503 kg
  **b)** 1.14 kg
**36.** $2.6 \times 10^8$ m/s
**37.** $2.12 \times 10^8$ m/s
**38.** $1333.33
**39.** $9.0 \times 10^{18}$ J
**40.** $3.6 \times 10^{-28}$ kg
**41.** $1.8 \times 10^{-13}$ J
**42.** $5.22 \times 10^{-4}$ kg
**43.** $4.59 \times 10^{20}$ J
**44.** $1.64 \times 10^{-13}$ J

In questions, all angles without decimal places are assumed exact.

## Chapter 10

**16. a)** 4 m
  **b)** 10 cm
  **c)** 8.0 s
  **d)** 0.12 s$^{-1}$
  **e)** 0.5 m/s
**17. a)** 8 m, 10 cm, 16.0 s, 0.062 s$^{-1}$,
   0.5 m/s
  **b)** 2 m, 10 cm, 4.0 s, 0.25 s$^{-1}$,
   0.5 m/s
**18.** 0.32 s, 3.1 s$^{-1}$
**19.** 0.83 s, 1.2 s

**20.** 0.017 s
**21. a)** 2.5 rev/s
  **b)** 0.4 s
**22. i)** 1.3 Hz, 0.77 s
  **ii)** 0.75 Hz, 1.3 s
  **iii)** 0.555 Hz, 1.80 s
**22. i)** 4800
  **ii)** 2800
  **iii)** 2100
**24. a)** $4.62 \times 10^{16}$ Hz
  **b)** $5.00 \times 10^{16}$ Hz
  **c)** $5.17 \times 10^{16}$ Hz
  **d)** $5.77 \times 10^{16}$ Hz
  **e)** $6.32 \times 10^{16}$ Hz
  **f)** $7.5 \times 10^{16}$ Hz
**25. a)** 0.138 h
  **b)** $3.53 \times 10^{-4}$ h
  **c)** 5.36 h
  **d)** 0.0842 h
**26. a) i)** $1.79 \times 10^9$ s
   **ii)** $4.56 \times 10^6$ s
   **iii)** $6.96 \times 10^{10}$ s
   **iv)** $1.092 \times 10^9$ s
  **b) i)** $1.79 \times 10^7$ s
   **ii)** $4.59 \times 10^4$ s
   **iii)** $6.96 \times 10^8$ s
   **iv)** $1.092 \times 10^7$ s
**27.** $9.4608 \times 10^{15}$ m
**28.** 100 years
**29.** $5.33 \times 10^{-7}$ s
**30.** $1.38 \times 10^7$
**31.** $-0.8$
**32.** 0.8 cm, $-0.8$
**33.** 618 cm
**34.** 128 m
**35.** 65 cm
**36.** 20.5 cm
**40.** yes, yes, no, no
**41.** 23°
**42.** 50°
**44.** 4.5 m
**45.** no
**46.** (1) inverted, real, same size
   (2) inverted, real, larger
   (3) inverted, real, smaller
**47.** virtual, larger, upright
**48.** at focus
**49.** 20 cm, 100 cm
**50.** virtual, smaller, upright
**54. a)** 60 cm
  **b)** 0.2
  **c)** 1.6 cm
  **d)** real, inverted, smaller
**55. a)** 30 cm
  **b)** 30 cm
  **c)** $-1$

  **d)** 1.5 cm
  **e)** inverted, real, same size
**56. a)** $-41$ cm
  **b)** 3.4
  **c)** 75 cm
  **d)** upright larger, virtual
**57. a)** at focus (20 cm)
  **b)** $\infty$
**58. a)** 18 m
  **b)** $1.21 \times 10^{-10}$
  **c)** 17.0 cm
**59. a)** diverging
  **b)** negative
  **c)** $-3.55$ cm
  **d)** 0.355, 3.55 cm
  **e)** virtual, smaller, upright
**61. a)** $-8.3$ m
  **b)** 0.83, 1.5 m
  **c)** virtual, smaller, upright
**62.** 20 cm
**63. a)** 10 cm
  **b)** $-20$ cm
  **c)** virtual, upright, larger

## Chapter 11

**28. a)** $1.24 \times 10^8$ m/s
  **b)** $1.97 \times 10^8$ m/s
  **c)** $2.26 \times 10^8$ m/s
  **d)** $2.31 \times 10^8$ m/s
**29. a)** 0.413
  **b)** 0.658
  **c)** 0.752
  **d)** 0.769
**30. a)** 1.90
  **b)** 1.46
  **c)** 1.50
  **d)** 0.79
**31.** $5.32 \times 10^{-5}$ s
**32. a)** $1.25 \times 10^8$ m/s
  **b)** 2.4
  **c)** diamond
**33. a)** 0.5
  **b)** 0.87
  **c)** 0.71
  **d)** 0.218
  **e)** 0.96
  **f)** 0.0
  **g)** 1.0
**34. a)** 20.0°
  **b)** 40.0°
  **c)** 44.4°
  **d)** 19.4°
  **e)** 90.0°
**35. a)** 22.1°
  **b)** 11.9°

**c)** 21.6°
**d)** 15.3°
**36. a)** 29.2°
**b)** 15.6°
**c)** 28.6°
**d)** 20.0°
**37. a)** 24.8°
**b)** 4.11°
**c)** 7.50°
**d)** 5.48°
**38. a)** 1.28
**b)** 2.40
**c)** 1.27
**39. a)** 1.71
**b)** 3.20
**c)** 1.69
**40.** air → glass 13.0°
glass → water 14.9°
glass → air 10°
water → glass 13°
**41.** $2.26 \times 10^8$ m/s
**42.** 2.3 m
**43.** 2.0 m
**44.** 319 cm
**45. a)** red: 19.2°, violet: 18.9°
**b)** red: 29.99°, violet: 29.92°
**50. a)** 24.4°
**b)** 48.8°
**c)** 41.8°
**d)** 33.3°
**51. a)** 2.00
**b)** 2.66
**52.** glass → water 61.0°
glass → air 41.1°
**53.** diamond → zircon 51.7°
diamond → ice 32.5°
zircon → ice 43.2°
**54. a)** inverted, same size, real
**b)** inverted, larger, real
**c)** no image
**d)** upright, real, larger
**55. a)** smaller, virtual, upright
**b)** smaller, virtual, upright
**c)** smaller, virtual, upright
**d)** smaller, virtual, upright
**56. a)** smaller, inverted
**b)** larger, inverted
**c)** larger, virtual
**57. a)** −380 cm, 60 mm
**b)** −60 cm, 12 mm
**c)** −20 cm, 6 mm
**d)** −5 cm, 3.8 mm
**58. a)** virtual, smaller, upright
**b)** virtual, smaller, upright
**c)** virtual, smaller, upright
**e)** virtual, smaller, upright

**61.** 0.4
**62.** 0.14
**64. a)** 30 cm, −1, −5 cm
**b)** 37.5 cm, −1.25, −6.25 cm
**c)** no image
**d)** −30 cm, 1, 5 cm
**65. a)** −10 cm, 0.33 cm, 1.7 cm
**b)** −9.375 cm, 0.3125, 1.56 cm
**c)** −7.5 cm, 0.5, 2.5 cm
**d)** −6.0 cm, 0.6, 3.0 cm
**66. a)** 6.25 cm, −0.25, −1.25 cm
**b)** 100 cm, −4, −20 cm
**c)** −50 cm, 2, 10 cm
**67. a)** −380 cm, 20, 60 mm
**b)** −60 cm, 4, 12 mm
**c)** −20 cm, 2, 6 mm
**d)** −5 cm, 1.25, 3.8 mm
**68. a)** −9.74 cm, 0.65, 2.0 mm
**b)** −8.7 cm, 0.58, 1.7 mm
**c)** −6.67 cm, 0.44, 1.3 mm
**d)** −3.33 cm, 0.22, 0.66 mm
**69.** 35 mm: 0.035 m, −0.007,
−1.05 cm
100 mm: 0.102 m, 0.020, 3.0 cm
**70.** 35 mm
**71.** −10 cm, 2, 12 mm
**72. a)** −10 cm
**b)** 5.0 cm
**c)** convex
**75. a)** 10 diopters
**b)** 3.3 diopters
**c)** −2.5 diopters
**76. a)** −0.20 m
**b)** 2
**c)** convex
**71. a)** 0.8 m
**b)** −0.4 m
**c)** concave
**78. a)** 12.75 cm
**b)** real image
**c)** −3.33 cm
**d)** virtual image
**e)** −20 mm
**f)** 20
**g)** upright

## Chapter 12

**17.** $6.65 \times 10^{14}$ s$^{-1}$
**18.** $5.5 \times 10^{14}$ s$^{-1}$
**19. a)** $7.35 \times 10^{14}$ s$^{-1}$
**b)** $6.5 \times 10^{14}$ s$^{-1}$
**20. a)** moving away
**b)** $2.00 \times 10^6$ m/s
**c)** 596 Nm
**21.** 138 km/h

**22. a)** 188 km/h
**b)** 88 km/h
**23.** $2.03 \times 10^{10}$ s$^{-1}$
**24. a)** 53.1°
**b)** 56.3°
**c)** 41.6°
**d)** 45.7°
**25.** 1.73
**27. a)** 97.0%
**b)** 75%
**c)** 11.7%
**d)** 0.76%
**28.** 39.2°
**29.** 2.9%
**30. a)** more than red
**b)** 1.75
**31.** 468 Nm
**32.** $4.0 \times 10^{-12}$
**33. a)** $\frac{\lambda}{2}$
**b)** $\frac{3\lambda}{4}$
**c)** $\frac{\lambda}{4}$
**35. a)** 7.9°
**b)** 4.0°
**c)** 24.4°
**d)** 20°
**36.** $3.2 \times 10^{-6}$ m
**37.** $5.36 \times 10^{-6}$ m
**38.** $2.14 \times 10^{-4}$ m
**39.** 0.3°
**40.** 15
**41.** 21.6 m
**42. a)** $3.25 \times 10^{-7}$ m
**b)** $\frac{1}{2}$
**43. a)** 7.4°
**b)** 5.5°
**44.** $8.37 \times 10^{-7}$ m
**45.** $6.74 \times 10^{-6}$ m
**46. a)** 17.4 cm
**b)** 14.5 m
**47.** 5.39°
**48. a)** 6.2 mm
**b)** 0.10°
**49. a)** λ < w
**b)** 1
**50. a)** constructive
**b)** destructive
**c)** constructive
**d)** constructive
**51.** minimum (dark)
**52. a)** $1.5 \times 10^{-7}$ m
**b)** $3.00 \times 10^{-7}$ m
**53. a)** $2.25 \times 10^{-7}$ m
**b)** $1.38 \times 10^{-7}$ m

# Chapter 13

24. a) 125 Hz
    b) 0.008 s
25. a) 0.92 Hz
    b) 1.08 s
26. a) 0.75 m
    b) 0.80 m
    c) 0.77 m
27. a) 350 m/s
    b) 1260 km/h
28. $\lambda$ = 187 500 m
    750 football fields
29. a) 3.4 m
    b) 0.008 s
    c) 425 m/s
30. a) 0.15 m/s
    b) 200 m/s
    c) 15 m/s
    d) 2500 m/s
    e) $5.1 \times 10^7$ m/s
31. a) $\vec{v}$ = 38 m/s
    b) $\vec{v}$ = 50 m/s
    c) $\vec{v}$ = 0.0063 m/s
    d) $\vec{v}$ = $3.5 \times 10^{-4}$ m/s
32. $\lambda$ = 0.782 m
    383 wavelengths
33. a) 2.06 s
    b) 1.38 s
    c) 0.39 s
    d) 4.26 s
34. a) 1.23 m
    b) 1.267 m
    c) 0.1119 m
    d) 0.3428 m
35. a) 332 m/s
    b) 347 m/s
    c) 350 m/s
    d) 323 m/s
36. $3.84 \times 10^{-3}$ m
37. 2454.2 m
38. 48.7 m
39. 13.3°C boxed too!
    $v$ = 340 m/s boxed too!
40. 690 m
41. $\Delta d$ = 5100 m
    $\Delta t$ = 14.8 s
42. a) $\Delta t$ = 1.00 s you
    b) $\Delta t$ = $1.0 \times 10^{-5}$ s friend
    friend hears it first
43. 0.676 m (air)
    2.90 m (water)
    4.3
44. a) 2, supersonic
    b) 0.91, subsonic

c) 0.12, subsonic
    d) 6.0, supersonic
45. a) 0.95
    b) 1.04
    c) 4.90
    d) 5.14
46. 2550 m
47. 5.29
48. a) $7.86 \times 10^3$ m/s
    b) 3140 m/s
49. a) $1.5 \times 10^{-6}$ w/m$^2$
    b) $3.8 \times 10^{-7}$ w/m$^2$
    c) $2.4 \times 10^{-5}$ w/m$^2$
    d) $5.4 \times 10^{-5}$ w/m$^2$
50. 3.5 m away
51. $5.45 \times 10^{-4}$ w/m$^2$
52. a) 62.5 m$^2$
    b) 11.4
    c) 3.37
53. a) 2
    b) 3
    c) −2
    d) −3.46
    e) 6.75
    f) 0
    g) does not exist
54. a) log 100
    b) log 1000000
    c) log 0.01
    d) log 0.000001
    e) log 3162.28
    f) log 2.24
55. a) 1.26
    b) 2.51
    c) 0.79
    d) 0.50
    e) 1.78
    f) 1.12
56. a) $10^7$
    b) $10^{11}$
    c) 10
    d) $3.2 \times 10^5$
57. a) $8.75 \times 10^{-7}$ w/m$^2$
    b) 6 dB
58. a) 1000
    b) 158.5
    c) 77.6
59. 250
60. 20 m back
61. 100
62. 10
63. 316 228
64. a) 1840 Hz
    b) 1580 Hz
    c) 1930 Hz

65. a) 1830 Hz
    b) 1590 Hz
    c) 1910 Hz
66. 9.49 m/s
67. 58 m/s
68. 86 m/s
69. 344 Hz
70. a) 1960 Hz
    b) 1640 Hz
71. a) 1980 Hz
    b) 1650 Hz

# Chapter 14

6. a) bottle
   b) skin on drum
   c) pipes
   d) strings
   e) door
17. 0.32 m
18. $f_1 = f_2 = 1.0 = 10^3$ Hz (unchanged)
19. 4315 Hz
21. #3, mechanical resonance
22. 0.480 m, decrease base
    fundamental frequency
23. 0.40 m
24. a) 347 m/s
    b) 0.365 m
    c) 18.3 cm
25. 8.54 cm
26. a) 92.0 cm, 120 cm
    b) 371 Hz, 284 Hz
    c) 15°C
27. a) 20 cm
    b) 1720 Hz
28. 578 Hz
29. a) 347 m/s
    b) 1.7 m
    c) $2.1 \times 10^2$ Hz
30. 1448 Hz
31. a) 900 Hz
    b) 1150 Hz
    c) 970 Hz
    d) 1035 Hz
32. a) 1100 Hz
    b) 778 Hz
33. b) 4.0 cm
    c) $8.6 \times 10^3$ Hz
34. 424 Hz
35. 197 Hz
36. 2$^{nd}$ – 1536 Hz, 4$^{th}$ – 2560 Hz,
    5$^{th}$ – 3072 Hz
37. a) 12 Hz
    b) 5 Hz
    c) 24 Hz

**38.** yes, 444 Hz and 436 Hz,
   444 Hz—reduce tension,
   436 Hz—increase tension
**39.** 515 Hz and 509 Hz

## Chapter 15

**10.** (+) protons, (−) electrons
**11. a)** 0
   **b)** −
   **c)** +
   **d)** 0 neutral
   **e)** +
**12. a)** rubber (−)
   **b)** silk (+)
   **c)** acetate (−)
   **d)** glass (+)
**13. a)** negative(−)
   **b)** electrons
**14.** glass (+), silk (−)
**15.** same as balloon (−)
**16. a)** insulator
   **b)** conductor
   **c)** insulator
   **d)** insulator
   **e)** insulator
   **f)** insulator
**17.** shortest path to ground
**19.** detect charge
**20. a)** positive, contact
   **b)** repel
   **c)** return to normal
**21.** $9.38 \times 10^{19}$ electrons
**22.** $6.98 \times 10^{12}$ electrons
**23.** $+ 6.4 \times 10^{-8}$ C
**24.** $4.3 \times 10^{-11}$ C
**25.** $1.5 \times 10^{7}$ electrons

## Chapter 16

**9.** $1.3 \times 10^{3}$ s
**10.** $9.1 \times 10^{2}$ C
**11.** $2.0 \times 10^{3}$ V
**12.** 3.8 V
**13.** $8.01 \times 10^{-14}$ J
**14.** $4.1 \times 10^{3}$ J
**15.** $1.2 \times 10^{2}$ V
**16.** $6.0 \times 10^{4}$ J
**17.** 6.9 A
**18.** $4.6 \times 10^{4}$ J
**19.** $2.4 \times 10^{2}$ V
**20. a)** $1.5 \times 10^{3}$ A
   **b)** $4.5 \times 10^{9}$ J
**21.** $1.602 \times 10^{-19}$ C
**22.** $9.1 \times 10^{5}$ J
**23.** $20 \ \Omega$

**24.** 0.33 A
**25.** $1.1 \times 10^{2}$ V
**26.** $200 \ \Omega$
**27.** $2000 \ \Omega$
**28.** $2.2 \ \Omega$
**29. a)** $3.2 \times 10^{1} \ \Omega$
   **b)** $1.3 \ \Omega$
   **c)** 4.8 V
**30. a)** $2.3 \times 10^{1} \ \Omega$
   **b)** $12 \ \Omega$
**31. a)** $110 \ \Omega$
   **b)** $3.2 \ \Omega$
   **c)** $5.8 \ \Omega$
**32.** 5
**33.** $10 \ \Omega$
**34.** $35 \ \Omega$
**35. a)** $V_1 = 24$ V, $I_1 = 3$ A, $R_1 = 8 \ \Omega$
   $V_2 = 9$ V, $I_2 = 3$ A, $R_2 = 3 \ \Omega$
   $V_3 = 21$ V, $I_3 = 3$ A, $R_3 = 7 \ \Omega$
   $V_T = 54$ V, $I_T = 3$ A, $R_T = 18 \ \Omega$
**35. b)** $V_1 = 9$ V, $I_1 = 2$ A, $R_1 = 4.5 \ \Omega$
   $V_2 = 9$ V, $I_2 = 2$ A, $R_2 = 4.5 \ \Omega$
   $V_T = 9$ V, $I_T = 4$ A, $R_T = 2.25 \ \Omega$
**35. c)** $V_1 = 24.2$ V, $I_1 = 0.97$ A,
   $R_1 = 25 \ \Omega$
   $V_2 = 24.2$ V, $I_2 = 1.01$ A,
   $R_2 = 15 \ \Omega$
   $V_3 = 25.8$ V, $I_3 = 2.58$ A,
   $R_3 = 10 \ \Omega$
   $V_T = 50$ V, $I_T = 2.58$ A,
   $R_T = 19.4 \ \Omega$
**35. d)** $V_1 = 75$ V, $I_1 = 3$ A, $R_1 = 25 \ \Omega$
   $V_2 = 20$ V, $I_2 = 2$ A, $R_2 = 10 \ \Omega$
   $V_3 = 5$ V, $I_3 = 1$ A, $R_3 = 5 \ \Omega$
   $V_4 = 15$ V, $I_4 = 1$ A, $R_4 = 15 \ \Omega$
   $V_T = 95$ V, $I_T = 3$ A,
   $R_T = 31.7 \ \Omega$
**35. e)** $V_1 = 29.5$ V, $I_1 = 5.9$ A,
   $R_1 = 5 \ \Omega$
   $V_2 = 2.5$ V, $I_2 = 2.5$ A,
   $R_2 = 1 \ \Omega$
   $V_3 = 2.5$ V, $I_3 = 0.17$ A,
   $R_3 = 15 \ \Omega$
   $V_4 = 2.5$ V, $I_4 = 0.25$ A,
   $R_4 = 10 \ \Omega$
   $V_5 = 2.5$ V, $I_5 = 2.5$ A,
   $R_5 = 1 \ \Omega$
   $V_6 = 118$ V, $I_6 = 5.9$ A,
   $R_6 = 20 \ \Omega$
   $V_T = 150$ V, $I_T = 5.9$ A,
   $R_T = 25.5 \ \Omega$
**35. f)** $V_1 = 6$ V, $I_1 = 0.40$ A,
   $R_1 = 15 \ \Omega$
   $V_2 = 1.2$ V, $I_2 = 0.12$ A,
   $R_2 = 10 \ \Omega$

$V_3 = 1.2$ V, $I_3 = 0.24$ A,
   $R_3 = 5 \ \Omega$
   $V_4 = 4.8$ V, $I_4 = 0.40$ A,
   $R_4 = 12 \ \Omega$
   $V_T = 12$ V, $I_T = 0.40$ A,
   $R_T = 30.3 \ \Omega$
**36. a)** $3.12 \times 10^{3}$ W
   **b)** $1.4 \times 10^{3}$ W
   **c)** 7.00 W
**37. a)** 1800 W
   **b)** 0 A
   **c)** 7.00 W
**38. a)** 10 A
   **b)** 20 A
   **c)** 4800 W
   **d)** conductor burn out
**39.** $15.08/year
**40.** $9.41

## Chapter 17

**20. a)** in to page, over top
   **b)** clockwise
   **c)** out of page from the top
   **d)** counterclockwise
   **e)** out of page from the top
**21. a)** in to page (X)
   **b)** in left (X), out right (•)
   **c)** right to left
   **d)** out of page (•)
   **e)** in right (X), out left (•)
   **f)** left to right
**22. a)** north (top), south (bottom)
   **b)** north (top), south (bottom)
   **c)** north (top/right),
   south (bottom/left)
   **d)** north (top/left),
   south (bottom/right)
**23. a)** in left, out right
   **b)** in right, out left
**24. a)** 16 N
   **b)** 20 N
   **c)** 15 N
**25.** 14.4 V
   **b)** 12 V
**26. a)** field (down), force (right)
   **b)** north (top), force (left)
**27. a)** field (up), current in (X)
   **b)** north (top), current in (X)
**28. a)** north (bottom), field (up)
   **b)** north (top), field (down)
**29. a)** top (in), bottom (out)
   **b)** top (in), bottom (out)
**30.** north lower left, turns counterclockwise

# Chapter 18

**21.** $V = 100$ V, $I = 12$ A
**22. a)** 55 turns
    **b)** 27.5 turns
**23. a)** 0.57
    **b)** 21 V
    **c)** step-up
**24. a)** $3.33 \times 10^3$ W
    **b)** 27.8 A
    **c)** 0.12
**25. a)** step-up
    **b)** converted to AC
    **c)** 0.1
    **d)** 5 A
**26.** 8.3 V
**27. a)** 11.5 V
    **b)** $5.8 \times 10^{-2}$ A
    **c)** 41.8 W
**28. a)** 120 V
    **b)** 90 A
    **c)** $1.1 \times 10^4$ W
**29. a)** 2
    **b)** 5 A
**30. a)** step-up, turn ratio of $8.7 \times 10^{-2}$
    **b)** 5.2 A
**31. a)** 164 A
    **b)** 1210 W
    **c)** 0.67 %
**32. a)** 562 W
    **b)** 28.7 m

# Chapter 19

**12.**

| Symbol | Z | A | N | $^A_Z X$ |
|--------|-----|-----|-----|----------|
| H | 1 | 3 | 2 | $^3_1$H |
| Li | 3 | 7 | 4 | $^7_3$Li |
| C | 6 | 14 | 8 | $^{14}_6$C |
| N | 7 | 14 | 7 | $^{14}_7$N |
| Na | 11 | 24 | 13 | $^{24}_{11}$Na |
| Co | 27 | 59 | 32 | $^{59}_{27}$Co |
| Sr | 38 | 88 | 50 | $^{88}_{38}$Sr |
| U | 92 | 238 | 146 | $^{238}_{92}$U |
| Pu | 94 | 239 | 145 | $^{239}_{94}$Pu |

**13. a)** $^1_1 p^+$
    **b)** $^4_2 He^{2+}$
    **c)** $^1_0 n$
    **d)** $^0_{-1} e$
**14. a)** $^{14}_7 N$
    **b)** $^1_0 n$
    **c)** $^4_2 He$
    **d)** $^0_{-1} e$
    **e)** $^{20}_{10} Ne$
**15. a)** $^0_{-1} e$ (beta)
    **b)** $^4_2 He$ (alpha)
    **c)** $^2_1 H$
    **d)** $^4_2 He$ (alpha)

    **e)** $^0_{-1} e$ (beta)
    **f)** $^0_{-1} e$ (beta)
**17.** 45 hours
**18. a)** $1.8 \times 10^6$ Bq
    **b)** $1.16 \times 10^4$ days
**19.** $1.15 \times 10^4$ a
**20.** 75.0 d
**21. a)** $5.0 \times 10^5$ kJ
    **b)** $5.6 \times 10^{-12}$ kg
    **c)** $1.4 \times 10^{-11}$ %
**22. a)** $6.1 \times 10^2$ kg/day
    **b)** $3.7 \times 10^{-18}$ %/year
**23.** $1.20 \times 10^{22}$ fissions/s
**24.** 0.38 %

# Numerical Answers to Applying the Concepts

## 1.2

**3. a)** $3.34 \times 10^{13}$ vibrations
**b)** $2.48 \times 10^5 \lambda$

## 1.3

**2. a)** 4
**b)** 5
**c)** 7
**d)** 1
**e)** 4
**f)** 6
**3. a)** 3.1 m
**b)** 3.2 m
**c)** 3.4 m
**d)** 3.6 m
**e)** 3.4 m
**4. a)** 3.745 m
**b)** 309.6 m
**c)** 120 s
**d)** 671.6
**e)** 461.7 s
**5. a)** 4.0 m
**b)** 3 m
**c)** 3.3333
**d)** 0
**e)** 0

## 1.4

**1. a) i)** $1.50 \times 10^{-4}$ months (assuming 30 d/month)
**ii)** 6.48 min
**iii)** $1.23 \times 10^{-5}$ a
**iv)** $3.89 \times 10^8$ µs
**b) i)** 60 months
**ii)** $2.6 \times 10^6$ min
**iii)** $1.8 \times 10^3$ d
**iv)** $1.6 \times 10^8$ s

## 2.4

**1. a)** $\vec{v}_2 = 1.6 \times 10^2$ m/s
**b)** $\Delta \vec{d} = 3200$ m
**2. a)** $\vec{a} = -14.6$ m/s$^2$
**b)** $\Delta t = 4.56$ s
$\Delta \vec{d} = 152$ m
**3. a)** $\vec{v} = 9.43.1$ m/s
**b)** $\Delta t = \Delta d = 471.5$ m
**c)** $\vec{a} = 78.59$ m/s
**d)** $\vec{v}_1 = 2.6 \times 10^2$ m/s

## 3.1

**1. a)** $x$: 10 km $\quad$ $y$: −17 km
**b)** $x$: −20 km $\quad$ $y$: 35 km
**c)** $x$: 1.7 km $\quad$ $y$: 9.8 km
**d)** $x$: −20 km $\quad$ $y$: −4.6 km
**e)** $x$: −8.5 km $\quad$ $y$: 8.5 km
**f)** $x$: 10 km $\quad$ $y$: 0 km
**2.** 230 m [W23°N]

## 3.3

**1. a)** $t = 4.525$
**b)** $t = 5.65$
**c)** $t = 3.65$
**d) i)** 23 m
**ii)** 28 m
**iii)** 18 m
**2. a)** $t = 1.08$ s
**b)** $\Delta d_y = 0.539$ m
**c)** $t = 0.33$ s
**d)** 32 m
**e)** 22.9 m/s [S82°E]

## 3.4

**2. a)** 59.84 m/s [N22°E]
**b)** 50.86 m/s [N24°W]
**c)** 52.3 m/s [E86°N]

## 3.5

**2. a)** 78 m/s$^2$ [W45°N]
**b)** 112 m/s$^2$ [W33°N]
**c)** 103 m/s$^2$ [W29°N]

## 4.3

**1. a)** 0 $\quad$ **b)** 0 $\quad$ **c)** +
**d)** − $\quad$ **e)** $F_{net_y} = 0$, $a_x$ +
**2. a)** $\vec{a} = 1.0$ m/s$^2$
**b)** $\vec{a} = 0.33$ m/s$^2$
**c)** $\vec{a} = -0.33$ m/s$^2$
**d)** $\vec{a} = 0.50$ m/s$^2$

## 4.4

**1. a)** $1.7 \times 10^5$ N [N45°E]
**b)** $2.1 \times 10^5$ N [E]
**c)** $2.3 \times 10^5$ N [N85°E]
**d) i)** $1.4 \times 10^5$ [N30°E]
**ii)** $1.6 \times 10^5$ N [E]
**iii)** $1.8 \times 10^5$ N [N84°E]

## 5.3

**1. a)** $1.18 \times 10^5$ N
**b)** $9.82 \times 10^4$ N
**c)** $6.00 \times 10^5$ N
**d)** $1.94 \times 10^4$ N

## 5.4

**1. a)** $6.9 \times 10^2$ N
**b)** $6.9 \times 10^2$ N
**c)** $5.5 \times 10^2$ N
**d)** 0 N

## 5.5

**3. a)** $1.5 \times 10^2$ N
**b)** 100 N
**c)** 0.34
**d)** 314 N
**i)** $1.6 \times 10^2$ N
**ii)** 100 N
**iii)** 0.32
**e) i)** $1.4 \times 10^2$ N
**ii)** 100 N
**iii)** 0.36

## 5.6

**3. a)** $8.3 \times 10^2$ N/m
**b)** 1.7 N
**c)** 6.7 M
**d)** $4.9 \times 10^2$ N/m

## 6.1

**a)** $4.0 \times 10^2$ kg m/s
**b)** $7.2 \times 10^5$ kg m/s
**c)** $6.8 \times 10^{10}$ kg m/s

## 6.2

**a)** 60 km/s
**b)** −60 kg/m
**c)** 0

## 6.3

**1. a)** 3.0 m/s
**b)** 1.7 m/s
**c)** 0.88 m/s
**d)** 0.17 m/s

## 7.2

**3. a)** 80 Nm
  **b)** 96 Nm
  **c)** $2.2 \times 10^3$ Nm

## 7.3

**1.** $4.8 \times 10^2$ J/s
**2.** 0

## 7.4

**1. a)** kg m$^2$/s$^2$
  **b)** N·m
**3. a)** 16 J
  **b)** 31 J
  **c)** 12 J
  **d)** 100 J
  **e)** 10 m/s

## 7.5

**1. a)** $2.4 \times 10^2$ J
  **b)** 18.8 J
  **c)** $1.32 \times 10^4$ J
**3.** $2.45 \times 10^5$ MJ

## 7.7

**1. a)** $1.1 \times 10^3$ J
  **b)** $7.7 \times 10^3$ J
  **c)** $8.7 \times 10^3$ J
  **d)** $8.7 \times 10^3$ J
  **e)** 39 m/s
  **f)** 52 m/s
  **g)** 136 m
**3.** 18 m/s

## 8.4

**3.** gold   $5.5 \times 10^3$ J
  iron   $1.9 \times 10^4$ J
  silver $9.7 \times 10^3$ J

## 8.5

**2.** $3.08 \times 10^{-2}$ L

## 8.6

**2. a)** 29.9°C
  **b)** 462 J/kg°C

## 9.3

**4. a)** 1.9 a
  **b)** 2278 kg
  **c)** 11 m

## 10.1

**1. a)** $4.5 \times 10^3$ s
  **b)** 0.67 s
  **c)** 1.8 s
  **d)** 0.95 s
**2. i) a)** 60 Hz **b)** 0.75 Hz
    **c)** $9.3 \times 10^{-3}$ Hz **d)** 1.4 Hz
  **ii) a)** 0.017 s **b)** 1.3 s
    **c)** 1.08 s **d)** 0.71 s

## 10.2

**1. a)** $4.69 \times 10^{14}$ Hz
  **b)** $2.50 \times 10^8$ Hz
  **c)** $1.50 \times 10^{17}$ Hz
**2. a)** $2.0 \times 10^{-5}$ m
  **b)** 0.15 m
  **c)** $1.0 \times 10^{-14}$ m

## 10.3

**1. a)** $2.1 \times 10^{-3}$
  **b)** $5.5 \times 10^{-2}$
**2. a)** 0.15 m
  **b)** 0.042   $h_i = 0.18$ m

## 10.8

**1. a)** $d_i = 20$ cm    $m = -0.67$
  **b)** 24 cm    $-1$
  **c)** 36 cm    $-2$
  **d)** $-12$ cm    2
**2. a)** $-8.6$ cm    0.29
  **b)** $-8.0$ cm    0.33
  **c)** $-7.2$ cm    0.40
  **d)** $-4.0$ cm    0.67

## 11.2

**1. a)** $2.26 \times 10^8$ m/s
  **b)** $1.24 \times 10^8$ m/s
  **c)** $1.99 \times 10^8$ m/s
**2. a)** 1.43 **b)** 2 **c)** 1.27
**3. a)** 18.5°
  **b)** 10.1°
  **c)** 16.3°
**4. a)** more dense
  **b)** 1.76
  **c)** $1.70 \times 10^8$ m/s
  **d)** less dense 1.08 $2.78 \times 10^8$ m/s

## 11.3

**2. a)**

| | $n_1$ | $n_2$ |
|---|---|---|
| case 1 | 1.2 | 2.3 |
| case 2 | 1.2 | 1.52 |
| case 3 | 1.2 | 1.65 |
| case 4 | 1.52 | 1.65 |
| case 5 | 1.52 | 2.3 |
| case 6 | 1.65 | 2.3 |

**b)** 31.4°, 41.4°, 45.8°, 46.7°, 52.1°, 67°

## 12.1

**1.** 32.6 m/s
**3. a)** $2.00 \times 10^7$ m/s
  **b)** red shift
  **c)** moving away
  **d)** $\vec{v}_r = -1.88 \times 10^7$ m/s

## 12.4

**2. a)** 26°
  **b)** 0.63°
**3. a)** 0.44 m
  **b)** $1.1 \times 10^{-2}$ m

## 12.5

**2. a)** 3.6°
  **b)** 2.9°
**3. a)** $3.8 \times 10^{-2}$ m
    $5.0 \times 10^{-2}$ m

## 12.6

**2.** Destructive

## 13.1

**1. a)** 300 Hz, $3.3 \times 10^{-3}$ s
  **b)** 1.15 m
**2. a)** $5.0 \times 10^{-3}$ s, 200 Hz
  **c)** 1.7 m
**3.** 0.04 s, 25 Hz

## 13.2

**2.** 11.8 times faster
**3. a)** $4.08 \times 10^3$ m
  **b)** $4.16 \times 10^3$ m
  **c)** $4.31 \times 10^3$ m
  **d)** $4.01 \times 10^3$ m

## 13.3

**1. a)** $7.0 \times 10^2$ m/s
  **b)** $1.4 \times 10^2$ m/s
  **c)** $6.3 \times 10^2$ m/s
  **d)** $1.7 \times 10^3$ m/s
**2. a)** $2.5 \times 10^3$ km/h
  **b)** $5.1 \times 10^2$ km/h
  **c)** $2.3 \times 10^3$ km/h
  **d)** $6.1 \times 10^3$ km/h

## 13.4

**2. a)** decrease by factor of 4
   **b)** decrease by factor of 28
   **c)** increase by factor of 9
   **d)** increase by factor of 11
**3. a)** 0.10 w/m$^2$
   **b)** $1.0 \times 10^{-10}$ w/m$^2$
   **c)** $3.2 \times 10^{-7}$ w/m$^2$
   **d)** $6.3 \times 10^{-5}$ w/m$^2$
**4. a)** 100 times louder
   **b)** 100 times softer
   **c)** $3.2 \times 20^6$ times louder
   **d)** 891 times softer

## 13.5

**3. a)** 662 Hz
   **b)** 341 Hz

## 14.3

**1. a)** 15.4 m
   **b)** 6.0 m

## 14.4

**2. a)** 0.3 m
   **b)** 6 m/s

## 14.6

**1. a) i)** 2.4 m  **ii)** 0.8 m  **iii)** 0.4 m
   **b) i)** 143 Hz **ii)** 429 Hz **iii)** 858 Hz
**2. a)** 4.8 m, 0.96 m, 0.44 m
   **b)** 71.7 Hz, 358 Hz, 788 Hz
**3. a)** 450 Hz
   **b)** 283 Hz
   **c)** 253 Hz
   **d)** 200 Hz

## 14.8

**1.** 997 Hz, 1003 Hz

## 15.4

**2. a)** $1.6 \times 10^{-19}$ C
   **b)** 1 C = $6.25 \times 10^{18}$ electrons

## 16.2

**2. a)** 11A
   **b)** $3.7 \times 10^{10}$A
**3. a)** $1.4 \times 10^{-2}$ s
   **b)** $4.38 \times 10^{21}$ electrons

## 16.3

**3. a)** $1.1 \times 10^3$ C
   **b)** $6.8 \times 10^{21}$ $e$
   **c)** $4.3 \times 10^2$ A
**4. a)** 25 C
   **b)** $1.5 \times 10^{20}$ $e$
   **c)** $9.8 \times 10^5$ A

## 16.5

**2. a)** 0.19 $\Omega$
   **b)** 4.6 $\Omega$

## 16.6

**1. a)** 60 $\Omega$
   **b)** 6.7 $\Omega$
   **c)** 66.7 $\Omega$
**2.** 26 $\Omega$, 19 $\Omega$, 22 $\Omega$
**3. a)** $1.0 \times 10^6$ $\Omega$
   **b)** 1.0 $\Omega$

## 16.7

**1. a)** 0.11 A
   1.1 V, 1.7 V, 2.2 V
   **b)** 0.5 A, 0.33 A, 0.25 A
   5 V
   **c) i)** For 10 $\Omega$     0.115A     1.152 V
   For 15 $\Omega$     7.68 $\times$
       $10^{-2}$A     1.152 V
   For 20 $\Omega$     0.192 A     3.84 V
   **ii)** 10 $\Omega$     0.27 A     2.7 V
   15 $\Omega$     0.15 A     2.3 V
   20 $\Omega$     0.115 A     2.3 V
   **iii)** 10 $\Omega$     0.153 A     1.53 V
   15 $\Omega$     0.23 A     3.46 V
   20 $\Omega$     0.77 A     1.53 V

## 16.8

**1. a)** 120 W
   **b)** 24 W
**2. a)** 8.33 A
   **b)** No
**3. a)** 500 C
   **b)** $3.125 \times 10^{21}$ $e$
**3. c)** $6.0 \times 10^4$ J
   **c)** 120 $\Omega$

## 16.9

**1. a)** 35.4¢
   **b)** 3¢

## 2.

**2. a)** \$3.60/month
   **b)** 7.50/month
   **c)** 11.52¢/month
   **d)** \$1.85/month
   **e)** \$13.59/month

## 17.2

**2. a)** 1.5 times stronger
   **b)** 1.23 times stronger
   **c)** 2 times stronger
   **d)** $\frac{1}{3}$
   **e)** 1.23 times stronger

## 18.5

**1. a)** 0.2
   **b)** 2 V
   **c)** 12.5 A
   **d)** 25 W
   **e)** 25 W
   **f)** 4 $\Omega$
**2. a)** 9.2 V
   **b)** 10.4 A
   **c)** 0.88 $\Omega$
   **d)** 96 W
   **e)** 96 W

## 19.3

**1.**

| | | | |
|---|---|---|---|
| $^{10}$C | #$p$ = 6 | #$n$ = 4 | #$e$ = 6 |
| $^{11}$C | 6 | 5 | 6 |
| $^{13}$C | 6 | 7 | 6 |
| $^{14}$C | 6 | 8 | 6 |

**2. a)** $^{35}_{18}$A$_r$
   **b)** $^{212}_{83}$B$_c$
   **c)** $^{141}_{59}$P$_r$
   **d)** $^{227}_{90}$T$_h$
   **e)** $^{239}_{93}$N$_p$
   **f)** $^{14}_{7}$N
**3. a)** $^{234}_{90}$Th
   **b)** $^{222}_{86}$Rn
   **c)** $^{206}_{82}$Pb
   **d)** $^{214}_{82}$Pb

## 19.4

**1. a)** 50 %
   **b)** 23 %
   **c)** $4.9 \times 10^{-5}$ %
   **d)** 99.96 %

# Glossary

**Absolute index of refraction**—the ratio of the speed of light in a vacuum to the speed of light in another optical medium

**Absorption (of sound)**—the process whereby a sound's energy is quickly dissipated by being transformed into other forms of energy

**Acceleration**—the process of changing velocity

**Accommodation**—contracting or relaxing the muscles of the eye connected to the lens, which changes the shape and focal length of the lens

**Acoustic pressure**—the change in air pressure produced by sound waves

**Acoustical engineer**—a person who designs structures and devices based on the effects of sound and noise on people

**Active sound control (ASC)**—a process that senses the unwanted sound pollution (noise), then generates an opposite phase signal to cancel the disturbance

**Activity (nuclear)**—the amount of radiation emitted from an atom's nucleus every second

**Acuity**—the sharpness or clarity of an image

**Air resistance**—force of friction on a moving object produced by interaction with the air it is passing through

**Alpha particles**—positively charged particles (helium nuclei) ejected at high speed from a radioactive nucleus

**Alpha radiation**—alpha particles emitted from a radioactive nucleus

**Alternating current (AC)**—current that continually changes direction

**Ammeter**—a current-measuring device

**Ampere (A)**—the base unit for current

**Amplitude**—the maximum displacement of a wave from its zero point

**Anechoic chamber**—a sound-proof room that can virtually eliminate the internal reflection or transmission of sound through its walls

**Antinodes**—regions of a standing wave that alternate between constructive "supercrests" and "supertroughs"

**Apparent weight**—the total upward force being exerted on an object

**Arthroscopic surgery**—surgery through small incisions that uses lasers, video cameras with fibre optic cables, and small surgical instruments

**Astronomical Unit (AU)**—the mean radius of Earth's orbit around the Sun

**Atomic mass number ($A$)**—the total number of protons plus neutrons in an atom's nucleus

**Atomic number (Z)**—the total number of protons in an atom's nucleus

**Average speed**—total distance travelled divided by the time taken

**Average velocity**—the displacement per unit time; requires a direction

**Beam**—a series of incident rays

**Beat frequency**—the frequency of a pulsating sound

**Beta decay**—the emission of an electron from the nucleus of an unstable atom

**Beta particles**—streams of high-energy electrons ejected at various speeds as high as close to the speed of light

**Big Bang**—a theory that the universe originated from a single source

**Binding energy**—a measure of the strength of the nuclear forces between neutrons and protons

**Birefringent**—exhibiting different refractive indices

**Blue shifted**—light from a celestial object that is compressed (has a smaller wavelength) because the object is moving toward the observer

**Bore**—the body of a wind instrument (e.g., clarinet, saxophone)

**Brewster's angle**—a special angle of incidence at which 100 % polarization can occur

**Brownian motion**—the constant, random, erratic movement of all matter at the molecular level

**Calandria**—the reactor vessel in a **CANDU** nuclear reactor

**Calorimetry**—the process of determining the amount of heat contained in, or given off by, bodies

**CANDU**—(**Can**adian, **D**euterium, **U**ranium) a nuclear reactor designed and built by Atomic Energy of Canada Limited

**Cardiac defribrillator**—a device used to reset the natural rhythm of the heart by applying a high-voltage shock when the heart's natural electric currents are disrupted

**Celsius**—a scale for measuring temperature in which the freezing point of water is 0° and the boiling point is 100°

**Chain reaction (nuclear)**—a reaction during which the number of subsequent fission reactions increases at a geometric rate

**Charge**—the electric state of an object

**Chemical potential energy**—energy that is stored in the chemical bonds of matter and can be released by way of a chemical reaction

**Circuit**—the path of electric current flow from and to the power supply

**Circuit analysis**—the study of how the parameters of current and voltage are distributed in a circuit

**Club head loft**—the angle between the golf club's face and an imaginary line perpendicular to the ground

**Cochlea**—the spiral-shaped part of the inner ear that contains fine hairs, the sensory ends of the auditory nerve

**Coefficient of kinetic friction ($\mu_k$)**—the ratio between the force of friction and the normal force when the object is moving

**Coefficient of static friction ($\mu_s$)**—the ratio between the force of friction and the normal force when the object is at rest; $\mu_s > \mu_k$

**Coherent (light)**—the waves of both light sources maintain a constant phase relationship at all times

**Cold nuclear fusion**—an as yet unproven process for producing nuclear fusion energy at room temperature

**Components**—two vectors, perpendicular to each other, which produce the original vector when added

**Compressions**—the dense areas of a longitudinal wave

**Concave**—curves inward

**Conduction**—the process of transferring heat by particle collision, or flow of electric charge

**Conductor**—a material that allows heat or electrons to transfer easily through it

**Constructive interference**—amplitudes of waves, both in the same direction, are added together

**Contact**—touch

**Convection**—the process of transferring heat by a circulating path of fluid

**Conventional current**—the model of positive charge flow

**Converging lens**—an optical device that bends parallel rays inward to a focal point

**Convex**—curves outward

**Critical angle**—the angle in the incident medium that makes the refracted angle 90°

**Critical mass**—the minimum mass of nuclear material needed for a self-sustaining chain reaction to take place

**Current**—the total amount of charge moving past a point in a conductor, divided by the time taken

**Cycle**—a complete sequence of motion that repeats itself

**Demagnetization**—loss of magnetic strength in a ferromagnetic material

**Destructive interference**—the resulting decrease in amplitude when two pulses in opposite phase combine

**Deuterium ($^2$H)**—an isotope of hydrogen used in the nuclear industry; contains a proton and a neutron in its nucleus

**Diffraction gratings**—a large number of closely spaced parallel slits

**Diffraction**—the bending of waves around obstacles

**Diffuse**—the characteristic of light rays reflected from a rough surface

**Diopter**—unit of measure for the refractive power of a lens

**Dipoles**—the small and flexible magnets that make up a large magnet

**Direct current (DC)**—current that flows in a single direction from the power supply through the conductor to a **load** and back to the power supply

**Dispersion**—separation of white light into its component colours

**Displacement**—the net travel of an object as measured from its starting point to its end point in a straight line, with direction

**Distance**—a measure of the total travel of the object, regardless of direction

**Diverging lens**—a lens that bends parallel rays outward

**Diverging**—spreading outward

**Domain theory of magnets**—all large magnets are made up of many smaller and flexible magnets that can interact with each other

**Doppler effect**—changes in the pitch of sound from a moving source

**Double slit formula**—an equation that predicts where maxima or minima occur given the slit separation distance, the wavelength of light used, and the order number

**Dynamics**—the study of the cause of motion

*e* **ray**—extraordinary ray; its speed varies depending on the angle at which it enters a birefringent crystal

**Echolocation (sonar)**—using sounds used to locate objects

**Efficiency**—the completeness of energy transfer

**Elastic potential energy**—energy stored by bending, stretching, or compressing matter

**Electric current**—a flow of charge

**Electric field**—the space around a single charge or an array of charges in which electric forces act

**Electric generator**—a device made up of a permanent magnet and coils of wire designed to produce a continuous flow of electric current when there is an input of some rotational mechanical energy

**Electric motor**—a device that uses an electromagnet with permanent magnets to convert electric energy to kinetic energy

**Electric potential difference**—the **electric potential energy** for each coulomb of charge in a circuit

**Electric potential energy**—energy stored when static electric charges are held a certain distance apart

**Electrocardiogram**—a graph of the voltage fluctuations plotted against time for the heart

**Electrocardiograph**—a device used to measure the heart's electrical activity

**Electrocauterization**—a process that uses a spark from an electric current to control severe bleeding by burning tissue to create a seal

**Electromagnet**—a coil of wire around a soft iron core, which uses electric current to produce a magnetic field

**Electromagnetic induction**—inducing a current in a conductor by changing the magnetic field around the conductor

**Electromagnetic spectrum**—the whole range of wavelengths, from longest to shortest

**Electromotive force (EMF)**—the electric potential difference (voltage) between two points where no external current flows

**Electrons**—negatively charged particles

**Electrostatics**—electricity at rest

**Endoscope**—a device used for looking inside the body

**Energy**—the ability to do work

**Ether**—thought to be the universal medium or frame of reference against which all other motions could be measured

**Eustachian tube**—a tube that connects the middle part of the ear to the throat

**Fahrenheit**—a system of measuring temperature whereby the freezing point of water is 32° and the boiling point of water is 212°

**Far point**—the distance to the farthest object that a fully relaxed eye can focus on

**Fast-breeder reactor**—a nuclear reactor designed to "breed" more fuel as it operates, thus extending the life of the nuclear fuel

**FBD**—see **free-body diagram**

**Ferromagnetic metals**—metals such as iron, nickel, cobalt, or mixtures of these three that attract magnets

**Fibre optic cable**—a flexible, transparent cable that transmits light according to the principle of total internal reflection

**Field lines**—the paths along which a test object travels if it is affected by a field (gravitational, electric, or magnetic)

**Field map**—a fairly complete set of lines that represent the shape of a magnetic, electric, or gravitational field around a body

**Field theory**—a theory that describes physical reality by means of the influence of a field, such as gravity, on objects

**Field**—a region of influence in the space around a body that is the source of this field. Common fields are gravitational, magnetic and electric.

**First harmonic**—see **fundamental frequency**

**Focus**—the point of convergence of parallel incident rays

**Force**—any cause that produces, changes, or stops the motion of an object

**Frame of reference**—the point of view from which one observes motion

**Free-body diagram**—a diagram that simplifies a force problem by isolating the studied object and the forces on it from its environment

**Frequency (f)**—the number of cycles that occur in a given time period, usually a second

**Friction**—a force produced from contact between two surfaces; opposite to the direction of motion

**Fundamental frequency**—the lowest frequency of a vibrating string

**Fusion**—joining

**Gamma rays**—electromagnetic radiation of very short wavelength

**Gas-cooled reactor**—a nuclear reactor that passes heat to helium or carbon dioxide gas, which heats water to drive a steam turbine and generator

**Gauge number**—the number on a wire that indicates its cross-sectional area

**Gaussian lens formula**—see **thin lens formula**

**Geiger counter**—a radiation detector that measures activity from a radioactive source

**Glare**—the effect caused by light reflecting off shiny surfaces such as glass, water, and bald heads

**Grand Unified Theory (GUT)**—a theory that would show the interdependence of the electromagnet, weak, and strong forces

**Gravitational potential energy**—energy stored in an object due to its height in an area where the force of gravity can act on it to make it fall

**Grid**—a network of electric lines and connections

**Half-life**—the amount of time required for half the number of unstable nuclei in an isotope to decay

**Harmonics**—multiples of the fundamental frequency in a standing wave pattern

**Head**—term used for the end of a vector arrow

**Head-to-tail**—a method of connecting vectors for vector addition

**Heat conductor**—a material that allows heat to transfer easily through it

**Heat insulator**—a material that does not allow heat to transfer easily through it

**Heat**—the energy of motion or the kinetic energy of matter at the atomic and molecular levels

**Hertz (Hz)**—the unit of measure of frequency; one cycle per second (1/s)

**High-level radioactive waste**—highly radioactive material, such as spent nuclear fuel

**Hypersonic**—travelling at speeds greater than or equal to **Mach** 5

**Impulse**—the product of the force and the time during which it acts

**Incident ray**—a ray of light striking a surface

**Index of refraction**—the ratio of the speeds of light as light passes from one material to another

**Induce**—to cause a change without contact

**Induction**—the act of inducing

**Inertia**—the ability of an object to resist changing its motion

**Inertial frame of reference**—a frame of reference that is not accelerating

**Infrasonic**—at frequencies below the lower limit of human hearing

**Instantaneous velocity**—velocity at a single instant in time

**Insulator**—a material that doesn't allow easy heat transfer between its molecules, or the easy transfer of electrons through it

**Intensity of sound (I)**—the amount of power (P) that passes through a surface with an area (A) perpendicular to the wave's direction

**Interference**—the result of two or more waves meeting each other at a particular point in space at the same time

**Interferometer**—an instrument that uses interference of light to measure small distances

**Inter-nodal distance ($d_n$)**—a distance that is equivalent to one-half the wavelength of the wave source; the distance between two consecutive nodes

**Isotopes**—atoms of the same element type that have differing numbers of neutrons

**Kelvin**—a system of measuring temperature whereby the freezing point of water is 273 K and the boiling point of water is 373 K. The lowest temperature is called absolute zero (0 K) and is determined experimentally to be $-273\,°C$

**Kinematics**—a sub-branch of mechanics dealing with motion only, without regard to any underlying causes

**Kinetic**—pertaining to motion

**Kinetic energy**—the energy of motion

**Laparoscope**—a fibre optic instrument used to view procedures during surgery

**Latent heat of fusion ($L_f$)**—the heat required to change 1.0 kg of a substance from solid to liquid form

**Latent heat of vapourization ($L_v$)**—the heat required to change 1.0 kg of a substance from a liquid to a gas

**Latent heat**—the heat released during condensation and freezing, and stored when heat is added during melting and vapourization

**Lateral inversion**—switched from left to right

**Light pipe**—see **fibre optic cable**

**Light year**—the distance light travels in one year

**Lightning rod**—an object that doesn't attract lightning, but allows excess charge in the atmosphere to be slowly transferred to the ground

**Linearly polarized**—see **plane polarized**

**Load**—a device that converts electric energy to other forms of energy

**Logarithmic system**—a mathematical system using the exponents of the base number 10

**Longitudinal waves**—waves where particles of the medium vibrate parallel to the direction of wave motion

**Longitudinal**—parallel to the motion of the source

**Loudness**—the amplitude of a sound wave

**Mach number**—the ratio of the speed of a body to the speed of sound in the surrounding medium, used to express the speeds of objects that travel faster than the speed of sound

**Magnetic domain**—the effect produced when **dipoles** of a magnet line up

**Magnetic induction**—the ability of ferromagnetic materials to be magnetized

**Magnetic potential energy**—the energy stored in the space between two magnets

**Magnification**—the factor by which the image size compares to the object size

**Magnitude**—a number and a unit without direction

**Mass**—the amount of matter in an object

**Mass defect**—the slight decrease in mass that accompanies the release of energy stored in nuclei and molecules

**Matter**—everything around us that has mass and takes up space

**Maxima**—points at which waves constructively interfere

**Mechanical resonance**—the vibrating response of an object to a periodic force from a source that has the same frequency as the natural frequency of the object

**Mechanics**—the study of motions and forces

**Microscopic welds**—bonds that form at the microscopic level between two surfaces in contact; require a force to be broken and move the surfaces apart

**Minima**—points at which waves destructively interfere

**Model**—a physical or mental representation of a phenomenon or process that cannot be shown otherwise

**Moderation**—the process of slowing down neutrons

**Momentum**—the product of mass and velocity of an object

**Near point**—the closest distance to an object that the eye can focus on clearly

**Net force**—the result of adding all the vector forces acting on an object

**Neutrons**—neutral particles in an atom's nucleus with no electric charge

**Nodal lines**—areas of destructive interference

**Nodes**—points at which destructive interference occurs

**Normal force**—the reaction force pressing back on the object exerting an action force; perpendicular to the surface on which the action force acts

**Normal**—a line drawn perpendicular to a surface

**Nuclear force**—force between particles of the nucleus

**Nuclear fusion**—the combining of two smaller nuclei to produce a larger one, with the release of energy

**Nuclear potential energy**—energy that is stored in an atom's nucleus

**Nuclear reactors**—devices that transform nuclear energy into useful heat and electrical energy

**Nucleons**—the particles that make up an atom's nucleus; neutrons and protons

**Nucleus**—the central, positively charged part of an atom, made up of protons and neutrons

**Nuclide**—an atom or nucleus characterized by a specific number of protons and neutrons

**Null result**—the result obtained regardless of the way an experiment is done

**$o$ ray**—the ordinary ray through a birefringent crystal

**Optic axis**—an imaginary line or measured direction used to measure polarization and refraction in an anisotropic crystal

**Optics**—the study of light

**Order number**—the number from the centre of a pattern of light wave interference

**Orthogonal system**—a two-dimensional plane defined by two perpendicular directions, usually designated $x$ and $y$

**Oscilloscope**—an electronic device that displays a complex longitudinal sound wave as a more simple transverse wave

**Overtones**—frequencies that are whole multiples of the fundamental frequency

**Parabolic motion**—the curved motion that occurs when a projected object is accelerated by a constant force in a given direction

**Paradox**—a statement or situation that seems to be contradictory to popular belief but which is true

**Parallel circuit**—a circuit in which loads are connected side by side

**Parsec (pc)**—an astronomical unit of measure based on the distance from Earth where stellar parallax is one second of an arc

**Period (*T*)**—the amount of time it takes a wave to complete one cycle

**Phase shift**—the relative position of the wave compared to a standard representation

**Phase**—the relationship of position and time between two points on a wave

**Pitch**—the highness or lowness of a musical note

**Plane polarized**—light that has had one of the components of its electric field absorbed, so its field lines oscillate in one plane only

**Plutonic rock**—stable rock formations in the Canadian shield

**Point of incidence**—the place where a light ray makes contact with a mirror's surface

**Polarization**—the removal of one component of the electric field of light such that it is no longer randomly oriented

**Polaroid**—a material that polarizes light that passes through it (i.e., removes a component of its electric field)

**Positron**—the anti-particle of an electron

**Potential energy**—energy that is stored or energy that is not actually in use at the present moment

**Power**—the rate at which work is done

**Preferential direction of transmission**—a characteristic of a Polaroid (polarizing filter) that causes it to absorb one component of light's electric field, allowing only one component to pass through

**Pressured-water reactor**—a nuclear reactor that uses normal water instead of heavy water as a moderator

**Prism**—a transparent body with triangular bases, rectangular sides, and refracting surfaces at an acute angle to each other that separates white light into a spectrum of colours

**Projectile motion**—see **parabolic motion**

**Protons**—positively charged particles

**Quality of sound**—the degree of richness of a sound, such as that produced by a symphony orchestra

**Radial keratotomy**—a laser procedure performed on the eye to correct vision

**Radiant energy**—energy that is carried by electromagnetic waves

**Radiation**—the transfer of heat energy through electromagnetic radiant energy

**Radioactive tailings**—radioactive material exposed by uranium mining

**Radioisotopes**—isotopes that are radioactive

**Range**—displacement in the horizontal direction

**Rarefactions**—the less dense areas of a longitudinal wave

**Ray**—an arrow used to indicate the direction of motion of waves

**Real images**—images that can be projected onto a screen

**Rectilinear propagation of light**—light travelling in a straight line

**Red shift**—light from a celestial object that is stretched out (has a longer wavelength) because the object is moving away from the observer

**Reed**—a thin sliver of wood that vibrates to produce sound in a woodwind instrument

**Reference frame**—the object or system with respect to which velocity is measured

**Reflection**—the effect of light bouncing off materials

**Reflectoscope**—a device that uses ultrasound to find flaws in materials such as tires and castings

**Refraction**—the bending of transmitted light when it enters another material of different optical density

**Regular reflection**—reflection where the incident and reflected angles are equal

**Relative index of refraction**—see **index of refraction**

**Relative motion**—motion of one object with respect to another

**Resistance ratio**—ratio of the resistance of one resistor compared to the total resistance

**Resistance (electrical)**—a measure of the opposition to current flow

**Resonators**—the collective term for the pharynx, mouth, and nasal cavity; they amplify and modify sound waves made by humans and some animals

**Resultant vector**—the final vector when vectors are added or subtracted

**Reverse magnetization**—reversal of the polarity of a magnet

**rpm**—revolutions per minute

**rps**—revolutions per second

**Scalar**—a quantity specified by a value (magnitude) only and no direction

**Series circuit**—a circuit in which loads are connected one after another in a single path

**Shells**—orbits of electrons around an atom's nucleus in which electrons have approximately the same amount of energy

**Simple harmonic motion**—motion of an object that repeats itself back and forth over the same path

**Solenoid**—a coiled conductor that acts like a magnet when current is passed through it

**Sonar**—**so**und **na**vigation **a**nd **r**anging; used to determine the depth of water under a boat or ship or to find sunken objects

**Sonic shock (wave)**—the buildup of energy as a sound source approaches the speed of sound

**Specific heat capacity**—the amount of heat required to increase the temperature of 1.0 kg of a material 1°C

**Spectrometer**—a device that measures wavelengths of light accurately using a diffraction grating

**Specular reflection**—see **regular reflection**

**Spherical mirrors**—convex (diverging) and concave (converging) mirrors; originate from a sphere

**Spring constant**—a constant that indicates the strength of a spring

**Standard reference system**—a system of direction that designates up and to the right and North and East as positive and the opposite directions as negative

**Standing wave**—a fixed pattern of nodes and antinodes that form when two identical waves meet and interfere

**Static**—stationary, not moving

**Step-down transformer**—an electromagnetic device that has more turns in its primary than in its secondary coil, allowing it to decrease electric potential and increase current

**Step-up transformer**—an electromagnetic device that has more turns in its secondary than in its primary coil, allowing it to increase electric potential and decrease current

**Subsonic**—travelling at a speed below **Mach** 1

**Supersonic**—travelling at a speed greater than **Mach** 1

**Tail**—the beginning of a vector arrow

**Temperature**—a measure of the average kinetic energy of all of the particles in a quantity of matter

**Terminal velocity**—velocity reached when the upward frictional force on a falling object balances the downward force of gravity

**Tesla (T)**—the unit of measure of magnetic field strength

**Test charge**—a small charge used to check for the presence of an electric field

**Test compass**—a compass used to check for the presence of a magnetic field

**Theory of Everything (TOE)**—a theory that would explain the origin of the four fundamental forces of nature

**Thermal energy**—heat energy or the energy that makes objects hot; a form of kinetic energy at the microscopic level

**Thermal expansion**—the increase in volume of a substance when it is heated up

**Thermal pollution**—the transfer of waste heat into the atmosphere

**Thermometer**—a device for measuring temperature; operates according to the principle of thermal expansion

**Thin lens formula**—a formula that relies on the assumption that air is one of the mediums and that the thickness of the lens is small compared with its focal length

**Time dilation**—the change in the rate time passes as an object approaches the speed of light

**Total internal reflection of light**—a phenomenon that occurs only when light travels from a more optically dense to a less optically dense medium and the refracted angle is 90°, causing the incident ray to be reflected back into the more dense medium; the principle behind fibre optic cables used in the telecommunications industry

**Total displacement**—the resultant vector when adding displacement

**Transducer**—a device that transmits and receives sound waves

**Transformer**—a device which uses electromagnetic induction to increase or decrease AC voltage

**Transmission**—the process of light passing through materials

**Transverse wave**—a wave the direction of which is perpendicular to the direction of vibration of the particles of the medium

**Tritium ($^3$H)**—an isotope of hydrogen produced in nuclear reactors, containing one proton and two neutrons

**Ultrasonic**—at frequencies past the upper limit of human hearing

**Unpolarized light**—light in which the electric field oscillates in any direction, perpendicular to the direction of wave motion

**Vectors**—quantities that are specified by both a magnitude and a direction

**Velocity**—displacement per unit time

**Virtual images**—images that cannot be projected onto a screen

**Voltage**—see **electric potential difference**

**Voltmeter**—an instrument used to measure potential difference between any two points

**Waste heat**—excess heat not used in an industrial process

**Wavefront**—a surface on which all the wave points are in the same phase

**Wavelength**—the length of one complete cycle of a wave

**Weight**—the gravitational pull on an object towards the centre of Earth

**White noise**—nondescript background noise that has a fairly steady intensity over a broad range of frequencies

**Wind instruments**—musical instruments in which a column of air vibrates to produce sound

**Work**—the process of energy transfer from one of its many forms to another

**Xerography**—the process of making copies of written or printed material, pictures, etc., by electromagnetic attraction

# Index

Kensington, Maryland; Fig.STSE.11.1 CP Picture Archive (Jonathan Hayward); CHAPTER 12: Opener: CP Picture Archives (Brian Donogh); Fig.12.3 CP Picture Archives (Brian Donogh); Fig. 12.4 CP Picture Archives (Vicki Cronis); Figs. 12.6, 7 and 8: Light And Vision, Conrad G. Mueller, Mae Rudolph and the Editors of Life, Life Science Library, 1966 Time Inc.; Figs. 12.13A and Fig.12.13B: 1992 Diane Hirsch, Fundamental Photographs NYC; Fig. 12.14 (c)1994 Michael Dalton, Fundamental Photographs NYC; Fig. 12.16 Optics, 3rd ed., by Hecht Jajac (c) 1974/Addison, Wesley, Longman; Fig. 12.19 Ed Bock/Firstlight.ca; Fig. 12.22 (first photo) Firstlight.ca; (fourth photo) Susan Berger, Irwin Publishing Ltd., Fig. 12.27 from Matter And Energy MacLachlan/McNeill/Bell/Spencer, (c) Irwin Publishing Inc., 1977; Fig. 12.31 Northwest Scientific Supply Ltd., Fig. 12.32, 33 and 35 Light And Vision, Conrad G. Mueller, Mae Rudolph and the Editors of Life, Life Science Library, 1966 Time Inc; UNIT D: Opener: David Jett/Firstlight.ca; CHAPTER 13: Opener: CORBIS/Magma Photos; Fig.13.1 CP Picture Archives (Sam Morris); Fig.13.8B Amos Machoum/Firstlight.ca; Fig.13.15 (first photo) B. Rondel/Firstlight.ca; (second, third, fourth photos) NASA; Fig.13.18 (top photo) Doug Wilson/Firstlight.ca; Fig.13.18 (bottom right) NASA; Fig.13.23 NEIL PRESTON/CORBIS/MAGMA; Fig.13.25A Hulton Getty Fig.13.25B Jonathan Morgan/Stone; Fig.13.33 Bruce Coleman/Firstlight.ca; Figs.13.41 (left) Tom and Dee Ann McCarthy/Firstlight.ca; (right) Benelux Press/Firstlight.ca; CHAPTER 14: Opener: Roger Ball/Firstlight.ca; Fig.14.5 Roger Ball/Firstlight.ca; Fig.14.11 Matter and Energy, MacLachlan, McNeill/Bell/Spencer, (c) Irwin Publishing Inc., 1977; Figs.14.18 MSCUA, University of Washington Libraries, (first photo) Farquharson #11, Collection 290; (second photo) Farquharson #12, Collection 290; (third photo) Farquharson #8, Collection 290; Figs.14.19 (a) Mike Magnuson/Stone; (b) Benelux Press/Firstlight.ca; Fig. 14.20A CP Picture Archives (Hans Deryk); Fig.14.21 Joyce Tannassee, Irwin Publishing Ltd., Fig. 14.29 Matter and Energy, MacLachlan, McNeill/Bell, Spencer, (c) Irwin Publishing Inc., 1977; Fig.14.40 CP Picture Archive (Greg Gibson); UNIT E: Opener: Tony Hutchings/Stone. CHAPTER 15: Opener: Jim Zuckerman/Firstlight.ca; Fig.15.10: Courtesy the CN Tower; Fig.15.13 Phil Degginger/Stone; Fig. 15.16 Glenco Physics: Principles & Problems, 1999 edition/Kodansha Ltd., Tokyo; Table 15.2 (a) www.hitachiplant.hbi.ne.jp/English/ep/03/index.htm; Table 15.2 (c) Andy Sacks/Stone; Table 15.2 (d) www.mosquito-zapper.com/images/FLOWbk40.jpg; Table 15.2 (e) Xerox Canada LtdSTSE.15.1, STSE.15.2; Fig. STSE.15.3; Fig. STSE.15.5; Fig. STSE.15.6 Sparktec, Stoney Creek; CHAPTER 16: Opener: Applications of Electrical Construction, Third Edition, Robert K. Clidero, Kennerth H. Sharpe, Copyright (c) 1991 Irwin Publishing; Fig.16.4A Brian Heimbecker; Fig.16.4B Courtesy of Fluke Electronics Canada; Fig. STSE.16.4 Brian Heimbecker; Fig.STSE.16.5B Brian Heimbecker; CHAPTER 17: Opener: 1988 Wayne Decker, Fundamental Photographs, NYC; Fig.17.1 Merrill Physics: Principles & Problems, Canadian Edition, 1992; Fig.17.4(a) Merrill Physics: Principles and Problems, Canadian Edition, 1992; Fig.17.4 (b) Matter and Energy, Third Edition, Peter T. Spencer, Kenneth G. McNeill, James H. MacLachlan, Irwin Publishing, 1987; Fig.17.6: Dennis Galante/Stone; Figs.17.8(a) and (b) Matter and Energy, Third Edition, Peter T. Spencer, Kenneth G.McNeill, James H. MacLachlan, Irwin Publishing, Toronto, 1987; Table 17.3 (top photo) (c) 1988 Wayne Decker, Fundamental Photographs, NYC; (middle photo) Applied Electricity and Electronics, Clair A. Bayne, The Goodheart-Willcox Company, Inc., Tinley Park, Illinois, 2000; (bottom photo) www.umei.com/fire-protection-accessories/fire-alarm-bells/fire-alarm-bell-1-10.htm; Fig.17.23 Sargent-Welch/CENCO Physics; Table 14 (first photo) Matter And Energy, Third edition, Peter T. Spencer, Kenneth G. McNeill, James H. MacLachlan, Irwin Publishing, Toronto, 1987; Fig.17.24A: "copyright ISTEC Tokyo JAPAN. All Rights Reserved; Fig.17.24C MAGLEVINC; CHAPTER 18: Opener: Dave Reede/Firstlight.ca; Fig.18.12A eStock Photography/Everett Johnson; Fig.STSE 18.1 James Marshall/Firstlight.ca; Fig.STSE.18.2 Stockphoto.com/Images/Firstlight.ca; CHAPTER 19: Opener: Gary J. Ehrhardt, Ph.D., University of Missouri, Development Group; Fig.19.12 CP Picture Archive (Monty Davis); Fig.19.14 CP Picture Archive (Katsumi Kasahara); Fig.19.21 NASA; Fig.19.23 CP Picture Archives; Fig.19.25 Ontario Hydro; Fig.19.26 Atomic Energy of Canada Limited (AECL); Fig.19.28 Atomic Energy of Canada Limited (AECL); Fig.19.30 Pennsylvania State University, Engineering Library; Fig.19.31 Atomic Energy of Canada Limited (AECL); Fig.STSE.19.1 (c) 1990 Richard Megna, Fundamental Photos, NYC; APPENDICES: Opener: Loren Santow/Stone.

# Photograph Credits:

Every effort has been made to find and to acknowledge correctly the sources of the material reproduced in this book. The publisher welcomes any information that will enable it to rectify, in subsequent editions, any errors or omissions.

COVER PAGE: Brian Erler/FPG

UNIT A: Opener: Paramount Canada's Wonderland; Page 2: CP Picture Archive (Elise Amendola); CHAPTER 1: Opener: Alan Thornton/Stone; Fig.1.1 CP Picture Archive (Peter Power) Fig. 1.4 Provincial Archives of Manitoba, George E Cripps Collection #21, dated 1927; Fig. 1.5 "Photo courtesy of Six Flags Magic Mountain-BATMAN, SUPERMAN and all related characters, names, ride and attraction names, and indicia are trademarks of DC Comics (c)2001,Valencia, CA; Fig.1.13A Joe McBride/Stone; Fig.1.25 Alan Schein/Firstlight.ca; Fig. 1.26 CNE, Toronto; Fig.1.28 Paramount; Canada's Wonderland; Fig.1.35 CP Picture Archive (Cesar Rangel); Fig.1.36 NASA; CHAPTER 2: Opener: Arno Turk; Fig.2.16 Paramount Canada's Wonderland; Fig.2.22 Mug Shots/First Light.ca; Fig.2.24 REUTERS/Corbis MAGMA; Fig.2.27 CP Picture Archive (Matt York); Fig.2.28 Richard Olivier/CORBIS/ MAGMA; Fig. STSE.2.2 Joe McBride/First Light.ca; Fig.STSE.2.3 Joe McBride/Stone; Fig.2.33; www.supphoto.net/ photo/tgv/tgv-post.jpg; Fig.2.37 Eric Sanford/Firstlight.ca; CHAPTER 3: Opener: CP Picture Archive (Clement Allard); Fig.3.12 Matter and Energy, Third Edition, Peter T. Spencer, Kenneth G. McNeill, James H. MacLachlan, (c) 1987 Irwin Publishing Inc.; Fig.3.19 (two photos) (c) Underwood & Underwood/ CORBIS/MAGMA; Figs.STSE.3.3 (both photos) "Courtesy of Wherify Wireless, Inc. www.wherifywireless.com; CHAPTER 4: Opener: CP Picture Archive (Cesar Rangel); Fig.4.5 NASA; Fig.4.8 (top photo) BETTMANN/CORBIS/MAGMA; (middle photo) CORBIS/MAGMA; (bottom photo) BETTMAN/ CORBIS/MAGMA; Fig.4.21B NASA; Fig. 4.26 NASA; Fig. STSE.4.1 RICHARD OLIVIER/CORBIS/MAGMA; CHAPTER 5: Opener: Alese & Mort Phechter; Fig.5.2: (first photo) Photo Bank Yokohama/Firstlight.ca; (second photo) CP Picture Archive (Darrald Bennett); (third photo) Photo Bank Yokohama/Firstlight.ca; Fig. 5.12A NASA; Fig. 5.18A Images/Firstlight.ca; 5.18B NASA; Fig. 5.33 NASA; Fig.5.36 NASA; Fig.STSE 5.2 Auto Fundamentals, Martin W. Stockel, Martin T. Stockel, Chris Johanson, The Goodheart-Willcox Company, Inc., Tinley Park, Illinois, 1996; CHAPTER 6: Opener: TIM WRIGHT/CORBIS/MAGMA; Fig.6.4 NASA; Fig.6.7 (first photo) Mendola/Bill Vann/Firstlight.ca; (second photo) CP Picture Archive (Ryan Remiorz); (third photo) COMSTOCK IMAGES/Russ Kinne; Fig. 6.14B Photo Bank Yokohama/Firstlight.ca; Fig.6.16 NASA; Fig. 6.18 CP Picture Archive (Adrian Wyld); Fig. 6.19 Les Jones-Covershots; Fig. 6.20 (three photos) TIM WRIGHT/CORBIS/MAGMA; UNIT B: Cover: Ontario Hydro; Page 213 top left: Bob McCloskey, top right: Leo Baeck Institute, NYC; (middle) CP Picture Archive (Alan Marler); CHAPTER 7: Opener: Split

Image/Firstlight.ca; Fig.7.11 Rick Gomez/Firstlight.ca; Fig.7.18B CP Picture Archive (Lionel Cironneau), Fig.7.20 (top) CP Picture Archive (Victoria Arocho); (bottom) CP Picture Archive (Joe Bryska); Fig.STSE.7.1 Photo Bank Yokohama/Firstlight.ca; Fig.7.25 Paramount Canada's Wonderland; CHAPTER 8: Chapter Opener: Jerry Kobalenko/Firstlight.ca, Fig.8.12 Easy Radiant Works; Fig. 8.13 Thermos Company; Fig. 8.14 Triple Seal Ltd.,Fig. 8.17 CP Picture Archives (Greg Marinovich); Fig.8.20, top left: CP Picture Archives (Robert Galbraith); top right: CP Picture Archives (Ryan Remiorz); CHAPTER 9: Chapter Opener: Fermilab photo: inside view of drift tube of 200 MeV section of Linac at Fermi National Accelerator Laboratory; Fig.9.4 BETTMAN/CORBIS/MAGMA; Fig.9.14 Photo CERN, Switzerland; Figs.9.15 Leo Baeck Institute, NYC; Fig.STSE.1, Fig.STSE.2, Fig.STSE.3 Photos CERN, Switzerland; UNIT C: Opener: SIRTF Science Center/IPAC; page 305 Bob McCloskey; CHAPTER 10: Opener: James Marshall/First Light.ca; Fig.10.1 John Gillmoure/First Light.ca; Fig.10.3 First Light.ca; Fig.10.9 North Carolina State University; Fig.10.20 NASA; Fig.10.23 Jim Cooper/Stone; Fig.10.29 (left) Mug Shots/Firstlight.ca; Fig.10.29 (right) Bryan Allen/Firstlight.ca; Fig.10.30 Adam Peiperl/Firstlight.ca; Figs.10.31 (both) (c)2001 Richard Megna, Fundamental Photos NYC; Fig.10.34 William James Warren/Firstlight.ca; Fig.10.45 (c)2001 Richard Megna, Fundamental Photos NYC; Fig.10.51 bbst1.lu.rp.schule.de/leonardo/projekte/Energy/solarfurnaces/SOLARFUR.html; Figs.10.52 (first photo) Images/ Firstlight.ca; (second photo) Celestron International; Torrance, CA; (third photo) NASA; (fourth photo) Photo courtesy of the Canada Science and Technology Museum, Ottawa. Photo; Fig.10.54 Massimio Mastrorillo/Firstlight.ca; Fig.10.55 www.naic.edu/pictour/phplato.htm; Fig.10.56 NASA; Figs.STSE.10.2, 10.3, 10.4, 10.5 Brian Heimbecker; CHAPTER 11: Opener: Bob McCloskey; Fig.11.19 from Johnson PHYSICS FIFTH EDITION, reprinted by permission of Wiley-Liss, Inc., a subsidiary of John Wiley & Sons, Inc., Fig.11.23 Mug Shots/First Light.ca; Fig.11.26A Greg Pease/Stone; Fig. 11.26B Steve Taylor/Stone; Fig.11.27A David Joel/Stone; Fig.11.27B Copyright KRT Graphics/The Toronto Star. Reprinted with permission-The Toronto Star Syndicate; Fig.11.28 Contributor/Custom Medical Stock Photo; Figs.11.32 (top) Charles O'Rear/First Light.ca; (photo under) William Whitehurst/First Light.ca; Fig.11.40 Light and Vision, Conrad G. Mueller, Mae Rudolph and the Editors of Life Science Library, 1966 Time Inc.; Fig.11.42 The National Post/Dr.Omar Hakim of TLC Laser Eye Centers, Toronto; Fig.11.43 Eye Disease in Clinical Practice: A Concise Colour Atlas by Peter Shaw, Andrew S Jacks and Peng T Khaw, Manticore Europe Limited 1999; Figs.11.44, 11.45 from The Visual Dictionary of Physics/Dorling Kindersley, UK; Fig.11.47 George B. Diebold/Firstlight.ca; Fig.11.48 (c) 1991 Richard Megna/Fundamental Photographs, NYC; Fig.11.49 provided by Andrew Berger, O.D., F.A.A.O.,

# Physics Formulas

## Motion

$$\vec{v}_{avg} = \frac{\vec{v}_1 + \vec{v}_2}{2}$$

$$\Delta = 2^{nd}\ value - 1^{st}\ value$$

$$\Delta\vec{d} = \vec{v}_{avg}\Delta t$$

$$\Delta\vec{d} = \left(\frac{\vec{v}_1 + \vec{v}_2}{2}\right)\Delta t$$

$$\Delta\vec{d} = \vec{v}_1\Delta t + \tfrac{1}{2}\vec{a}\Delta t^2$$

$$\Delta\vec{d} = \vec{v}_2\Delta t - \tfrac{1}{2}\vec{a}\Delta t^2$$

$$\vec{a} = \frac{\vec{v}_2 - \vec{v}_1}{\Delta t}$$

$$\vec{v}_2^2 = \vec{v}_1^2 + 2\vec{a}\Delta\vec{d}$$

## Force

$$\vec{F}_{net} = m\vec{a}$$

$$\vec{F} = mg$$

$$\frac{\vec{F}_{g_1}}{\vec{F}_{g_2}} = \frac{r_2^2}{r_1^2}$$

$$\vec{F}_g = \frac{Gm_1m_2}{r^2}$$

$$\vec{F}_s = kx$$

$$\vec{F}_f = \mu\vec{F}_N = \mu mg\cos\theta$$

## Work, Power, Energy

$$W = \vec{F}\cdot\Delta\vec{d} = F\Delta d\cos\theta$$

$$W = mg\cdot\Delta d$$

$$E_g = mg\Delta h$$

$$P = \frac{W}{t} = \frac{E}{t}$$

$$E_k = \tfrac{1}{2}mv^2$$

$$mg\Delta h_1 + \tfrac{1}{2}mv_1^2 = mg\Delta h_2 + \tfrac{1}{2}mv_2^2$$

$$Efficiency = \left(\frac{Useful\ output\ energy}{Input\ energy}\right)100\%$$

## Heat

$$E_H = mc\Delta t$$

$$mc\Delta t = -(mc\Delta t)$$

$$L_F = \frac{E_H}{m}$$

$$L_v = \frac{E_H}{m}$$

## Momentum

$$\vec{p} = m\vec{v}$$

$$\Delta\vec{p} = \vec{F}\Delta t$$

$$\vec{p}_{Total} = \vec{p}_{Total_{initial}} = \vec{p}_{Total_{final}}$$

## Relativity

$$t = \frac{t_o}{\sqrt{1 - \dfrac{v^2}{c^2}}}$$

$$L = L_o\sqrt{1 - \frac{v^2}{c^2}}$$

$$m = \frac{m_0}{\sqrt{1 - \dfrac{v^2}{c^2}}}$$

$$E = mc^2$$

## Nuclear

$$^A_Z X \rightarrow\ ^{A-4}_{Z-2}Y + ^4_2He$$

$$^A_Z X \rightarrow\ ^A_{Z+1}Y + ^{\ 0}_{-1}e\ (\beta\ electron\ emission)$$

$$^A_Z X \rightarrow\ ^A_{Z-1}Y + ^0_{+1}e^+\ (\beta^+\ positron\ emission)$$

$$^A_Z X + ^{\ 0}_{-1}e \rightarrow\ ^A_{Z-1}Y$$

$$^A_Z X \rightarrow\ ^A_Z X + ^0_0\gamma\ (gamma\ emission)$$

$$A = A_o\left(\frac{1}{2}\right)^{\frac{t}{T_{\frac{1}{2}}}} \text{ or } M = M_o\left(\frac{1}{2}\right)^{\frac{t}{T_{\frac{1}{2}}}}$$

$$N = N_o e^{-\lambda t},\ \lambda = \frac{0.693}{T_{\frac{1}{2}}}$$

## Light: Optics

$$f = \frac{1}{T}$$

$$T = \frac{1}{f}$$

$$c = f\lambda$$

$$n = \frac{c}{v_{medium}}$$

$$n_1\sin\theta_1 = n_2\sin\theta_2$$

$$\frac{1}{f} = \frac{1}{d_o} + \frac{1}{d_i}$$

$$M = \frac{h_i}{h_o} = -\frac{d_i}{d_o}$$

$$P = \frac{1}{f}\ diopters$$

## Electricity

$$Q = Ne$$

$$I = \frac{Q}{t}$$

$$V = \frac{E}{Q} = \frac{W}{Q}$$

$$E = VIt$$

$$V = IR$$

$$\frac{R_1}{R_2} = \frac{A_2}{A_1}$$

$$V_T = V_1 + V_2 + V_3$$
from Kirchhoff's law
*Series resistors*

$$I_T = I_1 = I_2 = I_3$$
from Kirchhoff's law

$$R_T = R_1 + R_2 + R_3$$
$$R_T = R_1 + R_2 + R_3 \dots R_N$$
$$R_T = N(R)$$

*where N is the total number of resistors and R is the value of the individual resistor*

$$I_T = I_1 + I_2 + I_3$$
from Kirchhoff's law

$$V_T = V_1 = V_2 = V_3$$
from Kirchhoff's law
*Parallel resistors*

$$\frac{1}{R_T} = \frac{1}{R_1} + \frac{1}{R_2} + \frac{1}{R_3}$$

$$\frac{1}{R_T} = \frac{1}{R_1} + \frac{1}{R_2} + \frac{1}{R_3} \dots \frac{1}{R_N}$$

$$R_T = \frac{R}{N}$$

*where N is the total number of resistors and R is the value of the individual resistor*

$$P = IV$$

$$P = \frac{V^2}{R}$$

$$P = I^2R$$

$$Cost = P\ (in\ kW) \times t(hours) \times cost\ rate$$

$$\frac{V_p}{V_s} = \frac{N_p}{N_s} = \frac{I_s}{I_p}$$